# SMALL ARMS

OVER 250 OF THE WORLD'S FINEST PERSONAL WEAPONS

# SMALL ARMS

OVER 250 OF THE WORLD'S FINEST PERSONAL WEAPONS

CHRIS CHANT

SB

Published by
Silverdale Books
an imprint of Bookmart Ltd
Registered Number 2372865
Trading as Bookmart Ltd
Blaby Road
Wigston
Leicester LE18 4SE



Reprinted 2004



A catalogue record for this book is available from the British Library.

ISBN 1-85605-790-9

Produced by
Amber Books Ltd
Bradley's Close
74-77 White Lion Street
London N1 9PF
www.amberbooks.co.uk

Picture credits: photographs courtesy of US DOD, IWM, US National Archives.

Previously published as part of the reference set *War Machine*.

Printed in Italy

# Contents


Introduction 7

Fire and manoeuvre 8

What use is a pistol in combat? 10
World War I pistols 12
World War II pistols 24
Modern pistols 34

Firepower in the hand 46
World War II sub-machine guns 48
Modern sub-machine guns 64

Rifles 80
World War I rifles 82
World War II rifles 90
Post war rifles 100

Development of the assault rifle 108
Modern assault rifles 110

Sniper rifles 126
Marksmanship 128
Sniping rifles 130

Machine guns 140
World War I machine-guns 142
World War II machine-guns 152
Modern machine-guns 164

Support weapons 178
World War II anti-tank weapons 180
World War II flamethrowers 192

Mortars in action 200
World War II mortars 202
Modern mortars and infantry support 212

Shotguns 222
Combat shotguns 224

Riot control 232
Riot control weapons 234

Land warrior 244
21st century combat weapons 246

Appendices and Further Reading 250
Glossary 251
Index 252

# Introduction

Throughout history, the humble footsoldier has depended on his personal weapon in combat, and today's soldiers are no exception. In fact the twentieth century saw a rapid development of the small arm, which shows little sign of slowing in the new millennium. *Small Arms* covers personal weapons from 1914 to the present day, moving from bolt-action rifles and revolvers to sub-machine guns, flamethrowers, assault rifles, and even non-lethal weaponry. The basic mechanical principles of firearms have not changed greatly since World War I, but modern small arms such as the M-16A4 are made from lighter yet harder-wearing materials, are designed to minimise recoil and remain fully operational even in the toughest of conditions.

Types of weapons move in or out of fashion – the sub-machine gun, so popular in the two world wars, is now a rare sight in a soldier's armoury, having been replaced by the assault rifle. Flamethrowers, too, are no longer common. However, shotguns are now accepted as important tools for urban and jungle fighting, while the increased likelihood of fighting in areas with high numbers of civilians has meant that non-lethal weaponry is an area which is being actively researched in many countries.

It is likely that major technological advances will change the nature of small arms in the near future. Heckler and Koch have already demonstrated their G11 rifle, which uses caseless ammunition – the propellant encases the bullet, and completely combusts on firing, meaning that no ejector system is necessary, resulting in a high rate of fire. Electromagnetically-propelled bullets are now being 'fired' soundlessly in experimental trials, and – perhaps a little further off yet – it seems portable beam weapons will no longer be the stuff of science fiction.

# Fire and manoeuvre

**Combat leaders at every military command level, from the two-man fire team to the multi-division corps, must know how to control, mass and combine fire with manoeuvre. They must identify the most critical targets quickly, direct fire onto them, and ensure that the volume of fire is sufficient to keep the enemy from returning fire effectively, and the unit from expending ammunition needlessly.**

*The essence of the fire and manoeuvre concept is that, in any team, one part is moving as the other provides, or is prepared to provide, fire for the first part's support or cover.*

The US army defines manoeuvre as the movement of forces supported by fire to achieve a position of advantage from which to destroy or threaten destruction of the enemy. Infantry forces move to gain a position of advantage over the enemy and to hold that advantage. They manoeuvre to attack enemy flanks, rear areas, logistics points and command posts. Manoeuvre, properly supported by fire, allows the infantry to close with the enemy and gain a decision in combat.

Firepower is the capacity of a unit to deliver effective fire on a target. Firepower kills or suppresses the enemy in his positions, deceives the enemy and supports manoeuvre. Without effective supporting fire, the infantry cannot manoeuvre. Before attempting to manoeuvre, units must establish a base of fire. A base of fire is placed on an enemy force or position to reduce or eliminate its ability to interfere with friendly manoeuvre elements.

## Basic unit

Fire and manoeuvre tactics are used by individual soldiers, fire teams, sections, squads and platoons, but the basic unit is usually the section or the squad.

In most armies, this consists of between eight and 10 men, commanded by a junior NCO. The section is divided into a rifle group and machine-gun group. The rifle group consists of up to six riflemen, who can act in pairs or in groups of four and two. The machine-gun group consists of the gunner and another NCO, who also serves as second-in-command of the section.

## Mutual support

Section tactics are based on the principle of simultaneous fire and movement. Thus, if the rifle group is moving, the machine-gun group should be static and ready to provide support or, if necessary, actually support the rifle group with fire. Clearly, the rifle group is vulnerable while on the move, and anything that can be done to keep the enemy's head down can only be helpful.

Likewise, particularly during the final stages of an assault, fire and manoeuvre will often be needed within the rifle group itself.

## Use of terrain

'Fire and manoeuvre' involves the combined use of weapons, movement and ground. The objective is to move with the minimum of casualties when in contact with the enemy. Suitable ground is used to protect the section from enemy fire when on the move, while fire from the static element of the section or platoon suppresses enemy fire at the moving element.

Fire and manoeuvre is practised at all levels so that, in a major attack involving a company or battalion, a combination of supporting fire from artillery, mortar, tanks, anti-tank guided weapons and aircraft are used to get dismounted infantry onto an objective.

At a much lower level, fire

*A British infantryman dives for cover. Any such position, with protection offered by a tree or raised earth round the tree's roots, provides a measure of protection and thereby enhances the man's ability to provide supporting fire.*

***Armed with M16A1 assault rifles, these American infantry of the Vietnam War are moving along a path in the standard file disposition, which offers good capacity for returning flank fire.***

and manoeuvre is used within a platoon by using one section as the fire section and the other two sections as manoeuvre groups. Similarly, fire and manoeuvre can be used within a section between individual riflemen for fighting through the enemy position.

## Paired operations

Riflemen within a section are paired off not just so that they can fire and manoeuvre, but also so that they can help each other in a number of other practical ways. For instance, while one member of a pair is on sentry duty, the other could be preparing a meal; or if one is wounded, the other can apply first aid.

The basic section formations are Single File, File, Arrowhead, Spearhead, Diamond, and Extended Line. The formation that the section should adopt depends on six factors:
1. The country in which it is moving.
2. The likely direction of enemy fire.
3. How far the soldiers can see.
4. How the section can best be controlled.
5. The need to produce the maximum fire effect.
6. Who has control of the air.

## Formations

Single File is the most basic form of military formation, and may be the only one possible in jungle. It is excellent for moving along hedges or the edge of a wood, and ideal for moving through a narrow gap in, for instance, a minefield. It is easy to control, particularly at night, and it is least vulnerable to fire from a flank. However, it is very vulnerable to frontal fire, and makes it difficult to fire to the front.

File can be used for movement along a path or track wide enough to permit men to move on both of its sides. Again, this formation is easy to control and useful at night, but it makes a concentrated target for enemy fire.

Arrowhead is probably the most widely used formation for moving across country. The machine-gun group is put on the flank from which an attack is most likely.

Spearhead is a variant of Arrowhead, and can be used when there is no need to deploy the gun group to one particular flank. The gun group is kept in the centre, forming the shaft of the 'spear', ready to deploy to either flank depending on the threat.

Both Arrowhead and Spearhead are good for producing fire against frontal attack. However, both formations are difficult to control, particularly when engaged by flanking fire.

Diamond is often used when crossing open ground at night. It is easy to control and affords good all-round observation and protection. Fire can be returned in any direction. It can present a concentrated target, however.

Extended Line can be used as an assault formation, but it is difficult to control.

## Tactical flexibility

Whatever formation is chosen, the gun group should normally be on the open flank, or the flank that provides the best potential fire positions, such as undulating or high ground. The degree to which section members should be spaced depends on the ground, but as a rule they should be in range of the section commander's voice control.

***Supervised by an instructor, these British infantrymen are moving across a simulated battlefield in line formation, offering good firepower to the front but only limited defence against fire from a flank.***

# What use is a pistol in combat?

**The pistol has been a factor in warfare almost from the invention of the firearm. In the early days, its use was confined to officers and cavalrymen, and with longer ranges between opponents becoming the norm it seemed that the inherent short range of the weapon meant that the use of the pistol in battle was coming to an end. Paradoxically, however, soldiers continued to favour the pistol as a specialist personal weapon. Clearly it is of some use after all.**

*The modern handgun is essentially a close-range weapon. An expert can shoot accurately out to around 50 m (164 ft), providing they are not under pressure, but in untrained hands it is rarely so accurate.*

An easy answer to the often-posed question 'What use is a pistol in combat?' is 'not much'. The pistol, be it a revolver or automatic, has only a very limited range and at best (and in the hands of a trained marksman) it has very little other than a nuisance value beyond a range of 40-50 m (45-55 yards). It is also a weapon that is very prone to be pointed in the wrong direction – it is relatively easy to keep a long weapon such as a rifle pointed towards an enemy, but all too easy to point a pistol at a friend in the heat of the moment. For such a small weapon, the pistol is quite demanding of industrial potential and skills, and even a simple example is not cheap when compared with, say, a much more lethal weapon such as a hand grenade. Another factor in combat is that the average projectile fired from a pistol has only a limited lethality and, although it may have a terrific impact at short ranges, it is not as lethal as a high-velocity projectile.

### Combat weapon

For all that, the handgun is still a much favoured combat weapon and even today soldiers venture into battle wearing pistols about their persons. There are two main reasons for this, and they can be oversimplified by being labelled 'convenience' and 'morale'.

The convenience factor is brought about by the simple fact that for many personnel on active service there is no alternative. There are numerous combat roles carried out by all manner of soldiers, airmen and sailors where it is quite simply impractical to carry any form of weapon larger than a pistol. Categories that come to mind without difficulty include tank crews, aircrew, frogmen and men carrying heavy equipment such as radio sets. They have no hands free to carry a weapon and very little space about the person or place of operations to stow anything larger than a pistol. On big vehicles such as tanks or trucks it is possible to carry a submachine gun or carbine, but on smaller vehicles this is not possible. Even so, at some stage in any combat operations it may be necessary to leave the sheltering confines of the vehicle, and some sort of weapon is still required for self-defence or survival. The latter factor is particularly important for aircrew who might be forced down behind enemy lines. Under such circumstances there is no alternative to the pistol.

### Confidence builder

The morale factor may be subdivided into two aspects. One is that wearing or flourishing a pistol gives an air of authority. The other aspect relates to morale alone: the carrying of a weapon such as

*Inaccurate though it is, the pistol does have an important military function. Many soldiers work in confined spaces, such as the interior of a tank, and only the pistol is small enough to allow a tank crewman to carry it as a self-defence weapon. Here a Panzer Leutnant fires his Walther P 38 against enemy tank-killing infantry as he bails out.*

a pistol imparts a measure of self confidence to the carrier. The air of authority is easily understood, for anyone pointing or holding a pistol is immediately regarded as someone who should be obeyed. Thus pistols become important symbols when dealing with sn unarmed or demoralised enemy, such as prisoners of war.

The self-confidence factor is less easily explained but is one that is understood by anyone who is operating or travelling in an unknown or hostile environment. This fact was well understood by the German forces who had to live and work in the occupied territories during World War II; every serviceman had to be armed for virtually his entire waking existence. Pistols were an easy way to interpret armed status, and consequently the servicemen had the secure knowledge that some form of weapon was always to hand should it become necessary. This self-confidence factor may perhaps be overstated but it is a factor that is well known to anyone who has ever had to operate in an unknown territory or situation, and in modern war combat is rarely confined to an easily defined front-line. Soldiers in rear areas are just as likely to come under attack from partisans or SAS-type units as their front-line counterparts are to come under attack from a known enemy.

***One major advantage which pistols have is that they are small, and can easily be hidden. For people who could not afford to be seen carrying weapons, like the French Resistance during World War II, that is a vital characteristic.***

### Status symbol

There is one further reason why the pistol is still carried in combat, and that is perhaps an offshoot of the two factors already described. Pistols are classic symbols of military status, and perhaps this is the reason why so many staff officers far from the battle area strap pistols to themselves.

Even so, many pistols carried by officers of staff rank are small-calibre weapons of very limited combat value and a far cry from the relatively large-calibre pistols carried by combat personnel.

There is one factor that has further limited the use of the pistol in combat, and that is that the factors listed above are as recognisable to an enemy as they are to the user. This was particularly true during World War I, when marksmen in the front-line trenches learned that attacking soldiers carrying pistols were more likely to be officers or senior NCOs and thus unit leaders.

Picking them off first tended to reduce the combat efficiency of the unit concerned; it was not long before even the most hidebound officers learned to carry rifles that rendered them indistinguishable from their men.

Their trouble was that once in the trench system the rifle was too cumbersome for the dangerous task of trench clearing. Close-quarter combat tasks such as trench clearing are to this day one aspect of combat where the pistol still has an important role to play.

## SERVICE PISTOLS MAIN TYPES

**Revolvers** generally fire more powerful rounds than automatics, but they require more training to be used effectively and are generally used by military police and security personnel.

**Self-loading pistols** are easier to use, and usually carry more rounds than a revolver.

**Concealed carry** pistols are small. They are designed for use in plain clothes or by off-duty soldiers, where it may be necessary to hide the fact that one is carrying a gun.

***Above right: Pistols designed for concealed carry are small, making them easier to hide in a pocket or in a holster concealed by a jacket. They are often issued to off-duty soldiers in high-risk areas.***

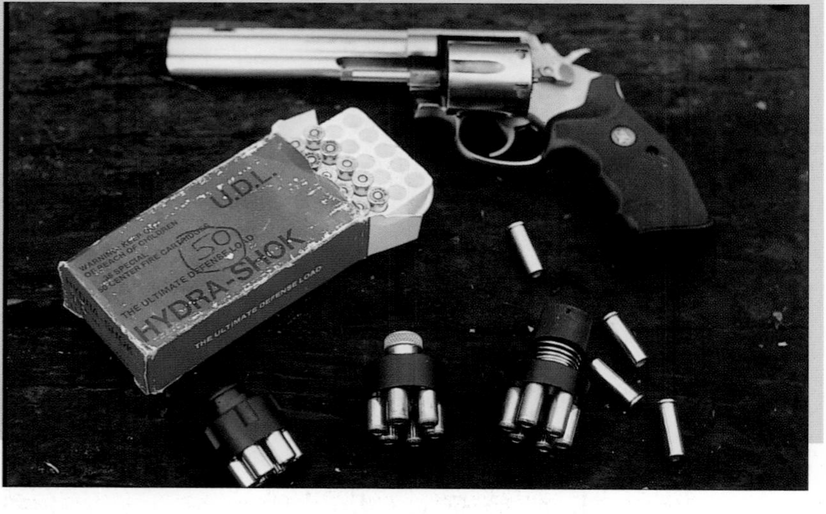


***Right: Revolvers are less complex and more rugged than automatics, and can fire more powerful rounds. But that power makes them quite a handful to shoot, requiring extensive training to achieve maximum efficiency.***

***Left: Self-loading service pistols are primarily self-defence weapons, but they are also used in roles such as house clearing and hostage rescue, where their short barrels make them quick to handle. Their higher magazine capacity gives the user extra firepower.***

# Austro-Hungarian pistols 8-mm and 9-mm pistols

The basic pistol of the Austro-Hungarian armies throughout World War I was the **8-mm Rast und Gasser Revolver M.1898**. This was a very robust and well made revolver, and was issued in large numbers to officers and NCOs of the imperial armies. But it was unusual on two counts: one was that it fired its own special 8-mm (0.315-in) cartridge, and the other was the unusual method of stripping. This was carried out by pulling down the trigger guard to expose the entire interior workings of the weapon for cleaning and repair. The latter was seldom needed as the M.1898 was an extraordinarily tough and reliable weapon. In fact the standard of production was so high that many were still in use during World War II.

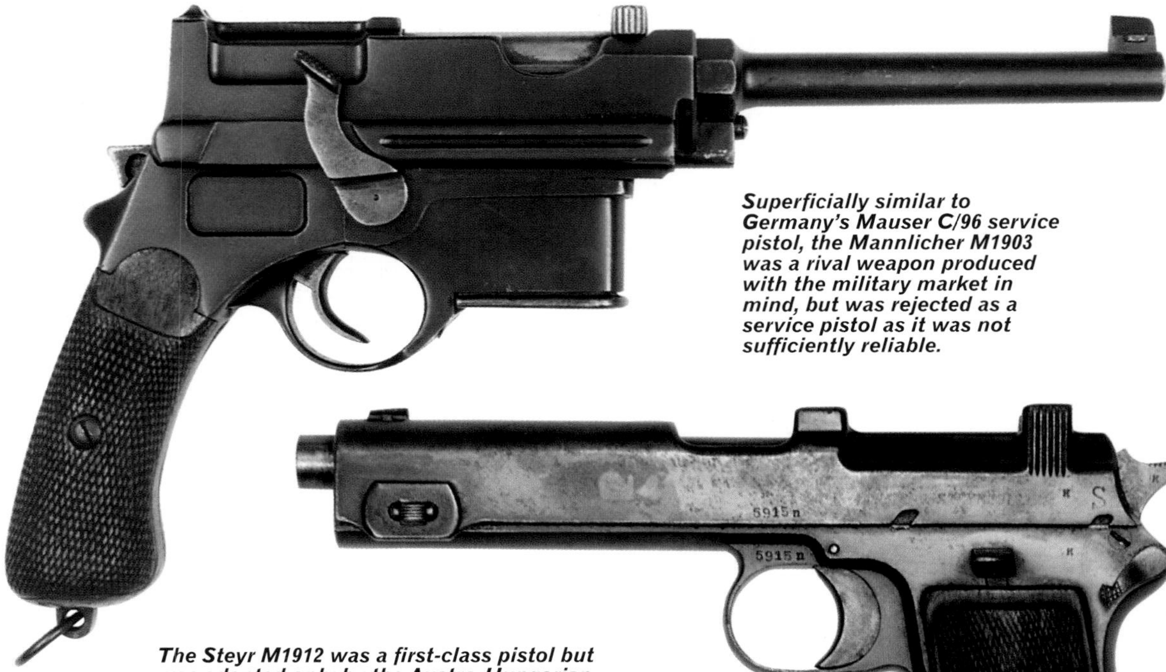

***Superficially similar to Germany's Mauser C/96 service pistol, the Mannlicher M1903 was a rival weapon produced with the military market in mind, but was rejected as a service pistol as it was not sufficiently reliable.***

***The Steyr M1912 was a first-class pistol but was adopted only by the Austro-Hungarian army, perhaps because it fired a unique 9-mm cartridge that was more powerful than the increasingly popular 9-mm Parabellum. It was called 'Steyr-Hahn' ('Steyr-Hammer') to distinguish it from the Roth-Steyr.***

## Automatic pistol

Despite the widespread issue of the M1898 revolver, in 1907 the Austro-Hungarian army decided also to adopt an automatic pistol. This was the **8-mm Repetierpistole M.07** (also known as the **Roth-Steyr**), a weapon that used a unique mechanism that no one has seen fit to copy. The M.07 used a long bolt that initially moved backward together with the barrel on firing, and then continued its rearward movement once the barrel had been held by stops. The complicated process of ejection and feeding the next round then commenced, ceasing only when the bolt and the barrel were back in their initial position. The process involved a straight travel and at one point rotary movement.

Despite all this complexity the M.07 was a sound service pistol, but was produced only for Austro-Hungarian military service. It too had a cartridge all of its own.

The M.07 was difficult to produce and in 1912 there appeared the **9-mm Repetierpistole M.12**. Widely known as the **Steyr-Hahn**, the M.12 used what was probably the strongest pistol action ever made, with a locked-breech mechanism operated by a rotating barrel. The 9-mm (0.354-in) cartridge was again special to the weapon, and therefore used by no other pistol. Another odd feature was the use of a fixed magazine, which was reloaded through the top by means of a charger clip.

The M.12 was officially the standard Austro-Hungarian side-arm of World War I and many were still used in World War II, by then in the hands of the Germans, to whom it was known as the **Pistole 12(oe)** after revision for the 9-mm Parabellum cartridge.

**SPECIFICATIONS**

| M.07 | M.12 |
|---|---|
| **Calibre:** 8 mm (0.315 in) | **Calibre:** 9 mm (0.354 in) |
| **Weight:** 1.03 kg (2.27 lb) | **Weight:** 1.02 kg (2.25 lb) |
| **Overall length:** 233 mm (9.17 in) | **Overall length:** 216 mm (8.5 in) |
| **Barrel length:** 131 mm (5.16 in) | **Barrel length:** 128 mm (5.1 in) |
| **Muzzle velocity:** 332 m (1,089 ft) per second | **Muzzle velocity:** 340 m (1,115 ft) per second |
| **Magazine capacity:** 10 rounds | **Magazine capacity:** 8 rounds |

# Browning pistols

The Belgian Fabrique Nationale d'Armes de Guerre (FN) was formed in association with John M. Browning after the latter left Colt, and the association produced many excellent weapon designs. The first pistol produced by the Browning/FN combination was the **Browning Modèle 1900**, a fairly straightforward pistol with few frills and chambered for the Browning 7.65-mm (0.301-in) cartridge. The first pistol based successfully on the blowback operating principle, the Modèle 1900 was never officially adopted as a standard service weapon, but the Modèle 1900 was produced and used in very large numbers (more than one million had been completed by 1912), many thousands finding their way into military hands, usually those of officers who had to supply their own side-arms. The weapon was also copied in very substantial numbers in China and Spain, usually without the benefit of any licence agreement. The Germans used the Modèle 1900 in World War II as the **Pistole 620(b)**, the main user being the Luftwaffe.

The **Modèle 1903** was the Belgian version of a Browning-designed Colt pistol produced to use a European cartridge known as the 9-mm Browning Long. The Modèle 1903 employed a straightforward blowback mechanism that could be used because of the relatively low power of the cartridge. The Modèle 1903 was adopted by the Belgian army and was also licence-produced in Sweden. Other user nations were Turkey, Serbia,

***The Modèle 1900 has the distinction of being the first Browning design to be made by FN of Herstal, the beginning of a long and successful association.***

Denmark and the Netherlands, and to the Germans in World War II the weapon was the **Pistole 622(b)**. Some versions could be used with a detachable shoulder stock that doubled as the weapon's holster.

### Modèle 1910

Perhaps the most important of the World War I Browning pistols was the attractive **Modèle 1910**. This weapon was placed on the market in 1912, and was immediately recognised as an ideal officer's side-arm. It was also accorded the accolade of being copied widely, often without any form of licence agreement. Produced to fire either the 7.65-mm (0.301-in) or 9-mm (0.354-in) Short cartridge, the latter also known as the 0.380 ACP, the

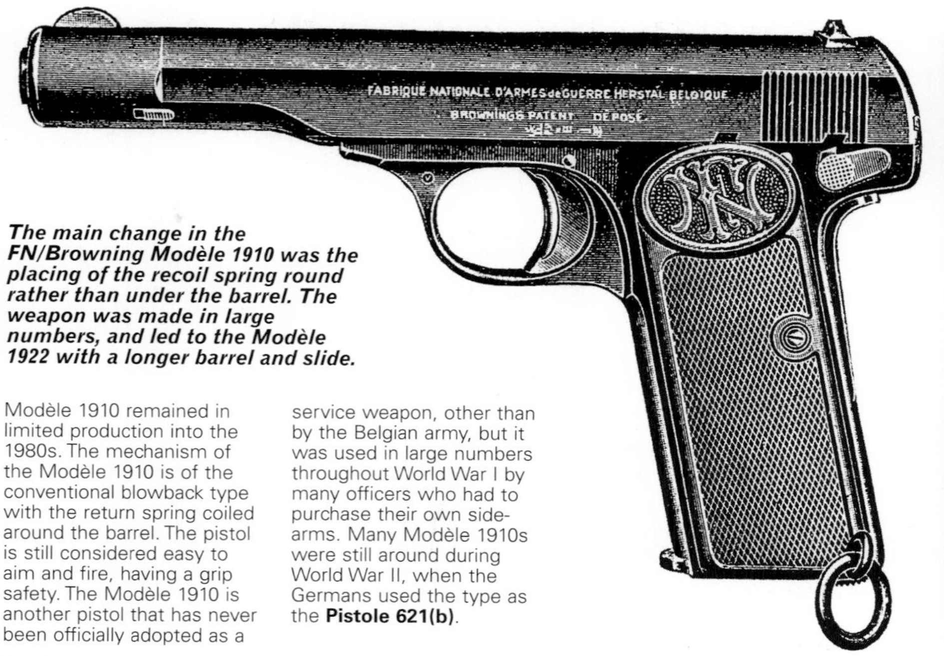


***The main change in the FN/Browning Modèle 1910 was the placing of the recoil spring round rather than under the barrel. The weapon was made in large numbers, and led to the Modèle 1922 with a longer barrel and slide.***

Modèle 1910 remained in limited production into the 1980s. The mechanism of the Modèle 1910 is of the conventional blowback type with the return spring coiled around the barrel. The pistol is still considered easy to aim and fire, having a grip safety. The Modèle 1910 is another pistol that has never been officially adopted as a service weapon, other than by the Belgian army, but it was used in large numbers throughout World War I by many officers who had to purchase their own side-arms. Many Modèle 1910s were still around during World War II, when the Germans used the type as the **Pistole 621(b)**.

**SPECIFICATIONS**

**Modèle 1900**
**Calibre:** 7.65 mm (0.301 in)
**Weight:** 0.625 kg (1.378 lb)
**Overall length:** 162.5 mm (6.4 in)
**Barrel length:** 102 mm (4.02 in)
**Muzzle velocity:** 290 m (951 ft) per second
**Magazine capacity:** 7 rounds

**Modèle 1903**
**Calibre:** 9 mm (0.354 in)
**Weight:** 0.91 kg (2 lb)
**Overall length:** 203 mm (8 in)
**Barrel length:** 127 mm (5 in)
**Muzzle velocity:** 320 m (1,050 ft) per second
**Magazine capacity:** 7 rounds

**Modèle 1910**
**Calibre:** 7.65 or 9 mm (0.301 or 0.354 in)
**Weight:** 0.57 kg (1.26 lb)
**Overall length:** 154 mm (6.06 in)
**Barrel length:** 88.5 mm (3.48 in)
**Muzzle velocity:** 299 m (981 ft) per second
**Magazine capacity:** 7 rounds

# Lebel revolvers Modèles 1873, 1874 and 1892

The first French military revolvers were the **Modèle 1873** and **Modèle 1874**. When they were first issued they fired an 11-mm (0.433-in) cartridge that used black powder, although after 1890 a more modern propellant was substituted and some were even converted to fire the new 8-mm (0.315-in) cartridge. The only visual differences between the Modèles 1873 and 1874 was that the Modèle 1874 had cylinder flutes while the Modèle 1873 did not.

### Long service history

With their fixed frames and gate-loaded cylinders, these two revolvers were still in use during World War I (many in fact survived until World War II), but were largely replaced by a more modern design known officially as the **Pistol Revolveur Modèle 1892** or the **Modèle d'Ordnance**. To most soldiers it was simply the **Lebel**. The Lebel had evolved via an interim design that fired a new 8-mm cartridge, but this interim model was not considered satisfactory and was redesigned to the model 1892 standard by the design staff of the Saint Etienne arsenal. The Lebel was the first European revolver to incorporate a swing-out cylinder that considerably assisted rapid reloading: the cylinder hinged out to the right and spent cases were ejected using a central hand-operated rod that was normally situated under the barrel.

The Lebel fired a special 8-mm cartridge using a trigger mechanism of the double-action type, and the action was very robust and heavy, which was good enough for short-range work but not forgiving enough for target-range accuracy. To clean and repair the action the Lebel had what must be one of the best mechanism access systems of any revolver. A plate at the lower left-hand side of the frame could be hinged open in a forward direction to expose the entire trigger and cylinder operating systems. Changing or cleaning any part was then very simple.

The main drawback to the Lebel when used in close-quarter action was its cartridge, which was seriously underpowered and even at short ranges inflicted wounds that only rarely knocked down an enemy. Unless a bullet found a vital spot an enemy could still continue to function – after a fashion. This drawback did not detract from the in-service popularity of the Lebel during World War I, for many front-line soldiers valued its reliability under adverse conditions more than its hitting power. Being the first of its kind in Europe the Lebel was copied in both Spain and Belgium.

**SPECIFICATION**

**Modèle 1892**
**Calibre:** 8 mm (0.315 in)
**Weight:** 0.792 kg (1.75 lb)
**Overall length:** 235 mm (9.25 in)
**Barrel length:** 118.5 mm (4.665 in)
**Muzzle velocity:** 225 m (738 ft) per second
**Cylinder capacity:** 6 rounds

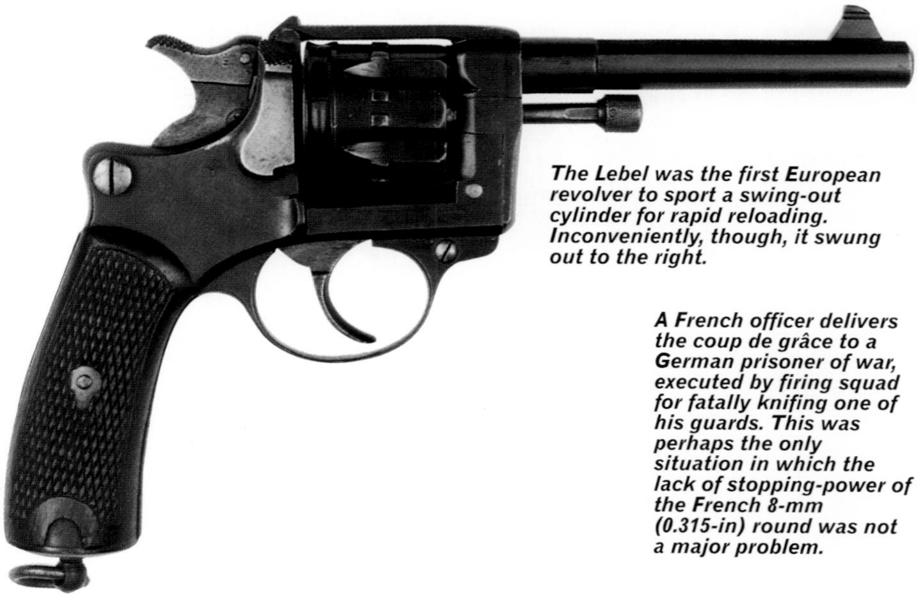

***The Lebel was the first European revolver to sport a swing-out cylinder for rapid reloading. Inconveniently, though, it swung out to the right.***

***A French officer delivers the coup de grâce to a German prisoner of war, executed by firing squad for fatally knifing one of his guards. This was perhaps the only situation in which the lack of stopping-power of the French 8-mm (0.315-in) round was not a major problem.***

# Beretta modello 1915
## 7.65-mm and 9-mm pistol

*The Beretta modello 1915 semi-automatic pistol had a somewhat 'rough and ready' look to it, but was nonetheless an effective and reliable weapon, well suited to the Italian army's needs in World War I.*

The **Pistola Automatica Beretta modello 1915** was the first of the Beretta semi-automatic pistols, but it lacked the degree of manufacturing finesse that became the hallmark of later Beretta models. This was a result mainly of the speed with with it was created and then manufactured. When Italy entered World War I in the course of May 1915, it did so at a time when the levels of all kinds of weapons in Italian service were very low, and pistols were no exception to this failing. Italian industry was rushed into a higher gear to churn out as many weapons as quickly as possible, and the Beretta modello 1915 was one of the results of this policy.

For all the rush with which it was created and placed into production, the modello 1915 was characterised by all the basic features that were to become typical of later Beretta semi-automatic pistol designs. The slide had the cut-away section over the barrel that was to become an instant recognition feature, but the overall appearance lacked the degree of balance and class that were to appear later.

*An Italian 'Deathshead' pioneer, in full trench raiding kit, has a medieval appearance. In the savage close quarter fighting in the trenches, the entrenching tool and pistol were more sensible weapons than a bulky rifle; the body armour was heavy, but provided good protection. Note the wire-cutters carried on the belt.*

### Several calibres

Modello 1915 pistols were initially issued in 7.65-mm (0.301-in) calibre, but some were later produced to fire the special 9-mm (0.354-in) Glisenti cartridge; this later version had a more powerful return spring. A relatively small number were also produced to fire the 9-mm Short cartridge, a round much less powerful than the 9-mm Parabellum.

The mechanism of the modello 1915 was simple blowback and the firing mechanism used a concealed hammer. The 7.65-mm version did not use an ejector to force the spent cartridge cases from the weapon after firing. The cases were pushed out by coming into contact with the firing pin after this had been forced through the breech block by the hammer at full recoil; the versions firing the larger 9-mm cartridges all featured a conventional ejector stop.

As was to be expected under wartime conditions, there were several detail variations between models. A large safety catch with differing shapes and locations was one, and there were also changes in butt grip materials and finish. One thing these modello 1915 variants shared, as all its users appreciated, was an attractive combination of reliability and good handling. The modello 1915 introduced the basic pattern of what were later to become some of the finest automatic pistols ever produced. Even now the name Beretta stands for sound design and good finish, but any examination of a modello 1915 today reveals few of these features as obvious factors, though the examiner must also appreciate the rapidity with which the modello 1915 was committed to mass production.

The modello 1915 was not retained in service for long after the end of World War I, and by World War II the Italian forces had standardised another Beretta pistol, the modello 1934.

**SPECIFICATION**

| | |
|---|---|
| **Beretta modello 1915** | **Length of barrel:** 84 mm (3.31 in) |
| **Calibre:** 7.65-mm (0.301-in) or 9-mm (0.354-in) Glisenti | **Muzzle velocity:** (9-mm Glisenti) 266 m (873 ft) per second |
| **Weight:** 0.57 kg (1.25 lb) | **Magazine:** 8-round box |
| **Length overall:** 149 mm (5.87 in) | |

# Glisenti modello 1910 and Brixia modello 1912
## 9-mm pistols

The **Pistola Automatica Glisenti modello 1910** was often known just as the Glisenti, but an essentially similar pistol was also issued to the Italian army and known as the **Brixia**. The initial pistol, the Glisenti, was designed in Switzerland by two Swiss engineers, but initial production was undertaken in Italy during 1905 at the Turin factory of the Societa Siderurgica Glisenti. During 1910 the pistol was accepted for service with the Italian army. Two years later, there appeared the **modello 12** produced by the Brixia concern. The modello 1912 was almost identical in appearance and operation to the modello 1910, but lacked the grip safety. For simplicity's sake these two pistols will be treated as one and the same.

The Glisenti modello 1910 used a mechanism that employed a locked-breech system, but for various design reasons this system was not very effective. The pistol could not, therefore, make use of full-power cartridges such as the 9-mm (0.354-in) Parabellum type, but instead had to fire its own special cartridge with a less powerful charge. The difficulty with this special cartridge, not least for safety reasons, was that it was virtually identical in shape, appearance and weight to the Parabellum round, a fact which meant that the Parabellum cartridge was not all that infrequently loaded in place of the Glisenti round: the use of the Parabellum round in the Glisenti pistol could, and often did, cause trouble. Some of these troubles could be very hazardous to the firer. Under normal circumstances this potential problem was easy to avoid through a proper look at the base of the cartridge, but under combat conditions the two types of cartridge could easily be mixed up.

### Design flaw

When firing the correct Glisenti cartridge, the modello 10 proved to be reliable enough, but suffered from one basic design weakness. The designers had been at pains to ensure good maintenance access by allowing almost the entire left-hand side of the pistol frame to be removable. This certainly achieved its object of mak-

***The Glisenti modello 1910 was not as popular as the Beretta: the left-hand side of the frame was designed for easy removal, but this reduced its strength, and the breech also accepted the 9-mm (0.354-in) Parabellum cartridge – far more powerful than the 9-mm Glisenti cartridge and able to shatter the weapon.***

ing the pistol's mechanism readily accessible for good cleaning and repair, but the incorporation of this removable plate made the entire pistol weak on that side. Under combat conditions the pistol frame could become distorted to an unacceptable degree, causing jams and also opening the way for other and potentially more severe problems; alternatively, the access plate could simply fall off.

Thus the modello 1910 was regarded with an increasing degree of user suspicion and, whenever possible, knowledgeable users opted for other types of sidearm, even if this was an obsolete but structurally safe type such as the 10.35-mm (0.4075-in) Pistola a Rotazione modello 89, a six-round revolver first issued in 1889 but based on a design of 1872.

This did not prevent the Glisenti pistols from being carried and used throughout World War I, and during World War II the weapon was not a rarity. If looked after and not subjected to too much hard use, the Glisenti and Brixia pistols were sound enough, but under severe combat conditions they often proved to be far less than satisfactory.

**SPECIFICATION**

| | |
|---|---|
| **Glisenti modello 1910** | **Length of barrel:** 95 mm (3.74 in) |
| **Calibre:** 9 mm (0.354 in) Glisenti | **Muzzle velocity:** 258 m (846 ft) per second |
| **Weight:** 0.8 kg (1.76 lb) | **Magazine capacity:** 7 rounds |
| **Length overall:** 211.2 mm (8.315 in) | |

# Japanese pistols

During World War I the Japanese armed forces used two types of sidearm: the **Pistol Revolver Type 26** and the somewhat more modern **Pistol Automatic Type 4**.

The 9-mm (0.354-in) Type 26 revolver was adopted in 1893, initially for cavalry use. It was a Japanese design that was typical of its era, for it was a mix of Western design features: the overall appearance owed much to the Belgian Nagant revolvers, the cylinder swing-out system was borrowed from the American Smith & Wesson revolvers, the facility for swinging open the lock mechanism came from the French Lebel pistols, and the action was derived from those of several European designs.

The Japanese decided to add a touch of their own and made the pistol a weapon capable of only double-action operation. To this they added a unique 9-mm cartridge. The result was an odd revolver whose two main attributes were a moderately high degree of serviceability, and a degree of structural strength sufficient to permit the weapon's use in two world wars.

The Type 4 automatic pistol was designed by one Kijiro Nambu and was never officially accepted for service with the Imperial Japanese forces. So many of the weapons were purchased and used by Japanese officers from the late 1900s onwards, however, that the design was provided with the official Type 4 designation. To the West the pistol became known as the **Nambu**, and the weapon was so widely used that all subsequent Japanese pistols were called Nambus.

## A stronger Glisenti

The Type 4 fired an 8-mm (0.315-in) cartridge, and was based on the use of an action not unlike that of the Italian Glisenti but with features to improve its structural strength. The use of this action gave the Type 4 a distinctive appearance. This weak ammunition was also used in the Type 100 submachine gun, which as a result lacked long-range firepower. There were several variations of the basic Type 4, the most drastic of which was a special 7-mm (0.276-in) **'Baby Nambu'** for use by staff officers.

Despite its widespread use the Type 4 was apparently not a particularly satisfactory pistol. One source of trouble was the striker spring that sometimes became too weak to fire a cartridge. Another was the generally low standard of steel used in manufacture, so that some components often broke under all but light use. However, the Type 4 remained in service for many years. Many were still in use during World War II despite the introduction of a generally improved design of similar appearance known as the **Type 1914 Nambu** (introduced in 1937).

**SPECIFICATION**

| | |
|---|---|
| **Type 26** | **Type 4** |
| **Calibre:** 9-mm (0.354-in) | **Calibre:** 8-mm (0.315-in) |
| **Weight:** 0.9 kg (1.98 lb) | **Weight:** 0.9 kg (1.98 lb) |
| **Length overall:** 239 mm (9.4 in) | **Length overall:** 229 mm (9 in) |
| **Length of barrel:** 119 mm (4.7 in) | **Length of barrel:** 120 mm (4.7 in) |
| **Muzzle velocity:** 277 m (909 ft) per second | **Muzzle velocity:** 325 m (1,066 ft) per second |
| **Feed:** 6-round revolver cylinder | **Magazine:** 8-round straight box |

***During the period of Japanese empire-building in China, soldiers carried the Type 4 automatic pistol in standard clamshell-type leather holsters. The 8-mm Type 4 weapon was never formally accepted for military service, and in 1937, prior to the march on Nanking, the improved Type 1914 began to be issued as a sidearm.***

# 9-mm Pistole '08 Service pistol

The **9-mm Pistole '08** remains one of the 'classic' pistols and it is still almost universally known as the **Luger**, after its designer Georg Luger who developed the pistol in the 1890s. Luger was from the Tyrol and had served in the Austro-Hungarian army before moving to Germany to work for the company of Ludwig Löwe.

There he met designer Hugo Borchardt, who had spent time in the USA working for Colt and Winchester. Borchardt had created one of the world's first self-loading pistols, and it was from the **Borchardt** pistol that Luger was to evolve his own design. Luger tidied up the Borchardt considerably, developing the pistol into the familiar form first manufactured by Deutsche Waffen und Munitions-fabriken (DWM) in 1898.

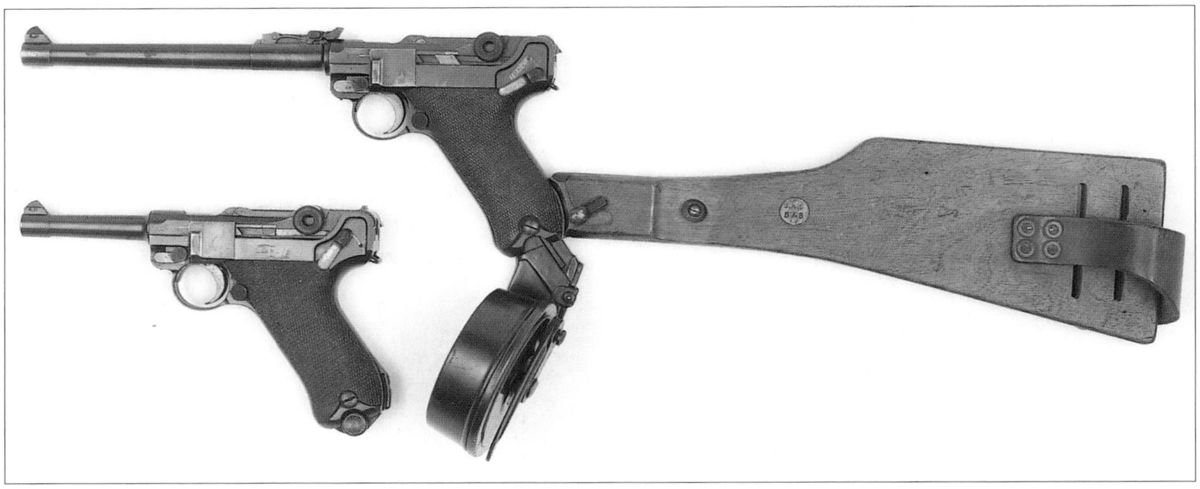

***Above: A standard Luger P '08 is shown beneath a long-barrelled 'Artillery' Model, introduced into service in 1917. The latter has been fitted with a 32-round 'snail' magazine, designed to provide extra firepower.***

## Luger enters service

Luger's design was very timely. At the end of the 19th century, armies all over the world had been developing an interest in magazine-fed, self-loading pistols to replace the large and heavy revolvers that they had been using for half a century. The automatic offered larger magazines in smaller packages, as well as a greater rate of fire. The only question was their reliability, which was then poor.

The first Luger pistols were sold to Switzerland in 1900, chambered for the 7.65-mm (0.301-in) cartridge. By 1904 the pistol was being re-chambered for the 9-mm (0.354-in) Parabellum cartridge, and this version was accepted for German navy use. In 1908 a slightly revised model was accepted by the German army and thereafter the P '08 was fabricated in hundreds of thousands.

These early models were produced in a variety of barrel lengths, the shortest being 103 mm (4.06 in) long. Other barrel lengths were 152 mm (6 in), 203 mm (8 in) and even 305 mm (12 in). These long-barrelled versions were usually issued with combined wooden shoulder stock/holster kits and were known as **Artillery Models**. They were frequently used with a 32-round 'snail' magazine.

## Working parts

All the variations of the P '08 used the same mechanism with its upward-opening toggle lock mechanism. As the pistol was fired all the hinge elements of the toggle were in line to lock the breech. The recoil forces had to overcome the mechanical advantage of the toggle mechanism before it would open, and once open the ejection and reloading processes could be carried out. A return spring in the butt reset everything ready to fire the next round.

The toggle device gave the P '08 a distinctive appearance, and the rake of the butt made the pistol a good one to aim and fire. The P '08 soon became a prized front-line weapon and war trophy, and there were never enough P '08s being produced to meet the ever-growing demands.

***The artillery model of the Luger had a 192-mm (7.5-in) barrel, and could be fitted with a flat board-like stock. It was designed to be used either as a pistol or as a short-range carbine.***

It was here that the disadvantages of the P '08 became apparent: the Luger was very well made but this meant that it was a difficult weapon to produce in quantity as virtually all its components had to be hand crafted. By 1917 much of the pistol's excellent pre-war detail finish had been omitted and the original grip safety was deleted altogether, never to return, even after 1918.

There was one other drawback to the P '08, and that was the fact that the toggle mechanism was not very tolerant of trench conditions; mud and dirt could all too easily clog the workings, often at the worst possible times, so the pistols demanded a lot of care. The soldiers did not mind, however; they liked the P '08, and after 1918 the model was kept in service. It was still in production in 1943 and even today many manufacturers find it well worth their while to produce 'look-alike' or direct copies for a seemingly insatiable market.

***As with all hand-held firearms, the Luger was used mainly as a secondary weapon, or as a personal protection weapon for troops working in confined spaces where a full-length rifle was not appropriate. Few worked in more confined spaces than the 18-man crew of Germany's first Panzer, the clumsy A7V.***

**SPECIFICATION**

**P '08**
**Calibre:** 9 mm (0.354 in) Parabellum
**Weight:** 0.876 kg (1.93 lb)
**Lengths:** overall 222 mm (8.76 in); barrel 103 mm (4.06 in)
**Muzzle velocity:** 320 m (1,050 ft) per second
**Effective range:** 50 m (55 yards)
**Magazine capacity:** (box) 8 rounds

# 9-mm Pistole '08 Parabellum

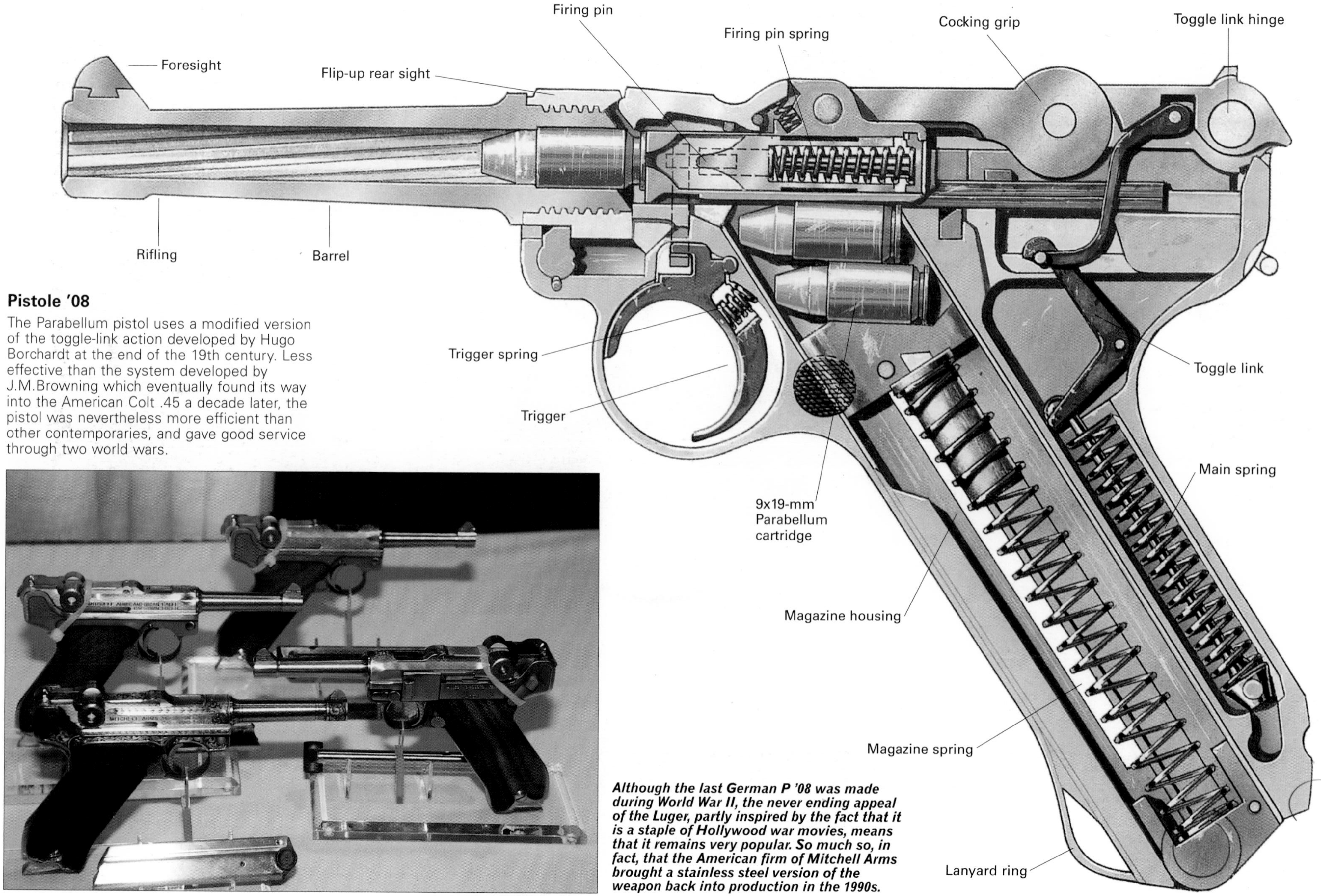


## Pistole '08

The Parabellum pistol uses a modified version of the toggle-link action developed by Hugo Borchardt at the end of the 19th century. Less effective than the system developed by J.M.Browning which eventually found its way into the American Colt .45 a decade later, the pistol was nevertheless more efficient than other contemporaries, and gave good service through two world wars.

***Although the last German P '08 was made during World War II, the never ending appeal of the Luger, partly inspired by the fact that it is a staple of Hollywood war movies, means that it remains very popular. So much so, in fact, that the American firm of Mitchell Arms brought a stainless steel version of the weapon back into production in the 1990s.***

# Mauser C/96 7.63-mm or 9-mm pistol

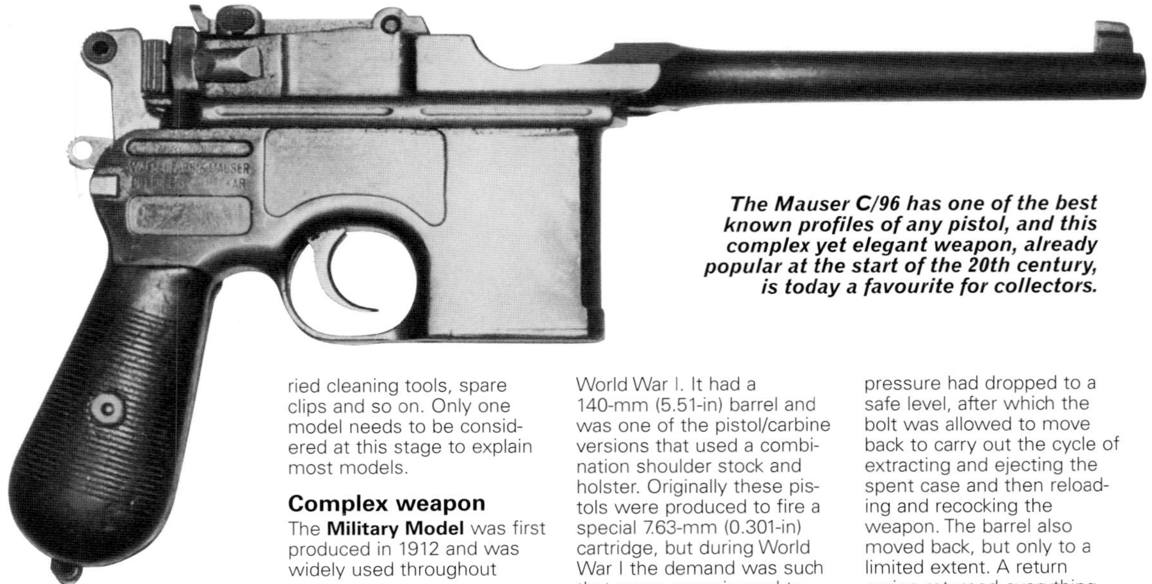

***The Mauser C/96 has one of the best known profiles of any pistol, and this complex yet elegant weapon, already popular at the start of the 20th century, is today a favourite for collectors.***

The original design of the **Mauser C/96** range of pistols was produced by three brothers named Feederle, who worked on the basic design until 1896 when it was placed in production by Mauser at Oberndorf-Neckar. Thereafter the C/96 and its derivatives were produced in a bewildering array of models to the extent that it is still a veritable minefield for the unwary historian.

The first C/96 pistols were pure hand guns, but it was not long before later models began to sprout shoulder stocks and other such appendages. Barrels started to increase in length until the weapons could be regarded almost as carbines rather than pistols, and some models of the C/96 became very complex pieces of kit together with their shoulder stock/holsters that also carried cleaning tools, spare clips and so on. Only one model needs to be considered at this stage to explain most models.

## Complex weapon

The **Military Model** was first produced in 1912 and was widely used throughout World War I. It had a 140-mm (5.51-in) barrel and was one of the pistol/carbine versions that used a combination shoulder stock and holster. Originally these pistols were produced to fire a special 7.63-mm (0.301-in) cartridge, but during World War I the demand was such that some were issued to fire the 9-mm (0.354-in) Parabellum cartridge: these had a large red number 9 engraved into their butts. Using both these cartridges the Military Model had a mechanism that can only be described as complicated. Rounds were fed into the magazine, situated in front of the trigger, from above by means of clips. At the moment of firing the breech was locked by a locking piece underneath the bolt that moved to and fro in a barrel extension. After firing, a system of tongues and bolt movement delayed the action until the chamber pressure had dropped to a safe level, after which the bolt was allowed to move back to carry out the cycle of extracting and ejecting the spent case and then reloading and recocking the weapon. The barrel also moved back, but only to a limited extent. A return spring returned everything for the next round. The mechanism depended on careful machining and exact tolerances, two factors that made the C/96 series difficult to manufacture and which led to its eventual military demise.

***Emperor Haile Selassie (seated) after his epic march back to Ethiopia. His bodyguard carried an extraordinary variety of weapons, including the Mauser C/96 sported by the man on the right.***

## Collectable item

The C/96 pistols were certainly formidable military weapons with a certain aura about them that survives to this day, for it seems that every pistol collector wants at least one C/96 in his collection. Such collectors have a wide choice, for the pistols were made in large numbers, not only in Germany but also in Spain and many other nations, including China, where the quantities involved were prodigious. Most of this 'overseas' production was entirely unofficial and therefore without a licence from Mauser.

**SPECIFICATION**

**Military Model**
**Calibre:** 7.63- or 9-mm (0.301- or 0.354-in)
**Weight:** 1.22 kg (2.69 lb)
**Length overall:** 308 mm (12.125 in)
**Length of barrel:** 140 mm (5.51 in)
**Muzzle velocity:** (7.63 mm) 433 m (1,420 ft) per second
**Magazine:** 10-round straight box

# Other German pistols

With trench warfare firmly established on the Western Front by the end of 1914, the armies of both sides demanded ever growing quantities of weapons and other war materials. Pistols were no exception to this general rule, and as most service pistols then in use had to be made virtually by hand, it was not easy to meet these demands in a hurry. Consequently something else had to be be found to equip the soldiers, and many store rooms were examined.

In some of them were found large numbers of **Reichs-Commissions-Revolver Modell 1879**. In fact some of them were still in reserve use by many units, despite their age. They fired an odd and low-powered 10.6-mm (0.417-in) cartridge, but were sturdy weapons as they had solid frames and a gate-loading system that required a rod to eject spent cartridge cases. These ancient revolvers were still around in 1918 and for many years after as they did not wear out. There was also a **Modell 1883** with a barrel shortened to a length of 126 mm (4.96 in).

**SPECIFICATION**

**Modell 1879**
**Calibre:** 10.6-mm (0.417-in)
**Weight:** 1.04 kg (2.29 lb)
**Length overall:** 310 mm (12.2 in)
**Length of barrel:** 183 mm (7.2 in)
**Muzzle velocity:** 205 m (673 ft) per second
**Cylinder capacity:** 6 rounds

## Commercial pistol

Another typical wartime expedient was the 7.65-mm (0.301-in) **Belholla-Selbstladepistole**. This was really a commercial semi-automatic pistol of wholly undistinguished design, but it was available in some numbers and was fairly easy to make. Many were issued to staff officers who had to carry a pistol and for whom the Belholla would be quite sufficient, freeing more useful combat pistols for front-line units. Thousands of Belholla pistols were made and issued, often under an array of sub-contractor names. The design was so simple that little thought was given to maintenance: the pistol could not be field stripped without recourse to a trained armourer with a substantial tool kit.

These two pistols were typical of the mix of commercial and ancient sidearms with which a great deal of the German army (and indeed other services) had to conduct their war. During this war the demand for pistols constantly outstripped supplies of these weapons, so it is hardly surprising that a wide assortment of other odd pistols was swept up into the German army's net. Pistols with such names as the **Dreyse** and the **Langenhan** were pressed into service as *Ersatz Pistolen* (substitute pistols) in quantities that ensured that their names would not be entirely forgotten, as otherwise they would probably have been, but few of them were designed for front-line service of the kind they often had to encounter, so many were less than satisfactory. The Langenhan pistol, made to the extent of at least 55,000 weapons between 1914 and 1917 by the Friedrich Langenhans Gewehr- und Fahrradfabrik of Zella St Basil, was the **FL-Selbstlader-Armee Modell Pistole**, a 7.65-mm (0.301-in) conventional blowback-operated weapon with feed for an eight-round box magazine carried in the butt. Many of these well-made Langenhans weapons were still being carried by German officers at the beginning of World War II.

***Above: A 7.65-mm (0.301-in) semi-automatic pistol designed for the commercial market, the Langenhan was adopted by the German army during World War I as demand for weapons exceeded the production capacity for current military side arms.***

***Left: One of the first commercial pistols to be produced in 9-mm (0.354-in) Parabellum was the RM & M Dreyse, which was manufactured only in limited numbers but nevertheless saw active service. The weapon was closely based on this earlier 7.65-mm (0.301-in) Dreyse Automatic.***

# Nagant Model 1895 7.62-mm pistol

The **Nagant Model 1895** revolver was originally a Belgian design produced as early as 1878. From then onwards the basic design was procured by Belgium, Argentina, Brazil, Denmark, Norway, Portugal, Romania, Serbia and Sweden, usually from Belgium and in various calibres (although copies were produced in Spain). However, the number of Nagant revolvers produced in Russia (initially under licence) dwarfed all output carried out elsewhere, to the extent that the Nagant is now regarded as a Russian weapon.

***The Nagant was a Belgian design adopted by many different armies, but so many were produced under licence in Russia that the revolver is now generally regarded as Russian. It incorporated an unusual gas-seal mechanism that added needless complication for little real benefit.***

## Early Russian pistols

The first Russian production of the Nagant was carried out at the Tula Arsenal in 1895 and continued until 1940. The version involved was the Model 1895, a variant designed to improve the overall efficiency of the basic revolver concept. The Model 1895 was an unusual revolver in many respects, not the least being the unique 7.62-mm (0.3-in) ammunition that used a brass cartridge case with a fully recessed bullet. The idea of this was that as the pistol was fired the cylinder was rammed forward into close contact against the end of the barrel, with the case forming a complete gas seal between the two assemblies. The idea behind this was supposedly to make the cartridge more efficient by minimising the loss of propellant gases through the small gap between the cylinder and the barrel. It was in fact a feature of doubtful value that added a degree of complexity to the requirement for a special cartridge, although the Russians thought much of it and retained the feature unchanged until production finally ceased.

## Two versions

The Tsarist army decided to perpetuate the differences between the ranks by issuing enlisted men with single-action revolvers while officers received double-action versions. There was also a noticeable difference between the finish of the two models, the single-action models often being left as bare metal while the officers' versions were plated or blued. Both were extremely sturdy and reliable weapons: they had to be to last under the conditions in which the Russian army usually fought. The frame was solid and the cylinder was fixed, with loading taking place through a gate on the right. A rod was used to eject spent cartridges cases.

The Model 1895 revolvers were produced in vast numbers, were used throughout World Wars I and II, and it was possible to encounter some examples in odd corners of the world into the 1980s. A few ammunition manufacturers still find it worth their commercial while to produce the special recessed ammunition, although today sales are only made to dedicated collectors.

**SPECIFICATION**

| | |
|---|---|
| **Nagant Model 1895** | **Length of barrel:** 110 mm (4.33 in) |
| **Calibre:** 7.62-mm (0.3-in) | **Muzzle velocity:** 272 m (892 ft) per second |
| **Weight:** 0.795 kg (1.75 lb) | **Cylinder capacity:** 6 rounds |
| **Length overall:** 230 mm (9.055 in) | |

# Webley & Scott self-loading pistols British 0.455-in pistols

The Webley & Scott self-loading pistols must rank as among the most awkward-looking pistols ever designed, but in use they proved reliable. The first of them was accepted for government service in 1912, mainly for police use, and by 1914 the **Webley Self-Loading Pistol Mk I** was in use by Royal Navy and Royal Marine landing or boarding parties. Later, more were issued to the newly formed Royal Flying Corps and to some Royal Horse Artillery battery personnel.

The basic design used a very positive locking system that ran in a series of angled grooves and lugs. This was just as well for the pistol continued to use the 0.455-in (actually 0.441-in/11.2-mm) cartridge but in a much more powerful form, so much so that for many years it remained the world's most powerful pistol cartridge. This cartridge had a charge so heavy that it could cause serious damage to pistol and user if fired from any other 0.455-in revolvers. Some pistols were produced to fire the 0.38-in (9.65-mm) Super Auto and 9-mm (0.354-in) Browning long cartridges, but few of these were used by the British military.

## Shoulder stock

The pistol had a a few odd design features all of its own, one being that it was possible to partially withdraw and lock the box magazine to allow single rounds to be fed into the chamber through the ejection slot, leaving the full magazine topped up for emergency use. There was provision on most versions for a flat wooden shoulder stock to be fitted to the butt for more accurate shooting at longer ranges.

These Webley & Scott self-loaders (the term 'automatic' was disliked by the British at the time) were massive pistols that took a lot of careful handling even at short combat ranges. They were well-built with a distinctive 'straight-line' appearance that was not helped by the almost square-set angle of the butt. This butt angle made the pistol rather difficult to fire instinctively, but deliberate shooting by a fully trained user could be quite accurate. If all else failed the pistols could be used as clubs as even when unloaded each weighed 1.13 kg (2.5 lb). However, these weapons were not generally liked. The Royal Horse Artillery got rid of theirs as soon as they could and the Royal Flying Corps were no more enthusiastic. As a result the Webley & Scott self-loaders were never accepted for full military service but the British armed forces continued to use the revolver for many years, officially until well after the end of World War II.

***Adopted by the Royal Navy in 1914 and later by the artillery and RFC, the ungainly Webley & Scott 0.455-in pistol was not particularly popular in service.***

***Naval aviation pioneer commander Samson and his Nieuport 10 prepare for another sortie over the Turkish lines at Gallipoli. Pistols were initially carried by airmen for personal defence in case of a forced landing.***

| SPECIFICATION | |
|---|---|
| **Webley Self-Loading Pistol Mk I** | barrel 127 mm (5 in) |
| **Calibre:** 0.441-in (11.2-mm) | **Muzzle velocity:** 236 m (775 ft) |
| **Weight:** 1.13 kg (2.5 lb) | per second |
| **Lengths:** overall 216 mm (8.5 in); | **Magazine capacity:** 7 rounds |

# Webley 0.455-in revolvers

## Webley & Scott Mks I and VI

The 0.455-in cartridge fired by the Webley revolvers had an actual calibre of 0.441 in (11.2 mm), and its design reflected experience gained in colonial warfare. The cartridge was designed to be a certain 'man-stopper' for close-range use against charging native hordes, and the heavy bullet and powerful charge were certainly adequate for the task. The pistol intended for use with this powerful cartridge was produced by Webley & Scott Limited of Birmingham, which produced its first 0.455-in pistol in late 1887.

The **Webley & Scott Mk I** was the forerunner of a host of similar models. The Mk I had a top-opening frame with an automatic ejecting device that pushed out spent cartridge cases as the frame opened. The butt had a distinctive shape that was termed a 'bird's head', and a lanyard ring was considered essential. A 102-mm (4-in) barrel was used, but later marks also used 152-mm (6-in) barrels.

## Submarks

After the Mk I came a large number of other marks and submarks with detail improvements and/or barrel length changes. The overall mechanism and design did not change much, although by the time the main World War I model appeared in 1915 the butt shape had changed and there had been some alterations to the sights. The **Mk VI** may be taken as typical of the World War I Webley 0.455-in revolvers, but in addition

***Webley revolvers are arguably the toughest and most accurate handguns ever made. Their calibre is 0.441 (11.2 mm) but, curiously, they have always been referred to as 0.455 (11.6 mm). The lower gun is the Mk I, introduced in 1887, the weapon above is the Mk IV of 1913.***

*Webley revolvers fired some powerful rounds, including the infamous hollow-pointed 'manstopper', but it needed a lot of training to master the recoil. After the war, the British Army reverted to 0.38-in calibre and since 1918 the trend in all armies has been away from large cartridges, despite the recent popularity of magnum loads in the civilian market.*

many of the earlier marks remained in use.

The Mk VI was a very well made and solid revolver. It was also large and something of a handful to tote and fire. The powerful cartridge produced an equally powerful recoil and it was considered to have a useful combat range of only a few metres. For trench warfare this was ideal, and the Webleys were a preferred weapon for trench raids and close-quarter fighting. Under such circumstances the Webleys had one major advantage and that was that they were very forgiving of the dirty and muddy conditions under which they were often used. Even if a Webley jammed or ran out of ammunition it could still be used as an effective club. This attribute was developed by the introduction of the Pritchard-Greener revolver bayonet, a spike-type bayonet/trench knife that fitted over the muzzle with the metal hilt resting against the revolver frame. This fearsome pistol/bayonet combination appears to have been little used as it was never approved officially.

A more useful device was a charger that held six cartridges ready for instant loading into the opened cylinder.

**SPECIFICATION**

| | |
|---|---|
| **Webley Mk VI** | barrel 152 mm (6 in) |
| **Calibre:** 0.441-in (11.2-mm) | **Muzzle velocity:** 189 m (620 ft) per second |
| **Weight:** 1.09 kg (2.4 lb) | **Cylinder capacity:** 6 rounds |
| **Lengths:** overall 286 mm (11.25 in); | |

# Webley Fosbery revolver 0.455-in automatic revolver

The **Webley Fosbery** revolver was designed by Colonel G. V. Fosbery VC, and is in a class of its own as it is an automatic revolver. The original patent was taken out in 1896 and production was taken up by Webley & Scott shortly after that, the resultant pistols being chambered for the standard 0.455-in (actually 0.441-in/11.2-mm) cartridge.

The action of the Webley Fosbery was unique. On firing, the recoil drove back the barrel, cylinder and top frame along a slide over the butt. This cocked the hammer and a return spring inside the butt then drove the whole assembly back to its initial position. As it did so a stud in the slide ran through an angled groove machined into the cylinder to turn it to the next cartridge position. The system had its attractions to those who thought that they had only to keep pulling the trigger to keep firing rapidly. In practice it was not that simple. One immediate drawback was that the action required a great deal of handling: the entire top frame moving back and forth added to the already considerable movement caused by the heavy recoil, and so made the pistol something of a brute to fire. Another drawback was that the firer had to hold the butt very firmly indeed or the entire system would not function, for the user's grip acted as the anchor for the entire mechanism.

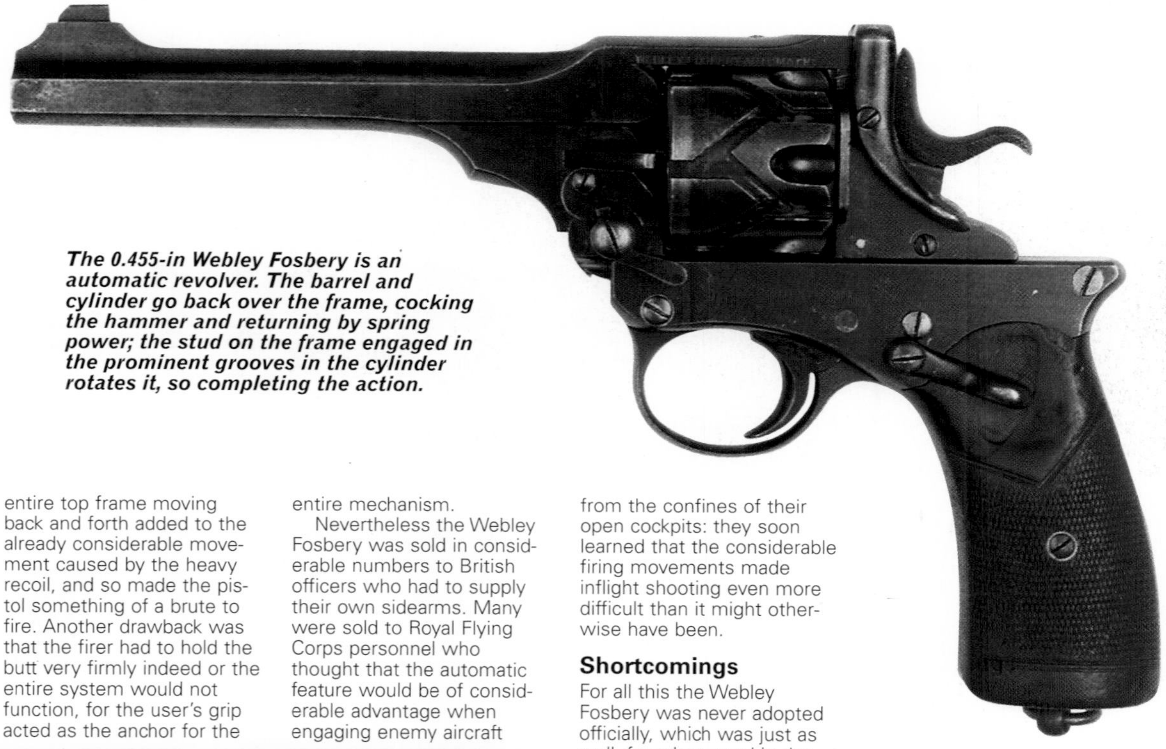

*The 0.455-in Webley Fosbery is an automatic revolver. The barrel and cylinder go back over the frame, cocking the hammer and returning by spring power; the stud on the frame engaged in the prominent grooves in the cylinder rotates it, so completing the action.*

Nevertheless the Webley Fosbery was sold in considerable numbers to British officers who had to supply their own sidearms. Many were sold to Royal Flying Corps personnel who thought that the automatic feature would be of considerable advantage when engaging enemy aircraft from the confines of their open cockpits: they soon learned that the considerable firing movements made inflight shooting even more difficult than it might otherwise have been.

## Shortcomings

For all this the Webley Fosbery was never adopted officially, which was just as well, for when used in the trenches the type's major drawback became all too obvious. This was that the action relied upon smooth movement through carefully machined grooves, any clogging of those grooves by dirt or mud resulted in a jam. As most of the grooves involved were fully exposed they soon became full of all manner of trench debris and it took constant attention to keep them clean. Many officers gave up the task and took up other less troublesome pistols.

*The Webley Fosbery revolver utilised a unique operation, but fell from favour as a result of its tendency to jam under trench conditions.*

**SPECIFICATION**

| | |
|---|---|
| **Webley Fosbery** | barrel 152 mm (6 in) |
| **Calibre:** 0.441-in (11.2-mm) | **Muzzle velocity:** 183 m (600 ft) per second |
| **Weight:** 1.25 kg (2.755 lb) | **Cylinder capacity:** 6 rounds |
| **Lengths:** overall 279 mm (11 in); | |

# Savage Model 1907 & Model 1915 Pistols

The **Savage Model 1907** pistol was produced by the Savage Arms Corporation located at Chicopee Falls, Massachusetts, and though it secured limited commercial sales, its only military customer was the Portuguese armed forces. This has led to the Savage pistols being identified almost exclusively with the Portuguese, though their origins were definitely American.

The Model 1907 was originally designed to take part in the US army trials that led to adoption of the Colt M1911 semi-automatic pistol. The Model 1907 showed up well in the trials, and although the decision went elsewhere the Savage Corporation attempted to sell the design abroad. It was not successful until 1914, when the Portuguese found themselves cut off from their usual German suppliers, who were selling them versions of the Pistole 08 (the Luger). Portugal therefore decided to adopt the Savage pistol in its original US Army competition form as the **M/908,** and in a slightly modified version as the **M/915**, both rechambered from their original 0.45 in (11.43 mm) to 7.65 mm (0.315 in).

## Retarded blowback

The Model 1907 used a retarded blowback mechanism, an operating system rarely used in pistols. On the Model 1907 this involved the barrel turning through lugs before the slide was allowed to move to the rear after firing, but the system adopted by Savage was only marginally more effective than a simple blowback. It was effective enough with the 7.65-mm cartridge employed but would probably have been less successful with a more powerful cartridge.

The Portuguese found the Savage pistols effective enough, but there was one unfortunate safety problem. It was possible to rest the striker attached to the cocking spur (the design featured a concealed hammer) in such a way that the striker touched the base of a round in the chamber. Any sudden jar could therefore fire the weapon, often to what was at best the user's disadvantage. This led the Portuguese to develop drills that ensured the pistol was cocked only when required and if no firing was carried out the pistol had to be unloaded again. This was obviously not a good feature for a combat pistol, so as soon as they could the Portuguese reverted to procurement of 9-mm Parabellum pistols of various types; they also used the British 0.455-in (11.56-in) Webley revolvers.

***This Savage Automatic belongs to the Weapons Museum at the School of Infantry, Warminster. The Savage design originated from the 1904 patent of E. H. Searle, and was an entry to the US army pistol trials of 1907, which were won by Colt.***

| SPECIFICATION | |
|---|---|
| **M/908** | **Weight:** 0.568 kg (1.252 lb) |
| **Calibre:** 7.65-mm (0.315-in) | **Muzzle velocity:** 290 m (950 ft) per second |
| **Length overall:** 165 mm (6.5 in) | **Feed:** 10-round straight box |
| **Length of barrel:** 95 mm (3.75 in) | |

# Revolver, Caliber .45, M1917 Pistols

By 1916 the demand for all types of war materials and weapons was outstripping the production capabilities of British and Commonwealth industries, so orders for various items were placed in the USA. Among these items were revolvers, and to save time it was decided to adopt American designs rechambered to accept the British 0.455-in (actually 0.441-in/11.2-mm) pistol cartridge. Many thousands of these pistols were accordingly placed into production by Smith & Wesson and the Colt Firearms Company, and were duly delivered to the British and Commonwealth armed forces.

Then in 1917 the USA entered World War I and found itself even shorter of weapons to equip its expeditionary force than the British had ever been. It was time for yet another hasty rearrangement of production priorities, and the British 0.455-in revolvers were quickly altered to accommodate the standard American 0.45-in (11.43-mm) pistol cartridge. This caused some problems, not in the pistol designs which remained unchanged (and virtually identical to each other) but in the loading. The British cartridge case had a distinct rim at its base while the American case, intended for use in automatic pistols, did not. Therefore as the cartridges were placed in the cylinder chambers they slipped through. This was avoided by loading the American rounds in pressed steel 'half-moon' clips, each holding three rounds. The clips allowed the rounds to be loaded quickly and held the cases in place for firing, and were also an aid to rapid unloading.

## Slight differences

Both weapons were produced with the basic designation Revolver, Caliber .45, M1917, the maker's name being inserted to denote the different models somewhat grandiloquently as the **Revolver, Caliber .45, Smith & Wesson Hand Ejector, M1917** and the

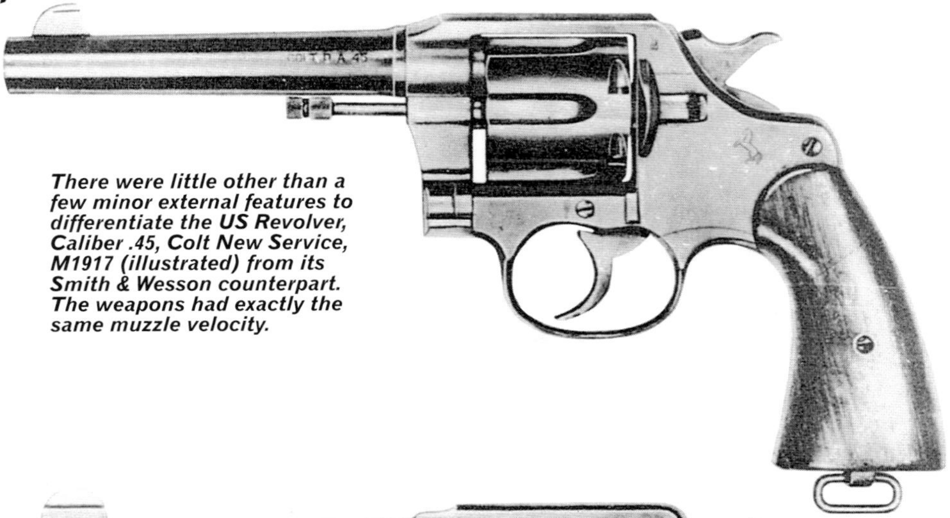

***There were little other than a few minor external features to differentiate the US Revolver, Caliber .45, Colt New Service, M1917 (illustrated) from its Smith & Wesson counterpart. The weapons had exactly the same muzzle velocity.***

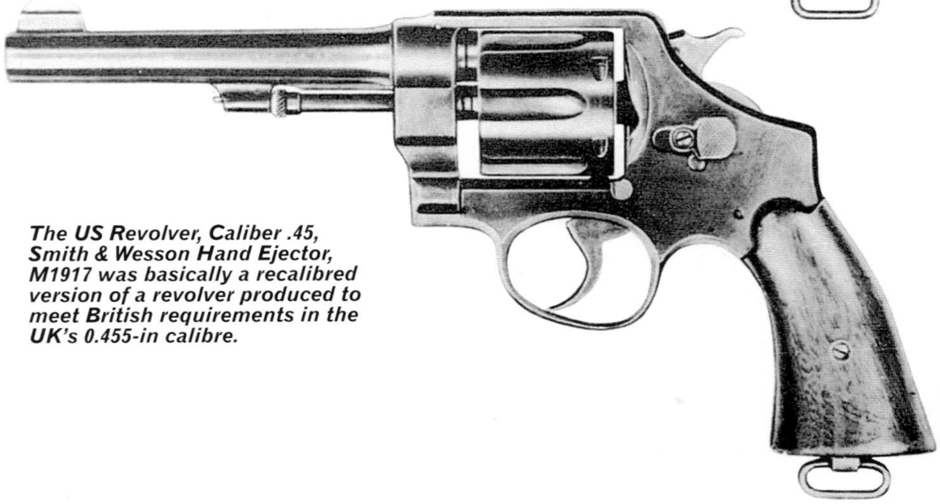

***The US Revolver, Caliber .45, Smith & Wesson Hand Ejector, M1917 was basically a recalibred version of a revolver produced to meet British requirements in the UK's 0.455-in calibre.***

| SPECIFICATION | |
|---|---|
| **Revolver, .45, M1917** | 1.02 kg (2.25 lb) |
| **Calibre:** 11.43-mm (0.45-in) | **Muzzle velocity:** 253 m (830 ft) per second |
| **Length overall:** 274 mm (10.8 in) | **Feed:** 6-round cylinder using two 3-round half-moon clips |
| **Length of barrel:** 140 mm (5.5 in) | |
| **Weight:** (Colt M1917) 1.134 kg (2.5 lb); (Smith & Wesson M1917) | |

**Revolver, Caliber .45, Colt New Service, M1917**.

Although the two revolver pistols seemed virtually identical to their users, they did in fact have a few slight differences. The Colt revolver was based on the 'New Service' model dating from 1897, while the Smith & Wesson pistol was a 'new' design based on the company's existing range of models. Both revolvers were based on the use of swing-out cylinders which, on the M1917 versions, had recesses in their rear faces to accommodate the two three-round half-moon clips. Another notable figure of the two weapons was that they were large and heavy revolvers offering a high degree of strength and therefore safety when firing the powerful round designed for a semi-automatic pistol.

Once they had been established in service with the US Army, both of these revolvers proved themselves to be rugged and reliable types. The three-round clip system gave no trouble and, in fact, proved to be so successful that it was even adopted for service by other nations such as Brazil, which made large-scale purchases of the Smith & Wesson M1917 in 1938. Both pistols were still in first-line service during World War II, although by then most were used by the British armed forces although the US military police retained the type, especially in its Colt version.

***In 1917 the US Army adopted revolvers chambered for the 0.45-in Auto cartridge of the M1911 automatic. US desire for 0.45-in calibre stemmed from the failure of 0.38-in weapons such as this Colt M1892 to stop charging Filipinos.***

# Colt M1911 Pistol

The semi-automatic pistol generally known as the **Colt M1911** is certainly one of the best known personal weapons ever placed in production. Though formally adopted for US army service in 1911, the pistol had its design origins in the Colt Browning Model 1900, which was chambered for the new 0.38-in (9.65-mm) Colt Automatic cartridge. The Model 1900 was a semi-automatic pistol of the recoil-operated type, and formed the basis of a larger-calibre hand gun required by the US army as a genuine 'man stopper' of a weapon. The need for such a capability had been discovered in the Philippines, where close-quarter combat against insurgents and rebels, often fighting in a drugged state, had revealed that the 0.38-in bullet lacked the kinetic energy to stop a charging man in his tracks and knock him backward before he could use his knife or short sword.

The new ACP (Automatic Colt Pistol) cartridge was of 0.45-in (11.43-mm) calibre. Competitive trials in 1907 led to the 1911 standardisation of the Colt pistol as the **Pistol, Automatic, Caliber .45, M1911**. Manufacture was slow to get into its stride, but on the USA entry into World War II in April 1917 the US army had received some 55,553 such pistols. Thereafter production accelerated rapidly, some 450,000 M1911 pistols having been completed by Colt and Remington by November 1918.

## Product improvement

Analysis of World War I operations on the Western Front suggested that the M1911 could be improved, and in 1926 the **M1911A1** was standardised. The changes introduced in this model were not major: the main-spring housing was changed for a smooth, flat surface to a knurled, arched surface; the trigger was shortened and given a serrated surface; the tang was lengthened; the front sight was widened; finger clearance cuts were introduced on the receiver immediately behind the trigger; the geometry of the rifling was altered; and the grip safety configuration and hammer spur outlines were modified.

The basic method of operation remained unaltered in a weapon that is characterised by one of the strongest mechanisms ever placed in production. However, there can be no denial of the fact that the pistol requires considerable user training for effective employment.

Production of the M1911A1 by Colt Firearms, Remington Rand, Union Switch & Signal, and Ithaca before and during World War II was some 1.95 million, and the weapon was also made in other countries, although often to lower standards. In World War II the Germans used modest quantities of captured weapons with the designation **Pistole 660(a)** or, for Norwegian-made weapons, the designation **P 657(n)**.

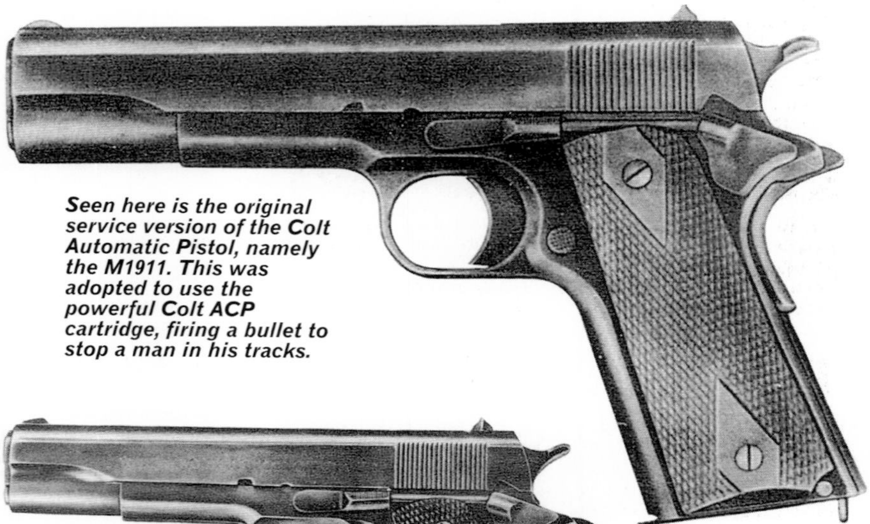

***Seen here is the original service version of the Colt Automatic Pistol, namely the M1911. This was adopted to use the powerful Colt ACP cartridge, firing a bullet to stop a man in his tracks.***

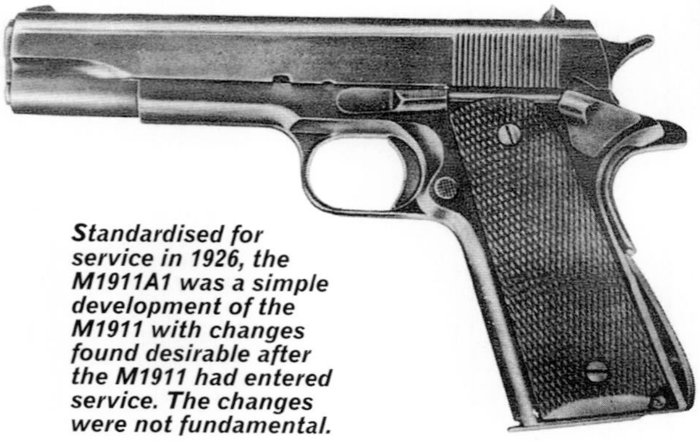

***Standardised for service in 1926, the M1911A1 was a simple development of the M1911 with changes found desirable after the M1911 had entered service. The changes were not fundamental.***

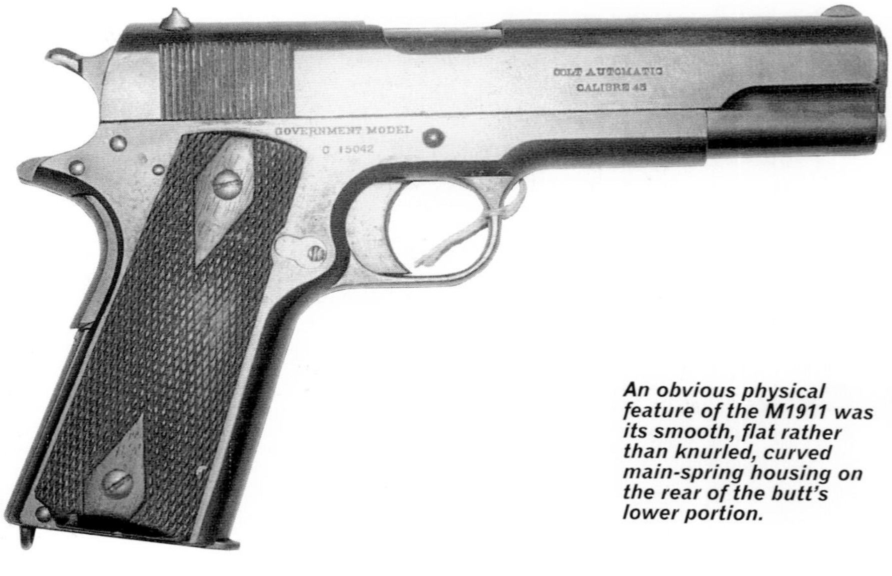


***An obvious physical feature of the M1911 was its smooth, flat rather than knurled, curved main-spring housing on the rear of the butt's lower portion.***

| SPECIFICATION | |
| --- | --- |
| **Colt M1911A1** | **Weight:** 1.36 kg (3 lb) |
| **Calibre:** 0.45-in (11.43-mm) | **Muzzle velocity:** 252 m (825 ft) per second |
| **Length overall:** 219 mm (8.6 in) | **Feed:** 7-round box magazine |
| **Length of barrel:** 128 mm (5.03 in) | |

# Enfield No. 2 Mk 1 and Webley Mk 4 Pistols

During World War I the standard British service pistol was the 0.455-in (11.56-mm) Webley revolver in one or other of its forms. These were very effective weapons for the type of close-quarter fighting that typified the trench combat of that war. However, their weight and bulk made the pistols notably difficult to handle correctly and effectively, unless a great deal of training had been provided and then followed by constant practice, both of them commodities that were in short supply at the time.

After 1919 the British army decided that a smaller pistol firing a heavy 0.38-in (9.65-mm) round would be just as effective as the larger-calibre weapon but would offer the advantages of being easier to handle and of requiring less training. As a result Webley and Scott, which up to that time had been pistol manufacturer of a virtually official status for the British armed forces, took its 0.455-in (11.56-mm) revolver, scaled it down and offered the result to the military.

## Double-action Enfield

To the company's chagrin, the military simply took the design, made a few minor alterations and placed the result in production as an 'official' government design produced at the Royal Small Arms Factory at Enfield Lock in Middlesex. This procedure took time, for Webley and Scott offered its design in 1923 and Enfield Lock took over the design in 1926. Webley and Scott was somewhat nonplussed at the course of events but proceeded to market its 0.38-in (9.65-mm) revolver, known as the **Webley Mk 4**, all over the world with limited success.

The Enfield product became the **Pistol, Revolver, No. 2 Mk 1**. In service the pistol proved to be sound and effective. However, the increasing degree of mechanisation in this period meant that large numbers of these pistols were issued to the crews of tanks and other mechanised equipments, who rapidly made the unfortunate discovery that the long hammer spur had a tendency to catch on the many internal fittings of tanks and other vehicles with what could be nasty results. This led to a redesign in which the Enfield pistol had its hammer spur removed altogether and its trigger mechanism lightened to enable the weapon to be fired only as a double-action pistol. This became the **Pistol, Revolver, No. 2 Mk 1***, and existing Mk 1 weapons were modified to the new standard. The double action made the pistol very difficult to use accurately at all except minimal range, but that was a matter of little consequence.

## World War II service

Webley and Scott re-entered the scene during World War II, when delivery of the Enfield pistol was too slow to meet ever-expanding demand. Thus the Webley Mk 4 was ordered to eke out supplies, and Webley and Scott went on to supply thousands of its design to the British army after all. The two pistols were virtually identical in appearance, but unfortunately there were enough minor differences between the two types to prevent interchangeability of parts.

***The Enfield No. 2 Mk 1* revolver was the most widely used pistol of all the British and Commonwealth armed forces. Firing a 0.38-in (9.65-mm) ball cartridge, it was an efficient combat pistol but lacked any finesse or frills; yet it was able to withstand the many knocks sustained during service life.***

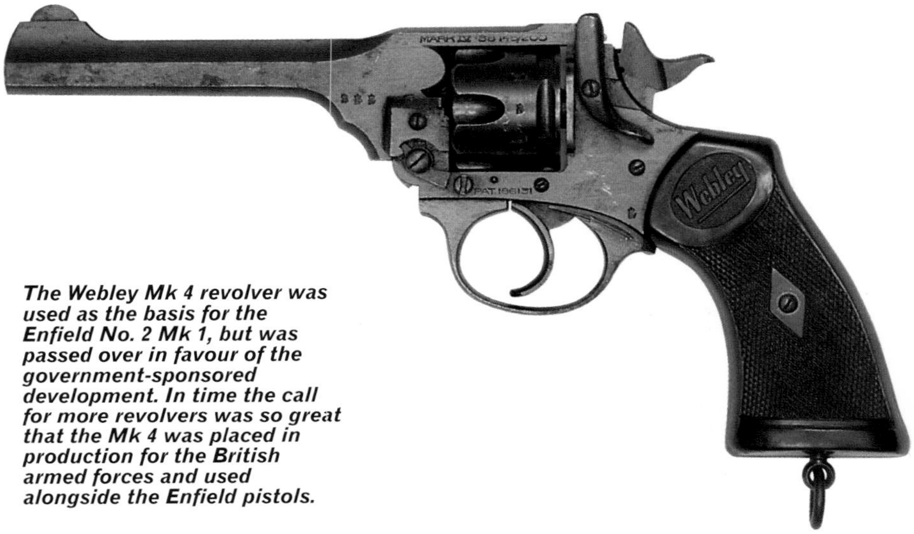


***The Webley Mk 4 revolver was used as the basis for the Enfield No. 2 Mk 1, but was passed over in favour of the government-sponsored development. In time the call for more revolvers was so great that the Mk 4 was placed in production for the British armed forces and used alongside the Enfield pistols.***

***An airborne soldier stands guard on a house in Holland during Operation Market Garden. The pistol is an Enfield No. 2 Mk 1* with the hammer spur removed to prevent snagging on clothing or within the close confines of vehicles or aircraft. These pistols were issued to airborne soldiers such as glider pilots.***

## Wartime service

Both pistols saw extensive use between 1939-45, and although the Enfield revolvers (there was also a **Pistol, Revolver, No. 2 Mk 1**** embodying wartime production expedients such as the elimination of the hammer safety stop) were the official standard pistols, the Webley Mk 4 was just as widely used among British and Commonwealth armed forces. Both remained in service until the 1960s, and were still encountered as service pistols up until the 1980s.

**SPECIFICATIONS**

| Pistol, Revolver, No. 2 Mk 1 | Webley Mk 4 |
|---|---|
| **Cartridge:** 0.38-in (9.65-mm) SAA ball | **Cartridge:** 0.38-in (9.65-mm) SAA ball |
| **Length overall:** 260 mm (10.25 in) | **Length overall:** 267 mm (10.5 in) |
| **Length of barrel:** 127 mm (5 in) | **Length of barrel:** 127 mm (5 in) |
| **Weight:** 0.767 kg (1.7 lb) | **Weight:** 0.767 kg (1.7 lb) |
| **Muzzle velocity:** 183 m (600 ft) per second | **Muzzle velocity:** 183 m (600 ft) per second |
| **Chamber capacity:** 6 rounds | **Chamber capacity:** 6 rounds |

# Tokarev TT-33 Pistol

***The Tokarev TT-33 was a sturdy and hard-wearing pistol that was used throughout World War II, but it never entirely replaced the Nagant Model 1895 revolver inherited from Tsarist days.***

The standard pistol of the Russian forces at the beginning of the 20th century and therefore inherited by the Soviet forces after the revolution of 1917, was the Nagant Model 1895G. This was a perfectly orthodox 7.62-mm (0.3-in) revolver with a seven-round cylinder. The weapon was of Belgian design, and although initially manufactured at Liège, was later made by the arsenal at Tula after its adoption for service with the Tsarist forces.

## Standard model

The first automatic pistol adopted for major employment by the Soviet forces was designed by Fyedor V. Tokarev and manufactured at Tula, which explains the use of the TT prefix in this weapon's designation. Standardised in 1930, as suggested by the numerical part of its designation, this weapon was the **TT-30**, but not many examples of this early weapon had been produced before a modified design known as the **TT-33** succeeded it in production during 1933. This TT-33 pistol was then adopted as the standard pistol in succession to the Nagant. In the event the TT-33 did not wholly replace the reliable Nagant until after the 1945 end of the 'Great Patriotic War', as the Soviets called their involvement in World War II. This was largely as a result of the fact that the revolver, which had been produced in very large numbers, was still a completely reliable and sturdy weapon under the rough active service conditions of the various fronts on which the Soviet forces fought from the time of the Russian Civil War onward.

## Soviet copy

Like the preceding TT-30, the TT-33 semi-automatic pistol was created as basically a Soviet version of the Colt-Browning pistols with a recoil-operated action, and used the swinging-link system of operation employed in the Americans' M1911 pistol designed as a 'man-stopper' for service with the US Army. The TT-33 was somewhat unusual, however, in having the hammer and its spring and other components combined as a single removable module fitting into the rear edge of the butt. However, the ever-practical Soviet designers introduced several other slight alterations (including locking lugs all round the barrel rather than just above it) that made the mechanism easier to produce and easier to maintain under field conditions, and production even went to the length of machining the vulnerable magazine feed lips into the main receiver to prevent damage and subsequent misfeeds if and when a slightly distorted magazine was loaded into the weapon. The result was a practical and sturdy weapon that, like all the best items of Soviet equipment, consistently proved itself able to absorb a surprising amount of hard use and still remain functional.

## Captured weaponry

The Germans made extensive use of captured weapons in World War II, and among this source of supply was a vast quantity of small arms seized during the initially successful days of Germany's advance into the Soviet Union as far to the east as Moscow. Examples of the TT-30 and TT-33 were issued to German army units, and also to field formations of the German air force, with the designation **Pistole 615(r)**. This German use was facilitated by the fact that the Soviet 7.62-mm Model 1930 Type P cartridge was in all essentials identical to the German 7.63-mm Mauser cartridge, which could therefore be used in the two Soviet pistols.

By 1945 the TT-33 had virtually replaced the Nagant revolver in service, and as Soviet influence spread over Europe and elsewhere, so did production and employment of the TT-33. Thus the TT-33 may be found in a variety of basically similar forms, one of which is the Chinese **Type 51**. Poland also produced the TT-33 for their own use and for export to East Germany and to Czechoslovakia. Yugoslavia manufactured the TT-33 for local and export service as the **M65**, while North Korea had its own variant in the form of the **M68**. The most prolific producer of the TT-33 was Hungary, which rejigged the design in several respects and recalibred it for the 9-mm Parabellum cartridge. The result was known as the **Model 48** or, in its export form for Egypt, the **Tikagypt** that was issued widely to the local police forces.

## Enter the Makarov

The TT-33 was replaced in first-line Soviet service by the Makarov PM blowback-operated semi-automatic pistol. Entering service in 1952 with a weight of 0.73 kg (1.61 lb) and ammunition feed from an eight-round detachable box magazine in the butt, the PM is chambered for the 9-mm Makarov cartridge created specifically to yield the maximum performance from a pistol firing from an unlocked breech.

The numbers of TT-33 pistols made and the type's ready availability to Soviet satellites and clients ensured that the type enjoyed a long period of service: the weapon was crudely finished by Western standards, but this proved to be of little significance to third world countries who prefered reliability and low cost to the 'flash factor' of more modern Western weapons.

Despite the introduction of the Makarov, many second-line and militia units within the Warsaw Pact organisation retained the TT-33 for many years after its replacement in first-line service, yet again the reason being the reliability and ruggedness of this readily available pistol.

| SPECIFICATION | |
|---|---|
| **TT-33** | **Weight:** 0.83 kg (1.83 lb) |
| **Cartridge:** 7.62-mm Type P (M30) | **Muzzle velocity:** 420 m (1,380 ft) per second |
| **Length overall:** 196 mm (7.68 in) | **Magazine:** 8-round box |
| **Length of barrel:** 116 mm (4.57 in) | |

***The Soviet Tokarev TT-33 in action in a well-posed propaganda photograph dating from about 1944. The officer is leading a section of assault infantry and has his pistol on the end of the usual lanyard. Snipers on all sides came to recognise such 'pistol wavers' as prime targets.***

# P 08 (Luger) Pistol

The pistol that is now generally, but misleadingly, known just as the **Luger** has its design origins in an automatic pistol design first produced in 1893 by one Hugo Borchardt. Georg Luger further developed this design to create the weapon that bears his name. The first Luger semi-automatic pistols were manufactured to fire a 7.65-mm (0.301-in) bottle-necked cartridge, and were first adopted by the Swiss army in 1900. Eventually, well over two million examples were produced by various manufacturers in at least 35 main variants.

## Standard weapon

The **Pistole 08** (or **P 08**) was one of the main variants. After the German navy had adopted a Luger pistol in 1904, the German army adopted a Luger pistol in 1908, and the weapon remained the standard German service pistol into the late 1930s. The Luger was produced in a number of calibres, but the primary calibre of the P 08 is 9 mm (0.354 in), and the 9-mm Parabellum cartridge was developed specifically for the Luger pistol in 1902. It should be noted, however, that versions were also made in 7.65-mm calibre.

The operating cycle of the P 08 is as follows. When the trigger is pulled, a connecting piece forces back a pin that drives out a spring-retaining lock, which allows the striker to move forward and fire the chambered cartridge. As the bullet passes down the barrel, the barrel and the recoiling mechanism, locked together, move back about 125 mm (0.49 in). Behind the breech block is a toggle joint with its rear fixed by a sturdy pin to the barrel extension. As the breech pressure drops to a safe level, the toggle joint's central element reaches a sloping section of the frame, breaking the toggle joint's straight line upward in exactly the same way that a knee bends, but still drawing the breech block straight back in the barrel extension's guide.

## Coil spring

As the action is opened, a short coil spring, which is located inside the breech block and whose function it is to drive the firing pin, is compressed and caught by the sear. The extractor in the upper part of the breech block's face pulls back the spent cartridge case to strike an ejector piece and be ejected out of the weapon, whereupon a small coil spring pushes the extractor back into place.

As the toggle joint buckles upward, a hook lever (hanging from its pin and hooked under claws that are connected to the recoil spring in the grip) compresses the recoil spring. The magazine spring lifts a fresh cartridge into alignment with the breech block. The compressed recoil spring can now pull down against the hook lever, driving down the bent toggle and pushing forward its front lever in a motion that drives the attached breech block straight ahead in its guide and strips the top cartridge from the magazine into the chamber.

The breech block and two toggle levers are now in a straight line with the toggle axis slightly lower than the other axes, locking the action. The sear now connects with the trigger mechanism, the trigger spring driving the trigger into position, and the pistol is ready to fire once more.

## Good 'pointability'

The P 08 handles well, is easy to 'point', is usually very well made, and relies on a rather complicated action. In fact it is arguable that this toggle action is basically undesirable in a service pistol. However, the P 08 was replaced in production and service by the P 38 only because it was too demanding in terms of production resources. It was late 1942 before the last 'German' examples came off the production lines, and the P 08 was never wholly replaced by the P 38 in German service. After 1945 the Luger was manufactured for the commercial market.

## A truly classic pistol

The standard P 08 had a barrel 103 mm (4.055 in) long, although some variants such as the **P 17 Artillerie** model had a 203-mm (8-in) or longer barrel and a snail-shaped magazine holding 32 rounds rather than the standard eight rounds. However, the P 17 Artillerie was no longer a service weapon by the beginning of World War II in 1939. Luger pistols were among the most prized of all World War I and II trophies, and many still survive today as collector's pieces. The type continues to attract the eye and attention of all pistol buffs throughout the world and the P 08 was, is, and will remain a classic of its type.

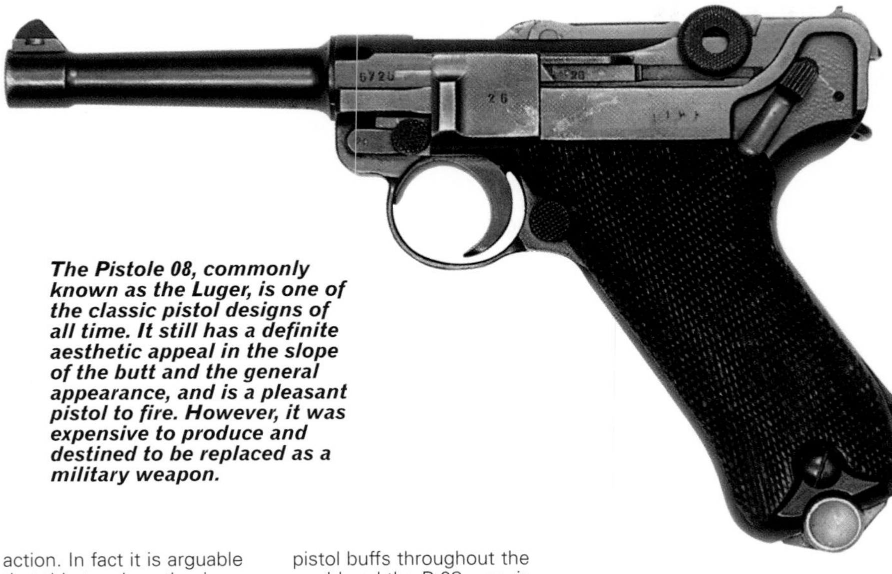

***The Pistole 08, commonly known as the Luger, is one of the classic pistol designs of all time. It still has a definite aesthetic appeal in the slope of the butt and the general appearance, and is a pleasant pistol to fire. However, it was expensive to produce and destined to be replaced as a military weapon.***

**SPECIFICATION**

| | |
|---|---|
| **Pistole 08** | **Weight:** 0.877 kg (1.92 lb) |
| **Cartridge:** 9-mm Parabellum | **Muzzle velocity:** 381 m (1,250 ft) per second |
| **Length overall:** 222 mm (8.75 in) | **Magazine:** 8-round detachable box |
| **Length of barrel:** 103 mm (4.055 in) | |

***Right: The P 08 in service with a section of house-clearing infantry during the early stages of the advance into the USSR during 1941. The soldier with the pistol is armed with Stielgranate 35 grenades and is festooned with ammunition belts for the section MG 34 machine-gun.***

***Left: A StuG III assault gun with a short 75-mm (2.95-in) weapon supports advancing infantry during an attack on the Voronezh front during January 1943. Although the pistol carried by the soldier on the right is blurred, it appears to be a P 08.***

# Walther PP & PPK Pistols

***The Walther PP pistol was, and still is, one of the best small pistol designs ever created. In German service it was used by various police organisations and also by Luftwaffe aircrew.***

The **Walther PP** (Polizei Pistole) was first produced in 1929 and marketed as a semi-automatic police weapon. In the 1930s it was adopted by many uniformed police forces. The PP is a light and handy design with few frills, but it is characterised by a clean overall shaping suiting it for holster carriage. The needs of plain clothes police units led to another model, the **PPK**, in which the designation's final letter indicated *Kurz* (short) or, according to other sources, *Kriminal*. The PPK was basically the PP reduced in overall size to enable it to be carried conveniently in a pocket. This reduction process trimmed overall length to 148 mm (5.83 in) and the weight to 0.568 kg (1.25 lb). The magazine carried six 9-mm (0.354-in) or seven 7.65-mm (0.301-in) rounds.

## Military adoption

Although intended as weapons for the use of civilian police forces, the PP and the PPK were adopted as military police weapons and, after 1939, were both kept in production for service use. Each model was widely used by the Luftwaffe, was often carried by the men of the many German police organisations, and was used by staff officers as a personal weapon. Both types could also be encountered in a range of calibres, the two main calibres being 9-mm Short and 7.65-mm, but versions were produced in the 5.56-mm (0.22-in LR) and 6.35-mm (0.25-in) calibres.

All these variants operated on a straightforward blowback principle, and more than adequate safety arrangements were incorporated. One of these safeties was later widely copied: a block was placed in the way of the firing pin when it moved forward, and was removed only when the trigger was given a definite pull. Another innovation was the provision of a signal pin above the hammer, which protruded when a round was actually in the chamber to provide a positive 'loaded' indication. This feature was omitted from wartime production, in which the general standard of finish was lower. Production resumed soon after 1945 in such countries as France and Turkey. Hungary also adopted the type for a while but production was then resumed once more at Ulm by the parent Walther company. Manufacture is still mainly for police duties but purely commercial sales are common to pistol shooters who appreciate the many fine points of the basic design.

## British use

One small item of interest regarding the PP centres on the fact that it is now a little known and rarely seen pistol used by the British armed forces as the **XL47E1**. This weapon has been used for the type of undercover operation in which civilian clothing has to be worn. The weapon was often issued to soldiers of the Ulster Defence Regiment for personal protection when off duty.

### SPECIFICATION

**Walther PP**
**Cartridge:** 9-mm short (0.38-in ACP), 7.65-mm (0.32-in ACP), 6.35-mm (0.25-in ACP) & 5.58-mm (0.22-in) LR
**Length overall:** 173 mm (6.8 in)
**Length of barrel:** 99 mm (3.9 in)
**Weight:** 0.682 kg (1.5 lb)
**Muzzle velocity:** 290 m (950 ft) per second
**Magazine:** 8-round box

**Walther PPK**
**Cartridge:** 9-mm short (0.38-in ACP), 7.65-mm (0.32-in ACP), 6.35-mm (0.25-in ACP) & 5.58-mm (0.22-in) LR
**Length overall:** 155 mm (6.1 in)
**Length of barrel:** 86 mm (3.39 in)
**Weight:** 0.568 kg (1.25 lb)
**Muzzle velocity:** 280 m (920 ft) per second
**Magazine:** 7-round box

# Walther P 38 Pistol

***Even today one of the best service pistols available, the Walther P 38 was developed to replace the Luger P 08 but by 1945 had only supplemented it. The pistol had many advanced features including a double-action trigger mechanism.***

The **Walther P 38** was developed primarily to replace the P 08, which was an excellent weapon but expensive to produce. After the National Socialist party came to power in Germany in 1933, it decided upon a deliberate programme of military expansion of the type in which the P 08 was only poorly suited. What was wanted at this stage was a pistol that could be produced both quickly and easily, but which nonetheless embodied all the many and various design features (such as a hand-cocked trigger and improved safeties) that were then becoming more common. Walther eventually received the contract for this new pistol in 1938, but only after a long programme of development.

Walther Waffenfabrik had produced its first original automatic pistol design back in 1908 and there followed a string of designs that led to the PP of 1929. The PP had many novel features, but had been created specifically as a police weapon and not a service pistol. Walther therefore developed a new semi-automatic weapon known as the AP (Armée Pistole, or army pistol), which did not have the protruding hammer of the PP but was chambered for the 9-mm (0.354-in) Parabellum cartridge. From this came the **HP** (**Heeres Pistole**, or Army Pistol), which had the overall appearance of the weapon that would become the P 38. But the German army requested the implementation of some small changes to facilitate rapid production, Walther obliged, and the P 38 was taken into German service use, the HP being kept in production for commercial sales. In the event, Walther was never able to meet demand for the P 38 and the bulk of the HP production also went to the German armed forces.

## Excellent pistol

From the beginning, the P 38 was an excellent service pistol which was robust, accurate and hard-wearing. Walther production versions, which were later supplemented by P 38 pistols produced by Mauser and Spreewerke, were always very well finished with shiny black plastic grips and an overall matt black plating. The weapon could be stripped easily and was well equipped with safety devices, including the hammer safety carried over from the PP along with the 'chamber loaded' indicator pin. It was a well-liked pistol and became a war trophy only slightly less prized than the P 08.

In 1957 the P 38 was put back into production for the West German army, this time as the **Pistole 1** (**P 1**) with a Dural slide in place of the original steel component. This pistol has enjoyed a long production run, and has been adopted by many nations.

### SPECIFICATION

**Walther P 38**
**Cartridge:** 9-mm Parabellum
**Length overall:** 219 mm (8.58 in)
**Length of barrel:** 124 mm (4.88 in)
**Weight:** 0.96 kg (2.12 lb)
**Muzzle velocity:** 350 m (1,150 ft) per second
**Magazine:** 8-round box

# Pistole Automatique Browning modèle 1910

## Automatic pistol

The **Pistole Automatique Browning modèle 1910** is something of an oddity among pistol designs, for although it remained in production virtually non-stop since 1910, it has never been officially adopted as a service weapon. Despite this it has been used widely by many armed forces at one time or another and the basic design has been widely copied and/or plagiarised by other designers.

### Pistol design

As the name implies, this blowback-operated automatic pistol was yet another product of the fertile mind of John Moses Browning. Nearly all the modèle 1910 weapons have been produced at the Fabrique Nationale d'Armes de Guerre (commonly known simply as FN) near Liège in Belgium. The reason why this particular pistol should have achieved such longevity is now not easy to determine, but the overall design is clean enough, with the forward part of the receiver slide around the barrel possessing a tubular appearance. This results from the fact that the recoil spring is wrapped around the barrel itself instead of being situated under or over the barrel as in most other designs of comparable type. This spring is held in place by a bayonet lug around the muzzle, providing the modèle 1910 with another recognition point. Grip and applied safeties are provided.

### Variants

The modèle 1910 may be encountered in one of two calibres, either 7.65 mm (0.32 ACP) or 9 mm (0.380 ACP) short. Externally the two variants are identical, and each uses a detachable seven-round inline box magazine. As is the case with all other FN products, the standard of manufacture and the finish are excellent, but copies made in such places as Spain lack this quality of finish. The excellent finish was continued with one of the few large-scale production runs for the modèle 1910. This occurred after 1940, when the German forces occupying Belgium required large numbers of pistols. The modèle 1910 was kept in production to meet this demand, the bulk of this new output being allocated to Luftwaffe aircrew who knew the type as the **Pistole P 621(b)**. Before that the modèle 1910 had been issued in small numbers to the Belgian armed forces, and many other nations obtained the type for limited use for their own military or police services. The numbers of modèle 1910s produced must have run into the hundreds of thousands.

***The Browning modèle 1910 was never officially adopted as a service pistol, but was nonetheless widely used and many of its design features were later incorporated in other pistol designs. The Belgian-made weapon was adopted in numbers as a sidearm by the Luftwaffe, who knew it as the P 621(b).***

| SPECIFICATION | |
|---|---|
| **Browning modèle 1910** | **Weight:** 0.562 kg (1.24 lb) |
| **Cartridge:** 7.65-mm (0.32 ACP) or 9-mm short (0.380 ACP) | **Muzzle velocity:** 299 m (980 ft) per second |
| **Length overall:** 152 mm (6 in) | **Magazine:** 7-round box |
| **Length of barrel:** 89 mm (3.5 in) | |

# Pistole Automatique Browning, modèle à Grande Puissance (Browning HP)

## 9-mm automatic pistol

The **Browning HP** may be regarded as one of the most successful pistol designs ever produced. Not only is it still in widespread service, in numbers that must surely exceed those of all other types combined, but it has also been produced at many locations in many countries.

### Into production

It was one of the last weapon designs produced by John Browning before he died in 1925, but it was not until 1935 that the HP was placed in production by FN at Herstal near Liège. From this derives the name which is generally given as the **HP** (High Power) or **Pistole Automatique Browning GP 35 (Grand Puissance modèle 1935)**. Numerous versions may be encountered, but they all fire the standard 9-mm (0.354-in) Parabellum cartridge. Versions exist with both fixed and adjustable rear sights, and some models were produced with a lug on the butt to enable a stock (usually the wooden holster) to be fitted, allowing the pistol to be fired as a form of carbine. Other versions exist with light alloy receiver slides to reduce weight.

Two factors that are common to all the numerous Browning HP variants are strength and reliability. Another desirable feature that has often proved invaluable is the large-capacity box magazine in the butt, which can hold a useful 13 rounds. Despite the width resulting from this, the grip is not too much of a handful, although training and general familiarisation are necessary to enable a firer to get the best out of the weapon. The weapon uses a recoil-operated mechanism powered by the blowback forces produced on firing and has an external hammer. In many ways the action can be regarded as the same as that of the Colt M1911 (also a Browning design), but it was adapted to suit production and to take advantage of the experience gained in the design.

### Service pistol

Within a few years of the start of production the Browning HP had been adopted as the service pistol of several nations including Belgium, Denmark, Lithuania and Romania. After 1940 production continued, but this time it was for the Germans, who adopted the type as the standard pistol of the Waffen SS, although other arms of the German forces also used the weapon. To the Germans the Browning HP was known as the **Pistole P 620(b)**. The Germans did not have the HP all to themselves, however, for a new production line was opened in Canada by the John Inglis Company of Toronto, and from there the HP was distributed to nearly all the Allied nations as the **Pistol, Browning, FN, 9-mm HP No. 1**, large numbers being sent to China to equip the nationalist forces. After 1945 the type was put back in production at Herstal, and many nations now use the weapon as their standard pistol. Various commercial models have been developed, and the type has even been adapted to produce a target-shooting model. The British Army still uses the Browning HP as the **Pistol, Automatic L9AI**. In 2001 the UK Ministry of Defence announced orders for a further 2,000 L9A1s to add to those already in service.

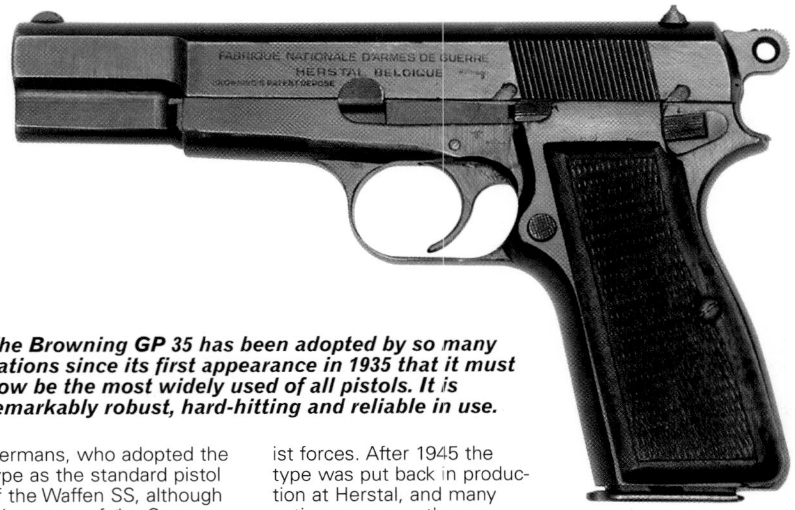

***The Browning GP 35 has been adopted by so many nations since its first appearance in 1935 that it must now be the most widely used of all pistols. It is remarkably robust, hard-hitting and reliable in use.***

| SPECIFICATION | |
|---|---|
| **Browning GP 35** | **Weight:** 1.01 kg (2.23 lb) |
| **Cartridge:** 9-mm (0.354-in) Parabellum | **Muzzle velocity:** 354 m (1,160 ft) per second |
| **Length overall:** 196 mm (7.75 in) | **Magazine:** 13-round box |
| **Length of barrel:** 112 mm (4.41 in) | |

# Liberator M1942 Assassination gun

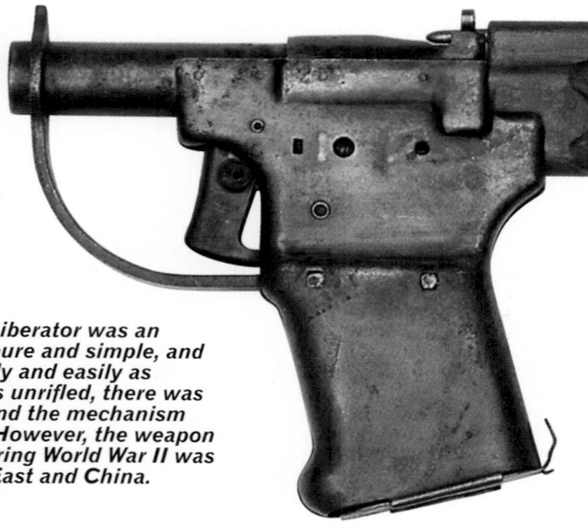

*The diminutive M1942 Liberator was an assassination weapon pure and simple, and was produced as cheaply and easily as possible. The barrel was unrifled, there was no spent case ejector, and the mechanism was crude to a degree. However, the weapon proved effective and during World War II was used mainly in the Far East and China.*

This very odd little pistol had its origins in the committee rooms of the US Army Joint Psychological Committee, which sold to the Office of Strategic Services the idea of a simple assassination weapon that could be used by anyone in occupied territory without the need for training or familiarisation. The OSS took up the idea and the US Army Ordnance Department then set to and produced drawings. The Guide Lamp Division of the General Motors Corporation was given the task of producing the weapon, and the division took the credit for churning out no less than one million between June and August 1942.

## Flare pistol

The 0.45-in (11.43-mm) **Pistol M1942** was provided with the cover name **Flare Pistol M1942**, but it was also known as the **Liberator** or the **OSS Pistol**. It was a very simple, even crude device that could fire only a single shot. It was constructed almost entirely of metal stampings and the barrel was a smooth-bore unit. The action was just as simple as the rest of the design: a cocking piece was grasped and pulled to the rear; once back a turn locked it in place as a single M1911 automatic cartridge was loaded, and the cocking piece was then swung back for release as the trigger was pulled. To clear the spent cartridge the cocking piece was once more moved out of the way, and the case was pushed out from the chamber by poking something suitable down the barrel from the muzzle.

## One-shot weapon

Each pistol was packed into a clear plastic bag together with 10 rounds, and a set of instructions in comic strip form provided, without words, enough information for any person finding the package to use the pistol. There was space in the butt to carry five of the rounds provided, but the pistol was virtually a one-shot weapon and had to be used at a minimal range to be effective. Each Liberator pistol cost the American government just $2.40. Exactly how effective it was is now difficult to say, for there seems to be no record of how these numerous pistols were ever employed or where they were distributed. It is known that some were parachuted into occupied Europe, but many more were used in the Far East and in China. The concept was certainly deemed good enough to be revived in 1964 when a much modernised equivalent to the Liberator, known as the 'Deer Gun', was produced for possible use in Vietnam. In the event several thousands were made but were never issued, maybe due to the fact that assassination-type weapons have a very nasty tendency to be double-edged.

| SPECIFICATION | |
|---|---|
| **M1942 Liberator** | **Muzzle velocity:** 336 m (1,100 ft) per second |
| **Cartridge:** 0.45-in (11.43-mm) ball M1911 | **Magazine:** none, but space in butt for five rounds |
| **Length overall:** 140 mm (5.55 in) | |
| **Length of barrel:** 102 mm (4 in) | |
| **Weight:** 0.454 kg (1 lb) | |

# Colt M1911 and M1911A1 Automatic pistols

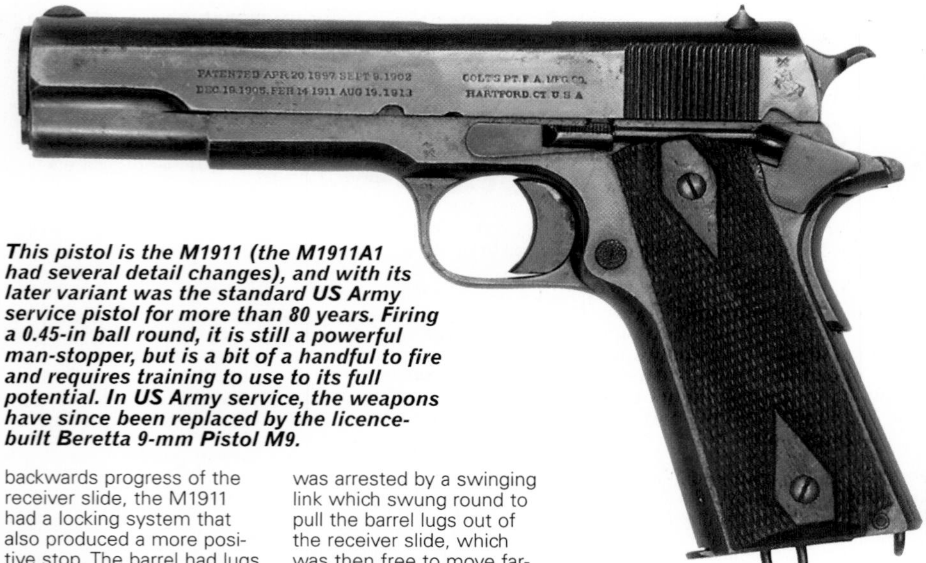

*This pistol is the M1911 (the M1911A1 had several detail changes), and with its later variant was the standard US Army service pistol for more than 80 years. Firing a 0.45-in ball round, it is still a powerful man-stopper, but is a bit of a handful to fire and requires training to use to its full potential. In US Army service, the weapons have since been replaced by the licence-built Beretta 9-mm Pistol M9.*

The **Colt M1911** vies with the Browning HP as one of the most successful pistol designs ever produced, for it has been manufactured in millions and is in widespread service all over the world some 90 years after it was first standardised for service in 1911.

## Colt-based design

The design had its origins well before then, however, for the weapon was based on a Colt Browning Model 1900 design. This weapon was taken as the basis for a new service pistol required by the US Army to fire a new 0.45-in (11.43-mm) cartridge deemed necessary as the then-standard calibre of 0.38 in (9.65 mm) was considered by many to be too light to stop a charging enemy. The result was a series of trials in 1907, and in 1911 the **Pistol, Automatic, Caliber .45, M1911** was accepted. Production was at first slow, but by 1917 was well enough under way to equip in part the rapid expansion of the US Army for its new role in France.

## Production changes

As the result of that battle experience it was decided to make some production changes to the basic design, and this led to the **M1911A1**. The changes were not extensive, being confined to items such as the grip safety configuration, the hammer spur outline and the mainspring housing. Overall the design and operation changed only little The basic method of operation remained the same, and this mechanism is one of the strongest ever made. Whereas many contemporary pistol designs employed a receiver stop to arrest the backwards progress of the receiver slide, the M1911 had a locking system that also produced a more positive stop. The barrel had lugs machined into its outer surface that fitted into corresponding lugs on the slide. When the pistol was fired the barrel and slide moved backwards a short distance with these lugs still engaged. At the end of this distance the barrel progress was arrested by a swinging link which swung round to pull the barrel lugs out of the receiver slide, which was then free to move farther and so eject the spent case and restart the loading cycle. This robust system, allied with a positive applied safety and a grip safety, make the M1911 and M1911A1 very safe weapons under service conditions. But the pistol is a bit of a handful to handle and fire correctly, and a good deal of training is required to use it to full effect.

The M1911 and M1911A1 were both been manufactured by numerous companies other than Colt Firearms, and have been widely copied direct in many parts of the world, not always to very high levels of manufacture. Modified 'fine tuned' variants continue to serve with the US Marine Corps and with special forces units.

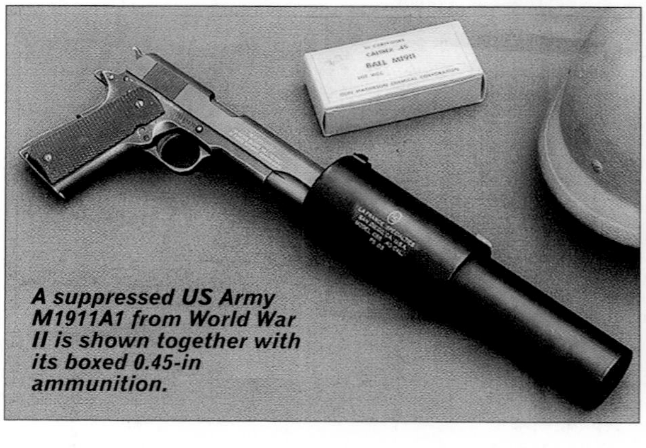

*A suppressed US Army M1911A1 from World War II is shown together with its boxed 0.45-in ammunition.*

| SPECIFICATION | |
|---|---|
| **Colt M1911A1** | **Weight:** 1.36 kg (3 lb) |
| **Cartridge:** 0.45-in (11.43-mm) ball M1911 | **Muzzle velocity:** 252 m (825 ft) per second |
| **Length overall:** 219 mm (8.6 in) | **Magazine:** 7-round box |
| **Length of barrel:** 128 mm (5.03 in) | |

# Smith & Wesson 0.38/200 Pistol

In 1940 the British army was in a desperate plight after the disaster of the French campaign and the evacuation from Dunkirk, with few combat-trained formations and even fewer weapons with which to equip them. Fortunately the USA, although not yet actually involved in World War II as a combatant, was at least sympathetic to the point where that nation would produce weapons for the British and to British designs. The British planned very substantial increases in military manpower levels, and was also faced with the problems of obtaining the weapons with which to equip them. Among the required weapons were pistols. Smith & Wesson was willing to produce revolvers to a British specification, however, and the result was the pistol known either as the **Revolver 0.38/200** or the **Pistol, Revolver, 0.38-n, Smith & Wesson No. 2.**

## Orthodox and sound

Whatever its designation, the pistol was a strictly orthodox concept that was conventional in every respect. It was straightforward in design and operation, and embodied not only Smith & Wesson craftsmanship but also British requirements, the resulting weapon being robust to an extreme. This was just as well, for the British pistol production lines were never able to catch up with demand and the British/American design more than filled the gap. The pistol was issued to all arms of the British forces, went to many Commonwealth forces as well, and was even handed out to various European resistance movements. Between 1940 and the time production ended in 1946 over 890,000 had been produced and issued. Many are still to be found in service, and it was well into the 1960s before the weapon was replaced in some British units by the Browning HP.

## Simple mechanism

The Revolver 0.38/200 fires a 200-grain bullet and uses the classic Smith & Wesson chamber release to the left. Once the weapon has been opened, fired cartridge cases can be cleared with a sprung plunger rod. The trigger action can be either single- or double-action. The finish of the pistols is plain, and at times was neglected in order that the numbers required could be churned out without production-line delay. But the standard of manufacture never wavered from a basic excellence, and only the finest materials were used.

Normally the pistol was carried in a closed leather or webbing holster that masked the hammer, so the snagging problem encountered with the Enfield revolver was not so acute, but a typical British touch was that the revolver was usually fitted to a waist or neck lanyard to prevent an enemy taking the pistol away from the firer at close quarters. The weapon appears never to have gone wrong, even when subjected to the worst possible treatment.

***A Canadian sergeant loads his Smith & Wesson 0.38/200 revolver. Empty cartridge cases were ejected by moving out the cylinder to the left and pressing a plunger normally under the barrel. All six spent cases were ejected together to allow each chamber to be reloaded one at a time, as seen here.***

**SPECIFICATION**

| | |
|---|---|
| **0.38/200 Revolver** | **Length of barrel:** 127 mm (5 in) |
| **Cartridge:** 9.65-mm (0.38-in) SAA ball | **Weight:** 0.88 kg (1.94 lb) |
| **Length overall:** 257 mm (10.125 in) | **Muzzle velocity:** 198 m (650 ft) per second |
| | **Chamber capacity:** 6 rounds |

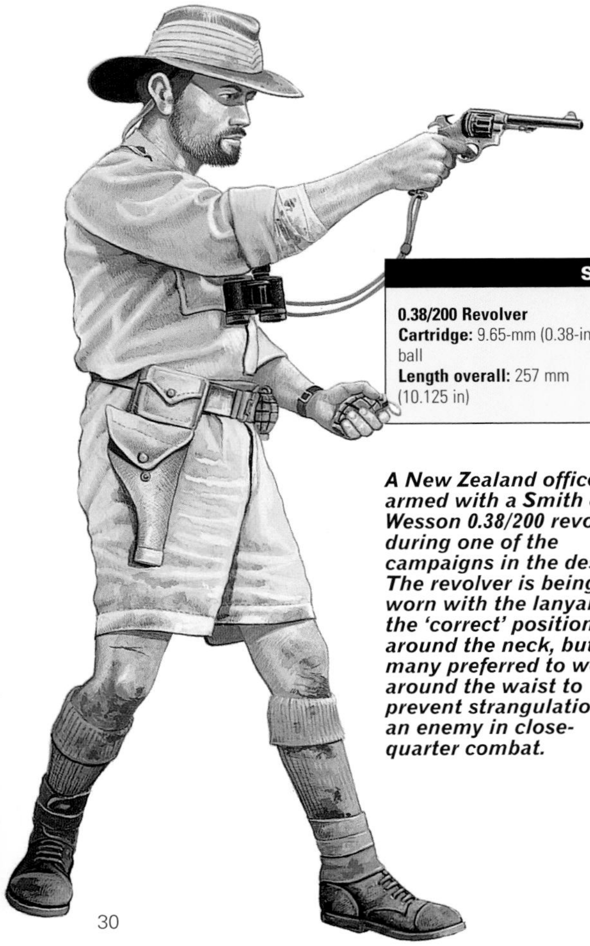

***A New Zealand officer armed with a Smith & Wesson 0.38/200 revolver during one of the campaigns in the desert. The revolver is being worn with the lanyard in the 'correct' position around the neck, but many preferred to wear it around the waist to prevent strangulation by an enemy in close-quarter combat.***

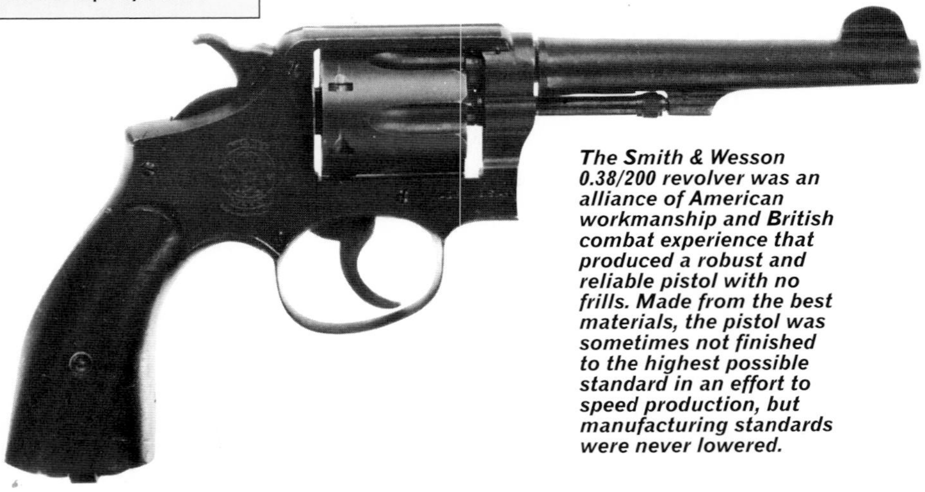

***The Smith & Wesson 0.38/200 revolver was an alliance of American workmanship and British combat experience that produced a robust and reliable pistol with no frills. Made from the best materials, the pistol was sometimes not finished to the highest possible standard in an effort to speed production, but manufacturing standards were never lowered.***

# Smith & Wesson M1917 Pistol

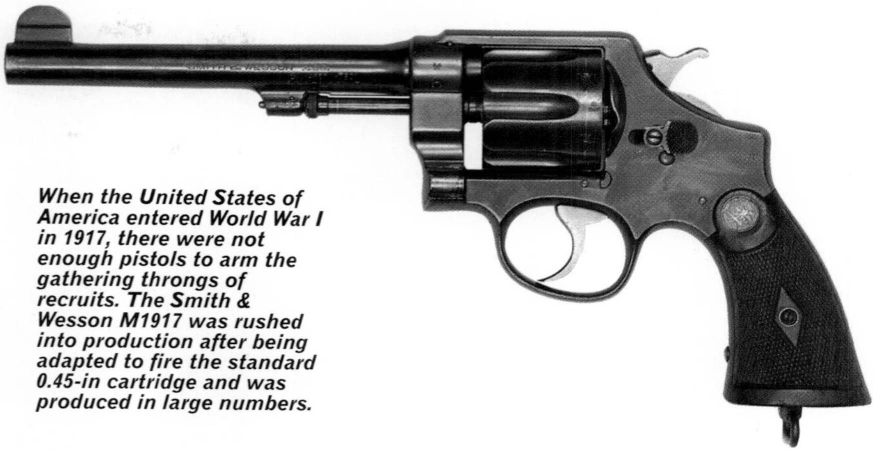

***When the United States of America entered World War I in 1917, there were not enough pistols to arm the gathering throngs of recruits. The Smith & Wesson M1917 was rushed into production after being adapted to fire the standard 0.45-in cartridge and was produced in large numbers.***

During World War I the UK placed sizeable orders in the USA for weapons of all types. One of these contracts was placed with Smith & Wesson of Springfield, Illinois, for the supply of military revolvers with a calibre of 11.56 mm (0.455 in), which was then standard for British military pistols. Many of the requested revolvers were supplied, however, only after the USA had entered the war in 1917. It was at this time that it was realised that large numbers of pistols would be needed to arm the rapidly expanding US Army, and that the output from Colt's production facilities of the M1911 pistol would fall considerably short of the numbers necessary to meet the growing requirement. As a direct result, Smith & Wesson's British contract was taken over for the American forces, only for a new problem to crop up once the pistol had been adapted to create a weapon chambered for the American 11.43-mm (0.45-in) cartridge.

### 'Half moon' clip

Nearly all pistol ammunition produced in 1917 was for the M1911 semi-automatic pistol and was thus of the rimless type. The use of rimless ammunition in the cylinder of a revolver posed several problems, however, as revolver cartridges are normally rimmed. This led to the adoption of a compromise solution, in the form of three M1911 cartridges held in a 'half moon' clip to keep the cartridges from slipping too far into the revolver chambers when loaded. After firing, the spent cartridges could be ejected in the normal way together with their clips, and the clips could be reused if necessary. This solved the problem and the revolver was taken into US Army service and subsequently saw service in France and elsewhere.

The **Revolver, Caliber .45, Smith & Wesson Hand Ejector, M1917**, as the pistol was designated in US service, is a large and notably robust weapon that is completely orthodox in design, operation and construction with the exception of the three-round 'half moon' clips. The revolving cylinder swings out to the left for loading and spent case ejection, and the action is of the single- or double-action type. Like many other pistols of its type, the M1917 is extremely robust and had already been well accepted by the British army before the US Army took over the type. The British used the weapon again in 1940, when large numbers of M1917 revolvers were sent over from the USA for issue to Home Guard units and for service with the Royal Navy.

Colt Firearms also produced a revolver very similar to the Smith & Wesson weapon as the **Revolver, Caliber .45, Colt New Service, M1917.** The weapon was also produced in 0.455-in calibre for British use, used a three-round 'half moon' clip, and included in its data a length of 274 mm (10.8 in), barrel length of 140 mm (5.5 in), weight of 1.135 kg (2.5 lb), and muzzle velocity of 253 m (830 ft) per second. Total production of both weapons was over 300,000, and in 1938 Brazil purchased some 25,000 Smith & Wesson revolvers, which many US military police units were still using as late as 1945.

| SPECIFICATION | |
|---|---|
| **Smith & Wesson M1917** | **Weight:** 1.02 kg (2.25 lb) |
| **Cartridge:** 0.45-in ball M1911 | **Muzzle velocity:** 253 m (830 ft) per second |
| **Length overall:** 274 mm (10.8 in) | **Chamber capacity:** 6 rounds |
| **Length of barrel:** 140 mm (5.5 in) | |

# Pistolet Radom wz.35 Pistol

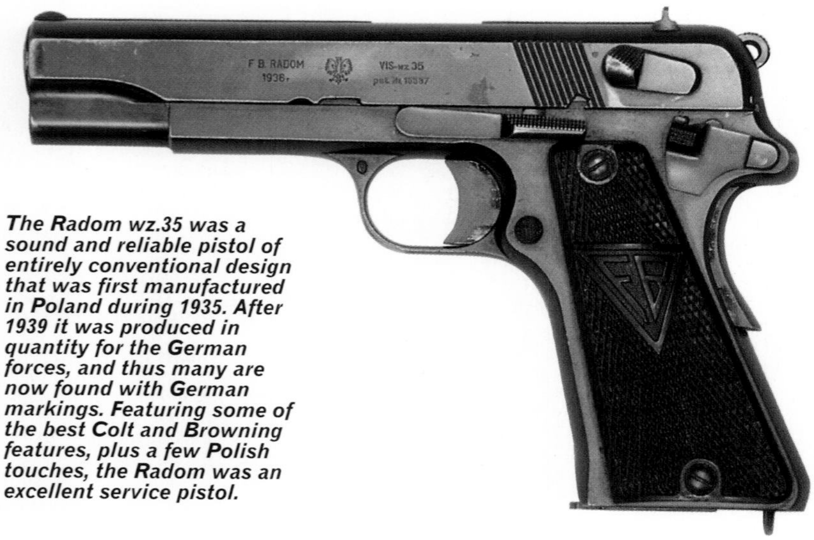

***The Radom wz.35 was a sound and reliable pistol of entirely conventional design that was first manufactured in Poland during 1935. After 1939 it was produced in quantity for the German forces, and thus many are now found with German markings. Featuring some of the best Colt and Browning features, plus a few Polish touches, the Radom was an excellent service pistol.***

By the early 1930s the Polish army, which had come into being only in the aftermath of World War I, was still trying to rationalize its equipment, much of it supplied as war-surplus items by a number of countries. The army currently had several pistol types in service, and sensibly wished to standardise on one weapon. An all-Polish design was created by P. Wilniewczyc and I. Skrzypinski, and this was put into production at the Fabryka Broni w Radomiu, initially under the supervision of Belgian engineers from the Fabrique Nationale organisation. The new 9-mm (0.354-in) weapon was selected in 1935 as the standard Polish service pistol with the designation **Pistolet Radom wz.35** or, in recognition of the designers, **Pistolet ViS wz.35,** with 'wz' standing for *wzor* (model).

### Mixed parentage

In overall concept, the wz.35 was a combination of Browning and Colt design features, adapted and finalised with a few Polish touches. The recoil-operated semi-automatic weapon is entirely conventional, but lacks an applied safety catch and therefore relies only a grip safety: the feature that appears to be the applied safety catch on the left-hand side of the receiver is in fact only a catch used when stripping the pistol. The weapon is chambered for the 9-mm Parabellum cartridge, but the discharge of this powerful round from the wz.35 is no great problem, for the size and mass of the pistol are such that the firing stresses are absorbed to a remarkable degree by the weapon without being passed on to the firer. This combination or size and mass also make the wz.35 a somewhat better-than-average pistol for the rigours of service life. The weapon's reliability and safety were also enhanced by the high standards of manufacture, materials and finish employed up to 1939, when Germany's invasion of Poland marked the beginning of World War II.

### German production

When the Germans overran Poland in September 1939, they took the Radom arsenal, complete with its pistol production line, essentially undamaged. Finding that the wz.35 was a thoroughly serviceable weapon firing a cartridge that was already standard in their own service, the Germans adopted the type as a service pistol and kept it in production for their own use under the formal designation **Pistole 645(p)** that for some reason was often rendered as **P 35(p).** The Germans' requirement for pistols was so great, however, that in an effort to speed production they eliminated some small features and reduced the overall standard of finish to the extent that the P 645(p) is readily distinguishable from the earlier wz.35 by its appearance alone. The Germans kept the pistol in full-scale production into 1944, when the surging westward advance of the Soviet forces destroyed the factory.

### Collector's item

When the new Polish army was re-established after 1945 it adopted the Soviet TT33 as its standard pistol. Many wz.35 pistols are still around as collectors' items, for the bulk of the German production went to the Waffen-SS and was marked appropriately. Thus these pistols have an added collection value for many pistol buffs. The wz.35 was one of the better service pistols of World War II.

| SPECIFICATION | |
|---|---|
| **Radom wz.35** | **Weight:** 1.022 kg (2.25 lb) |
| **Cartridge:** 9-mm Parabellum | **Muzzle velocity:** 351 m (1,150 ft) per second |
| **Length overall:** 197 mm (7.76 in) | **Magazine:** 8-round box |
| **Length of barrel:** 121 mm (4.76 in) | |

# Automaticky Pistole vz.38 (CZ 38) 9-mm automatic pistol

By the time that the German army marched into Czechoslovakia in 1938 and 1939 the Czechs had developed one of the most industrious and innovative armaments industries in all Europe. They were even supplying armour plate to the British for the Royal Navy's new battleships. Pistols were one of the many weapon types produced, mainly at the Ceska Zbrojovka (CZ) in Prague, and from there emanated a string of excellent designs that included the vz.22, 24, 27 and 30 (vz, stands for *vzor*, or model). These pistols all fired the 9-mm (0.354-in) short cartridge and had many features in common with the Walther pistols of the period, but in 1938 came a pistol that bore no relation to anything that had been produced before.

The new pistol was the **CZ 38** (otherwise known as the **Automaticky Pistole vz. 38**), and by all accounts this was not one of the better service pistols of the time. It was a large automatic weapon using a simple blowback mechanism, but it fired the 9-mm (0.354-in) short cartridge even though its size and weight could have accommodated a more powerful round. One feature that was unusual and outdated even at that time was that the trigger mechanism was double-action only. In other words, when you pulled the trigger you were cocking and releasing the hammer all in one motion – something that requires a much heavier pull than merely releasing the hammer. Because of the amount of force required to pull the trigger it is very difficult to shoot with any accuracy. Most other automatics carried an external hammer, so the weapon could be cocked prior to shooting. One redeeming feature of the design was that the pistol could be stripped very easily, simply by releasing a catch to allow the barrel to be cleaned once the slide was clear.

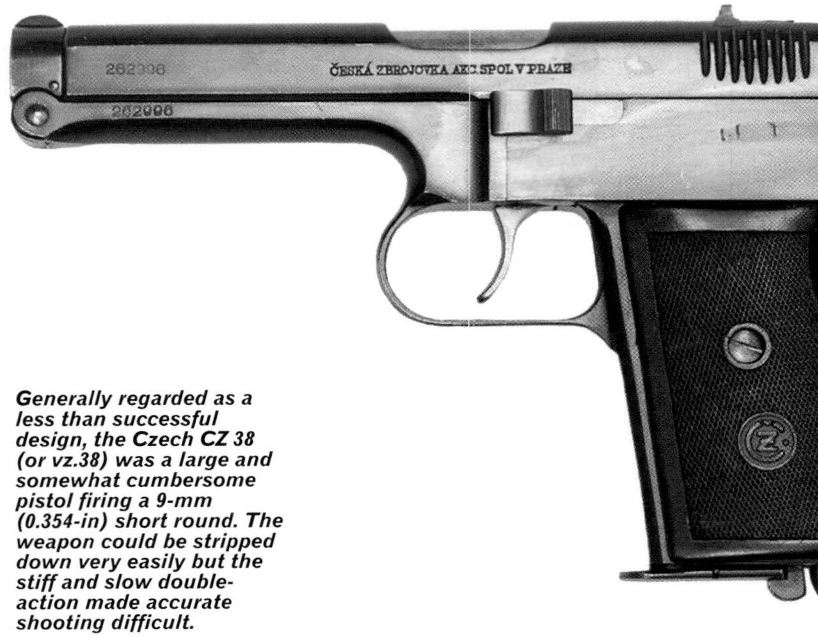


***Generally regarded as a less than successful design, the Czech CZ 38 (or vz.38) was a large and somewhat cumbersome pistol firing a 9-mm (0.354-in) short round. The weapon could be stripped down very easily but the stiff and slow double-action made accurate shooting difficult.***

### Under occupation

Not many of these pistols were produced for the Czech army before the Germans moved in, but the type was kept in production for some time. To the Germans the CZ 38 was known as the **Pistole P 39(t)**, but most of the production went to police forces and some second-line army and paramilitary units. Few survived after 1945. It is one of the few pistol designs that has not contributed some points to later designs.

**SPECIFICATION**

| | |
|---|---|
| **CZ 38 (vz.38)** | **Weight:** 0.909 kg (2 lb) |
| **Cartridge:** 9 mm short (0.380 ACP) | **Muzzle velocity:** 296 m (970 ft) per second |
| **Length overall:** 198 mm (7.8 in) | **Magazine:** 8-round box |
| **Length of barrel:** 119 mm (4.69 in) | |

# 94 Shiki Kenju 8-mm automatic pistol

In the 1930s the Japanese armed forces had in service a sound design of automatic pistol known to most Westerners as the 'Nambu' (8-mm Pistol Type 14), but following the large-scale Japanese incursions into China in the mid 1930s the demand for more pistols for the expanding Japanese forces could not be met. An easy solution appeared on the scene in the shape of an 8-mm (0.315-in) automatic pistol that had been commercially produced in 1934, but sales of this pistol had been few, as a result mainly of the odd and clumsy appearance of the weapon. The armed forces were then able to purchase existing stocks of these pistols and took over the production of more. The resultant weapons were initially issued to tank and air force personnel, but by the time production ended in 1945 (after more than over 70,000 had been made) its use had spread to other arms.

***Despite the fact that this Japanese captain is a tank officer, he is armed with a traditional sword in addition to the Type 94 pistol. The sword must have been rather unwieldy in the confines of a tank turret. However, it was almost certainly more reliable in a combat situation than the 94 Shiki Kenju, a weapon considered more dangerous to its firer than its target.***

### Inferior pistol

By all accounts this pistol, known as the **94 Shiki Kenju** (or Pistol type 94), was one of the worst service pistols ever produced. The basic design was unsound in several respects, the overall appearance was wrong and the weapon handled badly, but allied to this was the fact that it was often unsafe. Part of the trigger mechanism protruded from the left side of the frame, and if this was pushed when a round was in the chamber the pistol would fire. Another bad feature was the device to ensure that only single shots would be fired each time the trigger was pulled. Unfortunately this also made it possible to fire a cartridge before it was fully in the chamber. When these faults were combined with poor manufacture and low quality materials the result was a weapon that was probably more dangerous to its owner than the intended target.

Examples have been found that still bear file or other machine tool marks on the outside, and the degree of 'slop' in the mechanisms of some should signify that the Type 94 is a pistol that should not be carried or fired: it remains as a collector's piece only.

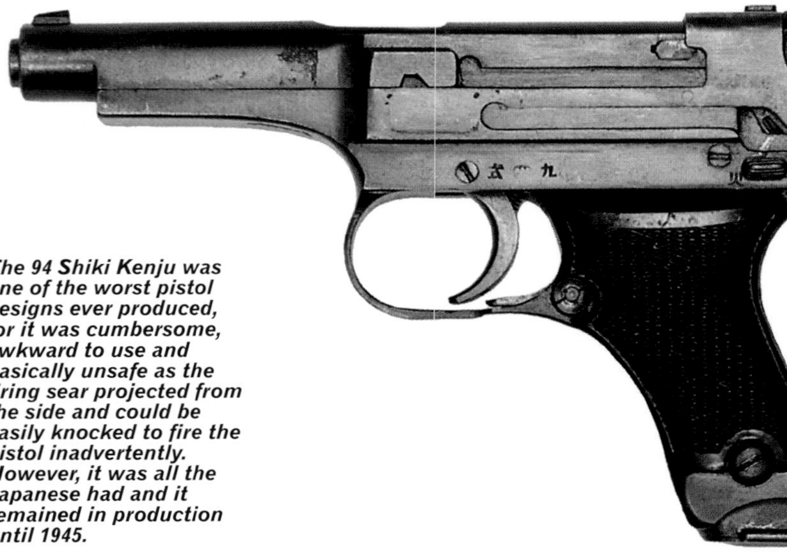

***The 94 Shiki Kenju was one of the worst pistol designs ever produced, for it was cumbersome, awkward to use and basically unsafe as the firing sear projected from the side and could be easily knocked to fire the pistol inadvertently. However, it was all the Japanese had and it remained in production until 1945.***

**SPECIFICATION**

| | |
|---|---|
| **Pistol Type 94** | **Weight:** 0.688 kg (1.52 lb) |
| **Cartridge:** 8 mm Taisho 14 | **Muzzle velocity:** 305 mm (1,000 ft) per second |
| **Length overall:** 183 mm (7.2 in) | **Magazine:** 6-round box |
| **Length of barrel:** 96 mm (3.78 in) | |

# Pistola Automatica Glisenti modello 1910 9-mm pistol

*The Glisenti modello 1910 was an unusual mixture of design innovations allied with a weak frame design. The pistol was chambered to fire a unique cartridge, the 9-mm Glisenti, which was similar to the 9-mm Parabellum with a reduced propellant load. In service, the pistol supplemented the modello 1889 revolver.*

The pistol that is now generally known as the **Pistola Automatica Glisenti modello 1910** was originally known as the **Brizia**, but the production and other patents were taken over by the Societa Siderugica Glisenti in the first decade of the 20th century. In 1910 this pistol was adopted by the Italian army as its standard service pistol, but for many years it managed only to supplement the earlier 10.35-mm (0.41-in) modello 1889 revolver, and in fact this ancient pistol remained in production until the 1930s.

## Unorthodox design

The Glisenti had several unusual features, and its mechanism was of a type little encountered in other designs. It used an operating system loosely described as a delayed blowback, in which the barrel and the receiver recoiled to the rear on firing. As it recoiled the action caused a rotary bolt to start to turn, and this rotation continued once the barrel had stopped moving after a distance of about 7 mm (0.276 in). The barrel was held in place by a rising wedge which was freed as the receiver moved forward again to chamber a fresh cartridge. All this movement had several effects: one was that while everything was moving the action was open and thus exposed to the ingress of debris such as sand (as in the North African deserts), and another was that the trigger pull was long and 'creepy', which made accurate fire that much more difficult. The action itself was made no more reliable by being constructed in such a way that the entire left side had no supporting frame and was held in place by a screwed-on cover plate. In prolonged use this plate could come separated from the pistol, causing it to jam. Even when in place the action was generally 'sloppy' and the moving parts displayed an unpleasant amount of internal movement.

To overcome the worst of this action the Italians introduced a special cartridge for this pistol known as the 9-mm Glisenti. In appearance and dimensions it resembled the standard 9-mm Parabellum, but the propellant load was reduced to produce less recoil and thus lower internal stress. However, the cartridge was unique to the Glisenti, and if normal 9-mm ammunition was inadvertently loaded and fired the results could be disastrous to pistol and firer! The Glisenti remained in production until the late 1920s but it was still in use in the Italian army until 1945. It is now a collector's piece only.

| SPECIFICATION | |
|---|---|
| **Glisenti modello 1910** | **Weight:** 0.909 kg (2 lb) |
| **Cartridge:** 9-mm Glisenti | **Muzzle velocity:** 320 m (1, 050 ft) per second |
| **Length overall:** 210 mm (8.27 in) | **Magazine:** 7-round box |
| **Length of barrel:** 102 mm (4.02 in) | |

# Pistola Automatica Beretta modello 1934 9-mm pistol

The diminutive **Pistola Automatica Beretta modello 1934** is today highly regarded by pistol collectors. It was adopted as the standard Italian army service pistol in 1934, but it was then only the latest step in a long series of automatic pistols that could be traced back as far as 1915. In that year numbers of a new pistol design were produced to meet the requirements of the expanding Italian army, and although the Pistola Automatica Beretta modello 1915 was widely used it was never officially accepted as a service model. These original Beretta had a calibre of 7.65 mm (0.301 in) although a few were made in 9-mm (0.354-in) short, the cartridge that was to be the ammunition for the later modello 1934.

***Beretta automatics were too light to be effective service pistols, but as personal weapons to officers such as the colonel depicted, they were highly prized.***

## Classic appearance

After 1919 other Beretta pistols appeared, all of them following the basic Beretta design. By the time the modello 1934 appeared the 'classic' appearance had been well established with the snub outline and the front of the cutaway receiver wrapped around the forward part of the barrel to carry the fixed foresight. The short pistol grip held only seven rounds and thus to ensure a better grip the characteristic 'spur' was carried over from a design introduced back in 1919. In operation it was a conventional blowback design without frills or anything unusual, but although the receiver was held open once the magazine was empty it moved forward again as soon as the magazine was removed for reloading. (Most pistols of this type were designed to keep the receiver slide open until the magazine had been replaced). The modello 1934 did have an exposed hammer which was not affected by the safety once applied, so although the trigger was locked when the safety was applied the hammer could be cocked either by hand or by accident, which was an unfortunate feature in an otherwise sound design.

The modello 1934 was almost always produced to an excellent standard of manufacture and finish, and the type became a sought-after trophy of war. British and American soldiers fighting at the front line in Italy in 1943-45 did a thriving trade in captured pistols to rear echelon personnel who wanted something to show for their war. Virtually the entire production run was taken for use by the Italian army, but there was a modello 1935 in 7.65 mm which was issued to the Italian air force and navy. Apart from its calibre this variant was identical to the modello 1934. The Germans used the type as the **Pistole P671(i)**. Despite its overall success the modello 1934 was technically underpowered, but it is still one of the most famous of all pistols used during World War II.

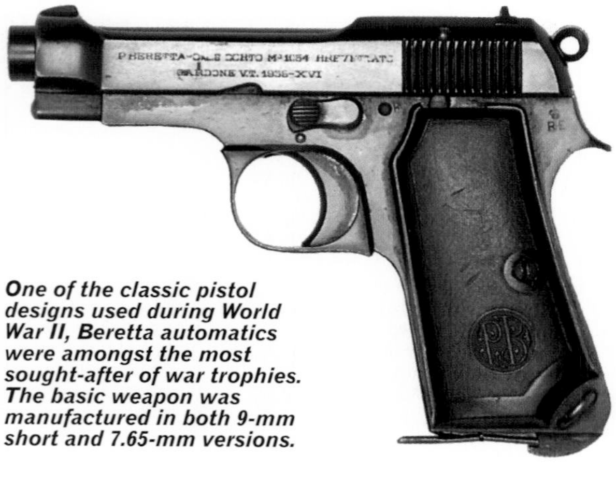

***One of the classic pistol designs used during World War II, Beretta automatics were amongst the most sought-after of war trophies. The basic weapon was manufactured in both 9-mm short and 7.65-mm versions.***

| SPECIFICATION | |
|---|---|
| **Beretta modello 1934** | **Muzzle velocity:** 290 m (950 ft) per second |
| **Cartridge:** 9-mm short (0.380 ACP) | **Magazine:** 7-round box |
| **Length overall:** 152 mm (6 in) | |
| **Length of barrel:** 90 mm (3.4 in) | |
| **Weight:** 0.568 kg (1.25 lb) | |

# Glock Self-loading pistol

Operation
The Glock is recoil operated; the reaction to firing forces the slide back and allows another round to be chambered.
Ammunition
The Glock 17 fires NATO standard 9x19-mm Parabellum ammunition. Other popular calibres include 10-mm, 0.40 S&W and 0.45 ACP.
Magazine
The Glock uses a double-row magazine holding 17 rounds.
Slide
Manufactured from high-strength polymer plastic, the Glock's slide will withstand temperatures ranging from -50° to +200°C.
Safety
The Glock has no manual safety catch; an automatic firing pin lock prevents the pistol from firing unless the trigger is pulled. The firing pin lock is disengaged by the simple catch mounted on the front of the trigger.
Weight
The use of plastic and light alloy means that the Glock is lighter than most pistols of similar size and ammunition capacity.
17
AUSTRIA
9x19

When it first appeared in the early 1980s, the Glock pistol seemed to break all the rules. Largely made of plastic, its design made no concessions to the popular view of what a pistol should look like. When it first appeared, there were widespread press reports about this sinister plastic pistol. Why plastic? Was it deliberately designed to be smuggled through security checkpoints at airports – was the Glock intended as the latest weapon in the terrorist arsenal?

In fact the Glock is firmly on the side of law and order. The slide, barrel and trigger group are all metal, so it is not X-ray proof. And the Glock is now in widespread service with armies and police forces worldwide, with over two million having been manufactured. Around 40 per cent of American law enforcement agencies that use automatic pistols have adopted the Glock.

## Non-traditional

Part of the reason for the Glock's unusual features comes from the fact that it was not designed by a traditional firearms maker. Glock was founded in Austria by Gaston Glock, an engineer who specialised in the manufacture of plastic and steel components. When the Austrian Army held a competition to find a new service pistol in the 1980s, Glock entered his revolutionary pistol design.

The Glock's receiver is made of tough plastic, resistant to both heat and cold. The old military adage of 'Keep It Simple' has been rigorously applied in the design of the Glock. It has only 33 parts, and can be stripped in a matter of seconds. Best of all, it has no external safety catch to release and so nothing to remember in the stress of action. Unlike almost all pistols in military service, the Glock is ready to fire from the moment it leaves your holster; draw and fire is all you need to do. A group of internal safety mechanisms keeps the weapon in a safe condition until the trigger is pulled.

## Military use

The 9-mm **Glock 17** is the most widely used version. Adopted by the Austrian army and by armies and special operations units all over the world, it is an outstanding handgun. The Glock 18 is a fully automatic version, used as a compact machine pistol. To prevent unauthorised conversions, the operating parts are not interchangeable with the Glock 17.

Its greatest commercial success has been in the United States, with police and civil users. To meet the needs of this rapidly expanding market, the basic design has been adapted to other calibres. Glock were one of the first manufacturers to launch a 10-mm (0.39-in) pistol, the **Glock 20**. One more step in search of the ultimate pistol cartridge, the 10-mm is a far more lethal round than the standard 9-mm (0.35-in) Parabellum used by most armies. The Glock 21 is chambered for the .45 ACP round, while the **Glock 22** and **23** fire the popular .40 Smith and Wesson round. Smaller examples of the Glock have been manufactured in all calibres, primarily for plain-clothed police officers to carry concealed.

A model of functional design, the Glock may have offended traditionalists but its world-wide success speaks for its quality.

| SPECIFICATION | |
|---|---|
| **Glock 17** | loaded 0.88 kg (1 lb 15 oz) |
| **Calibre:** 9x19 mm Parabellum | **Muzzle velocity:** 350 m (1,148 ft) per second |
| **Length:** overall 186 mm (7⅜ in); | **Magazine:** 17 rounds |
| **Barrel length:** 114 mm (4½ in) | |
| **Weights:** empty 0.63 kg (1 lb 5 oz); | |

***The Glock is an extremely simple design, with only 33 component parts. It is easy to strip and clean, which is a major plus for military use.***

***Light in weight, very tough, and accurate enough for all combat uses, the Glock is a firm favourite with military, special forces and law enforcement shooters.***

# Browning High Power Self-loading pistol

The **Browning High Power** was the last firearms design to come from the fertile brain of J.M. Browning, who died in 1926. His design was produced by Fabrique Nationale (FN) of Herstal, in Belgium. Serving through World War II on both sides, the High Power has been produced by the million, and is still in production.

The main producer is still FN, although spares are made in Canada following extensive World War II production in that country. During the 1990s, assembly was at a plant in Portugal from Belgian parts, but the factory was closed and full production has moved back to Herstal.

## Variants

FN has made several variants of the basic High Power. All are virtually identical internally, using the same basic Browning short recoil method of operation and the double-row magazine which made the High Power the first modern high-capacity pistol. However, the exterior fittings and finish vary considerably.

The military variants, the **High Power Mk 2** and **Mk 3**, are updated versions of the original with more modern finish and grip shape. The **High Power Standard** is the commercial model, while the **High Power Practical** is optimised for competition shooters.

## Compact carry

In recent years other versions of the High Power have appeared, some with specially lightened slides and components made from light alloys, to reduce weight. All these versions fire the 9-mm (0.35-in) Parabellum cartridge and all have found ready buyers, even in a world market sated with more modern pistol designs.

A double-action development, the BDA, was introduced in various calibres in the early 1980s, but did not sell as well as the original single-action pistol.

One factor that has consistently sold the classic Browning design has been the series' extreme robustness. The pistols can accept very hard use and will fire under the most adverse conditions, always providing that they are properly maintained and are loaded with decent ammunition.

The High Power can be a bit awkward to handle, especially for those with small hands, as the butt is rather wide to accommodate the double-stack box magazine. However, this does not detract from the pistol's many other virtues, and the Browning High Power has become the standard military issue sidearm in more than 50 countries.

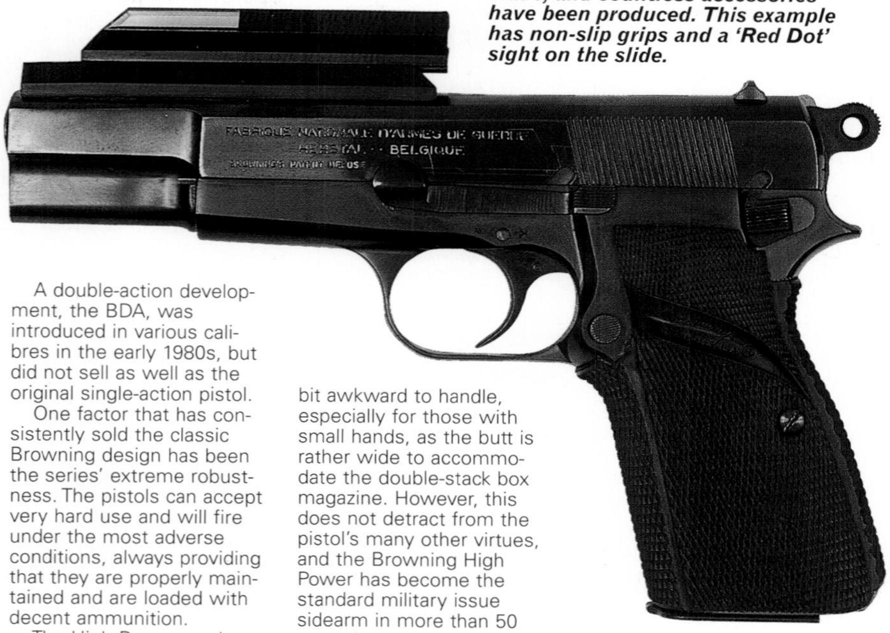

*Millions of High Powers have been made, and countless accessories have been produced. This example has non-slip grips and a 'Red Dot' sight on the slide.*

*Left: The reliability of the High Power made it the weapon of choice for Britain's SAS when the regiment set up one of the world's first hostage rescue teams.*

*Below: Hard-hitting and with a large magazine capacity, civilian High Powers have found a ready market with bodyguards all over the world.*

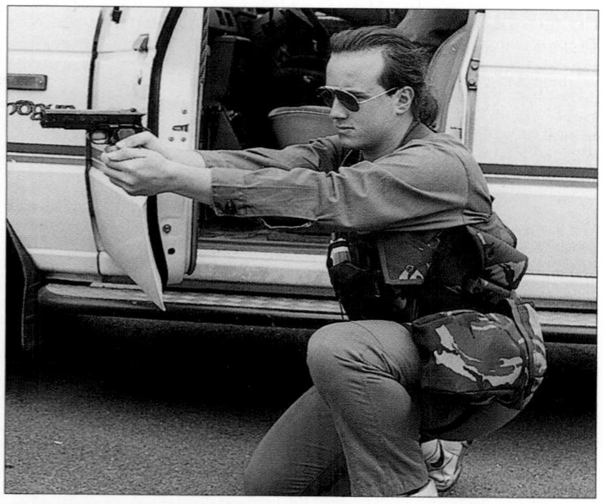

**SPECIFICATION**

**FN High Power**
**Calibre:** 9x19 mm
**Length:** overall 200 mm (7.85-in)
**Barrel length:** 118 mm (4.65-in)
**Weights:** empty 0.88 kg (1 lb 15 oz); loaded 1.04 kg (2 lb 4 oz)
**Muzzle velocity:** 350 m (1,148 ft) per second
**Magazine capacity:** 14 rounds

*Below: The axis of the High Power's bore sits low on the shooter's hand, reducing muzzle flip on firing. The well-positioned safety catch automatically drops the thumb into firing position when disengaged.*

# 9-mm FN High Power Belgian-made Browning

The **Browning High Power** pistol was created in 1925 by John Moses Browning, the famous American weapons designer, but the type is still in production and service to this day. The main producer of this fine weapon is still the Fabrique Nationale (FN) organisation of Herstal in Belgium, where manufacture began in 1935, although spares are also made in Canada following World War II production in that country by the Inglis company.

FN now makes several variants of the High Power in addition to the basic military version. All of these variants use the same basic Browning short recoil method of operation, and can easily be recognised as coming from the same stable. One notable modern variant is the **High Power Mk 2**, which can be regarded as an updated version of the original, characterised by a more modern finish and grip shape but retaining the original, reliable and well-proved operation without any significant modification. The **High Power Mk 3** is basically the High Power Mk 2 with an automatic firing pin safety device. The FN-made High Power carries the legend 'FABRIQUE NATIONALE HERSTAL BELGIUM BROWNING'S PATENT DEPOSE FN (year)' on the left-hand side of the slide.

There are three versions of the standard military model. The basic military model is now known to FN as the **BDA-9S**. The smaller **BDA-9M** uses the same frame as the BDA-9S but in combination with a shorter slide and barrel. The shorter slide and barrel are also used in the compact version of the family, the **BDA-9C**. This is a very small pistol for its calibre and has a much shortened butt holding only seven rounds instead of the 14 that are standard for the other models. The BDA-9C is intended as a 'pocket pistol' for use by plain clothes police units and by those involved in specialist tasks such as VIP protection.

In recent years other versions of the High Power have appeared, some with specially lightened slides to reduce weight and others with components made from light alloys, again to reduce weight. All these versions fire the standard 9-mm (0.35-in) Parabellum cartridge and all have found ready buyers, even in a world market that would appear to have been saturated with more modern pistol designs.

One factor that has consistently boosted sales of the High Power pistol has been its reputation for robustness and reliability. Both of these factors are inherent in Browning designs, and also in weapons of FN manufacture. The pistols are capable of accepting very hard use and will fire under the most adverse conditions, with the proviso – as with all weapons – that they are properly cleaned and maintained, and are also loaded with decent ammunition.

The High Power pistol can be a bit awkward to handle, for on all but the BDA-9C model the butt is wide, which results directly from the use of a double-stack box magazine to provide accommodation for the very useful total of 13 rounds. However, this has not prevented the High Power being used as a target pistol by some enthusiasts.

***This cutaway of the Browning High Power shows all the working parts of this automatic pistol. The name High Power was applied by the Belgians because it outperformed anything they had used previously.***

**SPECIFICATION**

| | |
|---|---|
| **9-mm FN High Power** | **Weight:** empty 0.882 kg (1.94 lb); loaded 1.04 kg (2.29 lb) |
| **Cartridge:** 9 mm (0.35 in) | **Muzzle velocity:** 350 m/s |
| **Length overall:** 200 mm (7.87 in) | **Magazine:** 13-round box |
| **Length of barrel:** 118 mm (4.65 in) | |

# Czech pistols CZ 75 and family

The design and manufacture of land warfare weapons, especially small arms and artillery, has long been a Czech speciality. The city of Brno in the central Czech republic is recognised as a centre of excellence for the manufacturer of small arms. Brno gave its name to the 'Br' part of the Bren gun. The Brno-based armaments firm, Ceská zbrojovka organisation, generally known as CZ, has been responsible for most of the country's pistol designs.

The first Czechoslovakian semi-automatic pistol was the VZ.22 recoil-operated weapon chambered for the 9.65-mm (0.38-in) short cartridge, but this was made only in small numbers before being replaced by the VZ.24 with a slightly modified locking and firing mechanisms. Next came the VZ.27, which was made in larger numbers that any other Czechoslovakian pistol of the period before World War II. Chambered for the 7.65-mm (0.32-in) ACP (Automatic Colt Pistol) cartridge, of which eight rounds were carried in the detachable inline box magazine, which fits inside the butt, the VZ.27 fitted was a blowback operating system which had used the momentum of the round leaving the chamber to extract another cartridge from the magazine. Made only in small numbers, the VZ.38 was chambered for the 9-mm (0.35-in) short cartridge, and was also a blowback weapon.

The next Czechoslovakian pistol to enter production was the 7.65-mm (0.30-in) VZ.50 with blowback operation and an eight-round magazine, and then came the VZ.52 firing the Czechoslovakian VZ.48 cartridge offering greater power than the Soviet Type P cartridge of the same calibre; the VZ.52 was a recoil-operated weapon with an eight-round magazine. One of the best pistols to be created in Europe after World War II, the **VZ.75**,

***The CZ 75 features a large grip that fills the hand and greatly improves both the handling and accuracy of the pistol. Note the adjacent double-row magazine.***

***Demonstrating the blowback mechanism, a second round can be seen underneath the main bullet which is ready to fire. The weapon is notably jam-resistant.***

**SPECIFICATION**

| | |
|---|---|
| **CZ.75B** | **Weight:** 1 kg (2.2 lb) with empty magazine |
| **Cartridge:** 9-mm (0.35 in) | **Muzzle velocity:** around 370 m/s |
| **Length overall:** 206 mm (8.1 in) | **Magazine:** 11- or 16-round box |
| **Length of barrel:** 120 mm (4.7 in) | |

increasingly known as the **CZ 75**, has been made in large numbers and has also been widely copied. This excellent 9-mm (0.35-in) Parabellum pistol is clearly derived from Browning design thinking with features from several other weapons. It is available in semi-automatic and automatic variants, and has a 16-round magazine. The **CZ 85** is basically similar to the **CZ 75** except for its ambidextrous safety catch and slide stop. The **CZ 85B** version adds a firing pin safety to enhance the drop safety of the pistol. The **CZ 85 Combat** is a CZ 85 development with additional features including an adjustable rear sight.

### Blowback

The **CZ 83** is a double-action pistol chambered for the 7.65-mm (0.30-in) ACP, 9-mm (0.35-in) short or 9-mm (0.35-in) Makarov rounds, of which 15, 13 or 13 respectively are carried. The **CZ 83** is a 'pocket' weapon with blowback operation; the trigger guard is large enough to admit a gloved finger.

The **CZ 92** is designed for personal defence, and is a double-action pistol working on the blowback system. The pistol is not equipped with a manual safety; after each shot the hammer returns to its released position, which enhances its safety against accidental discharge. The pistol is also fitted with a magazine safety catch so that removal of the magazine automatically blocks the trigger mechanism.

Belonging to a new range of pistols firing from a locked breech, the **CZ 100** is notable for its modern concept and the use of a high-impact plastic and steel slide for reduced weight. The trigger mechanism is of the double-action type and incorporates a firing pin safety, the pistol also being equipped with a single side slide stop and a magazine catch – the slide is locked open when the last round has been fired. The shaping of the weapon facilitates shooting with gloved hands, while the ergonomic shaping allows shooting with either left or right hand.

Finally, the **CZ 110** is based on the **CZ 100** but has semi-automatic and double-action firing modes. One major advantage of the weapon is that the pistol can be carried safely even with a cartridge in the chamber.

***This CZ 75 is ready to fire with a 9-mm (0.35-in) cartridge in the chamber. This pistol borrows much of its design from Browning. The ammunition of the basic model is carried in a 16-cartridge magazine.***

# French automatic pistols Model 1950 and PA15

The French **MAS Model 1950** 9-mm (0.35-in) pistol was designed by Nationale d'Armes, St-Étienne, eastern France, and manufactured at the Nationale d'Armes factory, Châtellerault, western France. From 1950 onwards it became the standard service pistol for the French army and the armies of several former French colonies.

The pistol is loaded by inserting nine 9-mm Parabellum cartridges into the magazine. A cartridge is positioned into the chamber by pulling back the slide and then releasing it. The gun's safety catch is located on the left rear side of the slide. If the safety catch lever is horizontal it indicates that the pistol is safe.

The locking ribs on top of the barrel are fitted into the grooves on the inside of the slide, causing the barrel to move backwards with the slide. The lower rear end of the barrel is attached to the receiver by means of a swinging link. The barrel and slide move back together for a short distance and then, since the lower portion of the link is attached to the non-recoiling frame, the link pulls the rear end of the barrel down. This separates the locking ribs of the barrel from the recesses inside the slide and, when the locking system is disconnected, the barrel is at rest and the slide continues to the rear under its own momentum. The empty case comes out on the breach face and stays there until it strikes the fixed ejector.

The weapon is reloaded when the return spring forces the slide forward and the face of the breech block carries the top cartridge in the magazine forward into the chamber. The breech block contacts the barrel and pushes it forward where the link raises the breech and the ribs on the top of the barrel enter the grooves on the slide, locking the two together. Forward movement ceases when the lug on the bottom of the barrel contacts the slide stop pin.

### MAB PA15

The MAB PA15 pistol was designed and introduced into the French Army in 1970 as the standard service pistol. It has a characteristic bulky grip giving better handling and increased accuracy, and the grip is also long enough to accommodate a magazine containing 15 9-mm (0.35-in) Parabellum cartridges. The weapon features a prominent spur towards the rear of the receiver; it also features a ring-type hammer.

Production of the MAB PA15 was terminated in the late 1980s, but it was announced in late 1991 that a deal had been concluded between the French and Yugoslav governments permitting the licensed manufacture of the MAB PA15 by Zastava Arms of Serbia. The gun is believed to be in service with some of the armies within the former Yugoslavia.

The MAB PA15 has a frame-mounted safety catch on the left hand side of the frame, and also features an internal magazine safety catch. This prevents the gun being fired if the magazine is removed. The reload of the chamber, after a round is fired, is by means of a delayed blowback action.

***The 9-mm (0.35-in) MAB PA15 pistol was, for over two decades, the standard service pistol of the French Army. Its large grip increased the weapon's accuracy. The PA15 utilises a delayed blowback mecanism.***

**SPECIFICATION**

| | |
|---|---|
| **MAS Model 1950** | **Weight:** 0.86 kg (1.89 lb) |
| **Cartridge:** 9-mm (0.35 in) | **Muzzle velocity:** 354 m/s |
| **Length:** 195 mm (7.68 in) | **Magazine:** 9-round box |
| **Length of barrel:** 112 mm (4.41 in) | |

***Until the appearance of the MAB PA15 in 1970, the MAS Model 1950 was the standard service pistol of the French Army and of several former French colonial nations. The safety catch is located on the left rear side of the slide.***

**SPECIFICATION**

| | |
|---|---|
| **MAB PA15** | **Weight:** 1.09 kg (2.43 lb) |
| **Cartridge:** 9 mm (0.35 in) | **Muzzle velocity:** 350 m/s |
| **Length overall:** 203 mm (7.99 in) | **Magazine:** 15-round box |
| **Length of barrel:** 114 mm (4.49 in) | |

# Heckler & Koch pistols

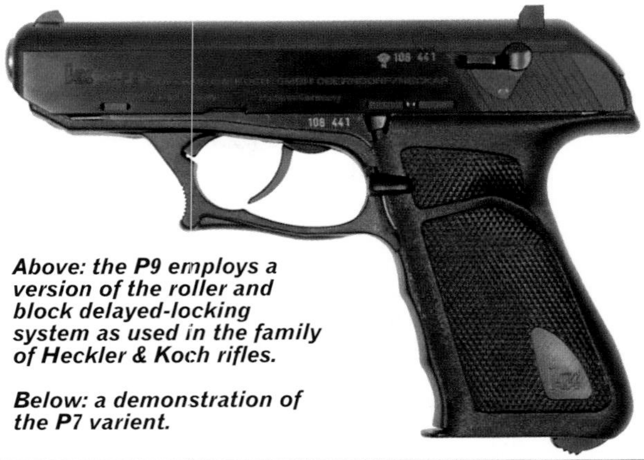

*Above: the P9 employs a version of the roller and block delayed-locking system as used in the family of Heckler & Koch rifles.*

Heckler & Koch GmbH was established in the 1950s and produced a pistol based on the Mauser HSc but with thumb-rests on the grip and a modernised profile. Manufactured in four calibres, the **HK4** was marketed in the US in the late 1960s but was not a great commercial success and manufacture ceased in the 1980s. The company, however, went from strength to strength after it won the contract to develop the G3 rifle for the newly established West German army. In 1990 the revolutionary G11 rifle was finally rejected as a replacement for the G3, however, and the company got into financial difficulty. It was bought by Royal Ordnance plc, a subsidiary of British Aerospace which already manufactured a number of Heckler & Koch weapons under licence.

The **P9** pistol has a delayed blowback action derived from that of the G3 rifle, involving a roller-locked breech block. Available in 7.65-mm (0.301-in) and 9-mm Parabellum (0.354-in) calibres, it has an internal hammer with a de-cocking lever on the left side of the receiver. The **P9S** is a double-action version. Both have been sold to a number of armies and paramilitary units, and a version chambered for the 0.45-in ACP (11.43-mm) cartridge was introduced in 1977 for the US market. The US Marine Corps acquired a number of P9s fitted with threaded barrels to accept a silencer. The P9 was taken out of production in 1990.

## VP70

From 1970 until the mid-1980s, Heckler & Koch manufactured a double-action automatic with a three-round burst facility. The **VP70** came with a detachable shoulder stock and was intended for the military market. Sales were limited to a few third-world armies, and neither this nor a 'civilian' version without the burst facility is widely encountered today.

## P7 variant

The **P7** was designed to a specification issued by the then West German police for an automatic that could be drawn and fired without releasing an external safety catch. Full production began in 1979, and the weapon is used by the German police and also by the Border Guard. Immediately recognisable by its grip, the P7 has a cocking lever built into the front of the handgrip: this must be squeezed in order for the pistol to operate. Releasing the grip disconnects the firing pin from the trigger rendering the weapon safe. The **P7K3**, chambered for the 9-mm Short (0.38-in) cartridge, is a simple blowback pistol adopted by the German army and some paramilitary forces. The **P7M8** and **P7M13** are models with 8- and 13-round magazines respectively, as well as a gas piston and cylinder for the delayed blowback action demanded by its more powerful 9-mm Parabellum cartridge. In 1987 the **P7M45** was introduced for the US market; chambered for the 0.45-in ACP cartridge, it uses an oil-filled cylinder rather than gas cylinder to delay the recoil of the slide, an interesting adaptation of an artillery mechanism to a hand gun. This made the P7M45 an expensive weapon and, at a time when competition was extremely fierce, its commercial failure could not have been a total surprise.

Developed in the 1980s was the **Mk 23**, which won a US Special Operations Command competition for a handgun for special forces missions, and entered service is 1996. Chambered for 0.45-in ACP, this large automatic has a double-action only trigger with safety and de-cocking levers. The frame is polymer with steel inserts and the pistol is built to mount laser aiming devices and/or tactical flashlights. The barrel is threaded to accept a silencer.

Heckler & Koch's other military pistol of recent years is a derivative of the **Universal Selbstlade Pistole** (universal self-loading pistol) that has been made in many variants in the last decade. A general purpose law enforcement and self-defence weapon, the USP includes sporting versions and the **USP Tactical**, a 0.45-in automatic used by some US Special Forces units instead of the huge Mk 23. The German army has acquired the USP which it designates **P8**, and the German police employs the **USP Compact** as the **P10**. Both German weapons are chambered for 9-mm Parabellum.

*Below: a demonstration of the P7 varient.*

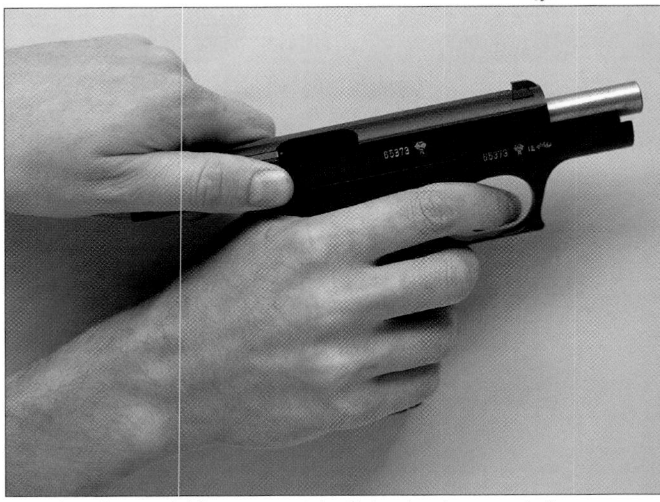

**SPECIFICATIONS**

**P7M8**
**Calibre:** 9-mm Parabellum
**Weights:** 0.8 kg (1.76 lb) empty; 0.95 kg (2.09 lb) loaded
**Lengths:** overall 171 mm (6.73 in); barrel 105 mm (4.13 in)
**Muzzle velocity:** 350 m (1,150 ft) per second
**Magazine capacity:** 8 rounds

**VP70**
**Calibre:** 9-mm Parabellum
**Weights:** 820 g (1.81 lb) empty; 1.14 kg (2.51 lb) loaded
**Lengths:** overall 204 mm (8.03 in); barrel 116 mm (4.57 in); with stock fitted 545 mm (21.45 in)
**Muzzle velocity:** 360 m (1,180 ft) per second
**Magazine capacity:** 18 rounds

**P9**
**Calibre:** 9-mm Parabellum
**Weights:** 0.88 kg (1.94 lb) empty; 1.07 kg (2.35 lb) loaded
**Lengths:** overall 192 mm (7.56 in); barrel 102 mm (4 in)
**Muzzle Velocity:** 350 m (1,150 ft) per second
**Magazine capacity:** 9 rounds

**USP**
**Calibre:** 9-mm Parabellum, 0.40-in S&W, 0.45-in ACP, 0.357-in SIG
**Weight:** 720 g (1.59 lb)
**Magazine capacity:** 15 rounds (9-mm version)

**Mk 23**
**Calibre:** 0.45-in ACP
**Weight:** 1100 g (2.425 lb) empty
**Length:** 245 mm (9.65 in) overall
**Magazine capacity:** 12 rounds

# Walther PP and PPK

Walther introduced its **PP** (**Polizei Pistole**) pistol in 1929, and the weapon is still in production. It was widely used by the German armed forces and their allies during World War II. The **PPK** (**Polizei Pistole Kurz**, or short police pistol) was a more compact version for the use of the police, and especially the plain clothes police, of which Germany had something of a surplus during the 1940s. Introduced in 1931, it has also been waved about in many a spy movie from James Bond down. (Bond has just upgraded to the more recent Walther P99). These were the first successful double-action automatics. Production ceased after the war but resumed in the mid-1960s, and the PP and PPK have remained in widespread service ever since. The original PP was offered in the 7.65-mm (0.301-in) and 9-mm Short (0.38-in) calibres; since the 1960s a version in 0.22-in Long Rifle (5.59-mm) calibre has been widely sold for plinking. A handful of PPs were made in 6.35-mm (0.25-in) calibre before the war. One oddity is the **PPK/S**, a PP frame with the barrel and slide of the PPK: this was built to get around the 1968 US gun control laws

***Small, light and possessing no significant features to snag in clothes, the PP and its smaller half-brother, the PPK, were designed for police and paramilitary use rather than the more arduous demands of front-line military forces.***

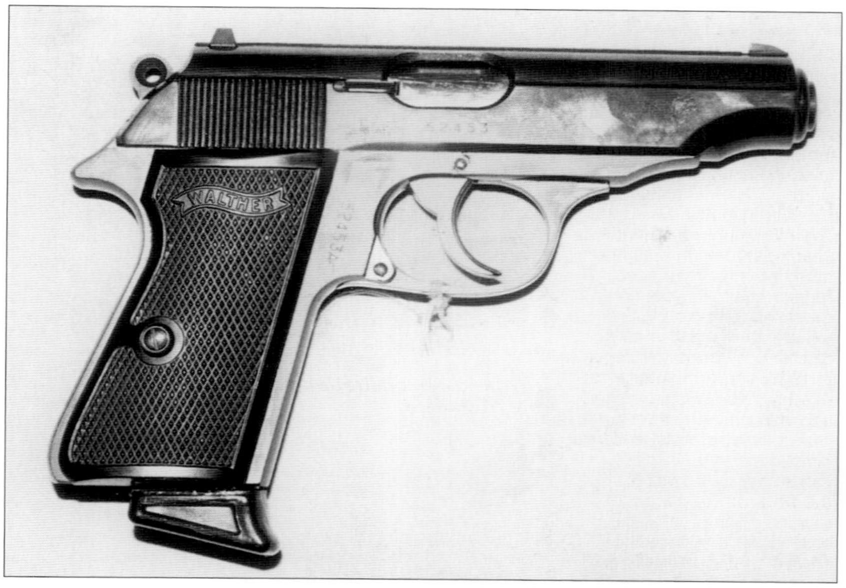


which introduced a minimum size for imported handguns. The **PP Super** has a trigger guard designed for two-handed use, and fires the 9-mm Police cartridge. The diminutive **TP** and **TPH** versions were discontinued in the 1970s, although they were manufactured under licence for a period in the US.

***The PP is a timeless automatic pistol whose excellent manufacturing and operational qualities have ensured a virtually constant manufacturing programme right up to the present day.***

All the models operate on a straightforward blowback principle, and good safety arrangements are incorporated. One of these safeties has been widely copied: a block is placed in the way of the firing pin when it moves forward, and is removed only when the trigger is given a definite pull. Another innovation is the incorporation of a signal pin above the hammer, which protrudes when a round is actually in the chamber to provide a positive 'loaded' indication. This feature was omitted from production in the course of World War II.

**SPECIFICATION**

**PPK**
**Calibre:** 7.65-mm
**Weight:** 0.58 kg (1.28 lb) empty
**Length:** 154 mm (6 in) overall; barrel 84 mm (3.31 in)
**Magazine capacity:** 7 rounds

# Modern Walther pistols P5, P88 and P99

Walther's P38 automatic pistol of World War II fame was revived as a production item in the course of 1979, the modernised version being designated as the **P5**. The main improvements are to the weapon's safety. Used by police arms including German and Dutch forces, and ordered by several African armies, the P5 is also manufactured in a compact format with a length of 169 mm (6.65 in) and an 8-round magazine.

In 1988 Walther departed from its standard operating design feature, the wedge lock, and produced a pistol with Colt/Browning toggle locking. This **P88** was tested by a number of armies looking for a new service sidearm, including the British Army. However, it did not attract sufficient interest to warrant a large-scale production programme.

The **P99** began life in the mid-1990s in an effort to overcome the problems of the P88: it is much cheaper than the P88 and yet incorporates the simple features modern armies prefer. It has no manual safeties, instead using three automatic safety features: trigger safety, out-of-battery safety, and striker safety. There is a de-cocking button in the upper part of the slide. The 'military' version's polymer slide is coloured olive green rather than the standard black.

Smith & Wesson manufactures the weapon under licence in the US as the **S&W99**: the frame and action are German-made, while the US manufacturer supplies the slide and undertakes final assembly of the weapon for the local market. The version chambered for the 0.40-in S&W cartridge has the reduced magazine capacity of 12 rounds.

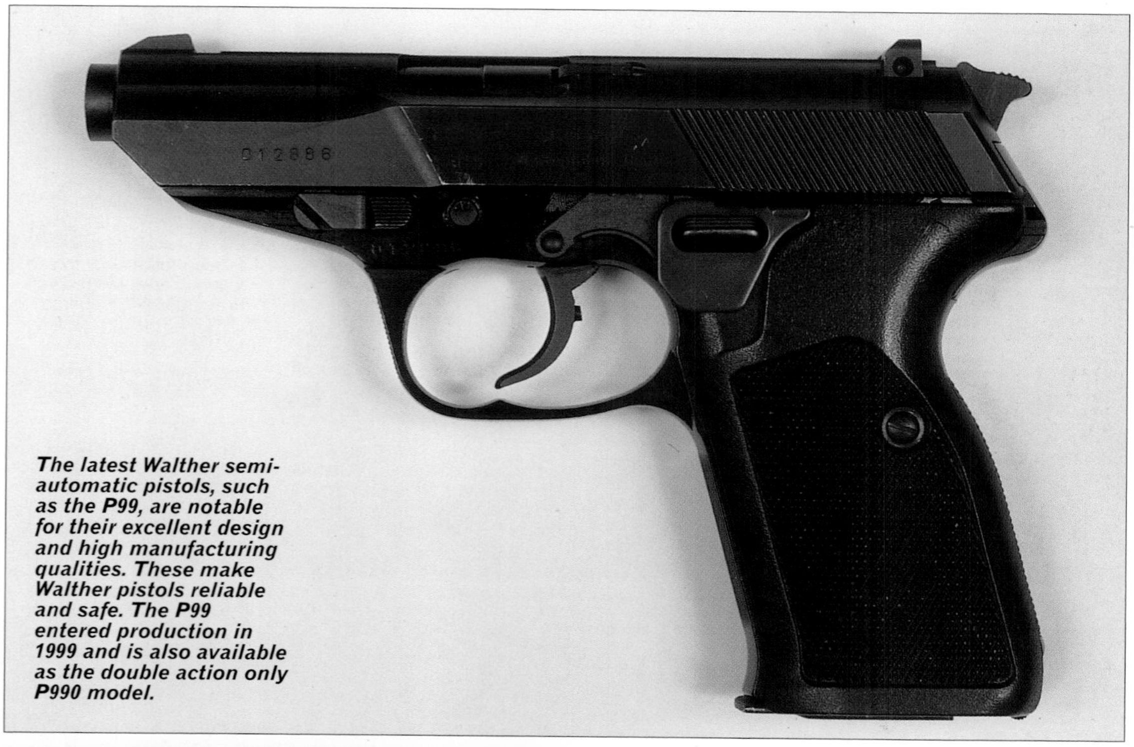

***The latest Walther semi-automatic pistols, such as the P99, are notable for their excellent design and high manufacturing qualities. These make Walther pistols reliable and safe. The P99 entered production in 1999 and is also available as the double action only P990 model.***

***Left: The P38 and its linear descendant, the P5, represent a continuous line of design thinking between the middle of the 1930s and the late 1970s, when the P5 was introduced as a modernised P38. The legend on the left-hand side of the slide, to the rear of the Walther banner emblem, reads 'P5/Carl Walther Waffenfabrik Ulm/Do'. The weapon's serial number is marked on the right-hand side of the frame. The Walther P5's basic specification was provided by the German police.***

**SPECIFICATIONS**

**P5**
**Calibre:** 9-mm Parabellum
**Lengths:** overall 180 mm (7.09 in); barrel 90 mm (3.54 in)
**Weight:** 0.795 kg (1.75 lb)
**Magazine capacity:** 8

**P88**
**Calibre:** 9-mm Parabellum
**Lengths:** overall 187 mm (7.36 in); barrel 102 mm (4 in)
**Weight:** 0.9 kg (1.98 lb)
**Magazine capacity:** 15 rounds

**P99**
**Calibre:** 9-mm Parabellum
**Weight:** 0.72 kg (1.59 lb) unloaded
**Lengths:** overall 180 mm (7.09 in); barrel 102 mm (4 in)
**Magazine capacity:** 16 rounds

# IMI Desert Eagle Pistol

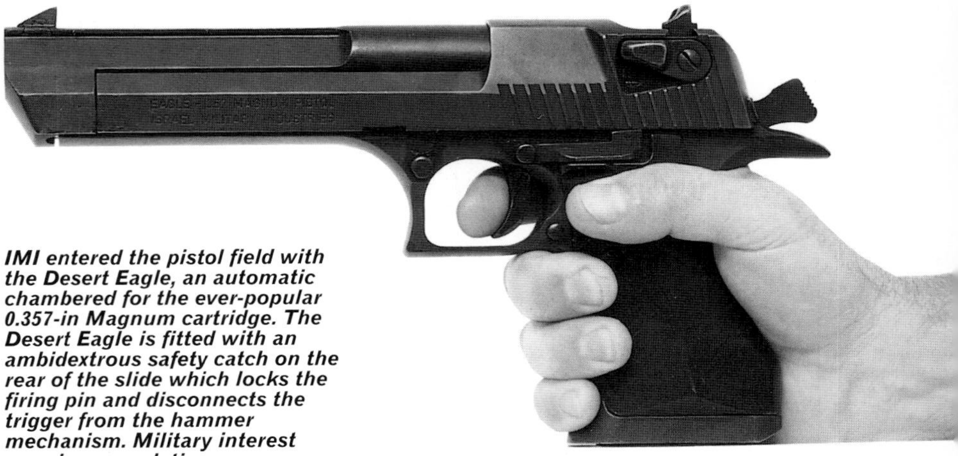

*IMI entered the pistol field with the Desert Eagle, an automatic chambered for the ever-popular 0.357-in Magnum cartridge. The Desert Eagle is fitted with an ambidextrous safety catch on the rear of the slide which locks the firing pin and disconnects the trigger from the hammer mechanism. Military interest remains speculative.*

The automatic pistol produced by Israel Military Industries and known as the **IMI Desert Eagle** was originally an American design proposed by M.R.I. Limited of Minneapolis, Minnesota. The basic concept has been developed in Israel to the point where the Desert Eagle is an extremely advanced and powerful weapon. Predictably, it has captured the imagination of film makers and has been wielded on screen in many an action movie.

The Desert Eagle can be converted to fire either the 0.357-in Magnum (9-mm) cartridge or the even more powerful 0.44-in Magnum (10.92-mm) round; the latter cartridge is one of the most powerful pistol rounds available. All that is required to convert the pistol from one calibre to the other is the replacement of a few parts. To ensure complete safety when using these large rounds the Desert Eagle uses a rotating bolt for a maximum locking action, The safety catch can be engaged by either the right or left hand, and when in position on 'Safe' the hammer is disconnected from the trigger and the firing pin is immobilized.

## Extended barrels

The pistol uses a 152-mm (6-in) barrel as standard, but this basic barrel is interchangeable with barrels 203 mm (8 in), 254 mm (10 in), and 356 mm (14 in) long. The extended barrels are intended for long-range target shooting and may be used with a telescopic sight fitted to a mounting on top of the receiver. No special tools are required to change the barrels. Several other options are available for the Desert Eagle. The trigger can be made adjustable and several different types of fixed sight can be fitted. The trigger guard is shaped to be used with a two-handed grip, although special grips can be fitted if required. The normal construction is of high-quality steels, but an aluminium frame can be supplied.

To date the Desert Eagle has been marketed with the civilian target shooter or enthusiast in mind, but it could also make a powerful military or police weapon. However, most military authorities usually frown upon the use of Magnum cartridges as they are too powerful for general military use because they require a great deal of training for their best capabilities to be realised. It is one of the ironies of the modern military that pistols, issued as sidearms to personnel who are not normally expected to get into a firefight, actually require more training than any other firearm for a shooter to become proficient. And it is not just a matter of learning the basic skill: regular practice is essential. Even among well trained military forces, accidents with pistols are depressingly common. Thus weapons such as the Desert Eagle seem destined to remain with special police units and enthusiasts who simply want the best and most powerful handguns available.

*The 0.357 Magnum is the cartridge favoured by most US police units and significantly outperforms the 9-mm Parabellum and 0.38 special. Recoil is sharp but controllable, despite gas operation.*

**SPECIFICATION**

**Desert Eagle**
**Calibre:** 0.357 in (9-mm) or 0.44 in (10.92-mm) Magnum
**Weight:** empty 1.701 kg (3.75 lb)
**Lengths:** overall with 6-in barrel 260 mm (10.25 in); barrel 152.4 m (6 in)
**Muzzle velocity:** 0.357 Magnum 436 m (1,430 ft) per second; 0.44 Magnum 448 m (1,470 ft) per second
**Magazine capacity:** 0.357 Magnum 9 rounds; 0.44 Magnum 7 rounds

# Beretta Model 1951/Beretta 9-mm Model 92 series Pistol

The **Model 1951** retained the Beretta open-topped slide, but early hopes that this slide could be made from aluminium did not materialize and most production models use an all-steel unit.

The first examples of the Model 1951 did not appear until 1957 as a result mainly of attempts to develop a satisfactory light slide. In more recent years the aluminium slide has become available as an option.

## Standard pistol

The 9-mm (0.354-in) Model 1951 became the standard service pistol of Israel and Egypt as well as Italy. A production line was established in Egypt to manufacture the type and it is known in Egypt as the **Helwan**. The Model 1951 uses the basic Beretta layout, despite the adoption of the locked breech system. The recoil rod and spring are located under the largely open barrel, and the well-sloped butt holds the box magazine containing eight rounds. There is an external hammer and the safety catch engages the sear when in use. Both rear and fore sights are adjustable on most versions.

## New types

In 1976 Beretta placed in production two new families of automatic pistols, the **Model 81** which used a blowback operating system and was chambered for calibres such as 7.65 mm (0.301

*The Beretta Model 1951 was the standard pistol of the Italian armed forces, although numbers are now declining, and has been exported to a number of countries, including Israel and Egypt. This is an example manufactured in Egypt, where the locally produced model is called the Helwan.*

in), and the much larger **Beretta Model 92** which fires the usual 9-mm (0.354-in) Parabellum cartridge. One of its variants, the **Model 92F** or **M9**, is the US Army's standard automatic pistol and replaced the M1911A1 in service with that operator.

### Slide safety catch

Starting from the basic Model 92, the **Model 92S** has a revised safety catch on the slide rather than below it as on the basic Model 92. This allows the hammer to be lowered onto a loaded chamber with complete safety as the firing pin is taken out of line with the hammer.

The **Model 92SB** is essentially similar to the Model 92S, but the slide-mounted safety catch can be applied from each side of the slide. The **Model 92 SB-C** is a more compact and handier version of the Model 92SB.

### US Army variant

The Model 92F was a development of the Model 92SB for the US Army and has been produced in both Italy and the US. The main changes from the Model 92SB are a revised trigger guard outline to suit a two-handed grip, an extended magazine base, revised grips and a lanyard ring. The bore is chrome-plated and the exterior is coated in a Teflon-type material.

Following on from the Model 92F there is a **Model 92F Compact**, designed along the same lines as the Model 92 SB-C but using the features of the US Army's Model 92F.

Also produced along the same lines is the **Model 92 SB-C Type M** which has an eight-round magazine instead of the 15-round magazine. There are also two more models based on the Model 92 series but in a smaller calibre: the **Model 98** and **Model 99** (no longer in production), both in 7.65-mm calibre and based on the Model 92 SB-C and Model 92 SB-C Type M respectively.

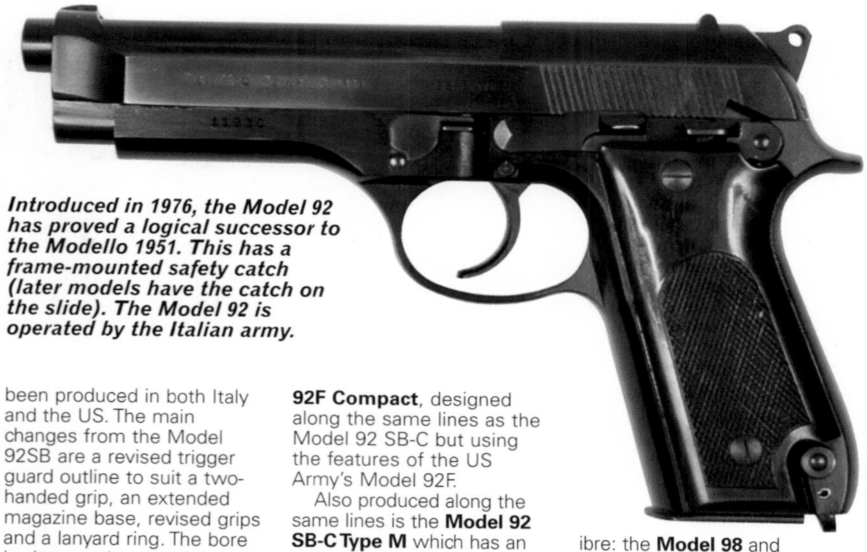

***Introduced in 1976, the Model 92 has proved a logical successor to the Modello 1951. This has a frame-mounted safety catch (later models have the catch on the slide). The Model 92 is operated by the Italian army.***

| SPECIFICATION | |
|---|---|
| **Model 1951**<br>**Calibre:** 9 mm (0.354 in)<br>**Weight:** empty 0.87 kg (1.918 lb)<br>**Lengths:** overall 203.2 mm (8 in); barrel 114.2 mm (4.45 in)<br>**Muzzle velocity:** 350 m (1,148 ft) per second<br>**Magazine capacity:** 8 rounds | **Model 92F**<br>**Calibre:** 9 mm (0.354 in)<br>**Weight:** loaded 1.145 kg (2.524 lb)<br>**Lengths:** overall 217 mm (8.54 in); barrel 125 mm (4.92 in)<br>**Muzzle velocity:** about 390 m (1,280 ft) per second<br>**Magazine capacity:** 15 rounds |

# Beretta 9-mm Model 93R Pistol

With the **Beretta Model 93R** one is back in that no-man's land between true machine pistols and selective-fire pistols, for the Model 93R is another modern pistol design intended to fire three-round bursts. Derived from the Beretta Model 92, the Model 93R can be handled and fired as a normal automatic pistol, but when the three-round burst mode is selected, the firer has to use both hands to hold the pistol steady.

### Grip arrangement

To do this Beretta has designed a compact grip system on which the right hand carries out its normal function of operating the trigger and grasping the butt. For the left hand a small forehand grip is folded down from in front of the elongated trigger guard. The left thumb is inserted into the front of the trigger guard and the rest of the fingers grasp the forehand grip. For additional assistance in holding the pistol steady during firing, the end of the protruding barrel is equipped with a muzzle brake that also acts as a flash hider.

***A self-loading weapon capable of firing three-round bursts, the Model 93R is more accurately a 'machine pistol', although it is carried and handled in the manner of a conventional pistol.***

### Folding stock

To provide even more firing stability it is possible to fix a metal folding stock to the butt. When not in use this can be carried in a special holster, and when mounted on the pistol can be extended to two lengths to suit the firer.

Two types of box magazine can be used with the Model 93R, one holding 15 rounds and the other holding 20. The usual 9-mm (0.354-in) Parabellum cartridge is used.

The design detail incorporated into the Model 93R is considerable and one item that will no doubt be seen on future designs is the use of the foregrip in front of the trigger guard. This is so arranged that the two-handed grip derived from its use is much steadier than the usual two-handed grip with both hands wrapped around what is often a bulky pistol butt.

Using this foregrip it is quite possible to provide reasonably accurate burst fire as both hands are 'spaced' to produce a longer holding base and yet are close enough to prevent either hand wavering. It is possible to fire bursts without using the metal extending stock, but for really accurate fire (even with single shots) its use is recommended.

The Model 93R has now progressed from the development stage and is available on the open market. However, one problem encountered with the pistol seems to be that the three-round burst mechanism is rather complicated and at present requires the services of a trained technician to carry out maintenance and repairs.

Once this difficulty has been ironed out, the Model 93R will certainly make a formidable close-quarter self-defence weapon.

***The Model 93R has been adopted by the Italian armed forces and other special forces units. The weapon's basic frame is similar to that of the Model 92, but there is a burst-controlling mechanism in the right-hand butt grip. The front handgrip can quickly be extended for engaging targets at long range or in order to provide increased control at close ranges.***

| SPECIFICATION | |
|---|---|
| **Model 93R**<br>**Calibre:** 9 mm (0.354 in)<br>**Weights:** loaded with 15-round magazine 1.12 kg (2.47 lb); loaded with 20-round magazine 1.17 kg (2.58 lb) | **Lengths:** pistol 240 mm (9.45 in); barrel 156 mm (6.14 in)<br>**Muzzle velocity:** 375 m (1,230 ft) per second<br>**Magazine capacity:** 15 or 29 rounds |

# Makarov 9-mm pistol

The **Makarov** automatic pistol was developed in the USSR in the early 1950s and entered production during 1952, although it was first noticed by various Western intelligence agencies only during the early 1960s. In design terms it is believed to be an enlarged version of the German Walther PP, a semi-automatic pistol introduced in 1929 and since that time acknowledged to be one of the best weapons of its type. It is worth noting, however, that there are other suggestions for the design origins of the Makarov pistol. The Makarov uses a 9-mm (0.354-in) x 18 cartridge which, though of nominally the same dimensions as the Western 9-mm Police cartridge, is in fact different from any other in use. Developed for use from 1951 in the Stechkin machine pistol (basically a scaled-up Walther PP with full-automatic fire capability and a 20-round magazine), this cartridge is intermediate in power between the 9-mm Parabellum and the 9-mm Short. The Soviet cartridge appears to have been based on a German design of World War II, known as the Ultra: this was not accepted for German wartime service, but attracted some attention in the West for a while. The Ultra has not been produced in the West in any form, but the Soviets took to it as a cartridge ideal, in their thinking, for use in unlocked-breech weapons.

*The Makarov is a simple semi-automatic pistol working on the blowback principle and apparently based in general terms on the Walther PP and PPK designs, closely related German pistols of the period before World War II.*

*An officer of the Soviet Naval Infantry prepares to fire his 9-mm Makarov pistol. The Naval Infantry was small by comparison with most Soviet arms, but for its size was regarded as one of the most effective fighting forces possessed by the USSR.*

## Simple action

The availability of this cartridge made it possible for the Makarov to be designed on the basis of a straightforward blowback operating mechanism without the complications that would be needed with a more powerful cartridge. Another difference between the PP and the Makarov is the latter's trigger mechanism: this is simpler than that of the Walther pistol, but this simplicity was purchased only at the price of a very poor double-action pull.

The Soviets introduced the Makarov as the **PM** (**Pistole Makarova**). As well as being issued to all the branches of the Soviet armed forces, the Makarov was also used by the forces of virtually all the other countries of the Warsaw Pact organisation, and by a great many of the Eastern bloc police forces as well.

The Makarov is a sound, rugged and simple weapon that can be relied upon to operate even under severe conditions. Most accounts state that the pistol is rather awkward to handle as the butt is rather thick, but this is presumably no problem for Eastern bloc soldiers, many of whom have to wear heavy gloves during much of the year.

The Makarov has also been manufactured outside the USSR. One of the largest producers has been China, where the weapon is known as the **Type 59**. China has made some efforts to secure export orders for its Type 59 in direct competition to the USSR, which frequently included the Makarov within the context of its military aid packages. East Germany was another non-Soviet manufacturer of the Makarov pistol, producing a weapon that was virtually identical to the Makarov but known as the **Pistole M**, while Poland turned out yet another Makarov lookalike known as the **P-64**. The special Makarov ammunition has also been produced in all three of these countries.

## Unadopted successor

The primary limitations of the Makarov pistol in its basic forms are a relatively small magazine capacity and an underpowered cartridge. The Soviets appreciated this fact and from the early 1980s attempted unsuccessfully to overcome these shortcoming in the **PMM** (PM Modified) pistol with a 12-round double-stack magazine, and a cartridge based on a lighter bullet fired by a heavier propellant load for a muzzle velocity increased by 100 m (328 ft) per second.

**SPECIFICATION**

**Makarov**
**Calibre:** 9-mm (0.354-in) Makarov
**Weight:** empty 0.663 kg (1.46 lb)
**Length overall:** 160 mm (6.3 in)
**Length of barrel:** 91 mm (3.58 in)
**Muzzle velocity:** 315 m (1,033 ft) per second
**Magazine:** 8-round detachable box

# PSM 5.45-mm pistol

In the 1970s the Soviet authorities decided that a new, notably compact and lightweight semi-automatic pistol was needed as the personal defence weapon to be carried by senior military and security officers. The requirement demanded that the weapon be as slim as possible and lacking in external excrescences that might catch in clothing, the object clearly being the creation of a weapon that could be carried under clothing as unobtrusively as possible yet still possessing the capability for being drawn quickly and smoothly.

The new weapon was created round a newly developed cartridge, the 5.45-mm (0.215-in) x 18 round with a bottle-necked case and a spitzer-pointed jacketed bullet to provide capability superior to those offered by the 0.22-in (5.59-mm) LR and Browning 0.25-in (6.35-mm) ACP cartridges. Although this round offers only a modest muzzle velocity, the bullet is claimed by some sources to possess remarkable penetrative capabilities against some types of body armour.

## Small and light

The weapon designed to fire this useful cartridge is the **Pistolet Samozaryadnii Malogabaritnii** (**PSM**, or small self-loading pistol), which entered production in 1980 and reached service shortly after this time. The PSM is a perfectly conventional blowback-operated weapon with a double-action trigger and a manually operated safety catch (pulled back to make the weapon safe) mounted on the left-hand side of the slide's rear portion. There is no slide stop. The weapon is made primarily of steel, but the grip sideplates are fabricated from thin aluminium alloy in an effort to reduce weight and width, the latter being a mere 18 mm (0.71 in) and facilitating the weapon's easy concealment under the wearer's outer clothes.

The trigger guard is accommodated neatly on the underside of the weapon with curves optimised to ease the drawing of the weapon, the barrel has six rifling grooves with a right-hand twist, and the magazine is carried in the weapon's butt, as is standard for modern semi-automatic pistols.

### Small magazine

The magazine carries only eight rounds, a figure deemed acceptable for a snugly carried self-defence weapon, and is unloaded after its catch, in the heel of the butt, has been operated. Once the magazine has been removed, the weapon can be made safe and also checked as safe by pulling back the slide to eject (via the ejector port in the weapon's right-hand side) any round that may be in the chamber, looking through the ejector port to ensure that there is no round in the chamber, and finally releasing the slide before pulling the trigger.

The PSM is still in modest production for military and paramilitary service, and has also made its way onto the black market in Europe and elsewhere.

| SPECIFICATION | |
|---|---|
| **PSM**<br>**Calibre:** 5.45-mm (0.215-in) x 18 MPT<br>**Weight:** empty 0.46 kg (1.014 lb; loaded 0.51 kg (1.124 lb) | **Length overall:** 155 mm (6.1 in)<br>**Length of barrel:** 85 mm (3.35 in)<br>**Muzzle velocity:** approximately 315 m (1,033 ft) per second<br>**Magazine:** 8-round detachable box |

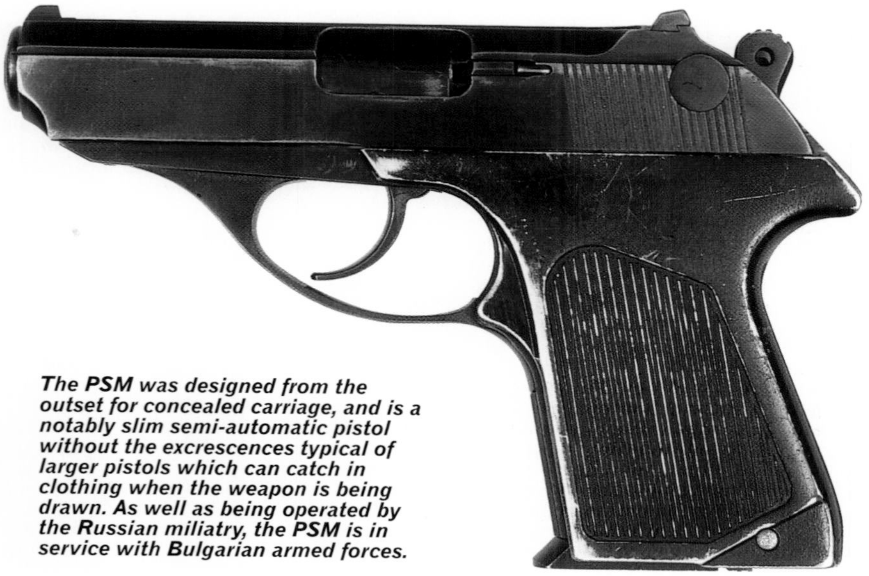

***The PSM was designed from the outset for concealed carriage, and is a notably slim semi-automatic pistol without the excrescences typical of larger pistols which can catch in clothing when the weapon is being drawn. As well as being operated by the Russian miliatry, the PSM is in service with Bulgarian armed forces.***

# SIG-Sauer P220 series Convertible-calibre pistols

For very many years the Schweizerische Industrie-Gesellschaft (SIG) has been producing excellent weapons in its production facility located at Neuhausen Rhinefalls. The company has always been restricted by the strict Swiss laws governing military exports from making any significant overseas sales, however, so by joining up with a German company, J. P. Sauer und Sohn, SIG was finally able to transfer production to West Germany and thus gain access to more markets. This was the original of the SIG-Sauer concern.

One of the first military pistols developed by the new organization was the **SIG-Sauer P220**, a mechanically locked single- or double-action semi-automatic pistol. When dealing with the P220 it is difficult to avoid superlatives, for in many ways this is a truly magnificent pistol. Its standards of manufacture and finish are superb, despite the extensive use of metal stampings and an aluminium frame to keep down weight and cost. The pistol handles very well, being one of those weapons that immediately feels 'right' in the hand as soon as it is picked up. It is accurate, and the overall design is such that it is difficult for dirt or dust to find its way into the interior and thereby cause stoppages. Despite this factor, the pistol is still easy to strip and maintain, and has all the usual pistol safeties.

### Four calibre options

One notable feature of the P220 in overall terms is the fact that it can be supplied in any one of four calibres. These are the usual 9-mm (0.354-in) Parabellum, 7.65-mm (0.301-in) Parabellum, 0.45-in (11.27-mm) ACP and 0.38-in Super (9-mm, but not to be confused with 9-mm Parabellum). It is possible to convert the P220 from one calibre to another, and there are also kits to convert the pistol to fire 0.22-in Long Rifle (5.59-mm) for training purposes. In its form to fire the 9-mm Parabellum cartridge, the pistol has a magazine holding nine rounds, but when firing 0.45-in ACP the magazine can carry only seven rounds.

The excellence of the P220 has rewarded SIG-Sauer with a stream of orders. The P220 is in service with the Swiss army, which knows it as the **9-mm Pistole 75**, a designation which sometimes provides the P220 with the name **Model 75**.

There is a later version of the P220 known as the **P225** which is a slightly more compact weapon chambered only for the 9-mm Parabellum cartridge. This version has been selected for Swiss and West German police use as the **P6**. The 9-mm Parabellum **P226** was developed with a 15-round magazine for the US competition to find an M1911A1 successor but proved too expensive. The **P228** was introduced in 1989 as a compact version of the P226 with a smaller magazine and was adopted as the US Air Force's **M11**, and the **P229** is the P228 chambered for 0.40-in SW.

***The superb SIG-Sauer P220 resulted from a collaborative effort between the Swiss SIG company and J. P. Sauer und Sohn to produce a pistol for export, unfettered by Swiss government restrictions. The P220 is available in up to five calibres: 0.45 ACP, 0.38-in Super, 9-mm Parabellum, 7.65-mm Parabellum and even 0.22-in LR.***

***Well over 150,000 examples of the SIG-Sauer P220 series have been produced, including 35,000 9-mm Pistole 75s for Swiss military use. The design has also apparently influenced the Iranian ZOAF pistol. This P226 is a limited edition, marking the Swiss concern's 125th anniversary in 1978.***

| SPECIFICATION | |
|---|---|
| **9-mm Pistole 75**<br>**Calibre:** 9-mm (0.354-in)<br>**Length overall:** 198 mm (7.8 in)<br>**Length of barrel:** 112 mm (4.4 in) | **Weight:** empty 0.83 kg (1.83 lb)<br>**Muzzle velocity:** 345 m (1,132 ft) per second<br>**Magazine:** 9-round detachable box |

# American
## Self-loading pistols

***The AMT On Duty pistol is typical of modern semi-automatic designs. Chambered for 9-mm or .40 S&W, it has a machined aluminium frame and other parts are made from steel castings. It can hold 15 rounds in its 9-mm version, with a capacity of 11 in the more powerful S&W .40 calibre.***

Although there are several American manufacturers who produce semi-automatic pistols of the type likely to be used by military, security and law enforcement bodies, the two with the largest grip on the market are Ruger and Smith & Wesson.

The most advanced of the Ruger pistols entered production in 1987 as the **Ruger P-85** in 9-mm (0.354-in) Parabellum, and the series has remained in manufacture since that time in a number of developed forms. All of the weapons are of the recoil-operated type, fire from a locked breech and, with the exception of the polymer-framed 9-mm **P-95** and 0.45-in (11.43-mm) **P-97**, are based on an aluminium frame.

The weapons differ from each other mainly in the details of their triggers, barrel lengths and magazine capacities. Taken out of production in 1991, the P-85 has a double-action trigger, 114-mm (4.5-in) barrel and 15-round magazine; the 9-mm **P-89** entered production in 1991 and differs in its options of double-action, double-action with decocker and double-action only trigger; the **P-90** is a 0.45-in weapon with double-action and double-action with decocker trigger options, and a seven-round magazine; the **P-91** in 0.4-in (10.16-mm) calibre was made between 1992 and 1994 with a 110-mm (4.33-in) barrel, double-action with decocker and double-action only options, and an 11-round magazine; the 9-mm **P-93** of 1994 has a 99-mm (3.9-in) barrel, double-action with decocker and double-action only options, and a 10-round magazine; the 9-mm **P-94** and 0.4-in **P-944** of the same year have 108-mm (4.25-in) barrels, all three trigger options and a 10-round magazine; the 9-mm P-95 of 1996 has a 99-mm barrel, all three trigger options and a 10-round magazine; and finally the 0.45-in **P-97** of 1998 also has a 99-mm barrel, all three trigger options and an eight-round magazine.

### S&W pistols

Smith & Wesson has also produced large numbers of semi-automatic pistols, starting with the 9-mm **Smith & Wesson Model 39** of 1949, based on a recoil-operated mechanism and steel, stainless steel and aluminium alloy construction. The Model 39 and companion **Model 59** with a 14- rather than eight-round magazine were the first-generation of S&W semi-automatic pistols, and were taken out of production in 1980. The second generation of S&W pistols was introduced in 1980 on the basis of the Models 39 and 59, had three-digit model numbers and different frame materials, and with double-stack magazines and traditional double-action triggers with safety/decockers. The key to understanding second-generation model numbers is a first digit of 4, 5 or 6 indicating an aluminium alloy, carbon steel or stainless steel frame; second and third digits indicating magazine capacity and frame size (59 for 9-mm and double-stack, 39 for 9-mm and single-stack magazines, 69 for 9-mm compact size and double-stack magazine).

The third-generation pistols were made from 1990 and have four-digit model numbers, an ambidextrous safety/decocker lever, double-action only and decocker only models, and calibres such as 0.4-in, 0.45-in and 10-mm (0.39-in). The key to third-generation pistols is the first two digits for the calibre and frame type (39 for 9-mm with single stack magazine, 59 for 9-mm with double-stack magazine, 69 for 9-mm compact with a double-stack magazine etc), third digit for the trigger type and frame size (5 for double-action only and compact etc), and a fourth digit for frame material (3 and 6 for aluminium alloy and stainless steel). All models have a stainless steel slide.

**SPECIFICATION**

**Ruger P-97**
**Calibre:** 0.45-in (11.43-mm)
**Length overall:** 185 mm (7.28 in)
**Length of barrel:**: 99 mm (3.9 in)
**Weight:** 0.86 kg (1.9 lb)
**Muzzle velocity:** not available
**Feed:** 8-round straight box magazine

***Above: Pistols have always had marginal military use, being primarily issued as personal protection weapons. However, they are much more important as police and paramilitary weapons, and constant training is essential to maintain proficiency.***

***Right: Colt's venerable Model 1911 has been updated by a number of arms makers as well as by Colt. The Delta Elite is a modernised version of the M1911, rechambered to fire the powerful 10-mm round now popular with law-enforcement officers.***

# Smith & Wesson, Colt and Ruger Revolvers

Smith & Wesson no longer manufactures a revolver specifically for military use, but many armed forces use Smith & Wesson revolvers, generally for the military and security police roles.

Top of the current list come the weapons chambered for Magnum cartridges offering prodigious stopping power. Primary among these is the **No. 29** firing the 0.44-in (10.92-mm) Magnum round and introduced in 1955. The No. 29 is too much of a handful for most users since its recoil is very considerable, so the **No. 57** was introduced in 1964 to use the less potent 0.41-in (10.41-mm) Magnum round. This revolver has the same overall dimensions as the No. 29, and retains much of its stopping power, but is rather more manageable.

Smith & Wesson also offers several 0.38-in (9-mm) revolvers. A typical weapon is the **No. 38 Bodyguard**, a snub-nosed revolver with a shrouded hammer and a five-round cylinder. The generally similar **No. 49** differs only its its steel rather than aluminium alloy body.

## Colt revolvers

Modern Colt military revolvers are double-action designs. The best known of these weapons is the **Python**. Introduced in 1955, this has a shrouded barrel with a distinctive appearance and is chambered for one cartridge only, the 0.357-in Magnum. The Python is a very powerful weapon, but to absorb some of the effects of the heavy cartridge load it has to be constructed in an equally heavy fashion – it is thus very heavy (1.16 kg/2.56 lb). The Python is available in two barrel lengths, 102 and 152 mm (4 and 6 in).

Appearing in 1953, the **Trooper** was available in a variety of barrel lengths and in various calibres. The Trooper was replaced by the **Lawman Mk III**, which is produced only in 0.357-in Magnum and with barrels as short as 51 mm (2 in).

## Ruger revolvers

When planning its revolver range, Sturm, Ruger and Co. decided to examine the fundamental design aspects of the revolver and came up with what was a very modern version of a weapon that had been around for nearly a century. New types of steel and other materials (especially springs) were introduced and the manufacture was developed into a modular system in which components could be added or subtracted to form any particular model.

Ruger revolvers are offered with various barrel lengths and in varying finishes, including stainless steel. The revolvers are also available in a wide range of calibres from 0.38-in Special up to the Magnums. Typical of the service revolvers is the **Service-Six** chambered for either the 0.38 Special or 0.357 Magnum cartridges. The Service-Six can be fitted with either a 70- or 102-mm (2.75- or 4-in) barrel, while the generally similar **Security-Six**, intended for police use, can have even longer barrels. The trigger actions of both are single- and double-action. Some Ruger revolvers fire rimless 9-mm Parabellum ammunition, so for loading these rounds special 'half moon' clips, each holding three rounds, have to be used.

A Ruger revolver that caused quite a stir on its introduction in 1955 is the **Blackhawk** firing the 0.44-in Magnum round. This was too much for most users, so the Blackhawk range was extended to include other less potent cartridges, and it is still in great demand by many pistol enthusiasts.

***The Ruger Speed-Six is known to the US Army as the GS-32N. It is made in two versions: one for 0.357-in Magnum/0.38-in Special and one for 9-mm Parabellum. The 9-mm is a rimless cartridge, so three-round 'half-moon' clips are used to ensure ejection.***

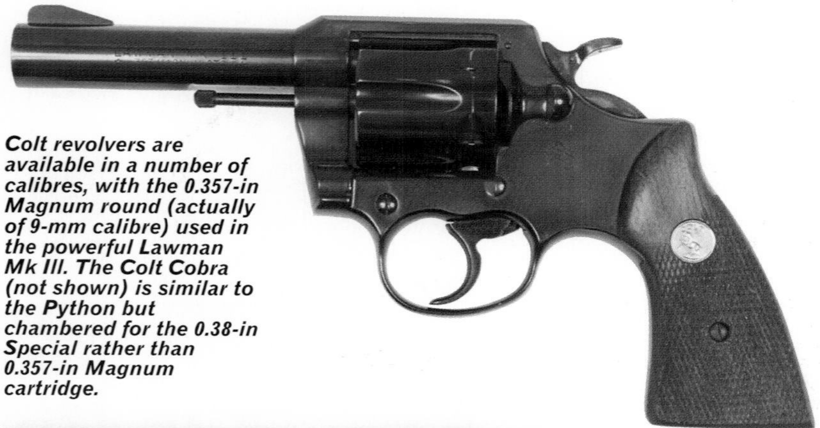

***Colt revolvers are available in a number of calibres, with the 0.357-in Magnum round (actually of 9-mm calibre) used in the powerful Lawman Mk III. The Colt Cobra (not shown) is similar to the Python but chambered for the 0.38-in Special rather than 0.357-in Magnum cartridge.***

**SPECIFICATION**

**No. 38 Bodyguard**
**Calibre:** 0.38-in (9-mm)
**Length overall:** 165 mm (6.5 in)
**Length of barrel:** 51 mm (2 in)
**Weight:** 0.411 kg (0.9 lb)
**Muzzle velocity:** 260 m (853 ft) per second
**Chamber capacity:** 5 rounds

**Lawman Mk III**
**Calibre:** 0.357-in (9-mm)
**Length overall:** 235 mm (9.25 in)
**Length of barrel:** see text
**Weight:** 1.022 kg (2.253 lb)
**Muzzle velocity:** about 436 m (1,430 ft) per second
**Chamber capacity:** 6 rounds

**0.38-in Service-Six**
**Calibre:** 0.38-in (9-mm)
**Length overall:** 235 mm (9.25 in)
**Length of barrel:** 102 mm (4 in)
**Weight:** 0.935 kg (2.06 lb)
**Muzzle velocity:** 260 m (853 ft) per second
**Chamber capacity:** 6 rounds

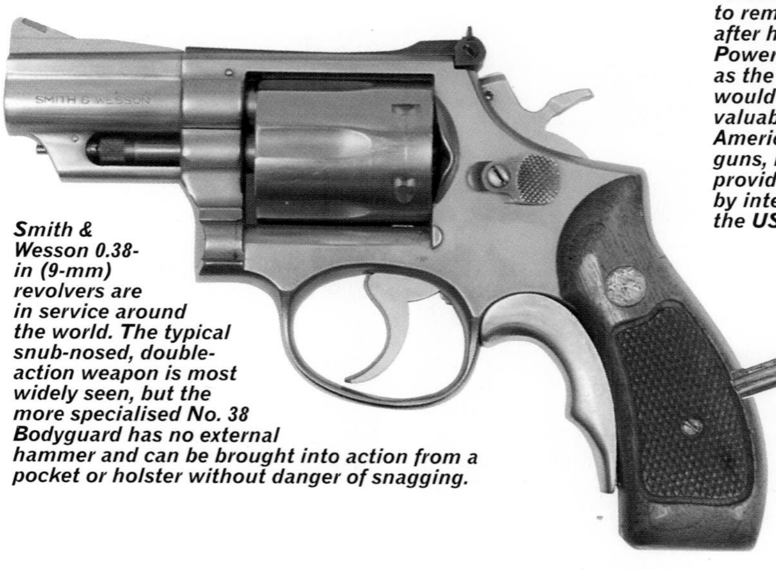

***Smith & Wesson 0.38-in (9-mm) revolvers are in service around the world. The typical snub-nosed, double-action weapon is most widely seen, but the more specialised No. 38 Bodyguard has no external hammer and can be brought into action from a pocket or holster without danger of snagging.***

***One advantage of the revolver is its capacity to remain in operation after harsh treatment. Powerful weapons such as the Colt Python would be extremely valuable to a Central American guerrilla, with guns, rounds and spares provided in many cases by interested parties in the USA.***

# Firepower in the hand

## Sub-machine guns in action

**The sub-machine gun has found a new role in special operations, counter-terrorism and law-enforcement. It is a powerful self-protection weapon, combining compact size and ease of handling with controllable firepower.**

Special forces carry them on deep penetration missions behind enemy lines. You can see them in the hands of the police at international airports. You don't see them, but you know they are there, in the entourage of the President of the United States. His bodyguards keep them hidden in their cars, or in innocent-looking briefcases.

They come in a variety of shapes and sizes, but sub-machine guns all have one thing in common. They provide the maximum amount of controllable short-range firepower in the smallest possible package.

### Evolution

Sub-machine guns evolved during World War I. In the confined, close quarter fighting of the trenches, troops needed a special kind of weapon; capable of automatic fire like a machine-gun, but less of a handful in a trench than a bayonetted rifle. A number of designs were tried, but the German Bergmann MP18 was the first really practical weapon to reach the troops.

### The first SMG

Even today, more than 80 years on, the MP18 displays the classic characteristics of the sub-machine gun. It fired a pistol cartridge using a simple 'blowback' mechanism. The low-power ammunition meant that it was relatively easy to control when firing on full auto; an important characteristic since a light weapon would be hard to control with full-power rounds.

Since then, sub-machine guns have appeared with a variety of complexity and finishes. They have ranged from the beautifully manufactured Steyr-Solothurn, made in Switzerland in the 1930s, to utilitarian designs turned out by the million during World War II. The most primitive of these, such as the British Sten gun, looked to be thrown together out of gas-pipe and pressed steel. But they worked.

However, the development of the assault rifle seemed to signal the end of the line. The trouble with sub-machine guns is that they are inaccurate. They are fine for spraying bullets – as long as you don't mind where they go. Carbine versions of the latest assault rifles are hardly larger than sub-machine guns, and can seemingly do everything that the simpler gun does, only more accurately and over longer distances. Yet not only is the sub-machine gun still in existence, but more and more designs are being marketed every year.

Part of the reason is that

***Sub-machine guns, also commonly known as machine pistols, offer an immense amount of firepower on one handy package. But while they are easy to use, they are very hard to use well.***

***Above: Modern sub-machine guns are most commonly used in the internal security role, partly because they are easy to handle in confined spaces, but partly because their firepower is vital to counter increasingly heavily armed terrorists and criminals.***

sub-machine guns are easy to make and maintain. It is much cheaper to build large numbers of simple weapons than to tool up for the more complex and expensive manufacture of sophisticated assault rifles.

### A new type of war

But there is a new type of war, and a new type of warrior. The alarming rise in crime and terrorism has turned the streets of the world into battlefields.

Security forces can rarely use conventional weapons. They need something easy to handle in confined spaces, such as in vehicles or buildings. It must have enough stopping power to handle an armed criminal or terrorist, yet not be so powerful as to harm innocent bystanders half a mile away.

### Expert tool

Special Forces in particular need such weapons. When you are on foot behind enemy lines, loaded with communications gear and explosives for some clandestine demolition work, you need simple, tough, reliable, firepower that does not weigh too much.

The sub-machine gun is the only practical weapon that comes near to matching all these needs, even though some were actually designed for very different reasons. The classic Uzi was produced in the 1950s when the state of Israel needed all the firepower it could get as quickly and as cheaply as possible.

By contrast, the Heckler & Koch MP5 is a scaled-down version of an assault rifle, and is much more complex than its rivals. The problem with the MP5 is the very complexity that makes it accurate. As long as you give it a thorough cleaning after every action, it will perform reliably and effectively. But give it the kind of battering that a soldier will subject it to in the field, and it will cease to function.

For a battlefield weapon, this is a serious problem, but hostage rescues are different. Action rarely lasts for more than a few minutes, and the troops who take part are all highly skilled weapons handlers. Accuracy is more important than the ability to fire after a week of mishandling, which weapons have to survive in the field.

Small, cheap and easily concealed, the modern sub-machine gun is one of the most important tools for combatting the urban terrors of the 21st Century. Technology may have changed its appearance in the last few years, and the people using it are a far cry from the German Stormtroopers of 1918, but the sub-machine gun of today is still the same handy package of firepower it has been for more than eight decades.

***Although most modern sub-machine guns, like this Austrian Steyr MPi machine pistol, are made of high-tech materials, in action they are virtually the same as the original SMGs introduced during and after World War I.***

# Owen Gun

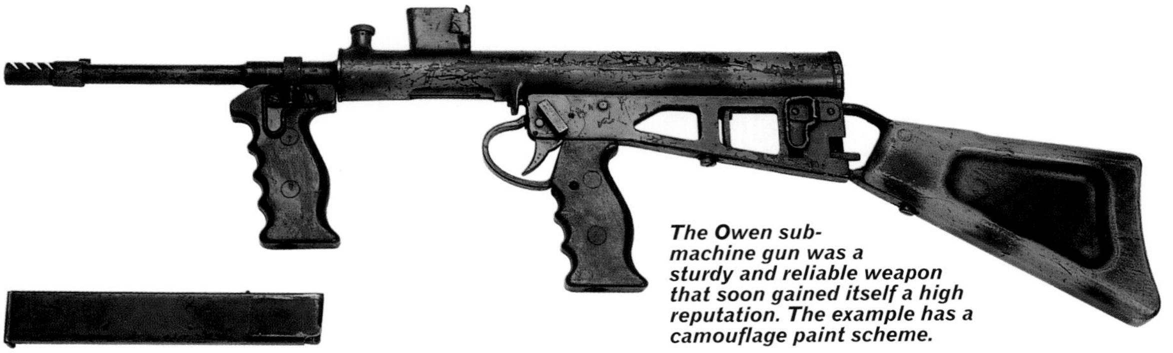

*The Owen sub-machine gun was a sturdy and reliable weapon that soon gained itself a high reputation. The example has a camouflage paint scheme.*

It took some time before Lieutenant Evelyn Owen was able to persuade the Australian military to adopt his design of sub-machine gun in 1940. At the time the Australian army had little or no interest in the sub-machine gun, and by the time it realised the weapon's importance it expected to receive all the Sten guns it required from the UK. It took some time for the army to appreciate that it was going to receive no Sten guns as the British army wanted all that could be produced. So finally the Australians adopted the **Owen** gun, but even then they were not sure in what calibre. Thus the first trials batches were produced in four calibres before the universal 9-mm was adopted.

## Overhead magazine

The Owen can be easily recognised by its magazine, which points vertically upward. This arrangement was apparently chosen for no other reason than that it worked, and it must be said that it worked very well. The Owen was kept in service until well into the 1960s and its successor retains the overhead magazine. The rest of the gun was fairly conventional and very robust under all conditions. As production increased, changes were introduced to the design. The early fins around the barrel were removed and some changes were made to the butt, which could be found in versions with just a wire skeleton, an all-wood design, and one version that was half outline and half wood.

*The Australian Owen sub-machine gun's most prominent recognition feature was the vertically-mounted box magazine. The example shown here is one of the early production models.*

Another feature unique to the Owen was its quick-change barrel. Why this feature was incorporated is uncertain, for it would have taken a long period of firing for the barrel to become unusably hot. Another odd point regarding the Owen was that once in service it was often painted in camouflage schemes to suit the terrain in New Guinea, where Australian soldiers found the Owen ideal for the close-quarter combat that the jungles enforced. It was true that the Owen was rather heavier than most comparable models but the forward-mounted grip and the pistol grip made it easy to handle.

The top-mounted magazine meant that the sights had to be offset to the right side of the body, but this was of little consequence as the Owen was almost always fired from the hip.

Production of the Owen ceased in 1945 but in 1952 many were virtually rebuilt and provision was made for a long bayonet to be fitted to the muzzle; some versions made in 1943 used a much shorter bayonet that fitted over the muzzle with an almost unique tubular mount.

**SPECIFICATION**

| | |
|---|---|
| **Owen Gun** | **Rate of fire, cyclic:** 700 rounds per minute |
| **Calibre:** 9-mm | **Muzzle velocity:** 420 m (1,380 ft) per second |
| **Length overall:** 813 mm (32 in) | **Magazine:** 33-round vertical box |
| **Length of barrel:** 250 mm (9.84 in) | |
| **Weight loaded:** 4.815 kg (10.6 lb) | |

# ZK 383 Gun

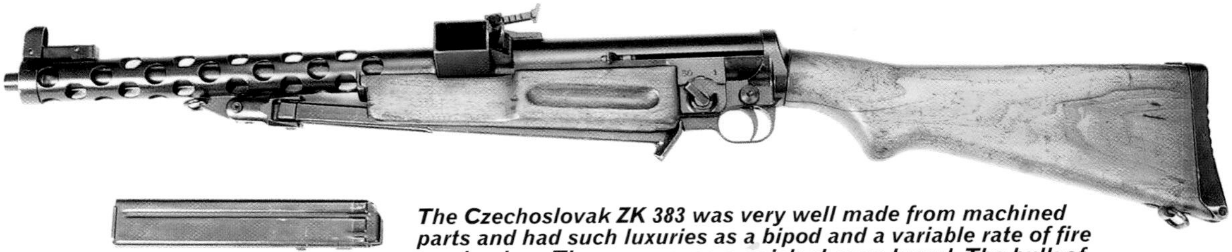

*The Czechoslovak ZK 383 was very well made from machined parts and had such luxuries as a bipod and a variable rate of fire mechanism. There was even a quick-change barrel. The bulk of these weapons was later produced for the German Waffen SS, whose men found it a heavy but reliable weapon.*

The Czechoslovak **ZK 383** is one of those sub-machine guns that is virtually unknown in the West as it was little used outside Eastern Europe and its combat use was limited mainly to the war against the USSR. The ZK 383 was a very important weapon type for its time, however, and remained in production from the late 1930s until 1948.

Designed during the early 1930s, the ZK 383 went into production at the famous Brno arms plant, known for the later introduction of what was to be the Bren gun. The ZK 383 was a relatively large and heavy weapon for the sub-machine gun class, a feature emphasised by uncommon application of a bipod under the barrel on some models. This bipod was the result of the Czech army's tactical philosophy, for it regarded the weapon as a form of light machine-gun, in direct contradiction of the usually accepted role of a close-quarter combat weapon. This odd approach was further emphasised by the use of what was one of the ZK 383's oddest features, namely a capability for two rates of fire (500 or 700 rounds per minute) provided by the addition or subtraction of a small 0.17-kg (0.37-lb) weight to the breech block – with the weight removed, the breech block could move faster and thus the rate of fire could be increased. The slower rate of fire was used when the ZK 383 was used with its bipod as a light machine-gun, and the faster fire rate when the ZK was carried as an assault weapon.

## Limited export

But that was only the Czechoslovak army's point of view, and the feature does not appear to have been used much by the other customers for the weapon. The Bulgarian army adopted the type as its standard sub-machine gun (it used the ZK 383 until at least the early 1960s), but by far the largest number of ZK 383s were produced after 1939 for the German army. When they took over Czechoslovakia in 1939 the Germans found the ZK 383 production line still intact, and it was a sensible move as far as they were concerned to keep it intact for their own uses. The Brno factory was taken over for SS weapon production and thus the ZK 383 output was diverted to the Waffen SS, which used the weapon only on the Eastern Front. The Waffen SS examples were all known as the **vz 9** (vz for *vzor*, the Czech for model) and the Waffen SS found it effective enough for it to become one of their standard weapons. Numbers were kept in Czechoslovakia for use by the civil police who had their own version, the **ZK 383P**, which was produced without the bipod.

The only nations other than Czechoslovakia, Bulgaria and Germany that purchased the ZK 383 were Brazil and Venezuela, and even then the numbers involved were not large. Apart from its use in Eastern Europe, the ZK 383 had few points to attract attention and in many ways it was too complicated for the role it was called upon to play. The Czechoslovak army's predilection for the design as a light machine-gun led to all manner of detail extras that the weapon did not need.

The dual rate of fire feature has already been mentioned, as has the bipod, but the sub-machine gun does not really need a complex barrel-change mechanism, an all-machined mechanism made from the finest steels available or an angled breech block return spring angled into the butt. The ZK 383 had all these, making it a very reliable, sound weapon but one that was really too complex for its role.

**SPECIFICATION**

| | |
|---|---|
| **ZK 383** | **Muzzle velocity:** 365 m (1,200 ft) per second |
| **Calibre:** 9-mm | **Rate of fire, cyclic:** 500 or 700 rounds per minute |
| **Length overall:** 875 mm (34.45 in) | **Magazine:** 30-round straight box |
| **Length of barrel:** 325 mm (12.8 in) | |
| **Weight loaded:** 4.83 kg (10.65 lb) | |

# Suomi m/1931 Gun

*The Suomi m/1931 was one of the highest quality sub-machine guns ever manufactured, for practically every part was machined from solid metal.*

The **Suomi m/1931** resulted from German-inspired designs from the early 1920s. As sub-machine gun designs go, there was little remarkable about the m/1931, for it used a conventional blowback action and an orthodox layout. Where it did score over many existing designs was that it was extremely well made (to the point of lavishness in the quality of material used and the excellence of the machining) and used very good feed systems that were later copied widely. There were two main versions, one a 50-round vertical box and the other a 71-round drum. In the box magazine the normal lengthy bulk of 50 rounds of ammunition was overcome by having the magazine split into two vertical columns, rounds being fed from one column and then the other. In action this feed system was much favoured as it enabled a soldier to carry into action far more ready rounds than would be possible with a conventional magazine. Despite this, there was also a normal 30-round box magazine.

## Proved in service

The m/1931 was produced for the Finnish army in numbers and proved itself in action during the 'Winter War' of 1939-50 with the Soviets. There were several export models, some of them with small bipods under the barrel or body, and these were purchased by Sweden and Switzerland, which set up their own production lines, as did a company in Denmark. The type was adopted by the Polish police before 1939, and examples popped up during the Spanish Civil War on both sides. It was still in limited Scandinavian service until recent times, and this longevity can be explained by one factor other than its excellent construction: this is the weapon's reliability under any conditions without ever seeming to go wrong. These factors alone explain the high regard shown for the m/1931 in the past, but there was also another factor. When the m/1931 was produced, no pains were spared on detail machining; the whole of the gun, the body and bolt included, were machined from solid metal.

Consequently the gun was very accurate for its type. Most sub-machine gun types are accurate only to a few yards and most are almost useless at ranges over 50 m (55 yards). The m/1931 can be used accurately at ranges up to 300 m (330 yards). In relative terms, few were used in World War II but the influence of the design can be detected in many wartime models. The design was also made under licence in Switzerland for the Swiss army during 1943.

***The Suomi m/1931 in action, fitted with the 71-round magazine. Unlike many other sub-machine guns, the m/1931 had a long barrel that was accurate enough for aimed fire at most combat ranges.***

**SPECIFICATION**

**Suomi m/1931**
**Calibre:** 9-mm
**Length overall:** 870 mm (34.25 in) with the butt extended
**Length of barrel:** 314 mm (12.36 in)
**Weight loaded:** 7.04 kg (15.52 lb) with drum magazine
**Muzzle velocity:** 400 m (1,310 ft) per second
**Rate of fire, cyclic:** 900 rounds per minute
**Magazine:** 30- or 50-round box, or 71-round drum

# MAS Modèle 1938 Gun

***The MAS 1938 was a sound, advanced weapon. Unfortunately for its future prospects, it fired an underpowered cartridge available only in France, and was complicated and therefore slow and expensive to manufacture.***

Often quoted as the **MAS 38**, this French sub-machine gun was first produced at St Etienne in 1938, hence the model number. The MAS 38 was the outcome of a long period of development, and was the follow-on from a weapon produced in 1935. But it must be stated that the development period was well spent, for the MAS 38 proved to be a sound enough weapon well in advance of its period.

There were some rather odd features about the MAS 38, however. It was quite complicated and also fired a cartridge produced only in France. Both these features can be explained by the period when it was designed. At that time there appeared to be no reason to make the weapon as simple as possible, for existing production methods seemed adequate to churn out the limited numbers then required. The calibre can be explained by the fact that it was available at the time and so the MAS 38 had a calibre of 7.65 mm (0.301 in) and used a cartridge available only in France, the 7.65-mm Long. While this cartridge was accurate, it was not very powerful, and had the disadvantage that no one else was likely to adopt it once the 9-mm calibre had been universally adopted.

## Complex mechanism

The MAS 38 has a complex mechanism with a long bolt travel that was partially offset by having the gun body sloping down into the solid wooden butt. The cocking handle was separate from the bolt once firing started, a good but complex feature. Another good point was a flap over the magazine housing that closed as the magazine was withdrawn to keep out dust and dirt. Very few other designs had this feature and most of them managed to work perfectly well without it.

In fact the MAS 38 turned out to be rather too good for the customer, who at first decided that it did not want a sub-machine gun after all. The French army turned down the weapon when it was first offered, and the initial production examples went to some of the more para-military members of one of the French police forces. When hostilities did start in 1939, the French army soon changed its mind and ordered large quantities, but the complex machining that went into the MAS 38 resulted in a slow rate of introduction into service, and the French army was driven to ordering numbers of Thompson sub-machine guns from the USA. These arrived too late to make any difference to the events of May and June 1940, and France capitulated. When the French forces rearmed under the Vichy regime the MAS 38 was kept in production: in fact the weapon was kept in production until 1949, and it was used in the Indo-China War.

The MAS 38 never got the recognition it deserved. It was rather too complicated, fired an odd cartridge and it was never possible to produce it in quantity when it was required. It is therefore now little known outside France and few, if any, modern weapon designs owe anything to its influence. The only armies to use the MAS 38, other than some of the ex-French colonies, were the Germans who captured enough in 1940 to issue them as **Maschinenpistole 722(f)** weapons to their garrison forces in France.

**SPECIFICATION**

**MAS 38**
**Calibre:** 7.65-mm
**Length overall:** 623 mm (24.53 in)
**Length of barrel:** 224 mm (8.82 in)
**Weight loaded:** 3.356 kg (7.4 lb)
**Muzzle velocity:** 350 m (1,150 ft) per second
**Rate of fire, cyclic:** 600 rounds per minute
**Magazine:** 32-round straight box

# MP 38, MP 38/40 & MP 40 Sub-machine guns

*This MP 38 is of the original production version. Although the design was intended for mass production, the receiver and some other parts were machined – these were later replaced by the pressings and welds of the MP 40.*

When the **MP 38** was first produced in 1938 it revolutionised weapon design, not by any particular feature of the design but as a result of the method of manufacture employed. Gone was the accurate machine tooling of yesteryear, along with the finely produced wooden fittings, and the standard of finish upon which gunsmiths so prided themselves. With the introduction of the MP 38 came rough and simple metal stampings, die-cast parts, plastic instead of wood and a finish that lacked any finesse or even plating of any kind.

The MP 38 looked what it was: a weapon mass-produced to meet a precise military need, namely a simple and cheap weapon that would work when called upon to fire, and nothing more. On the MP 38 there was no wooden butt, just a bare folding heavy wire framework that folded under the body for use in close confines such as the back of a vehicle.

## Stamped metal parts

The body was produced from simple sheet metal stampings that could be churned out in any metal workshop, and the breech block was provided with only a minimum of machining. Most of the outer surfaces were left in their bare metal state and at best were just painted. Despite all these cost-cutting measures the MP38 had an immediate impact out of all proportion to its design attributes, for in the years after 1938 more and more weapons adopted similar mass-production techniques first introduced on the MP 38.

The MP 38 was quite orthodox so far as operation went. It had a conventionally functioning blowback bolt, and the vertical magazine under the body fed 9-mm (0.354-in) Parabellum rounds into a conventional feed system. A cocking handle along the left-hand side of the body operated in an open slot, but although dust and dirt could enter the internal workings the weapon could absorb an appreciable amount of foreign bodies before it jammed. Under the muzzle there was an odd projection that was designed to catch on the edge of vehicles to act as a firing rest but the same item also acted as a muzzle cover to keep out dirt.

Once in action in 1939, one rather nasty habit of the MP 38 came to light. The gun operated from the open-breech position (the bolt was cocked to the rear before the trigger could release it to fire) but if the gun was jarred the bolt could jump forward and start the firing cycle by itself. This nasty fault caused many casualties before it was modified out by the machining of a slot over the breech block's 'home' position, through which a pin could engage and lock after being pushed through a hole on the other side of the body. This modification turned the MP 38 into the **MP 38/40**.

## Further simplification

During 1940 the simple manufacture of the MP 38 was taken one stage further with the introduction of even more metal stampings and even simpler manufacturing methods. The new version was called the **MP 40**. To the soldier in the field it was little different from the MP 38/40, but for the German economy it meant that the MP 40 could be easily manufactured anywhere, with subassemblies produced in simple workshops and assembled at central workshops. The weapon was churned out in tens of thousands, and in the field proved a most popular and handy weapon, with Allied troops using any examples they could find or capture. The MP 38/40 was often used by resistance forces and partisans as well.

The only major change to the MP 40 after 1940 was the introduction of a twin-magazine feature with the **MP 40/2**. This was not a success and was little used. The MP 40 is still used in odd corners of the world, especially by guerrilla forces.

One odd word about this weapon: it is often known as the 'Schmeisser'. Exactly where this name came from is unknown, but it is incorrect as Hugo Schmeisser had nothing to do with the design, which originated with the Erma concern.

### SPECIFICATION

**MP 40**
**Calibre:** 9-mm Parabellum
**Length overall:** 833 mm (32.8 in) with the stock extended and 630 mm (24.8 in) with the stock folded
**Length of barrel:** 251 mm (9.88 in)
**Weight loaded:** 4.7 kg (10.36 lb)
**Muzzle velocity:** 365 m (1,200 ft) per second
**Rate of fire, cyclic:** 500 rounds per minute
**Magazine:** 32-round straight box

*Right: The MP 40, as used by this corporal during the invasion of the USSR, was almost identical to the MP 38 except that it was much simpler to manufacture.*

*Left: Two German army Panzergrenadiers armed with MP 40s occupy a shell hole on the outskirts of Stalingrad. As will be readily understood, the MP 40 was at a slight disadvantage in such positions, for the long downward-pointing magazine was no assistance when firing over the lip of such a shell hole.*

# MP 38

The MP 38 presaged a major shift in the world's thinking about the sub-machine gun. From this time onward, this type of close attack weapon was seen as semi-expendable and fit for manufacture by the cheapest possible process. Although this thinking found its first expression in the MP 38, this important German weapon was in fact a half-way stage in the process, for its still incorporated a relatively high proportion of high-quality machined elements.

***Above:* The MP 38 and its successors in the line-up of German sub-machine guns were appreciated by Allied soldiers for exactly the same reasons that the Germans liked the weapons. It was not uncommon for captured weapons to be turned against their former owners, especially as the ammunition was readily available.**

***Right:* An MP 40 in action during the Stalingrad fighting. Although many German propaganda photographs tend to give the impression that the MP 40 was in widespread use, its issue was restricted mainly to front-line divisions and Panzergrenadier units in particular.**

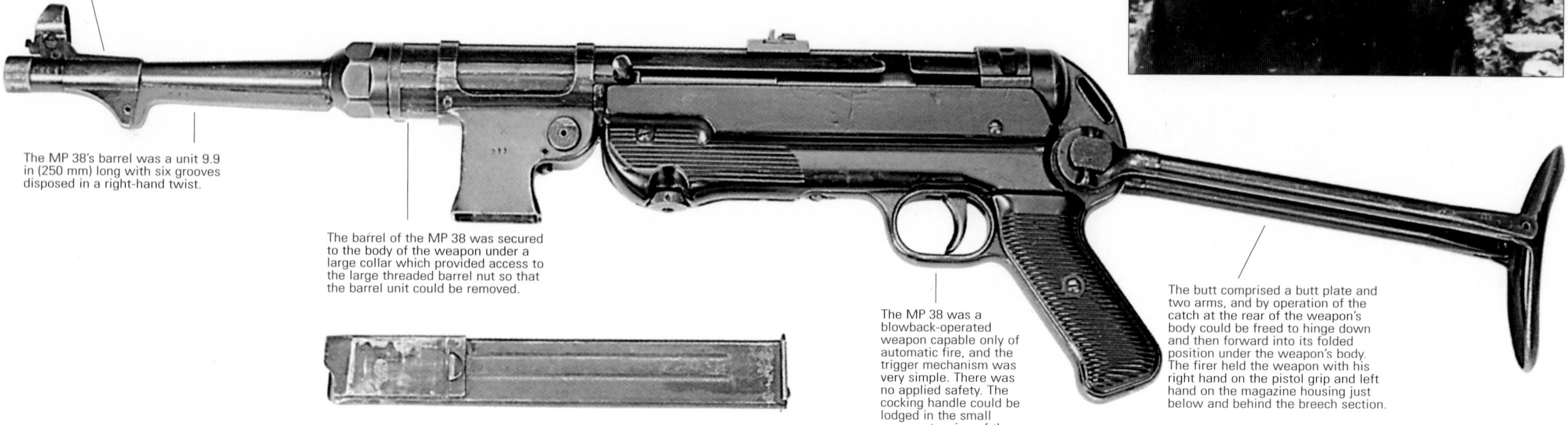

The muzzle end of the MP 38's barrel was fitted on its upper surface with a hooded barley corn fore sight and on its lower surface with a device designed to allow the firer to hook his weapon over the side of a vehicle such as a half-track carrier.

The MP 38's barrel was a unit 9.9 in (250 mm) long with six grooves disposed in a right-hand twist.

The barrel of the MP 38 was secured to the body of the weapon under a large collar which provided access to the large threaded barrel nut so that the barrel unit could be removed.

The MP 38 was a blowback-operated weapon capable only of automatic fire, and the trigger mechanism was very simple. There was no applied safety. The cocking handle could be lodged in the small upper extension of the handle's operating slot to hold the bolt in the rear position.

The butt comprised a butt plate and two arms, and by operation of the catch at the rear of the weapon's body could be freed to hinge down and then forward into its folded position under the weapon's body. The firer held the weapon with his right hand on the pistol grip and left hand on the magazine housing just below and behind the breech section.

# MP 18, MP 28, MP 34 & MP 35

## Sub-machine guns

***The MP 28 was a revised version of the original MP 18, retaining the general outline of its predecessor but able to deliver either single-shot or full automatic fire.***

Although it was preceded by the Italian Villar Perosa, the **MP 18** can be considered as the father of the modern sub-machine gun. In general concept, operating principle and all-round appearance, the MP 18 had all the features that became standard for such weapons.

The design of the MP18 began on a low priority in 1916 to provide front-line troops with a short-range rapid-fire weapon. The designer was Hugo Schmeisser, the man whose name later came to be synonymous with the sub-machine gun. It was not until 1918 that the new weapon, known to the Germans as a *Maschinen-Pistole* (hence MP, machine pistol), was issued to the troops on the Western Front. The MP 18 had little more than local impact at the time.

### Blowback operation

The MP 18 was a simple blowback weapon firing the classic 9-mm (0.354-in) Parabellum round. The MP 18 was well made, with a solid wooden stock and a 32-round 'snail' magazine mounted in a housing on the left of the body. The barrel was covered by a perforated jacket to aid barrel cooling after firing, and the weapon fired on full automatic only.

When Germany was largely disarmed after 1919, the MP 18 was passed to the police in an attempt to keep the concept alive. In police service the weapons were modified during the 1920s to replace the Luger 'snail' magazine with a simple inline box magazine that again became the virtual prototype of what was to follow. In 1928 the MP 18 was placed back into limited production in Germany, this time as the **MP 28**, with new sights, a single-shot fire capability, some small internal changes on the breech block, and extras such as the mounting for a bayonet. The MP 28 had the new box magazine as standard and the type was produced in Belgium, Spain and elsewhere for export all over the world.

### Pattern established

Perhaps the greatest importance of the MP 18 and MP 28 was not in their use as weapons but in their example for other designers to follow.

At first sight the **MP 34** and **MP 35** appeared to be direct copies of the MP 18 and MP 28, but there were in reality many differences. Easily missed at first glance was that on the MP 34 and MP 35 the magazine protrudes from the right- rather than left-hand side of the gun body. The trigger mechanism used double-pressure system to control the rate of fire: a light pull produced single shots, while full pressure provided automatic fire.

The MP 34 was designed by the Bergmann brothers, and improvements led to the MP 35. This was produced in long- and short-barrel versions, and niceties such as bayonet attachments and even light bipods were introduced.

### Reliability

It was reliability, largely due to the use of a rear-mounted rather than side-located cocking bolt to keep the weapon's body much clearer of dirt and debris, that brought the MP 35 to the attention of what was to be the biggest customer for the weapon.This was the Waffen SS, which was planning its own procurement arrangements separate from those of the German army. From late 1940 all MP 35 production went to the Waffen SS, continuing until World War II ended in 1945. Many of the weapons can still be found in use with South American police forces. The reason for this longevity is quite simply that the MP 34 and MP 35 were very well manufactured, with nearly all parts machined from the solid metal.

***After the arrival in service of later and more capable sub-machine guns, the older weapons were still effective and therefore allocated to troops operating in tasks such as rear-area security.***

***These truck-borne troops carry MP 28 sub-machine guns with bayonets fixed. The MP 28 was an excellent weapon in qualitative terms, but was too expensive for manufacture on a very large scale.***

**SPECIFICATION**

**MP 18**
**Calibre:** 9-mm (0.354-in) Parabellum
**Length overall:** 815 mm (32.09 in)
**Length of barrel:** 200 mm (7.87 in)
**Weight loaded:** 5.245 kg (11.56 lb)
**Muzzle velocity:** 365 m (1,200 ft) per second
**Rate of fire, cyclic:** 350-450 rpm
**Magazine:** 32-round 'snail', later 20- or 32-round box

**MP 35**
**Calibre:** 9-mm (0.354-in) Parabellum
**Length overall:** 840 mm (33.07 in) for the standard model
**Length of barrel:** 200 mm (7.87 in)
**Weight loaded:** 4.73 kg (10.43 lb)
**Muzzle velocity:** 365 m (1,200 ft) per second
**Rate of fire, cyclic:** 650 rpm
**Magazine:** 24- or 32-round box

# Beretta Sub-machine guns

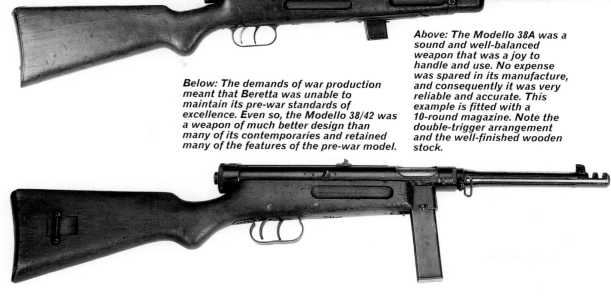

*Above: The Modello 38A was a sound and well-balanced weapon that was a joy to handle and use. No expense was spared in its manufacture, and consequently it was very reliable and accurate. This example is fitted with a 10-round magazine. Note the double-trigger arrangement and the well-finished wooden stock.*

*Below: The demands of war production meant that Beretta was unable to maintain its pre-war standards of excellence. Even so, the Modello 38/42 was a weapon of much better design than many of its contemporaries and retained many of the features of the pre-war model.*

The first of the Beretta series of sub-machine guns, designed by the company's highly talented chief designer, Tullio Marengoli, was the **Beretta Moschetto Automatico Modello 38A,** which was produced at the company's headquarters in the northern Italian city of Brescia. The first examples were produced in 1935, but it was not until 1938 that the first mass-produced examples appeared for issue to the Italian armed forces. The term 'mass production' is perhaps rather misleading for the Beretta sub-machine guns; although the weapons were produced on normal production lines, the care and attention that went into each example was so considerable that they can almost be regarded as hand-made. In fact the Beretta weapons are still regarded as some of the finest examples of the sub-machine gun that it is possible to obtain, and the early Modello 38A weapons were destined to become among the most prized of all.

## Simple but well made

In design terms the Beretta guns had little enough of note. They had a well finished wooden stock, a tubular body, a downward-pointing box magazine and a perforated barrel jacket (sometimes with provision for a folding bayonet at the muzzle). There was nothing really remarkable in these points, but what was very noticeable and indeed notable was the way in which the weapon was balanced and the way it handled in action. The Modello 38A turned out to be a truly remarkable sub-machine gun. The superb finish endeared it to all who used the type, and one result of the painstaking assembly and finishing was the emergence of a weapon that was highly reliable and very accurate under all combat conditions.

The ammunition feed proved to be exceptional, but only when the proper magazines were used. There were several sizes of magazines (holding 10, 20, 30 or 40 rounds), and these were issued together with a loading device. The round used on the early Beretta sub-machine guns was a special high-velocity 9-mm (0.354-in) cartridge, but this was later changed to the 9-mm Parabellum cartridge that was more readily obtainable as it was employed in large numbers of other weapons.

There were several variations on the Modello 38A theme. One of these lacked the bayonet and some of the refinements as it was intended as a special light-weight model for use in desert regions.

After Italy had entered World War II in June 1940, a small revision of manufacturing practices was made in an effort to streamline production and speed deliveries of the weapon, but the soldier at the front would be hard put to recognise the implementation of these changes, for the overall finish remained beautiful. Close examination revealed that the barrel jacket was altered into a stamped and welded component, but that was about the only concession to mass-production technology, and the Modello 38A retained its high reputation.

*The nature of the Italian Fascist state was such that by the time he entered the army, any youth was already well trained in the use of most of the service's standard weapons. This included the Beretta Modello 38A, seen here carried by a Young Fascist being decorated by General Bastico.*

## German use

By 1944 the war situation had changed radically, with Italy divided since the September 1943 armistice with the Allies between pro-Allied and pro-German portions in the south and north respectively, as one of the results of this division was the manufacture of Beretta sub-machine guns for the German army. By this time the basic design of the Modello 38A had been revised by the addition of simpler assembly and manufacturing methods to the point that it had become the **Modello 38/42**, while an even later version was the **Modello 1**. Relatively few of these two versions were produced, the bulk of them being produced after 1945. Both were easily recognisable as Berettas, and while they retained the overall excellence they were generally simpler and lacked some of the finesse of the Modello 1938A.

As mentioned above, by 1944 Berettas were being produced for the Germans, who used the Modello 38A and Modello 38/42 as the **MP 739(i)** and **MP 738(i)** respectively. Romania also used the Modello 38A and Modello 38/42.

Allied troops greatly prized the Berettas and used them in place of their own weapons whenever they could capture sufficient numbers, but their use by the Allies was restricted to a great extent by a shortage of Beretta magazines. Apparently the sub-machine guns were often captured without their vital magazines, which was perhaps just as well for the Italians.

*Italian troops in Tunisia, their Beretta Modello 1938s ready to hand. The weapon on the left is equipped with a 10-round magazine which was often employed when single-shot fire was required. The Modello 38A was very accurate and could be used in the manner of a rifle at combat ranges up to 300 m (330 yards).*

**SPECIFICATION**

**Moschetto Automatico Modello 38A**
**Calibre:** 9-mm (0.354-in)
**Length overall:** 946 mm (37.24 in)
**Length of barrel:** 315 mm (12.4 in)
**Weight loaded:** 4.97 kg (10.96 lb)
**Muzzle velocity:** 420 m (1,380 ft) per second
**Rate of fire, cyclic:** 600 rounds per minute
**Magazine:** 10-, 20-, 30- or 40-round box

# Type 100 Sub-machine gun

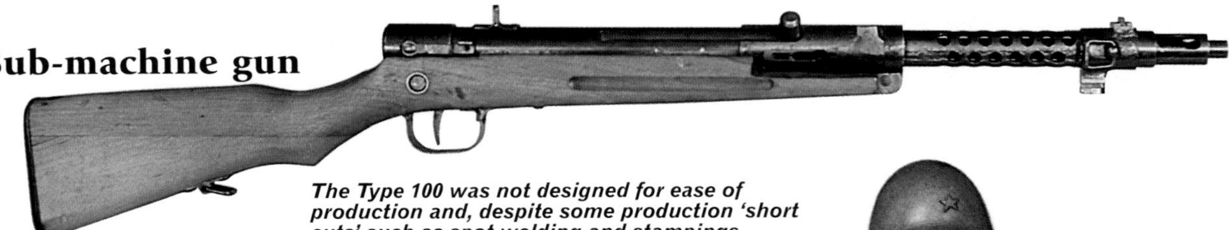

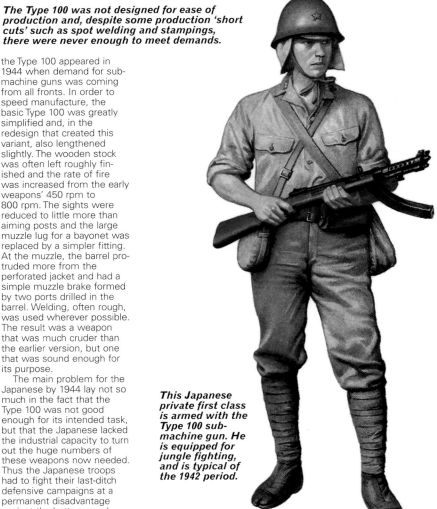

***The Type 100 was not designed for ease of production and, despite some production 'short cuts' such as spot welding and stampings, there were never enough to meet demands.***

The Japanese were surprisingly late entrants into the field of sub-machine gun design, a fact made all the more remarkable considering the combat experience their troops had gained in their protracted campaigns in China before 1941, and the number of different sub-machine gun designs that had been imported for service use or for evaluation. It was not until 1942, indeed, that the first example of what had already progressed through several years of low-priority development left the Nambu production lines in the form of the **Type 100** sub-machine gun, or **100 Shiki Kikanshoju**. This was a sound but unremarkable design that was destined to be the only sub-machine gun that the Japanese produced in any numbers.

## Complex devices

The Type 100 was moderately well made but had several rather odd features. One of these was a complex ammunition feed device that ensured that the round was fully chambered before the firing pin could be released. Other than the safety of the firer, the exact purpose of this feature is rather uncertain, for the cartridge used by the Type 100 sub-machine gun was the 8-mm (0.315-in) pistol round, a rather weak and ineffective cartridge that was also hampered by its bottle-necked layout, which added further problems to the creation of the feed mechanism. The Type 100's barrel was chrome-plated to aid cleaning and reduce wear, and to add to such niceties the design had complex sights and a curved magazine. Other oddities were the use of a complicated muzzle brake on some models and the fitting of a large bayonet-mounting lug under the barrel. Some versions also had a bipod for enhanced firing accuracy when the firer was lying down.

There were three different versions of the Type 100. The first is described above, and had an overall length of 867 mm (2 ft 10 in) and a barrel length of 228 mm (9 in). The second had a folding butt stock and was intended for service with the Japanese paratroop force: the stock was hinged just behind the gun body to fold forward along the side of the weapon, reducing length to 464 mm (22.2 in) but also weakening the weapon in combat situations, and relatively few examples were made. The third version of the Type 100 appeared in 1944 when demand for sub-machine guns was coming from all fronts. In order to speed manufacture, the basic Type 100 was greatly simplified and, in the redesign that created this variant, also lengthened slightly. The wooden stock was often left roughly finished and the rate of fire was increased from the early weapons' 450 rpm to 800 rpm. The sights were reduced to little more than aiming posts and the large muzzle lug for a bayonet was replaced by a simpler fitting. At the muzzle, the barrel protruded more from the perforated jacket and had a simple muzzle brake formed by two ports drilled in the barrel. Welding, often rough, was used wherever possible. The result was a weapon that was much cruder than the earlier version, but one that was sound enough for its purpose.

The main problem for the Japanese by 1944 lay not so much in the fact that the Type 100 was not good enough for its intended task, but that the Japanese lacked the industrial capacity to turn out the huge numbers of these weapons now needed. Thus the Japanese troops had to fight their last-ditch defensive campaigns at a permanent disadvantage against the better-armed Allied troops.

**SPECIFICATION**

| | |
|---|---|
| **Type 100 (1944 version)** | **Magazine:** 30-round curved box |
| **Calibre:** 8-mm (0.315-in) | **Rate of fire, cyclic:** 800 rounds per minute |
| **Length overall:** 900 mm (35.43 in) | **Muzzle velocity:** 335 m (1,100 ft) per second |
| **Length of barrel:** 230 mm (9.06 in) | |
| **Weight loaded:** 4.4 kg (9.70 lb) | |

***This Japanese private first class is armed with the Type 100 sub-machine gun. He is equipped for jungle fighting, and is typical of the 1942 period.***

# Steyr-Solothurn S1-100 Sub-machine gun

***The Steyr-Solothurn S1-100 was an Austrian version of the German MP18 produced during the 1920s and 1930s mainly for commercial sale on the export market. The type was well made and could be supplied with a range of accessories including tripods, bayonets and oversize magazines.***

Although the Steyr-Solothurn sub-machine gun is often designated as a Swiss weapon, for it was manufactured mainly in Switzerland, it was in fact designed in Austria. The complicated process whereby an Austrian sub-machine gun became a Swiss weapon had its origins in the end of World War I and the defeat of the Central Powers (Germany and Austria-Hungary). By the treaties that finalised their defeats, both Germany and Austria were severely restricted in the design and manufacture of automatic weapons. The German company Rheinmetall successfully sought to circumvent these restrictions by the purchase of Solothurn, a Swiss company, as its manufacturing arm in a neutral country. Under the supervision of its new German owner, Solothurn then acquired an interest in a major Austrian armaments manufacturer, the Österreichische Waffenfabrikk-Gesellschaft based in Steyr. It was this last company, which developed several sub-machine gun designs, that in the 1920s actually created the final design of the weapon that became known as the **Steyr-Solothurn S1-100** on the basis of Rheinmetall's original thinking by Louis Stange in 1920.

## Intended for export

In its full production form as the Steyr-Solothurn S1-100, this sub-machine gun was by 1930 in full production mainly for the export market. As with so many other designs of the period, the S1-100 was based on the general outlines and operating method of the MP18, a pioneering German sub-machine gun introduced late in World War I. However, by the time the Swiss manufacturer had finished its development of the design, the weapon had reached a high point of refinement and detail manufacture. The blowback-operated S1-100 was an excellent product that was very well designed and engineered, made from the finest materials and excellently finished, robust, reliable and adaptable. This last was notably important, for the nature and demands of the export market meant that the sub-machine gun had to be capable of production in a whole host of calibres and with a seemingly endless string of extra and accessories, the latter including a magazine filling slot on the magazine housing on the left-hand side of the weapon at the forward end of the weapon's wooden furniture.

*The Steyr-Solothurn S1-100 is seen here in a drill-book position, mainly because the picture has been taken from a German manual produced for the type after the Germans had taken over Austria and its arsenal during 1938.*

The S1-100 was produced in no less than three separate variations of the 9-mm (0.354-in) calibre. Apart from the usual 9-mm Parabellum, the weapon was thus produced in 9-mm Mauser and 9-mm Steyr, the latter specially produced for the S1-100. Models for export to China, Japan and South America were produced in 7.63-mm (0.3-in) Mauser calibre, and the Portuguese purchased a large batch chambered for the 7.65-mm (0.301-in) Parabellum cartridge. The extras were many and varied, the most outlandish perhaps being a tripod to convert the weapon into what must have been a rather ineffective light machine-gun: even so, a number of these tripod mountings were sold to China during the mid-1930s. There were also various forms of bayonet-securing devices, and several barrel lengths were available, some of them very long indeed for what were only pistol cartridges. Another Steyr-Solothurn selling ploy was to present the S1-100 to a customer packed in individually fitted chests containing not only the weapon but all manner of special magazines, special cleaning tools, spare parts, etc.

### German use

By the mid-1930s the S1-100 was the standard sub-machine gun of the Austrian army and police force, and after they had peacefully annexed Austria after the Anschluss of 1938 the Germans also took over the armoury of the Austrian armed forces. Thus the S1-100 became the German **Maschinenpistole 34(ö)**, a designation which must have caused at least some confusion with another MP 34 weapon, the Bergmann sub-machine gun. After a short period of front-line German service the confusion of no less than three types of 9-mm ammunition to be supplied for the type was too much even for the adaptable German army supply network, and the MP 34(ö) was therefore relegated to service with the German military police; it was also retained by what was left of the Austrian police forces.

Until recent times the S1-100 was still to be found in odd corners of the world, but only in very small numbers. Perhaps the most combat seen by the type was in China, where at one point the S1-100 was in use by both the Chinese and Japanese armies. The latter even produced their own copy at one point and used some of the design's features as the basis for their own 8-mm Type 100 sub-machine gun.

**SPECIFICATION**

**S1-100 (9-mm Parabellum)**
**Calibre:** 9-mm (0.354-in)
**Length overall:** 850 mm (33.46 in)
**Length of barrel:** 200 mm (7.87 in)
**Weight loaded:** 4.48 kg (9.88 kg)
**Magazine:** 32-round box
**Rate of fire, cyclic:** 500 rounds per minute
**Muzzle velocity:** 418 m (1,370 ft) per second

# Lanchester Sub-machine gun

*Obviously based on the German MP 28, the Lanchester was ideally suited to the rough-and-tumble of shipboard life. It had a one-piece wooden stock based on the outline of the Lee-Enfield No. 1 Mk 3 rifle, and there was a bayonet lug under the muzzle. The brass magazine housing can be seen.*

In 1940, with the Dunkirk evacuation completed and invasion apparently imminent, the Royal Air Force decided to adopt a sub-machine gun for airfield defence. With no time to spare for the development of a new weapon it decided to adopt a direct copy of the German MP 28. The period was so desperate that the Admiralty decided to join the RAF in adopting the new weapon, but in the event it was only the Admiralty which adopted the resultant weapon.

The British copy of the German MP 28 was called the Lanchester after George H. Lanchester, who was charged with producing the weapon at the Sterling Armament Company at Dagenham. The Lanchester emerged from its British development as a sound, sturdy weapon in many ways ideal for use by boarding and raiding parties. It was a very solid, soundly engineered piece of weaponry with all the trimmings of a former era. Nothing was left off from the gunsmith's art. The Lanchester had a well-machined wooden butt and stock, the blowback mechanism was very well made of the finest materials, the breech block well machined and, to cap it all, the magazine housing was fabricated from solid brass. A few typical British design details were added, such as a mounting on the muzzle for a long-blade British bayonet (very useful in boarding party situations), and the rifling differed from that of the German original in details to accommodate the different type of ammunition fired by the Lanchester.

### Large magazine

The magazine for the Lanchester was straight and carried a useful load of 50 rounds. Stripping was aided by a catch on top of the receiver, and the first model was the **Machine Carbine, 9-mm Lanchester, Mk I** capable of single-shot or automatic fire. On the **Lanchester Mk I*** this was changed to automatic fire only, and many Mk Is were converted to Mk I* standard at Royal Navy workshops.

The Lanchester was an unashamed copy of a German design, but gave good service to the Royal Navy throughout and after World War II. Many old sailors still speak of the Lanchester with respect but not with affection, for it was a heavy weapon and it had one rather off-putting feature: if the butt was given a hard knock or jar while the gun was cocked and loaded it would fire. The last example left Royal Navy use during the 1960s, and the Lanchester is now a collector's item.

**SPECIFICATION**

**Lanchester Mk I***
**Calibre:** 9-mm (0.354-in)
**Length overall:** 851 mm (33.50 in)
**Length of barrel:** 203 mm (8.00 in)
**Weight empty:** 4.34 kg (9.57 lb)
**Magazine:** 50-round box
**Rate of fire, cyclic:** 600 rounds per minute
**Muzzle velocity:** about 380 m (1,245 ft) per second

*Lanchesters in a typical naval environment as captured U-boat personnel are escorted ashore in a Canadian port – the blindfolds were a normal procedure. The Lanchesters are carried using Lee-Enfield rifle slings.*

# Sten Sub-machine gun

By the time the Sten Mk V entered production there had been time for some finesse to be added to the basic design. While the original outline was retained, a wooden butt and pistol grip, and a No. 4 rifle foresight had been added.

After the Dunkirk evacuation of mid-1940, the British army had few weapons left. In an attempt to launch rapid rearmament, the military authorities put out an urgent request for simple sub-machine guns that could be produced in quantity. Using the concept of the MP 38 as an example, the designers went to work. Within weeks the result was adopted. It was the product of two designers, Major R. V. Shepherd and H. J. Turpin who worked at the Enfield Lock Small Arms Factory, and from these three names came the universally accepted name **Sten** for the new weapon.

The first variant was the **Sten Mk I**, which must be regarded as one of the unloveliest weapon designs of all time. It was schemed for production as quickly and cheaply as possible using simple tools and a minimum of time-consuming machining, and so was made from steel tubes, sheet stampings and easily produced parts all held together with welds, pins and bolts. The main body was a steel tube and the butt a steel framework. The barrel was a drawn steel tube with either two or six rifling grooves, roughly carved. The magazine was again sheet steel and on the Sten Mk I the trigger mechanism was shrouded in a wooden stock. There was a small wooden foregrip and a rudimentary flash hider. It looked horrible and occasioned some very caustic comments when it was first issued, but it worked and troops soon learned to accept it for what it was, a basic killing device produced in extreme circumstances.

## Primitive yet effective

The Sten Mk I was produced to the tune of about 100,000 examples, all delivered within months. By 1941 the **Sten Mk II** was on the scene and this was even simpler than the Mk I. In time the Sten Mk II became regarded as the 'classic' Sten gun, and it was an all-metal version. Gone was the wooden stock over the trigger mechanism, replaced by a simple sheet-metal box. The butt became a single tube with a flat buttplate at its end. The barrel was redesigned to be unscrewed for changing, and the magazine housing (the box magazine protruded to the left) was designed as a simple unit that could be rotated downward, once the magazine had been removed, to keep out dust and dirt. The butt could be removed easily to provide access for the removal of the breech block and spring for cleaning.

By the time the weapon had been disassembled it occupied very little space, and this turned out to be one of the Sten's great advantages. When the initial needs of the armed forces had been met from several production lines, including those set up in Canada and New Zealand, the Sten was still produced in tens of thousands for paradrop into occupied Europe for resistance forces. The very simplicity of the Sten and the ease with which it could be broken proved a major asset.

A silenced version of the Sten Mk II was produced in small numbers as the **Sten Mk IIS** for commando and raiding forces. Then came the **Sten Mk III**. This was basically an even simpler version of the original Mk I as its barrel could not be removed and it was encased in a simple steel-tube barrel jacket. Again, tens of thousands were produced.

## Definitive model

The **Sten Mk IV** was a model intended for parachute troops but not placed in production. By the time the **Sten Mk V** was on the scene things were going better for the Allies and the Mk V could be produced with rather more finesse. The Mk V was easily the best of the Stens, for it was produced to much higher standards and had extras such as a wooden butt, forestock and a fitting for a small bayonet. It had the foresight of the Lee-Enfield No. 4 rifle. The Mk V was issued to the airborne troops in 1944, and after World War II became the standard British sub-machine gun.

The Sten was a crude weapon in nearly every way, but it worked and it could be produced in large numbers at a time when it was desperately needed. In occupied Europe it was revealed as an ideal resistance weapon and all over the world underground forces have copied the design almost direct. The Germans even produced their own copies in 1944 and 1945 to complement captured Mk III and Mk IIS weapons used with the designations **MP 749(e)** and **MP 751(e)** respectively.

**SPECIFICATION**

| | |
|---|---|
| **Sten Mk II** | **Weight loaded:** 3.7 kg (8.16 lb) |
| **Calibre:** 9-mm (0.354-in) Parabellum | **Muzzle velocity:** 365 m (1,200 ft) per second |
| **Length overall:** 762 mm (30 in) | **Rate of fire, cyclic:** 550 rpm |
| **Length of barrel:** 197 mm (7.75 in) | **Magazine:** 32-round straight box |

*The Sten was well suited to Resistance-style ambushes and nuisance raids. While giving more firepower to the Maquis, it could be broken down into components for easy concealment.*

*The Sten was one of the first weapons issued to the newly formed airborne troops of the British army, and this example is unusual in being fitted with a small spike bayonet.*

# Sten Mk II

Quickly designed, easy and very cheap to manufacture, and effective in use, the Sten sub-machine was an ideal weapon with which to begin the re-equipment of the British army in the dark days after its retirement from Europe in the Dunkirk evacuation of mid-1940. The weapon was extremely reliable, largely as a result of its simple design, and was steadily upgraded in features and basic finish as and when the time and manufacturing facilities became available later in World War II.

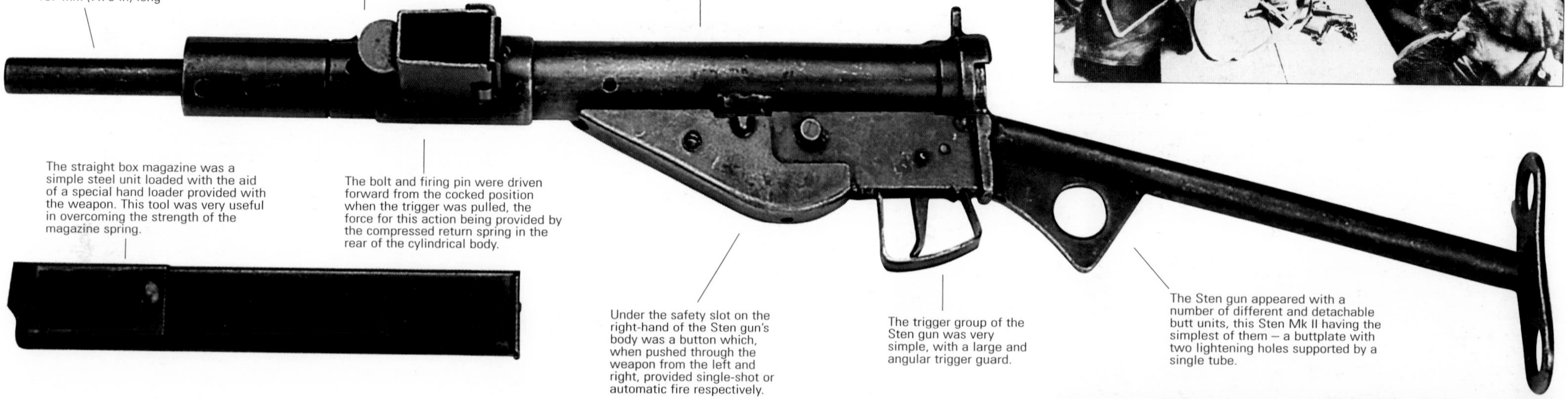

The barrel of the Sten sub-machine gun was a simple drawn steel tube with two or six rifling grooves with a right-hand twist. The barrel was 197 mm (7.75 in) long
The magazine housing, located just to the rear of the chamber on the left-hand side of the weapon's body, accepted and locked the 32-round box magazine. When not being used, the housing could be rotated downward to block the feed slot and so prevent dirt and debris entering the weapon
The Sten gun was cocked by pulling back the handle in the long slot on the right-hand side of the body, and until the weapon was needed the handle was then dropped into a small safety slot.
The straight box magazine was a simple steel unit loaded with the aid of a special hand loader provided with the weapon. This tool was very useful in overcoming the strength of the magazine spring.
The bolt and firing pin were driven forward from the cocked position when the trigger was pulled, the force for this action being provided by the compressed return spring in the rear of the cylindrical body.
Under the safety slot on the right-hand of the Sten gun's body was a button which, when pushed through the weapon from the left and right, provided single-shot or automatic fire respectively.
The trigger group of the Sten gun was very simple, with a large and angular trigger guard.
The Sten gun appeared with a number of different and detachable butt units, this Sten Mk II having the simplest of them – a buttplate with two lightening holes supported by a single tube.


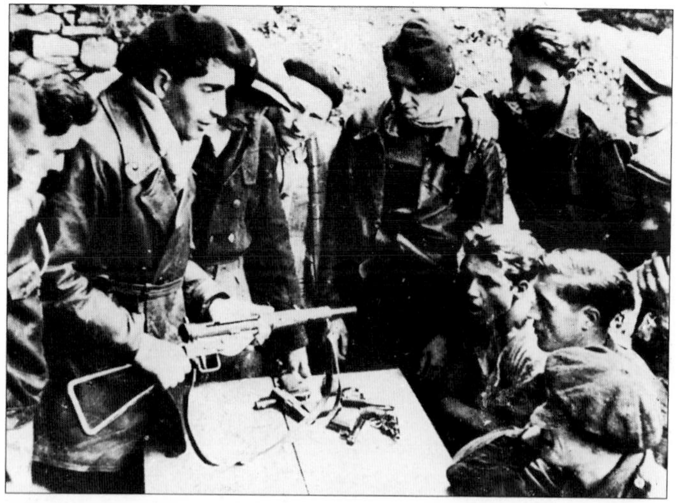

***Maquis in the Haute Loire conducting a weapon training session using the Sten Mk II as the subject. This Sten has the steel 'outline' butt in place of the more usual 'T-shape'. Both types could be easily removed.***

***Left: This is likely to be a posed picture (1944) of the French Resistance in action. It shows two Stens and a shotgun, a fairly typical Resistance weapon combination.***

***Above: Street fighting in the Mediterranean theatre. This example of the Sten has had a non-standard foregrip added to enhance its handling qualities.***

# M1 Thompson Sub-machine gun

One of the most famous weapons in history, the **Thompson sub-machine gun** is one of the few firearms whose nickname has become a generic term. Known universally, thanks to Hollywood, as the **'Tommy Gun'** the Thompson's origins date back to 1918 and the trenches of World War I.

The vicious close-quarters nature of trench fighting called for a short-range automatic weapon to 'sweep' the trenches clear of enemies. Since such a 'trench broom' needed to operate only at short ranges, a powerful long-range cartridge was not necessary.

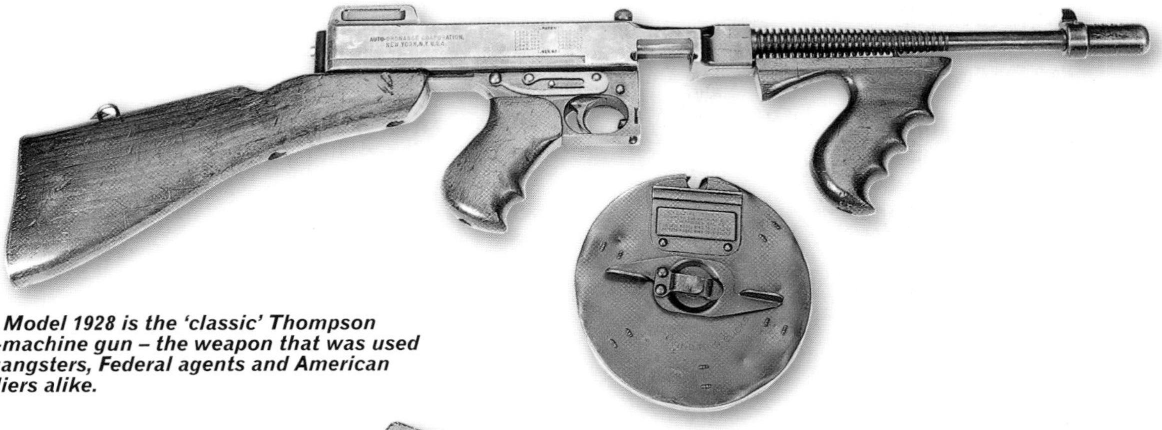

***The Model 1928 is the 'classic' Thompson sub-machine gun – the weapon that was used by gangsters, Federal agents and American soldiers alike.***

***Still indubitably a Thompson, the wartime M1A1 lacked the luxury finish of the M1928. Of simplified construction, it had a fixed firing pin and hammer, making the type a simple blow-back design.***

## The first SMGs

The German army had drawn the same conclusions and produced the MP 18. On the American side, a former ordnance officer, General John Thompson, initiated the development of an automatic weapon using the standard 0.45-in (11.43-mm) pistol cartridge. It became known as a sub-machine gun.

The **Thompson Gun**, as it was soon labelled, was produced in a variety of models. Military sales were limited with the end of the war, but the Thompson became notorious during the prohibition era. Gangsters and government agents both used the Thompson as their weapon of choice. When Hollywood started to make gangster films the gun became famous overnight.

The US Marines used a few Thompsons in Nicaragua in 1927, and the Navy adopted the type as the **Model 1928** a year later.

In 1940 several European nations were clamouring for Thompson guns. The unexpected employment by the Germans of sub-machine guns on a large scale in 1939 and 1940 produced requests for similar weapons from Britain and France, and the Thompson was the only example on offer. Large-scale production commenced for France, the UK and Yugoslavia, but the orders were overtaken by events.

The French and other orders were diverted to the United Kingdom, where the M1928 was used until the Sten became available. Even then Thompsons were issued for Commando raids and were used later in jungle fighting in Burma.

When the USA entered the war the US army also decided that it wanted sub-machine guns but the Thompson had to be redesigned for mass production. The Thompson was an awkward weapon to mass-produce because of the large number of complex machining processes involved.

The **M1 Thompson**, type-classified in April 1942, was a simpler weapon with a straightforward blowback action. The awkward drum magazine, so beloved by Hollywood, was replaced by a vertical box magazine. The even simpler **M1A1** which appeared in October 1942 did away with the foregrip and barrel ribbing, but it was still largely made from machined parts.

Although costs came down from over $200 per gun in 1939 to under $70 in 1944, the Thompson could not compete with the ugly but functional M3 Grease gun, which had a unit cost of $10 or less!

In spite of the fact that the M1 was heavy, difficult to strip and a problem to maintain in the field, its toughness made it a firm favourite with the troops. Total production, after the last US Army order was delivered at the end of 1944, had reached 1,750,000, most being made by the Savage Firearms Company between 1940 and 1944.

### SPECIFICATION

| | |
|---|---|
| **M1 Thompson** | **Muzzle velocity:** 280 m (920 ft) per second |
| **Calibre:** 0.45-in (11.43-mm) | **Rate of fire:** 700 rpm cyclic |
| **Weight:** loaded 4.74 kg (10.45 lb) | **Magazine:** 20- or 30-round box |
| **Length:** 813 mm (32 in); length of barrel 267 mm (10½ in) | |

***Left: Winston Churchill strikes a famous pose with a 'Tommy Gun'. The weapon has a 50-round drum magazine, a device that proved to be too complex for service use.***

***Below: A Thompson gunner in action on Okinawa in 1945. He is using an M1A1, fitted with a horizontal foregrip in place of the original forward pistol grip.***

# Thompson M1928

### Firing pin
The original Thompson guns used a separate firing pin struck by a hammer, but this was really too complex for the task and later models used a fixed firing pin – which was much cheaper to make.

### Sight
Thompsons of the 1920s had a finely machined Lyman rear gun sight calibrated to 50 m (165 ft) and (optimistically) to 550 m (1,800 ft). This was later replaced by a simple 'L'-shaped battle sight.

### Stock
If required, the butt could be easily removed by unscrewing the two screws shown. This was rarely utilised in action, as the butt stabilised the aim and reduced firing vibrations. The butt contained an oiling bottle behind a butt trap.

### Compensator
The Cutt's compensator was intended to divert some muzzle gases upwards to keep the muzzle down when firing. Being of limited value and complex to manufacture, it was simplified and eventually omitted from later models.

### Foregrip
The fore pistol grip is characteristic of early Thompson guns. However, the Marines found it unnecessary when they used the weapon in Nicaragua in the 1920s, and on military versions it was soon replaced by a simple horizontal foregrip.

### Magazine
The M1928 originally utilised a 20-round box magazine and the 50-round drum magazine made famous by Hollywood. However, during World War II a 30-round box magazine was most commonly fitted.

### Fire selector
The fire selector was on the left of the trigger group and could be set for semi-automatic (single shot) or full automatic at a cyclic rate of 725 rounds per minute for early guns. This was reduced to 600 rpm on the first military models of 1928 and on later weapons.

### Fixed stock
Wartime variants of the Thompson did away with the removable butt, the heavy wooden stock remaining fixed. Other changes included the removal of the foregrip, the elimination of the machined cooling fins on the barrel and the fitting of a simplified firing mechanism which allowed the removal of the cocking handle from the top of the receiver, as seen here, to the right side.

***Although its pistol cartridge meant that the Thompson had very little range, and its solid, heavy construction meant that it was something of a burden on the march, it was more popular with individual soldiers than its lighter, cheaper replacements.***

***Below: A Gurkha keeps watch on the upper floor of a ruined house in Cassino, during the fierce fighting for the strategically positioned Benedictine Abbey overlooking the town. Designed for action in trenches, the Thompson's compact size and close-range firepower made it equally suitable for fighting in built-up areas.***

***Above: The Thompson was very popular because of its solid reliability. After extensive service in World War II, it continued to be used by US troops in Korea and Vietnam, and can still be found in use in out-of-the-way wars.***

# M3 and M3A1

***The American M3 'Grease Gun' was the equivalent of the British Sten and the German MP40, for it was designed for mass production. It was a sound enough weapon but the American troops never really took to the type, preferring the Thompson.***

By the beginning of 1941, although the United States was not yet directly involved in World War II, the American military authorities had acknowledged that the sub-machine gun had a definite role to perform on the modern battlefield. They already had to hand numbers of Thompson guns and more were on their way, but the appearance of the German MP38 and the British Sten indicated the production methods that could be employed in future mass-produced designs. Using an imported Sten, the US Army Ordnance Board initiated a design study to produce an American Sten-type weapon. The study was handed over to a team of specialists who included the same George Hyde who had developed the Hyde M2 and to executives from General Motors, to whom the mass-production aspects were entrusted. In a very short time they had designed a weapon and development models were produced for trials.

***Unpopular with its users in Europe, the 'Grease Gun' gained acceptance in the Pacific, where there was no alternative weapon.***

## Sense of urgency

The first of these models was handed over for trials just before Pearl Harbor brought the United States into World War II. As a result the project got a higher priority and it was not long before the design was issued with the designation **M3**. The M3 was just as unpleasant looking as the Sten. Construction was all-metal with most parts simple steel stampings welded into place. Only the barrel, breech block and parts of the trigger mechanism required any machining. A telescopic wire butt was fitted and the design was simple to the point that there was no safety system fitted and the gun could fire fully-automatic only.

The main gun body was tubular and below it hung a long 30-round box magazine. An awkwardly placed and flimsy cocking handle was placed just forward of the trigger on the right-hand side, and the cartridge election port was under a hinged cover. The barrel screwed into the tubular body. Sights were very rudimentary and there were no luxuries such as sling swivels.

## Early problems

The M3 was rushed into production and once issued to the troops it soon ran into acceptance troubles. The very appearance of the weapon soon provided it with the nickname of 'Grease Gun' and it was regarded with about as much affection. Once in action though, it soon showed itself to be effective, but the rush into production on lines that were more used to producing motor car and lorry components led to all manner of in-service problems. The cocking handles broke off, the wire stocks bent in use, some important parts of the mechanism broke because they were made of too soft a metal, and so on. Consequently the M3 received more than its fair share of in-service development and modification, but what was more important at the time was that it rolled off the production lines in huge numbers for issue to the troops at the front.

## Unpopular model

The M3 never overcame the initial reception its appearance engendered. Whenever possible the troops in the front line opted for the Thompson M1 or used captured German MP38s and MP40s, but in the Pacific there was often no choice other than to use the M3 and when this happened the design often gained grudging acceptance. For some arms of the US forces the M3 became a virtual blanket issue. These arms included the drivers in the many transport units and tank crews, as for both the M3 was easy to stow and easy to handle in close confines.

From the outset the M3 had been designed to have the capability of being rapidly converted to 9-mm calibre by simply changing the barrel, magazine and breech block. This facility was sometimes employed in Europe when the M3 was dropped to resistance forces. A silenced variant of the M3 was produced in small numbers.

## Design modifications

Simple as the M3 was to produce it was decided in 1944 to make it even simpler. The result of combat experience allied with production know-how resulted in the **M3AI**, which followed the same general lines as the M3 but with some quite substantial changes. For the soldier the most important item was that the ejection cover was enlarged to the point where the full breech block travel was exposed. This enabled the firer to place his finger into a recess in the block to pull the block to the rear for cocking, thus doing away with the awkward and flimsy cocking handle. A flash hider was added to the muzzle and some other minor changes were incorporated. The M3A1 was still in production when the war ended, by which time it had been decided to phase out the Thompson guns in favour of the M3 and M3AI.

## Poor production

Apart from the appearance problem, the M3 guns were not perfect weapons. They were rather prone to breakages, the ammunition feed was often far from perfect and the lack of a safety often gave rise to alarm. But it worked and it was available, and in war those two factors are more important than hankering after something that might be better. Thus the M3 and M3A1 were used wherever the US Military went, and that was all over the world.

### SPECIFICATION

**M3**
**Calibre:** 0.45-in (11.43-mm) or 9-mm
**Length, butt extended:** 745 mm (29.33 in)
**Length, butt retracted:** 570 mm (22.44 in)
**Weight loaded:** 4.65 kg (10.25 lb)
**Magazine:** 30-round box
**Rate of fire:** 350-450 rpm
**Muzzle velocity:** 280 m (920 ft) per second

# UD M42

***The UD M42 was not accepted as an official US service weapon, but numbers were purchased for issue to some odd undercover and special mission units. It was a very well made and finished weapon and was popular with its users.***

In accounts of the American submachine gun scene between 1939 and 1945 one weapon is often not mentioned at all, and that is the submachine gun known under a number of names but usually called the **UD M42**. This weapon was designed in the days just prior to World War II as a commercial venture in 9-mm calibre. It was ordered under rather odd circumstances by an organisation known as the United Defense Supply Corporation, a US government body that ordered all manner of item for use overseas, but the main point of its existence was that it was an American secret service 'front' for all forms of underground activities.

Exactly why the United Defense (hence UD) concern ordered the design that was produced by the Marlin Firearms Company is now not known, but the name 'Marlin' was subsequently often given to the weapon that became the UD M42. The general impression given at the time was that the weapons were to be shipped to Europe for use by some underground organisations working for the US interest, but events in Europe overtook the scheme. Some UD M42s were certainly sent to the Dutch East Indies before the Japanese invasion of the area, but they vanished without trace.

Most of the UD M42s did find their way to Europe but in some very odd hands. Most were handed out to some of the numerous resistance and partisan groups that sprang up in and around the German- and Italian-occupied areas of the Mediterranean Sea. There they took part in some very odd actions, the most famous of which was when British agents kidnapped a German general on Crete. Other actions were just as dramatic but often took place so far from the public gaze that today these actions and the part the UD M42 took in them are virtually forgotten.

This is perhaps a pity for many weapon authorities now regard the UD LT42 as one of the finest submachine gun types used in World War II. Being made on a commercial and not a military basis it was well machined and very strong. The action was smooth and the gun very accurate, and by all accounts it was a joy to handle. It could withstand all manner of ill-treatment (including immersion in mud and water) and still work.

After all these years it now seems very unlikely that the full service record of the UD M42 will ever be told, but at least the very existence of the weapon should be better known.

**SPECIFICATION**

**Name:** UD M42
**Calibre:** 9-mm
**Length:** 807 mm (31.75 in)
**Length of barrel:** 279 mm (11.00 in)
**Weight loaded:** 4.54 kg (10,00 lb)
**Magazine:** 20-round box
**Rate of fire:** 700 rpm
**Muzzle velocity:** 400 m (1,310 ft) per second

# Reising Model 50 and Model 55

***The Reising Model 50 was one of the least successful of all American sub-machine guns to see service, for it employed a complex mechanism that added to the cost, performance and reliability of the weapon.***

***The Reising Model 55 differed from the Model 50 in that it dispensed with the wooden stock in favour of a folding wire butt for use by airborne troops. Like the Model 50, the weapon was not popular and was prone to malfunctioning due to the ingress of dirt.***

The **Reising Model 50** and the later **Model 55** are two more examples of how things can go wrong when the basic blow-back action used on the sub-machine gun is ignored and replaced with something that seems to offer a better action. On the Reising Model 50, which was first produced in 1940, the basic action was altered so that instead of the breech block moving forward to the chamber when the trigger was pulled, the action operated when the bolt was forward with a round in the chamber. This action can work quite well but it needs a system of levers to operate the firing pin in the breech block and these levers have to disconnect once the breech block moves. This all adds complexity and cost and adds something to the system which can break.

## Commercial venture

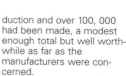

Thus it was with the Reising Model 50. The design was the result of a commercial venture and was thus not so influenced by military considerations as would have been the case a few years later, but the Model 50 was a well-made design with an unusual system of cocking the weapon by means of a small catch sliding in a slot under the fore-stock. This left the top of the gun body free of many of the usual hazards such as the cocking slot that usually provides an ingress for dirt to clog the system. But on the Model 50 all that happened was that the dirt got into the slot underneath and was difficult to clean out, thus providing one source of potential bother. From the outside the Model 50 looked a fairly simple weapon but the internal arrangements were complex to the point where there was too much to go wrong, hence there were more stoppages and general unreliability.

When the Reising Model 50 was first offered to the US forces the US Marine Corps was some way down the list of priorities, a position it was later dramatically to reverse, so in the absence of any other source of sub-machine guns it obtained numbers of the Model 50. Once the USMC had the Model 50 it soon found the weapon wanting and obtained other weapon types. Some Model 50s were obtained by a British Purchasing Commission but few were involved and some others went to Canada. Yet more were sent to the Soviet Union and by 1945 the Model 50 was still in production and over 100, 000 had been made, a modest enough total but well worthwhile as far as the manufacturers were concerned.

Some of this total was made up by the Model 55 which was the same as the Model 50 other than that the allwood stock of the Model 50 was replaced by a folding wire butt for use by airborne and other such units. The Model 55 was no more successful than the Model 50.

**SPECIFICATION**

**Model 50**
**Calibre:** 0.45-in (11.43-mm)
**Length:** 857 mm (33.75 in)
**Length of barrel:** 279 mm (11.00 in)
**Weight loaded:** 3.7 kg (8.16 lb)
**Magazine:** 12- or 20-round box
**Rate of fire, cyclic:** 550 rpm
**Muzzle velocity:** 280 m (920 ft) per second

# PPSh-41 Sub-machine gun

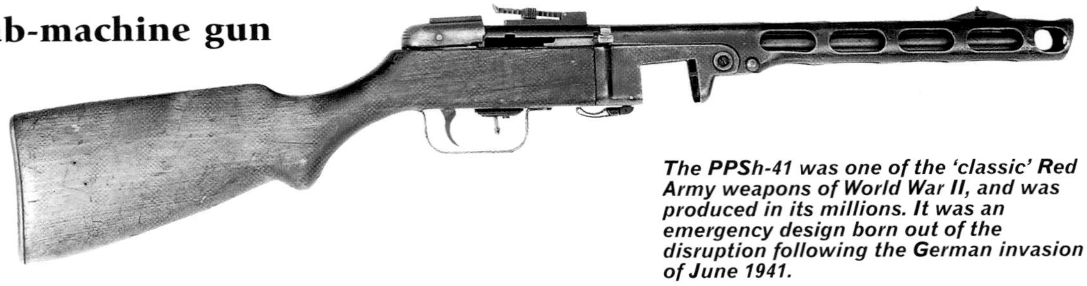

***The PPSh-41 was one of the 'classic' Red Army weapons of World War II, and was produced in its millions. It was an emergency design born out of the disruption following the German invasion of June 1941.***

In many ways the **Pistolet-Pulyemet Shpagina obrazets 1941g**, generally known as the **PPSh-41,** was to the Red Army what the Sten was to the British and the MP 40 to the Germans: in short, it was the Soviet equivalent of the mass-produced sub-machine gun making the maximum possible use in its concept of ways of simplifying the weapon, and in its construction of reducing to the lowest possible figure the number of costly and time-consuming machining operations. Unlike the Sten and the MP 40, however, the PPSh-41 was the result of a more measured and involved development process than had been possible with, for example, the Sten, and as a result the Soviet result was a much better all-round weapon.

## Huge production total

The PPSh-41 was designed and developed from 1940 by Georgi S. Shpagin, but it was not until a time early in 1942, in the wake of the upheavals of the German invasion from June of the previous year, that the first examples were issued to the Red Army on a large scale. As it had been designed from the outset for the very maximum ease of production, the PPSh-41 was churned out in the tens of thousands in all manner of workshops ranging from properly equipped arsenals to shed workshops in rural areas. It has been estimated that by the end of the 'Great Patriotic War' in 1945 that more than five million examples of the PPSh-41 had been produced.

Considering that it was a mass-produced weapon, the PPSh-41 was a well-made design with a heavy solid wooden butt. It used the conventional blowback operating system, but it had a high rate of fire and in order to absorb the shock of the recoiling breech block a buffer of laminated leather or felt blocks was provided at the rear of the breech block's travel. The gun body and the barrel jacket were simple shaped steel stampings, and the muzzle had a downward sloping shape that doubled as a rudimentary muzzle brake. The muzzle was also fitted with a device termed a compensator, and this was intended to reduce the amount of muzzle climb produced by the recoil forces when the gun was fired. The barrel was chrome-plated, a standard Soviet practice to ease cleaning and reduce barrel wear, but at one time the need for weapons was so great that the barrels were simply old Mosin-Nagant rifle barrels cut down to the appropriate length for use in the sub-machine gun.

The weapon was supplied with ammunition from a 35- or 71-round drum magazine, and this was of exactly the same type as that used on the earlier Soviet sub-machine guns. Fire selection (single shot or full automatic) was made by a simple lever located just forward of the trigger. In construction the PPSh-41 was wholly reliant on welding, pins and seam stampings. The overall result was a tough, reliable and highly effective weapon.

The PPSh-41 had to be tough, for once the Red Army started to receive the type in appreciable numbers it adopted the weapon in a way that no other army even attempted to consider. Quite simply the PPSh-41 was issued to entire infantry battalions and regiments, to the almost virtual exclusion of any type of weapon other than hand grenades. These units formed the vanguard of the shock assault units that were carried into the attack on the backs of T-34 medium tanks, from which these shock assault units descended only for an attack or for food and rest. These personnel of these units carried enough ammunition only for their immediate needs, their general life standards were low, and their combat lives were very short. But in their tens of thousands these hordes armed with the PPSh-41 sub-machine swept across eastern Russia and across Europe, carrying all before them. They were a fearful force and the PPSh-41 with which they were equipped became a virtual combat symbol of the Red Army.

## German service

Under such circumstances the PPSh-41 (known to its users as the 'Pah-Pah-Shah') received virtually no maintenance or even any cleaning. Under Eastern Front conditions it soon became apparent that the best way to keep the weapon going under summer dust or winter ice conditions was to keep it completely dry and free from any sort of oil, otherwise its action clogged or froze.

So many PPSh-41 sub-machine guns were produced that the type became a virtual standard weapon for the German army as well as the Red Army, the Germans even going to the extent of recalibring some of their captured hoard to their own 9-mm (0.354-in) Parabellum cartridge: this process required the replacement of the Soviet barrel and magazine housing by a new barrel and a housing able to accept the magazine of the MP 40. Unaltered weapons in German service received the official inventory designation **Maschinenpistole 717(r),** but the designation of recalibred weapons remains unknown. Partisan forces operating behind the German lines found the PPSh-41 an ideal weapon for their purposes, and after the war the type was used by virtually every nation that came within the Soviet sphere of influence. It still turns up in the hands of 'freedom fighters' all over the world, and it will no doubt be around for a long time to come.

***The German army was much impressed with the Soviet PPSh-41, and when supplies of their own MP 40 sub-machine guns were lacking they took to using large numbers of captured PPSh-41s. If Soviet 7.62-mm (0.3-in) ammunition was in short supply the weapon could fire the German 7.63-mm Mauser pistol round, and by 1945 numbers of PPSh-41s were being adapted to fire German 9-mm (0.354-in) ammunition.***

***Involvement in the fighting extended throughout the population, for during some of the many sieges, such as those at Leningrad, Sevastopol and Stalingrad, even women and children took up weapons.***

**SPECIFICATION**

**PPSh-41**
**Calibre:** 7.62-mm (0.3-in)
**Length overall:** 828 mm (32.60 in)
**Length of barrel:** 265 mm (10.43 in)
**Weight loaded:** 5.4 kg (11.90 lb)
**Magazine:** 71-round drum or 35-round box
**Rate of fire, cyclic:** 900 rounds per minute
**Muzzle velocity:** 488 m (1,600 ft) per minute

# PPD-1934/38 Sub-machine gun

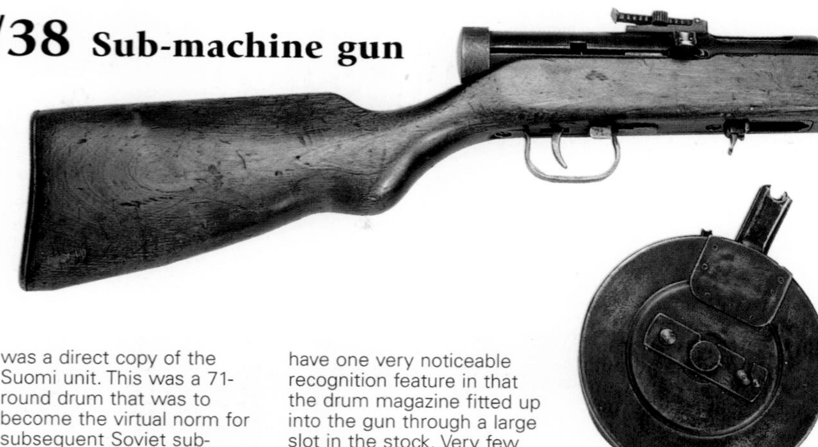

***The Soviet PPD-1934 introduced one feature later used on all Soviet sub-machine gun designs: the chromed barrel to reduce wear and ease cleaning.***

The USSR had sufficient troubles during the 1920s and 1930s without worrying too much about the design of modern weapons for its armed forces, but after matters had settled down enough for re-equipment of the Red Army to be contemplated, the creation of a sub-machine gun design was not very high on the list of Soviet military priorities. Rather than make any innovations in sub-machine gun design, Vasili A. Degtyarev opted to design a weapon combining features that had already appeared in other countries' weapons. The result was the **Pistolet-Pulyemet Degtyareva obrazets 1934g,** or **PPD-1934.**

## Derivative design

First produced in 1934, the blowback-operated weapon combined Finnish Suomi m/1931 and German MP 18 and MP 28 features. It remained in production until 1940, by which time the introduction of modifications justified the **PPD-1934/38** designation. There was nothing very remarkable about the PPD-1934/38. The mechanism was almost the same as that of the German weapons and the magazine was a direct copy of the Suomi unit. This was a 71-round drum that was to become the virtual norm for subsequent Soviet sub-machine guns, but a smaller 25-round box magazine was also issued on occasion. This box magazine had to be curved as the cartridge used for all the Soviet sub-machine guns was the 7.62-mm (0.3-in) Tokarev (Type P) rimless cartridge, which had a bottle-necked shape and would not therefore lie completely flat for feeding from the magazine lips into the gun body.

## General improvement

There was one variant of the PPD-1934/38, and this was placed in production during 1940 as the **PPD-1940**. The new variant offered a general all-round improvement over the earlier design. It did have one very noticeable recognition feature in that the drum magazine fitted up into the gun through a large slot in the stock. Very few other sub-machine gun designs used this magazine fixing system.

When the Germans and their allies invaded the USSR in 1941 the PPD guns were still in relatively short supply among Red Army units, and for this reason had little real effect on the outcome of events as the Axis forces drove east. The success of this initial phase of the Axis campaign meant that the Germans captured useful but not very large numbers of PPD sub-machine guns, which they issued to their own second-line units. In German service the PPD was known as the **Maschinenpistole 716(r),** and the Germans used either captured Soviet ammunition or alternatively the 7.63-mm (0.3-in) Mauser cartridge, which was virtually identical to the Soviet round. By the end of 1941 even the PPD-40 had passed out of production for the simple reason that the Germans had overrun the arsenals concerned, namely those at Tula and Sestroretsk, and there was no time to set up the extensive machine shops and production lines elsewhere. The Red Army therefore had to resort to newer and more easily produced sub-machine gun models.

**SPECIFICATION**

| | |
|---|---|
| **PPD-1934/38** | **Magazine:** 71-round drum or 25-round box |
| **Calibre:** 7.62-mm (0.3-in) | **Rate of fire, cyclic:** 800 rounds per minute |
| **Length overall:** 780 mm (30.71 in) | **Muzzle velocity:** 488 m (1,600 ft) per second |
| **Length of barrel:** 269 mm (10.60 in) | |
| **Weight loaded:** 5.69 kg (12.54 lb) | |

# PPS-42 and PPS-43 Sub-machine guns

***The Soviet PPS-43 was the full production version of the emergency-produced PPS-42 designed during the siege of Leningrad. The PPS-43 introduced a measure of finesse, but it was essentially a simple weapon.***

Few weapons can have been designed and produced under conditions as desperate as those that surrounded the advent of the Soviet **Pistolet-Pulyemet Sudareva obrazets 1942g** (or **PPS-42**) sub-machine gun. In 1942 the city of Leningrad (now St Petersburg) was under siege from the south and north by the German and Finnish armies respectively, and the trapped Red Army units were short of every war-making necessity including weapons. Leningrad contained a large number of manufacturing facilities and machine shops, so when it came to local production of weapons the fighting troops were relatively well off, but they needed these weapons as quickly as possible. Under such conditions the sub-machine gun provides an obvious basis on which to work, so it was a weapon of this type that the small arms designer A. I. Sudarev created.

## Crude yet effective

Sudarev was limited in the design he could create by the materials to hand and the type of machines that would be available to work these materials. By sheer pragmatic trial and error, Sudarev developed a sub-machine gun that embodied all the features to be found in other emergency designs such as the British Sten and American M3. The result was a simple and very robust gun manufactured from sheet metal stampings, most of them heavy as that was the only material to hand. The gun was held together by welds, rivets and pins, and a simple metal butt, capable of being folded, was provided. The 35-round magazine used on earlier Soviet sub-machine guns was adopted almost unchanged, for the simple reason that production of a drum magazine would have proved too difficult.

The firing trials were carried out quite simply by handing examples straight from the production shops to front-line soldiers. Their comments and results were fed straight back to the assembly shops where any changes were made on the spot. One of these changes involved the use of a curved steel plate, pierced by a central hole through which the bullet passed, over the muzzle to act as a partial compensator and muzzle brake, and this crude and simple device was retained when the weapon entered production. In time the new sub-machine gun received an official designation.

## Massive production

In action around Leningrad the PPS-42 proved to be a thoroughly sound design and one that could be produced quickly and cheaply. Thus it was not long after the 900-day siege of Leningrad had been lifted that the weapon was adopted for general Red Army service. When this took place there was opportunity to remove some of the more rushed and crude features of the weapon. The folding butt was revised so that it could be hinged upward to clear the ejection port, and the original rough wooden pistol grip was replaced by a hard rubber type. The overall finish was generally improved, and in this form the weapon became the **PPS-43**. In time the PPS-43 took its place in service with the units of the Red Army alongside the PPSh-41, but never in quite the same numbers.

Considering the inauspicious beginnings of the design it proved to be an excellent weapon in service wherever it was taken, and in 1944 it was adopted by the Finns as their standard sub-machine gun once they came into the Soviet sphere of influence. The Germans also used captured PPS-43s as **Maschinenpistole 709(r)** weapons. The PPS-43 has long been out of service with its parent country but remains in limited service elsewhere and, like the British Sten, has the distinction of being copied in many backyard workshops.

**SPECIFICATION**

| | |
|---|---|
| **PPS-43** | **Weight loaded:** 3.9 kg (8.60 lb) |
| **Calibre:** 7.62-mm (0.3-in) | **Magazine:** 35-round curved box |
| **Length:** 808 mm (31.81 in) with butt extended and 606 mm (23.86 in) with butt retracted | **Rate of fire, cyclic:** 700 rounds per minute |
| **Length of barrel:** 254 mm (10.0 in) | **Muzzle velocity:** 488 m (1,600 ft) per second |

# F1 Sub-machine gun

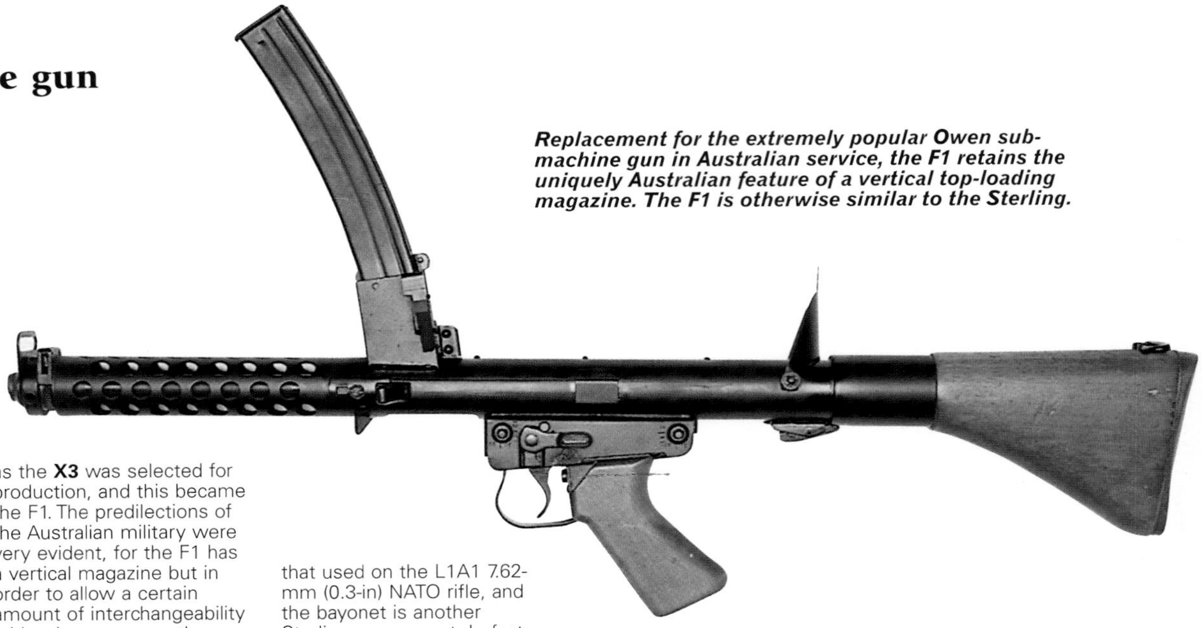

*Replacement for the extremely popular **Owen** sub-machine gun in Australian service, the **F1** retains the uniquely Australian feature of a vertical top-loading magazine. The **F1** is otherwise similar to the **Sterling**.*

Lieutenant Evelyn Owen created the sub-machine gun that bears his name, and this was used by Australian soldiers during World War II and for many years after. One of the most recognisable features of the Owen sub-machine gun was the vertical magazine, a feature with no particular merit or demerit but one that the Australians found very much to their liking. When the Australian army began searching for a new sub-machine gun, it was therefore not averse to choosing a design with an overhead vertical magazine.

Before selecting the design now known as the **F1**, the Australians looked at a number of experimental weapons that rejoiced in names such as 'Kokoda' and 'MCEM'. Some of these experimental designs had a number of advanced features, but they were generally regarded as not being 'soldier-proof' enough to suit Australian conditions. But in 1962 a design known as the **X3** was selected for production, and this became the F1. The predilections of the Australian military were very evident, for the F1 has a vertical magazine but in order to allow a certain amount of interchangeability with other weapons the magazine is now curved and identical to that of the British Sterling and the Canadian C1.

This interchangeability factor is also evident in several other features of the F1. The pistol grip is the same as that used on the L1A1 7.62-mm (0.3-in) NATO rifle, and the bayonet is another Sterling component. In fact it is tempting to regard the F1 as an Australian Sterling, but there are too many differences to support such a claim. The F1 uses a simple 'straight-through' design with the butt fixed in line with the tubular receiver, and the pistol grip group is arranged differently from that of the Sterling. The overhead magazine does produce one difficulty, namely sighting. In action deliberate aiming is not common but has to be taken into account, so a form of offset sighting system had to be introduced. On the F1 this comprises an offset leaf sight (folding down onto the tubular receiver) and an offset fixed foresight.

***Simple and effective, the F1 in its prototype X3 form performed extremely well in the Mekong Delta during the Vietnam War. Modern construction made it almost 1 kg (2.2 lb) lighter than its World War II ancestor.***

## Protective feature

The F1 has one unusual, yet simple and effective safety feature: on a short-barrel weapon it is often too easy to place the forward grip over the muzzle or too close to it for safety, but on the F1 a simple sling swivel bracket prevents the hand from getting too close to the muzzle.

The F1 has some other interesting design features. One is the cocking handle, which exactly duplicates the position and action of its counterpart on the L1A1 rifle: this handle has a cover which prevents dirt and debris getting into the action, though if enough dirt does get into the action to prevent the bolt closing, the cocking handle can be latched to the bolt for the firer to force it closed in an emergency.

For all its many attributes the F1 has not been bought outside Australia and some of its associated territories. At one time there was talk of its being replaced by the American M16A1 rifle, but the F1 is still used.

**SPECIFICATION**

| | |
|---|---|
| **F1** | with bayonet |
| **Calibre:** 9-mm (0.354-in) | **Muzzle velocity:** 366 m (1,200 ft) per second |
| **Length overall:** 714 mm (28.1 in) | **Rate of fire, cyclic:** 600-640 rounds per minute |
| **Length of barrel:** 213 mm (8.386 in) | **Feed:** 34-round curved magazine |
| **Weight:** loaded 4.3 kg (9.48 lb) | |

# FMK-3

## Sub-machine gun

***The FMK-3 has a straight-through design with a telescoped wrap-around bolt, retractable wire buttstock, plastic fore grip and metal rear grip carrying the magazine.***

From 1943 the Halcon small arms company of Buenos Aires in Argentina produced a series of blowback-operated sub-machine guns chambered for the 9-mm (0.354-in) Parabellum and 11.43-mm (0.45-in) ACP cartridges. None of them was ever adopted as a first-line weapon by the Argentine forces, but the weapons did see a measure of second-line and police use. The first of the weapons was the Model 1943 with a very distinctive appearance as a result of the fact that its buffer cap overhung a buttstock with a pistol grip built into its forward end. The Model 1946 differed mainly in having a metal rather than wood buttstock. The Light Model 57 marked a shift in design thinking, for the barrel lacked cooling fins, the receiver was cylindrical rather than rectangular, and the magazine was curved rather than straight. The final Light Model 60 was based on the Model 57 but with the fire selector removed from the receiver and a two-trigger arrangement introduced.

Manufactured by the Fabrica Militar de Armas Portatiles of Rosario, the PAM was a shorter and lighter variant of the American M3A1, and was produced in two models as the PAM-1 capable only of automatic fire, and the PAM-2 with full selective-fire capability.

## Advanced design

FMAP then moved forward to the creation of a more modern sub-machine as the PA3-DM. Like the PAM, it is a blowback-operated weapon firing the 9-mm Parabellum cartridge. This selective-fire weapon has a 25-round detachable and straight box magazine that slides into the pistol grip,

and a plastic fore grip under the receiver. The weapon was produced in two variants: one has a fixed wooden buttstock, and the other a sliding wire buttstock modelled on that of the M3. Other features of the PA3-DM include the use of a metal pressing at the body, a screw-threaded cap at the front for easy removal of the barrel, a wrap-around bolt and a cocking handle on the left-hand side of the receiver with a slide that covers the cocking handle's slot to keep out dirt and thus reduce the chances of the weapon jamming under adverse conditions.

The PA3-DM was accepted for first-line service with the Argentine forces, and was followed in the mid-1970s by the **FMK-3**. Produced by what is now the Fabricaciones Militares organisation, this sub-machine gun can be regarded as a modernised development of the PA3-DM, and is a selective-fire weapon that has also been produced in semi-automatic form as the **FMK-5** for sale to civilians.

Used by the Argentine army and also by the country's police, the FMK-3 is based on the use of a telescoped bolt that sleeves round the rear part of the barrel when closed, a double-row magazine, a receiver and pistol grip fabricated from steel stampings, and a safety and fire-selector switch on the left-hand side of the weapon above the pistol grip, which incorporates a grip safety in its rear.

The FMK-3's sights are of the flip-up type, with a rear sight blade of the L type and calibrated for 50- and 100-m (55- and 110-yard) ranges. The buttstock is of the retractable sliding steel wire type derived ultimately from that of the American M3.

***The FMK-3 is a wholly conventional and utilitarian sub-machine gun that was designed and manufactured in Argentina for the country's armed forces.***

**SPECIFICATION**

**FMK-3**
**Calibre:** 9-mm (0.354-in)
**Length overall:** 693 mm (27.3 in) with the buttstock extended and 523 mm (20.6 in) with the buttstock retracted
**Length of barrel:** 290 mm (11.42 in)
**Weight:** empty 3.4 kg (7.5 lb)
**Muzzle velocity:** 400 m (1,312 ft) per second
**Rate of fire, cyclic:** 650 rounds per minute
**Feed:** 25-, 32- and 40-round straight box magazine

# MPi 69 Sub-machine gun

Designed by a team under the supervision of Hugo Stowasser, the **MPi 69** (Maschinen-Pistole 1969) is a product of Steyr-Daimler-Puch AG (now known as Steyr-Mannlicher AG). This Austrian sub-machine gun bears a strong visual affinity to the Uzi weapon of Israeli design, but differs in a number of important respects and is in fact a simpler weapon than the Israeli gun. The MPi 69 is no longer in production, having been superseded by two other Steyr weapons, the TMP and AUG/Para.

***The MPi 69 is a sub-machine gun of straight-through concept, and the 25- or 32-round box magazine is loaded into the weapon's pistol grip.***

The MPi 69 works on the blowback principle, and is a selective-fire weapon offering a choice between single shot and full automatic. The forward end of the sling is attached to the simple pressed steel cocking piece, which is therefore operated by a tug on the sling.

The weapon's receiver is a pressing of light-gauge steel sheet which is welded into a hollow box with two openings (one in the middle to serve as the ejection port and one near the front to accept the barrel seating, barrel release catch and barrel locking nut) on its right-hand side. The ejector is a simple steel strip bent to the right shape and riveted into position on the base of the receiver to run in a groove let into the bottom of the breech block. Attached by spot welds under the rear of the receiver are the guides for the telescoping steel-wire buttstock and its release plungers, and also at the rear is the strip-down catch. Screws attach the optional Singlepoint sight to the top of the receiver, while under the receiver is a moulded nylon receiver cover that carries the trigger mechanism and the pistol grip complete with the magazine housing.

***The Austrian-designed MPi 69 was clearly influenced by the Uzi sub-machine gun of Israel, and fires the virtually universal 9-mm Parabellum cartridge.***

***The MPi 69 has a sliding wire buttstock, the spent cases are ejected from a port on the weapon's right side, and the swivels for the sling are located on the left.***

## Cold-forged barrel

The barrel is cold-forged on a mandrel in a process that is notably cheap and clean in its results. The breech block has a fixed firing pin on the bolt face, itself located at about the midpoint of this wrap-around unit, which is cut away on its right-hand side for ejection purposes. The fresh round is kept out of alignment with the firing pin until it is fully chambered, and this considerably enhances safety in conjunction with the applied safety device. A light pull on the trigger produces single-shot fire, while a strong pull generates automatic fire.

A later variant is the **MPi 81**, which differs in having a conventional cocking handle on the left of the receiver, and the rate of fire boosted to 700 rounds per minute.

**SPECIFICATION**

**MPi 69**
**Calibre:** 9-mm (0.354-in)
**Length overall:** 673 mm (26.5 in) with the buttstock extended and 470 mm (18.5 in) with the buttstock retracted
**Length of barrel:** 260 mm (10.24 in)
**Weight:** loaded 3.52 kg (7.76 lb)
**Muzzle velocity:** 381 m (1,250 ft) per second
**Rate of fire, cyclic:** 550 rounds per minute
**Feed:** 25- or 32-round straight box magazine

# Steyr AUG Para Sub-machine gun

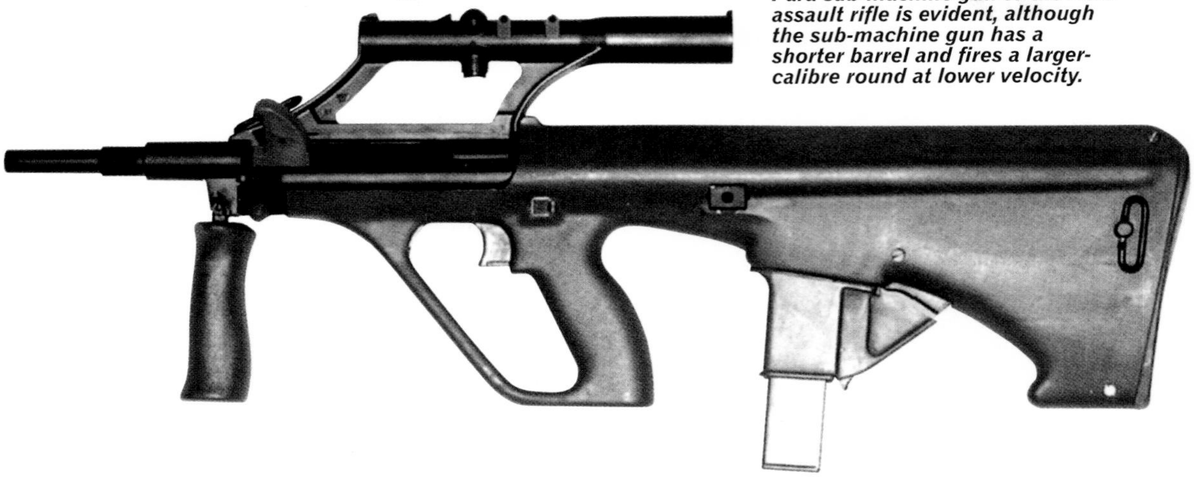

***The family kinship of the AUG Para sub-machine gun to the AUG assault rifle is evident, although the sub-machine gun has a shorter barrel and fires a larger-calibre round at lower velocity.***

Entering production in 1988, the **Steyr AUG Para** from the Steyr-Daimler-Puch AG is an Austrian sub-machine gun derived very simply from the same company's AUG (Armee Universal Gewehr) assault rifle. The process of converting the assault rifle, chambered for the NATO or SS109 5.56-mm (0.219-in) cartridge, into a sub-machine gun chambered for the 9-mm (0.354-in) Parabellum cartridge was essentially simple: a shorter barrel in the new calibre was introduced, the bolt assembly was changed, an adapter was added to allow the weapon to accept the 25- or 32-round magazine of the MPi 69 sub-machine gun, and the gas-operated mechanism of the assault rifle was disabled so that the weapon would operate on the blowback principle that is a standard physical feature of all modern sub-machine guns.

## Closed-bolt firing

Notable features of the AUG Para include firing from the closed bolt position for greater accuracy and safety, and a barrel that is longer than those of most sub-machine gun barrels and therefore provides a higher muzzle velocity (and therefore greater range and increased accuracy) than is usual among weapons chambered for the 9-mm Parabellum cartridge. The interior of the chamber is chromed for longer life and the useful advantage of reduced cleaning requirements.

The AUG Para, which is otherwise known as the **AUG 9**, also has a muzzle threaded to accept any of several types of silencer, and provision for the installation of a device to launch CS or CN grenades, or alternatively for the mounting of a bayonet, an item not frequently found on a sub-machine gun.

## Pioneering move

The Steyr company was one of the first small arms manufacturers to make the commercially and militarily sensible adaptation of an assault rifle to sub-machine-gun standard. A major attraction of the concept is that there is need for only a small number of different parts, which greater eases the operating service's spares holding and logistics requirements. To improve the versatility of the AUG assault rifle and AUG Para sub-machine gun family, the manufacturer also offers a kit of three major parts to allow the conversion of the weapon between the two primary standards in as little as 10 minutes.

The AUG Para retains the AUG's fixed optical sight over the rear part of the barrel and forward part of the receiver (with mechanical sights retained for emergency use) and its straight-through 'bullpup' design with the magazine located behind the trigger group and aiming accuracy enhanced by the provision of a forward pistol grip in addition to the rear pistol grip below the trigger. The furniture is made of moulded plastic.

## Safety and firing

The safety arrangements are based on a cross-bolt safety catch above the trigger: this is pushed firmly from right to left to make the weapon safe, and from left to right to allow the weapon to be fired. There is a firing pin safety integrated with this mechanism. The AUG 9 Para can be fired in two modes: the first pressure on the trigger fires the weapon in semi-automatic mode, while the second pressure yields fully automatic fire.

| SPECIFICATION | |
|---|---|
| **AUG Para**<br>**Calibre:** 9-mm (0.354-in) Parabellum<br>**Length overall:** 665 mm (26.18 in)<br>**Length of barrel:** 420 mm (16.54 in) | **Weight:** empty 3.3 kg (7.28 lb)<br>**Muzzle velocity:** not available<br>**Rate of fire, cyclic:** 700 rounds per minute<br>**Feed:** 25- or 32-round straight box magazine |

# Madsen Sub-machine guns

***World War II saw the development of a number of simple, cheap sub-machine guns. The Madsen Model 46 was specifically designed for ease of production and maintenance.***

Despite its small size and population, Denmark has been home to several manufacturers of small arms, of which the most notable was Madsen, more formally known as the Dansk Industri Syndikat. Although the sub-machine guns adopted by the Danish forces after World War II were of Finnish and Swedish design from the Suomi and Husqvarna organisations, Madsen had some export success with its own weapons.

The first Madsen sub-machine gun to appear after World War II was the **Model 45**, which had a number of interesting features but was not a success, but the following **Model 1946, Model 1950** and **Model 1953** were altogether more profitable for the company.

The Model 1945 (or **P13**) was chambered for the 9-mm (0.354-in) Parabellum cartridge, of which 50 were carried in a box magazine below the receiver. Despite the fact that the weapon had wooden furniture, the designers achieved the low empty weight of 3.2 kg (7.1 lb). Unusual features included a cocking slide rather than handle, a recoil spring wound round the barrel below this cocking slide, and a light breech block whose inertia was boosted by the mass of the moving spring and slide.

## Rapid obsolescence

The Model 1945 was rendered obsolete only a year later by the Model 1946 (or **P16**). This was schemed for ease of production, and the weapon's body comprised two pressed steel frames hinged together at the rear and held together at the front by the barrel locking nut. The butt comprised a length of metal tube bent into a rectangle open at the forward end, where its ends were hinged to the rear of the body and the heel of the pistol grip allowing the butt to be folded to the right so that it rested alongside the weapon's body. Like the Model 1945, the Model 1946 was chambered for the 9-mm Parabellum cartridge, of which 32 rounds were carried. The Model 1946's cyclic rate of fire was 480 rounds per minute rather than the Model 1945's figure of 850 rounds per minute. The Model 1946 also had a lower muzzle velocity than the Model 1945, the respective figures being 380 and 400 m (1,247 and 1,312 ft) per minute. The Model 1946 weighed only 3.175 kg (7 lb) without its magazine.

The Model 1946 had basically the same cocking arrangement as the Model 1945, namely a slide on the upper part of the body's rear with a pair of milled flanges extending outward and downward for the firer to grip. On the Model 1950 the flanges were replaced by a knob on top of the slide, which was integral with the bolt. The weapon had the same type of folding butt as the Model 1946, and was supplied with 32 rounds of ammunition from a straight, flat-sided box magazine under the weapon. Other details included a weight of 3.175 kg (7 lb), muzzle velocity of 380 m (1,247 ft) per second, and cyclic rate of 550 rounds per minute.

### British interest

The Model 1950 was demonstrated in many countries and secured some orders. The British at one time wanted to adopt this weapon for use by second-line troops as the EM-2 was adopted for first-line forces, but plans for both these weapons were abandoned, and the British instead adopted the Sterling sub-machine gun. The one major change that the British had demanded for the Model 1950 was the replacement of the Madsen type of single-row magazine by a double-row magazine that was curved and fullered to make it easier for the magazine spring to lift the rounds and for dirt and debris to fall to the bottom of the magazine without interfering with the gun's operation.

This type of magazine was adopted for the definitive Model 1953 sub-machine gun, which was otherwise still very clearly a linear descendant of the Model 1946 via the Model 1950. A closer examination revealed a reversal of the previous system to lock the two halves of the body to the rear of the barrel. Now the barrel locking nut screwed onto the barrel rather than onto the front of the receiver as had been the case with the Models 1946 and 1950. Also the rotation of the locking nut drew the barrel forward until a flange on the rear of the barrel met the inside of the body, in the process holding the whole assembly in a stronger and more rigid arrangement.

Another internal change was the improved shaping of the bolt for better functioning. An optional extra was a removable barrel jacket to which a special short bayonet could be attached. Like the other Madsen sub-machine guns, the Model 1953 was generally produced as an automatic weapon with provision for an alternative selective-fire mechanism, and had comprehensive safety features preventing, amongst other things, the accidental discharge of the weapon should it be jarred or dropped.

**SPECIFICATION**

**Model 1953**
**Calibre:** 9-mm (0.354-in)
**Length overall:** 808 mm (31.8 in) with butt extended
**Length of barrel:** 213 mm (8.4 in)
**Weight:** loaded 4 kg (8.82 lb)
**Muzzle velocity:** 385 m (1,263 m) per second
**Rate of fire, cyclic:** 600 rpm
**Feed:** 32-round curved magazine

# CZ vz 61 Skorpion Sub-machine gun/Machine-pistol

***Stock fully extended, the Type 61 can shoot with reasonable accuracy at up to 200 m (220 yards). It uses a simple blowback operation, but the empty case is ejected directly upwards.***

***The Model 61 Skorpion is a favourite weapon of the Palestine Liberation Organization, its small size making for easy concealment.***

A weapon that was manufactured in the period from about 1960 to 1975, the **Ceska Zbrojovka vz 61 Skorpion** is of Czechoslovak design and manufacturing origins, and lies in that no-man's land of small arms capability in which a weapon that is neither a pistol nor a true sub-machine gun is described as a 'machine pistol'. Such a weapon is small enough to be carried and fired as a pistol, but is also capable of fully automatic fire when this is required. Thus the vz 61 has the advantages and disadvantages of both types of weapon, and is perhaps below par in both capacities, but is nevertheless one of the most feared of all 'underground' arms, despite the fact that it was intended to be a standard service weapon for the conventional Czechoslovak armed forces and also for special forces requiring a close-combat weapon that could be concealed with ease.

### Personal weapon

The Skorpion was designed for use by tank crews, signallers and other personnel who have no normal need for anything larger than a pistol. But since a pistol is essentially a short-range weapon, the introduction of a fully automatic feature provided this small weapon with a considerable short-range firepower. The Skorpion resembles a pistol, though the magazine is not in the butt, but forward of the trigger assembly, and a folding wire butt is provided for aimed fire. The overall appearance is short and chunky, and the weapon is small enough to be carried in a somewhat oversized belt holster.

When fired in fully automatic mode the weapon has a cyclic rate of about 840 rounds per minute, which makes it formidable at short ranges, but this advantage is offset by two factors. One is that the firing of any machine pistol on full automatic makes the weapon almost impossible to aim accurately: the forces above the position of the hands and shoulder of the firer cause the muzzle to climb and judder, making it all but impossible to hold the weapon on the target for anything other than an instant. The other is that the Skorpion uses magazines with only 10- or 20-round capacities, and on automatic either is soon exhausted. But while the Skorpion fires, it creates an alarming swathe of fire at close quarters.

### Folding wire butt

The Skorpion operates on the blowback principle. Single shots can be selected, and the folding wire butt helps in aiming. The basic vz 61 Skorpion fires the American 0.32-in/7.65-mm cartridge – the only Warsaw Pact weapon to use this round – but the **vz 63** uses the 9-mm Short (0.38-in) round and the **vz 68** the 9-mm (0.354-in) Parabellum cartridge. There is also a silenced version.

### Terrorist weapon

Apart from its use by Czechoslovakia, the Skorpion was also sold to some African nations, but its main impact has been in the hands of guerrillas and 'freedom fighters'. The impact of the Skorpion at short range is considerable, which suits the requirements of assassination and terror squads, so the type is much favoured by such groups. With them it has turned up in parts of the world from Central America to the Middle East.

**SPECIFICATION**

**vz 61 Skorpion**
**Calibre:** 0.32-in (actual 7.65-mm)
**Length overall:** 513 mm (20.2 in) with butt extended and 269 mm (10.6 in) with butt folded
**Length of barrel:** 112 mm (4.4 in)
**Weight:** loaded 2 kg (4.4 lb)
**Muzzle velocity:** 317 m (1,040 ft) per second
**Rate of fire, cyclic:** 840 rpm
**Feed:** 10- or 20-round straight box magazine

# Jati-Matic
## Sub-machine gun

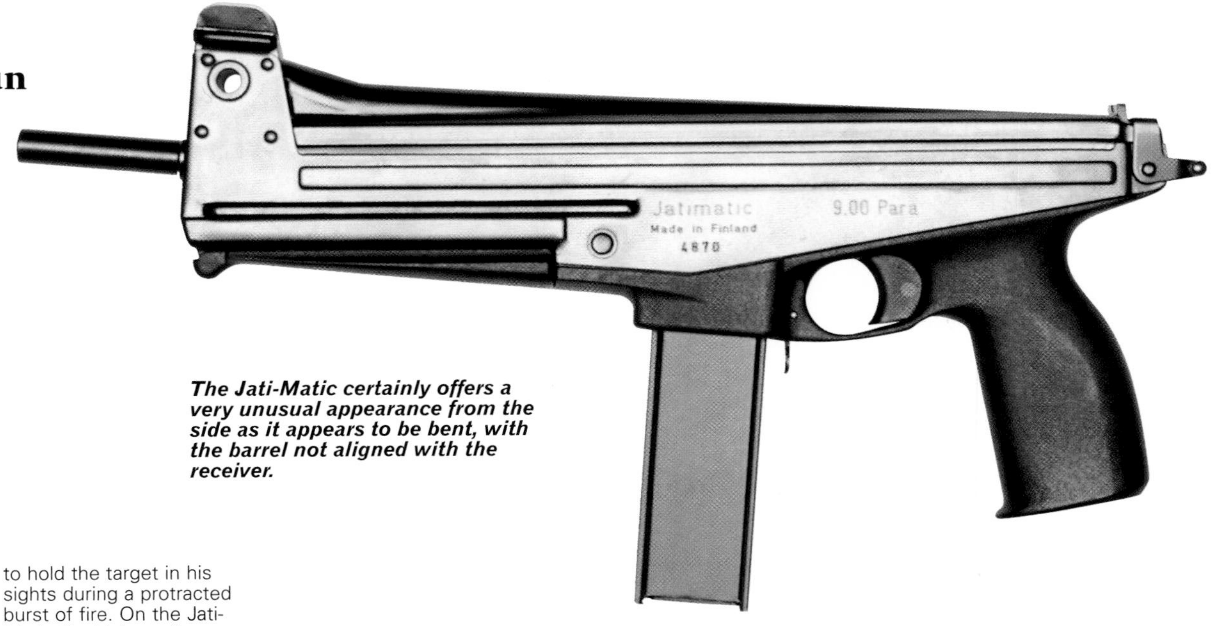


***The Jati-Matic certainly offers a very unusual appearance from the side as it appears to be bent, with the barrel not aligned with the receiver.***

During the 1970s Jaati Tumari was working in Finland to design a highly accurate 0.22-in (5.59-in) semi-automatic (self-loading) pistol for target shooting. While being test fired, the new pistol suddenly unleashed a burst of fully automatic fire, and on investigating the resulting impacts through the target Tumari found that the holes were very tightly grouped. Such are the semi-accidental design origins of the **Jati-Matic** sub-machine gun, which is chambered for the universally accepted 9-mm (0.354-in) Parabellum cartridge, and is certainly one of the most unusual-looking weapons of its type currently to be found in service anywhere in the world.

### Odd appearance

The striking and somewhat disconcerting appearance of the Jati-Matic is derived from the apparent misalignment of the barrel and the body of the weapon. This is the result of Tumari's patented inclined bolt system. Rather than operating in the same plane as the barrel, the Tumari type of bolt recoils up an inclined ramp, which helps to retard the bolt's movement to the rear, and at the same time forces the weapon down. This angling of elements in the receiver also permits the grip to be located in a position higher than would otherwise have been possible, and therefore in line with the barrel and the weapon's recoil. The result is a virtual elimination of the muzzle-climb tendency evident in most of the other sub-machine guns to be found anywhere in the world, which makes it virtually impossible for the firer to hold the target in his sights during a protracted burst of fire. On the Jati-Matic the higher grip ensures that the recoil force does not compel the weapon to rotate muzzle-upward in the firer's hands, but rather to push straight back and therefore leave the sights on the target. The one major limitation of the arrangement is that it reduces the natural 'pointability' of the sub-machine gun.

Other features of the Jati-Matic include a foregrip that is hinged at its upper end to fold to the rear, when it serves as a safety, provision for 20- and 40-round magazines inserted into the weapon just forward of the trigger group, and a trigger on which the first pressure yields single-shot fire and the second pressure produces fully automatic fire.

### Blowback operation

The Jati-Matic is a blowback-operated weapon, the receiver is made of pressed steel with a hinged cover, the foregrip serves as the cocking handle when lowered into the open position, and there is no stock, fixed or folding, control of the weapon being exercised by means of the foregrip and the pistol grip.

The Jati-Matic was manufactured in modest numbers between 1980 and 1987 by the Tampeeren Asepaja Oy, and then re-entered production in 1995 by another Finnish manufacturing concern, the Oy Golden Gun Ltd.

The model manufactured from 1995 is the **GG-95 PDW** (Personal Defence Weapon). This is basically a development of the Jati-Matic revised top surface to the receiver, eliminating much of the angularity that reduced the Jati-Matic's 'pointability'.

***The complete 'kit' for the Jati-Matic sub-machine gun includes a night sight, holsters, 20- and 40-round magazines, a carrying sling, and cleaning and maintenance equipment.***

***The foregrip of the Jati-Matic serves as a cocking handle when opened, and as a safety when closed. The blade on the lower part of its rear edge engages in the weapon's mechanism to prevent any movement of the bolt.***

**SPECIFICATION**

**Jati-Matic**
**Calibre:** 9-mm (0.354-in) Parabellum
**Length overall:** 400 mm (15.75 in)
**Length of barrel:** not available
**Weight:** empty 1.65 kg (3.64 lb)
**Muzzle velocity:** not available
**Rate of fire, cyclic:** 650 rounds per minute
**Feed:** 20- or 40-round straight box magazine

# MAT 49 Sub-machine gun

***Entering French service in 1949, the 9-mm MAT 49 is an extremely rugged design, made from heavy-gauge steel stampings. The pistol grip/magazine housing hinges forward for stowage and transport.***

In the immediate aftermath of World War II the French armed forces were equipped with a variety of weapons from a remarkable miscellany of origins and sources. As far as sub-machine guns were concerned, some of these were of French design and manufacture dating from before the start of World War II in 1939, and others were American and British weapons delivered to the revised French forces from the United States and the United Kingdom. While the weapons themselves were serviceable enough, the range of ammunition calibres and types was considered too large for logistical convenience and cost-effective stores holding. A selection and standardisation programme was therefore launched, resulting in the authorities' decision to standardise on the 9-mm (0.354-in) Parabellum cartridge for future sub-machine gun developments.

## New weapon

A new sub-machine gun of wholly French origin was also demanded, and three arsenals responded with new designs. That created by the Manufacture d'Armes de Tulle (hence MAT) was selected for service, and the new weapon went into production during 1949 within the context of re-equipping and strengthening the French armed forces with more capable weapons that were, wherever possible, of French design and manufacture.

This **MAT 49** sub-machine gun is still in fairly extensive service, for it is an efficient weapon that is also, unlike many other sub-machine guns of the period, very well manufactured. Although it uses the now commonplace constructional practice of parts and assemblies fabricated from steel from stampings, those of the MAT 49 were made from heavy-duty steels and are thus very strong and capable of absorbing a great deal of hard use. This was a factor of primary importance to the French, whose forces were committed to a large number of active operations over the following 15 years or so, many of them in parts of the world (such as Indo-China and North Africa) notably inhospitable to the continued smooth functioning of weapons.

***Designed with colonial service in mind, the MAT 49 was used extensively in Indo-China, as well as by the paratroops so notably involved in the bloody conflict in Algeria. It withstood such stern tests successfully.***

## Proven mechanism

The design uses the blowback principle but, in place of what is now described as a 'wraparound' breech block, to reduce the length of the receiver the MAT 49 has an arrangement in which a sizeable portion of the breech block enters the barrel chamber to have much the same effect. No other design uses this feature. There is another aspect of the MAT 49 which is typically French. This is the magazine housing, which can be folded forward with the magazine inserted to reduce the bulk of the weapon for stowage and transport. This feature is a carry-over from the pre-war MAS 38, and was considered so effective by the French army that it was retained in the MAT 49: a catch is depressed and the magazine housing (with a loaded magazine in place) is folded forward to lie under the barrel, while to use the weapon again the magazine is simply pulled back into place so that the housing acts as a foregrip. This foregrip is made all the more important by the fact that the MAT 49 can be fired only in full automatic mode, so a firm grip is needed to keep the weapon under control when fired.

Considerable pains were taken in the design of the MAT 49 to ensure that dust and dirt were kept out of the weapon's mechanism: this too was another historical carry-over from previous times as the MAT 49 was intended for use in the deserts of North Africa. Even when the magazine is in the forward position a flap moves into position to keep out foreign matter. If repairs or cleaning are required, the weapon can be easily stripped without tools. In action a grip safety locks both the trigger mechanism and any possible forward movement of the bolt.

Overall the MAT 49 is a sturdy and foolproof weapon. It is still used in limited numbers by the French armed forces and also by various of the French police and para-military units. It was also exported to many of the ex-French colonies and wherever French interests prevailed. The numbers in French service declined after the introduction of the 5.56-mm (0.219-in) FA MAS assault rifle, but there are enough operators left to ensure that the MAT 49 will remain around for some time.

### SPECIFICATION

**MAT 49**
**Calibre:** 9-mm (0.354-in) Parabellum
**Length:** 720 mm (28.34 in) with butt extended and 460 mm (18.1 in) with butt closed
**Length of barrel:** 228 mm (8.97 in)
**Weight:** loaded 4.17 kg (9.19 lb)
**Muzzle velocity:** 390 m (1,280 ft) per second
**Rate of fire, cyclic:** 600 rounds per minute
**Feed:** 20- or 32-round straight box magazine

# Heckler & Koch MP5

## Sub-machine gun

Heckler & Koch MP5A3

This MP5A3 is fitted with a sliding metal strut stock which can allow a considerable reduction in length. Early MP5s used a straight magazine.

Heckler & Koch MP5A2

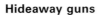

This MP5A2 has a fixed plastic stock. After 1978 all MP5s were fitted with a curved magazine to improve cartridge feed.

Since World War II, the German concern of Heckler und Koch has become one of Europe's largest and most important small-arms manufacturers. Its success has been based soundly on the production of its G3 rifle, which was a standard NATO weapon and is still in use all over the world. In the 1960s the company used the G3 as a basis on which to produce the **Heckler und Koch MP5** sub-machine gun

### Rifle-based

The MP5 was designed to fire the standard 9-mm (0.354-in) X 19 Parabellum cartridge. Although this is a relatively low-powered pistol round, the MP5 uses the same roller and inclined ramp locking mechanism as the G3, which fires a full-power rifle round. The complexity of this system is more than offset by its increased safety. Unlike other machine pistols, the MP5 fires from a closed bolt – the breech block is in the forward position when the trigger is pulled so there is no forward-moving mass to disturb the aim. This makes the MP5 much more accurate than other SMGs. The resemblance to the G3 is maintained by the use of many G3 components on the MP5.

Used by military and law enforcement units in more than 50 nations, the MP5 is firmly established as the world's pre-eminent submachine gun. Over 120 variants of the MP5 are available to address the widest range of tactical requirements. The weapon's unique modular design and a variety of optional buttstocks, forearms, sight mounts, and other accessories gives the MP5 extraordinary flexibility to meet almost any mission.

The main versions of the MP5 include the **MP5A2** with a fixed butt stock and the **MP5A3** with a sliding metal strut stock. The **MP5A4** and the **MP5A5** are the same weapons with the addition of a three-round burst fire capability.

The **MP5SD** is a silenced weapon for use in special or anti-terrorist warfare. The removable sound suppressor is integrated into the design and conforms to the normal length and profile of an unsuppressed weapon. The MP5SD uses an integral aluminum or optional wet technology stainless steel sound suppressor. Unlike most silenced weapons, it does not require use of subsonic ammunition for effective sound reduction.

Heckler & Koch MP5K

### Hideaway guns

The **MP5K** was introduced for use by special units, where weapon concealment is often essential. It is a very short version of the basic MP5, only 325 mm (12.8 in) long and recognizable by a small foregrip, under the almost non-existent muzzle. The **MP5KA1** is a special version of this variant with no protrusions so that it can be carried under clothing or in a special holster.

The **MP5N** or 'Navy' model is made for US Navy SEALs. Fully 'marinised' for operations in seawater, it comes standard with an ambidextrous trigger group and threaded barrel.

In spite of its complexity, the MP5 has proved to be an excellent and reliable submachine-gun. Its first users were West German police agencies and border guards, and soon numbers were purchased by Swiss police and the Netherlands armed forces. Single fire variants are widely used by law-enforcement officers in crowded public areas such as airports.

However, it is since the MP5 was adopted by the British SAS that it has become the weapon of choice for special forces worldwide. The MP5 is inherently accurate because it fires from a closed bolt, and pinpoint accuracy is an essential requirement of any weapon used in a hostage rescue, where innocent lives are at risk.

***The MP5 became a 'star' when it was used by the Special Air Service during the hostage rescue at Iran's London Embassy in 1980.***

**SPECIFICATION**

**MP5A2**
**Calibre:** 9 mm Parabellum
**Weight:** loaded 2.97 kg (6 lb 8 oz)
**Length:** 680 mm (26¾ in); length of barrel 225 mm (8⅞ in)
**Muzzle velocity:** 400 m (1,312 ft) per second
**Rate of fire:** 800 rpm cyclic
**Magazine:** 15- or 30-round box

**MP5K**
**Weight:** empty 2.1 kg (4 lb 7 oz)
**Length:** 325 mm (12⅘ in); length of barrel 115 mm (4½ in)
**Muzzle velocity:** 375 m (1,230 ft) per second
**Magazine:** 15- or 30-round box

**MP5SF**
**Calibre:** 0.40-in S&W
**Weight:** loaded 2.54 kg (5 lb 7 oz)
**Length:** 712 mm (28 in); length of barrel 225 mm (8⅞ in)
**Muzzle velocity:** 330 m (1,083 ft) per second
**Rate of fire:** semi-auto only

# Heckler & Koch MP5A3

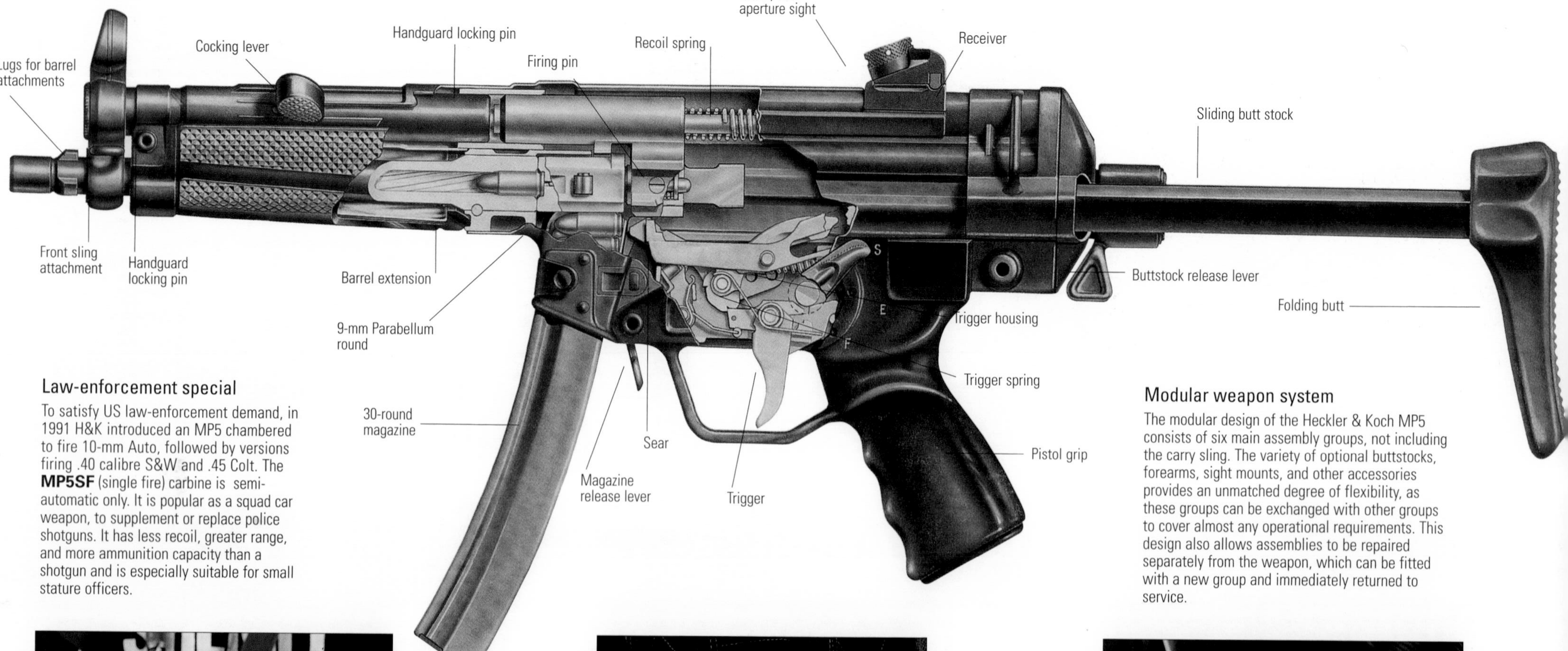


## Law-enforcement special

To satisfy US law-enforcement demand, in 1991 H&K introduced an MP5 chambered to fire 10-mm Auto, followed by versions firing .40 calibre S&W and .45 Colt. The **MP5SF** (single fire) carbine is semi-automatic only. It is popular as a squad car weapon, to supplement or replace police shotguns. It has less recoil, greater range, and more ammunition capacity than a shotgun and is especially suitable for small stature officers.

## Modular weapon system

The modular design of the Heckler & Koch MP5 consists of six main assembly groups, not including the carry sling. The variety of optional buttstocks, forearms, sight mounts, and other accessories provides an unmatched degree of flexibility, as these groups can be exchanged with other groups to cover almost any operational requirements. This design also allows assemblies to be repaired separately from the weapon, which can be fitted with a new group and immediately returned to service.

***Left:* Heckler & Koch have developed a whole range of accessories for the MP5. A variety of laser sights and torches have been developed for police use.**

***Right:* A selection of optional trigger groups allow for single fire only, full automatic, 2-round, and 3-round burst options. The selector switch is easy to use, even in gloves.**

***Right:* Magazine clips are a simple, cheap but very useful accessory. Full-size MP5s usually come with 15- or 30-round box magazines. Clipping together two magazines effectively doubles the MP5 user's firepower, enabling magazines to be changed and the weapon recharged in an instant.**

# Israel Military Industries Uzi
## Sub-machine gun

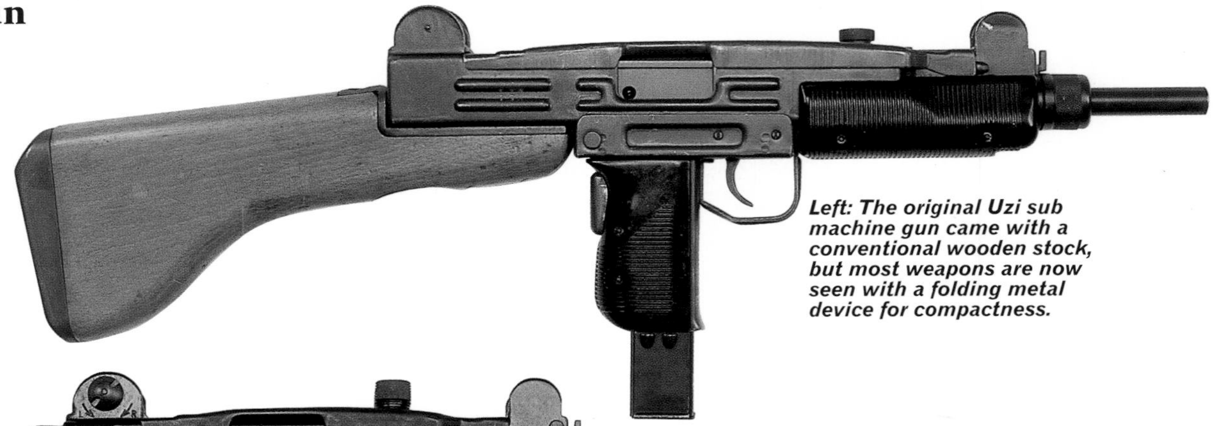

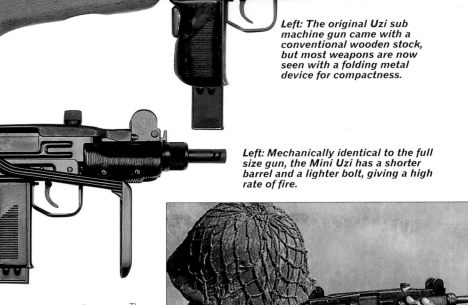

Left: ***The original Uzi sub machine gun came with a conventional wooden stock, but most weapons are now seen with a folding metal device for compactness.***

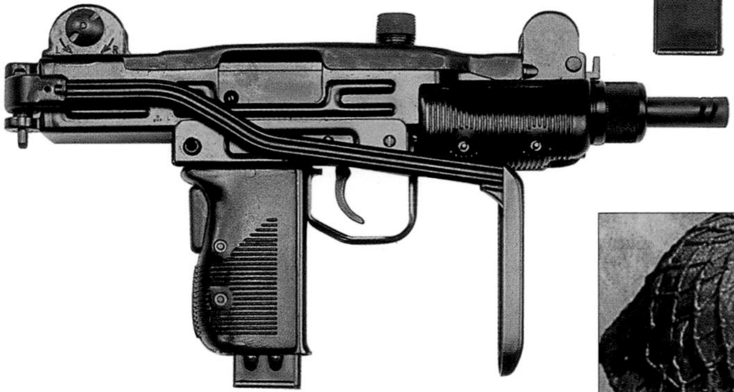

Left: ***Mechanically identical to the full size gun, the Mini Uzi has a shorter barrel and a lighter bolt, giving a high rate of fire.***

Even though its design dates back more than half a century, the **Uzi** remains one of the most effective sub-machine guns ever built. Named after designer Uziel Gal, the compact weapon was developed at a time when Israel was beset by enemies, yet had little in the way of manufacturing facilities. As a result the gun is largely made from cheap pressed-steel parts, easy to make and easy to maintain.

Gal was influenced by the pre-war Czech CZ 23. This featured a bolt that wrapped around the barrel, placing the mass well forward, while the breech remained at the rear. Although of short overall dimensions, the Uzi's barrel is actually longer than that of more conventional weapons.

### Cheaply made

The UZI is made largely from welded steel pressings. The main body is made from a single sheet of heavy gauge sheet steel, with grooves pressed into the sides to take any dust, dirt or sand that might get into the works. This simple feature makes the UZI capable of operation under even the most arduous conditions, and in military use it has gained an enviable reputation for reliability.

The barrel is secured to the body by a large nut just behind the muzzle. The trigger group is situated centrally, and the box magazine is inserted through the pistol grip. This makes reloading very easy in the dark, for 'hand will naturally find hand'. The normal combat magazine holds 32 rounds, but a common practice is to join two magazines together using a cross-over clip or tape to allow rapid changing. A grip safety is incorporated into the pistol grip, and a change lever just above the grip can be used to select semi-automatic (single-shot) fire. Originally built with a sturdy wooden butt stock, production was quickly switched to a version with a metal butt, which can be folded under the receiver to reduce overall length.

Even with the folding stock, there were many users who wanted an even more compact weapon. The **Mini-UZI** was developed by Israel Military Industries from the full scale UZI and differs from the original only in dimensions and weights. A few modifications have been introduced to the basic design, but these are only superficial while the operating system of the original has been retained unchanged. As the weapon is lighter than the full-size version, its breech block is lighter too and this provides a cyclic rate of fire of 950 rounds per minute, which is much higher than on the original. The most obvious difference is that the normal folding metal butt has been replaced by a single-strut butt stock that folds along the right hand side of the body. When folded the butt plate acts as a rudimentary foregrip.

### Reduced scale

The Micro-Uzi is even smaller, having been developed primarily for clandestine or security use. Barely larger than a heavy pistol, the small size and weight of the bolt would create an unacceptably high rate of fire, so a tungsten insert has been added to increase the mass. Even so, the Micro Uzi has a cyclic rate of more than 1,200 rounds per minute.

Other Uzi variants include the semi-automatic Carbine UZI, which has been produced to conform with the legal requirements of some American states that ban the private ownership of fully-automatic weapons. An Uzi pistol has also been developed.

The UZI became one of the symbols of Israeli military prowess, but Israel is not the only nation to use the type – it has been sold to police and military forces in at least 30 countries. The West German police and military forces bought large numbers of the gun, which was given the designation MP2. This model was produced under licence by FN in Belgium.

***Uzis fire from an open bolt, so they will never be blindingly accurate. However, at combat ranges they shoot straight enough to do the job.***

***Had he not been close enough to be tackled, would-be assassin John Hinckley would undoubtedly have been killed by the Uzis carried by President Ronald Reagan's Secret Service bodyguards.***

**SPECIFICATION**

**UZI**
**Calibre:** 9 mm (0.354 in) Parabellum
**Weight:** loaded with 32-round magazine 4.1 kg (9 lb)
**Length:** 650 mm (25.59 in) with wooden stock; 470 mm (18.5 in) with folding stock, retracted
**Length of barrel:** 260 mm (10 in)
**Muzzle velocity:** 400 m (1,312 ft) per second
**Effective range:** 200 m (656 ft)
**Cyclic rate of fire:** 600 rpm
**Magazine:** 25- or 32-round box

**Mini UZI**
**Calibre:** 9 mm (0.354 in) Parabellum
**Weight:** loaded with 20-round magazine 3.11 kg (6.85 lb)
**Length:** with stock extended 600 mm (24 in) and with stock folded 360 mm (14 in)
**Length of barrel:** 197 mm (7.75 in)
**Muzzle velocity:** 352 m (1,115 ft) per second
**Cyclic rate of fire:** 950 rpm
**Magazine:** 20-, 25- or 32-round box

# Beretta Model 12
## Sub-machine gun

***Left:** The PM12S can be distinguished from the earlier Model 12 by the single-lever fire-selector and safety. The white 'S' is for safe, 'I' is for semi-automatic and 'R' is for full-auto fire.*

***Below:** Although widely exported, the Model 12 and its derivatives were only issued to special operations units of the Italian army and security forces.*

During World War II, Beretta sub-machine guns were among the most highly-prized of all war trophies. They remained in service with both military and para-military formations for many years. After the war, Beretta introduced a new naming system, and post war weapons were known as the Models 4 and 5. The last of the variants on pre-war design came in 1949. It was extremely well-made – too well-made, in fact, since it was slow and expensive to produce.

### Modern design

During the 1950s, the company set about producing an entirely new submachine gun. The **Beretta Model 12** was introduced in 1958. This owed nothing to previous designs, and for the first time Beretta adopted the tubular receiver and stamped component construction that had long been employed by many other manufacturers.

Although it looked simple, the Model 12 was still a Beretta product, and was made to the customary high standard of finish and quality of manufacture.

The Model 12 was of fairly orthodox construction, although it was one of the earlier sub-machine guns to employ the 'wrap-around' or telescoping bolt that has now become commonplace. This allowed it to be short and handy, qualities enhanced by the fact that it could be fitted with a folding metal stock as well as a fixed stock. It was chambered for the 9-mm Parabellum cartridge which it took from a 20, 30 or 40 round magazine.

### Overseas sales

The Model 12 was a commercial success, sold extensively to nations in South America, Africa, the Middle East and Southeast Asia. Beretta was able to negotiate licence production of the Model 12 in Indonesia and Brazil for local sales and export. However, the Italian armed forces, who bought the weapon in 1961, acquired relatively small numbers, primarily for use by special units.

Production of the model 12 continued until 1978, when it was replaced by the improved Model 12S. Externally the Model 12S looks very like the Model 12 but there are some detail differences. The most obvious is the epoxy-resin finish, making the metal resistant to corrosion and wear.

The fire selector mechanism on the Model 12 was of the 'push through' type, operated by pushing a button from either side of the receiver just over the pistol grip. The Type 12S has a conventional single-lever mechanism with a safety catch that locks both the trigger and the grip safety.

### Modifications

The folding butt now has a more positive lock for both the open and the closed positions, and some changes have been made to the sights. One laudable feature that has been carried over from the original Model 12 is the retention of the raised grooves that run along each side of the tubular receiver. These grooves act as catchers for any dirt or debris that find their way into the interior, and enable the Model 12S to operate under adverse conditions.

The Model 12S has been purchased by the Italian armed forces and by several other armies. A production licence was taken out by FN of Herstal, Belgium, and the type is also manufactured by Forjas Taurus of Brazil.

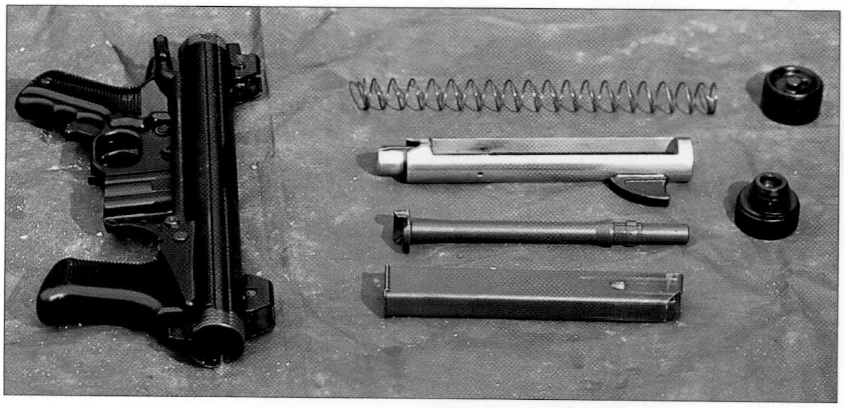

***Very different from pre-war Beretta designs, the Model 12 uses heavy sheet metal stampings to form the magazine housing and receiver.***

**SPECIFICATION**

**Beretta Model 12S**
**Calibre:** 9 mm (0.354 in) Parabellum
**Weight:** loaded with 32-round magazine 3.81 kg (8.4 lb)
**Length:** with stock extended 660 mm (26 in) and with stock folded 418 mm (16.45 in)
**Length of barrel:** 200 mm (7.87 in)
**Muzzle velocity:** 381 m/1,250 ft per second
**Cyclic rate of fire:** 500-550 rpm
**Magazine:** 20-, 32- or 40-round box

# Spectre Sub-machine gun

Created by the SITES company of Italy from the late 1970s and first offered for sale in 1983, the **Spectre** sub-machine gun is a capable weapon that is somewhat underrated and has therefore failed to gain the commercial success that its technical capabilities should have commanded. The weapon was designed for the close-range role, as are all sub-machine guns, but optimised for the police and anti-terrorist tasks rather than the battlefield role. This optimisation led to the evolution of a weapon notable for its compact overall dimensions, capability for being brought into action at a moment's notice, and high degree of safety in carriage and operation.

The Spectre has been offered in four forms as the **Spectre HC** semi-automatic pistol, **Spectre H4** fully automatic sub-machine gun, **Spectre PCC** with a 230 mm (9.06 in) barrel fitted with a silencer, and **Spectre Carbine** that has reached only prototype form with a 407-mm (16.02-in) barrel.

## Easy concealment

The Spectre is designed for maximum capability rather than lowest cost, even though its price is still lower than that of 'blue-ribband' weapons such as the Heckler & Koch MP5. It has a stamped steel receiver, polymer grips and a butt that folds flat over the top of the receiver and barrel jacked without protrusions that could catch in clothing, and then unfolds upward and rearward to lock into position as a brace against the shoulder.

The Spectre is a recoil-operated weapon that fires from a closed bolt, and is hammer-fired. Both of these are factors that enhance the weapon's safety. The weapon's action is controlled by two springs, and the fact that it fires from a closed bolt also enhances the weapon's stability when firing, in which there is a significantly lower level of vibration and muzzle climb than in most other sub-machine guns. The trigger group is more characteristic of the typical semi-automatic pistol than the standard type of sub-machine gun, and the trigger is of the double-action variety, the only known instance of this in a sub-machine gun. There is no manual safety on the weapon, but rather a de-cocking lever, whose use makes the accidental discharge of the weapon impossible. The Spectre can therefore be carried safely with a round in the chamber and the hammer down, but then be fired without delay by pressure on the trigger.

***Above:* The Spectre sub-machine gun is shown here as a silenced weapon, but in typical sales format with the high-capacity magazine removed from its housing in the fore grip.**

***Left:* The provision of two grips and a shoulder stock combines with the weapon's action to make the Spectre easy to hold on the target even when firing in full automatic mode.**

***Below:* Men of an African country's army receive instruction in the firing of the Spectre, which is a safe and highly cost-effective weapon of the sub-machine class but optimised for para-military service.**

### SPECIFICATION

**Spectre H4**
**Calibre:** 9-mm (0.354-in)
**Length overall:** 580 mm (22.835 in) with stock extended and 350 mm (13.78 in) with stock closed
**Length of barrel:** 130 mm (5.12 in)
**Weight:** 2.9 kg (6.39 lb)
**Muzzle velocity:** not available
**Rate of fire, cyclic:** 850 rounds per minute
**Feed:** 30- or 50-round straight box magazine

## Cooling arrangement

A particular feature of the bolt is that its action doubles as an air pump to drive air through the the barrel's shroud and thus improve the cooling of the barrel and action when long bursts are fired. Another notable feature embodied in the overall design of the Spectre is the compact magazine. This carries four rows of cartridges in an arrangement that makes the magazine comparatively wide but also fairly short: the 50-round magazine of the Spectre is about the same length as the 30-round magazine of the MP5. This is a notable advantage when concealed carriage of the weapon is desirable.

In an effort to maximise the Spectre's sales potential, the manufacturer also offers the weapon in calibres other than the standard 9-mm (0.354-in) Parabellum – these including 0.4-in (10.16-mm) S&W and 0.45-in (11.43-in) ACP.

# m/45 Sub-machine gun

The 9-mm (0.354-in) **m/45** sub-machine gun was originally produced by the Karl Gustav Stads Gevärsfaktori (now part of the FFV consortium), and is thus widely known as the **Carl Gustav**. The m/45 is an entirely orthodox design with no frills, and uses a simple tubular receiver and barrel cover with a simple folding butt hinged onto the pistol grip assembly. The usual blowback operating principle is employed, and in overall terms there is nothing remarkable about the m/45.

But the weapon does have one interesting point, namely its magazine. On many sub-machine guns the magazine is usually one of the most trouble-prone components, for the magazine relies upon simple spring pressure to push the rounds towards the receiver, whence they are fed into the firing system. It is all too easy for rounds to become misaligned or forced together, and the result is then a misfeed or jam, which can happen at inopportune moments in combat. On the original m/45 the magazine was that once used on the Suomi Model 37-39 of the period before World War II, a 50-round magazine considered at the time to be one of the best in use. But in 1948 a new magazine was introduced: this held 36 rounds in twin rows that were carefully tapered into a single row by the use of a wedge cross-section.

***Used by many countries, including Egypt (in the 1967 war with Israel) and the USA (in a silenced version by special forces in Vietnam), the Carl Gustav remains in large-scale service with the Swedish forces.***

***The m/45 is often known as the Carl Gustav. The weapon has been in service since 1945, and has been exported widely. The 9-mm (0.354-in) Parabellum round is known as the m/39B in Sweden.***

### Problem-free feed

This new magazine proved to be remarkably reliable and trouble-free in use, and was soon being widely copied elsewhere. Production examples of the m/45 were soon being offered with a revised magazine housing to accommodate either the Suomi magazine or the new wedge-shaped magazine, and this version was known as the **m/45B**. Later production models made provision for the wedge-shaped magazine only.

The m/45 and m/45B became one of Sweden's few major export weapons. Numbers were sold to Denmark and some other nations such as Eire. Egypt produced a licensed version of the m/45B as the **Port Said**, and copies were also produced in Indonesia. Perhaps the oddest service use of the m/45B was in Vietnam. Numbers of these weapons were obtained by the Central Intelligence Agency and converted in the USA with a special silenced barrel. These weapons were used in action in Vietnam by the US Special Forces on undercover missions. According to most reports the silencers were not particularly effective, and the weapons did not survive long in service.

Numerous accessories have been produced for the m/45, one of the oddest being a muzzle attachment that doubles as a blank firing device or a short-range target training device. The attachment is used with special plastic bullets which for safety are shredded as they leave the muzzle. These bullets generate enough gas pressure to operate the mechanism and if required enough pressure is available to project a steel ball from the attachment itself. This reusable steel ball can thus be used for short-range target practice.

**SPECIFICATION**

**m/45B**
**Calibre:** 9-mm (0.354-in)
**Length:** 808 mm (31.8 in) with butt extended and 551 mm (21.7 in) with butt folded
**Length of barrel:** 213 mm (8.385 in)
**Weight:** loaded 4.2 kg (9.25 lb)
**Muzzle velocity:** 365 m (1,198 ft) per second
**Rate of fire, cyclic:** 550-600 rounds per minute
**Feed:** 36-round straight box magazine

# Z-84 Sub-machine gun

The **Z-84** sub-machine gun was developed in the mid-1980s by the Star Bonifacio Echeverria SA company of Spain as successor to the Z-62 and Z-70B but, unlike these weapons, probably chambered only for the 9-mm (0.354-in) Parabellum round.

Compact, light and comfortable to handle and fire, the Z-84 is of modern concept and construction with a two-piece stamped steel receiver and the magazine housing built into the forward grip. The weapon works on the blowback principle, and has a wrap-around bolt that sleeves round the barrel for most of the bolt's length. The bolt travels on two guide rails, and the good clearance between the bolt and the inside of the receiver ensures that the weapon continues to work even when highly fouled.

### Safety features

The weapon fires from an open bolt, the safety is located inside the trigger guard to the rear of the trigger to lock the trigger when engaged and other safety features include interceptor notches on the bolt to catch the bolt if the cocking handle slips while the weapon is being cocked, and an inertia lock to hold the bolt in its forward position. On the left-hand side of the receiver is a fire selector offering single-shot or automatic fire.

**SPECIFICATION**

**Z-84**
**Calibre:** 9-mm (0.354-in)
**Length overall:** 615 mm (24.21 in) with stock extended and 410 mm (16.14 in) with stock folded
**Length of barrel:** 215 mm (8.465 in)
**Weight:** empty 3 kg (6.61 lb)
**Muzzle velocity:** not available
**Rate of fire, cyclic:** 600 rounds per minute
**Feed:** 25- or 30-round straight box magazine

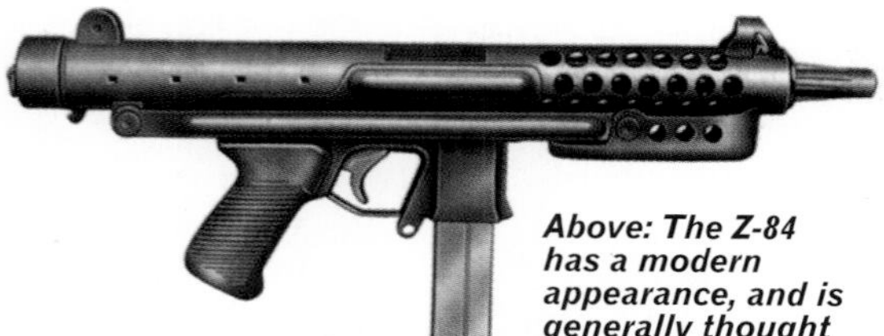

***Above: The Z-84 has a modern appearance, and is generally thought to be an excellent, safe and reliable weapon for military and police service.***

***Below: The Z-84 has thought to be easy to handle, and is sighted to 200 m (220 yards). The weapon is seen here with its but in the open position.***

# 9-mm L2A3 Sterling

## Sub-machine gun

***Replacing the ubiquitous Sten in British Army service, the Sterling 9-mm sub-machine gun, seen here with the stock extended, has proved effective and reliable under the most extreme conditions.***

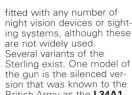

The sub-machine gun that is now almost universally known as the **Sterling** entered British Army use in 1955, although an earlier form, known as the **Patchett**, underwent troop trials during the latter stages of World War II. It was intended that the Patchett would replace the Sten gun, but in the event the Sten lasted in service until well into the 1960s.

The British Army model was designated the **L2A3** and equated to the **Sterling Mk 4** produced commercially by the Sterling Armament Company of Dagenham, Essex. This weapon is one of the major export successes of the post-war years, for it was sold to over 90 countries and in 2002 it remained in production in India. The basic service model is of simple design with the usual tubular receiver and a folding metal butt stock, but where the Sterling differs from many other designs is that it uses a curved box magazine that protrudes to the left. This arrangement has proved to be efficient in use and it has certainly created no problems for the army in India, or in Canada where the design was produced as the **C1** with some slight modifications.

### Blowback operation

The Sterling is a simple blowback weapon with a heavy bolt, but this bolt incorporates one of the best features of the design in that it has raised and inclined splines that help to remove any internal dust or dirt and push it out of the way. This enables the Sterling to be used under the worst possible conditions. The usual magazine holds 34 rounds, but a 10-round magazine is available along with a string of accessories including a bayonet. The weapon can be fitted with any number of night vision devices or sighting systems, although these are not widely used. Several variants of the Sterling exist. One model of the gun is the silenced version that was known to the British Army as the **L34A1**.

This uses a fixed silencer system allied to a special barrel that allows the firing gases to leak through the sides of the barrel into a rotary baffle silencer that is remarkably efficient and almost silent in use. There is also a whole range of what are known as paratrooper's pistols that use only the pistol group and the receiver allied to a short magazine and a very short barrel. These are available in single-shot or machine pistol versions.

The Sterling in all its forms has proven to be a very reliable and sturdy weapon. With many armies the weapon has been used to arm second-line personnel who do not have to carry normal service rifles, and on vehicles it can easily be folded away to take up very little stowage space. With the British Army the L2A3 was slowly replaced by the 5.56-mm (0.219-in) Individual Weapon, but the large numbers of Sterlings still around the world mean that it will remain a widely used type for some years to come.

***The Sterling saw considerable service in Malaya and Borneo, where the inherent inaccuracy of the sub-machine gun proved no handicap.***

***The Sterling is seen on exercise in the UK, at Bassingbourn. The Sterling was replaced by the improved 5.56-mm L85 Individual Weapon.***

**SPECIFICATION**

| L2A3 | L34A1 |
|---|---|
| **Calibre:** 9 mm (0.354 in) | **Calibre:** 9 mm (0.354 in) |
| **Weight:** 3.47 kg (7.65 lb) | **Weight:** loaded 3.6 kg (7.93 lb) |
| **Length:** with stock extended 690 mm (27.16 in) and with stock folded 483 mm (19 in) | **Length:** with stock extended 864 mm (34 in) and with stock folded 660 mm (26 in) |
| **Length of barrel:** 198 mm (7.88 in) | **Length of barrel:** 198 mm (7.88 in) |
| **Muzzle velocity:** 390 m (1,280 ft) per second | **Muzzle velocity:** 293-310 m (961-1,017 ft) per second |
| **Cyclic rate of fire:** 550 rpm | **Cyclic rate of fire:** 515-565 rpm |
| **Magazine:** 10- or 34-round box | **Magazine:** 34-round box |

# Ingram Model 10 9-mm and 0.45-in sub-machine gun

There have been few weapons that have 'enjoyed' the attentions of the Press and Hollywood to such an extent as that lavished on the Ingram sub-machine guns. Gordon B. Ingram had designed a whole string of sub-machine guns before he produced his **Ingram Model 10**, which was originally intended to be used with the Sionics Company suppressor. First produced during the mid-1960s, the diminutive Ingram Model 10 soon attracted a great deal of public attention because of its rate of fire, coupled with the highly efficient sound suppressor.

Hollywood and television films added their dramatic commentaries and the Ingram Model 10 soon became almost as widely known as the old Thompson sub-machine guns of the 1920s.

## Exceptional weapon

The Ingram Model 10 is indeed a remarkable weapon. It is constructed from sheet metal but manufactured to a very high standard and is extremely robust. This has to be, for it fires at a cyclic rate of over 1,000 rounds per minute, yet control of the weapon is still relatively easy thanks to the good balance imparted by the centrally-placed pistol group through which the box magazine is inserted. Most versions have a folding metal butt but this may be removed, and many weapons not fitted with the long tubular suppressor use a forward webbing hand-strap as a rudimentary foregrip. The muzzle on most models is threaded to accommodate the suppressor, and when fitted this is covered with a heat-resistant canvas or plastic webbing to allow it to be used as a forward grip. The cocking handle is on top of the slab-sided receiver and when turned through 90° acts as a safety lock. As this handle is slotted for sighting purposes the firer can soon notice if this safety is applied, and there is a normal trigger safety as well.

***Ingram fire selection is determined by the pressure put on the trigger: the initial pressure produces single shots, whilst more pressure gives automatic fire.***

## Model 10

The Model 10 may be encountered chambered for either the well-known 0.45-in (11.43-mm) cartridge or the more usual 9-mm (0.354-in) Parabellum. The latter round may also be used on the smaller **Model 11** which is normally chambered for the less powerful 9-mm Short (0.380 ACP). In all these calibres the Ingram is a dreadfully efficient weapon and unsurprisingly it has been sold widely to customers ranging from paramilitary forces to bodyguard and security agencies.

## Covert operators

Military sales on any large scale have been few but several nations have acquired numbers for 'testing and evaluation'. The British SAS is known to have obtained a small quantity for testing. Sales have not been encouraged by the fact that the ownership and manufacturing rights have changed hands several times, but both the Model 10 and Model 11 are now effectively back in production as the **Cobray M11**. This, again, is available in either 9-mm Short or 9-mm Parabellum versions. In order to keep sales rolling several variants of the basic Ingram design were made. Versions firing single-shot only and without the folding butt are available, and at one point a long-barrelled version was produced, though only in limited numbers as the type did not find a ready market.

In the meantime Ingrams can be found in countries as diverse as Greece, Israel and Portugal, while the weapon is also retained in small numbers by the US Navy. Many of these weapons been sold to Central and South American nations, including Bolivia, Colombia, Guatemala, Honduras and Venezuela.

**SPECIFICATION**

| | |
|---|---|
| **Model 10 (0.45-in model)** | **Length of barrel:** 146 mm (5.75 in) |
| **Calibre:** 0.45 in (11.43 mm) | **Length of suppressor:** 291 mm (11.46 in) |
| **Weight:** loaded with 30-round magazine 3.818 kg (8.4 lb) | **Muzzle velocity:** 280 m (918 ft) per second |
| **Length:** with stock extended 548 mm (21.575 in) and with stock folded 269 mm (10.59 in) | **Cyclic rate of fire:** 1,145 rpm |
| | **Magazine:** 30-round box |

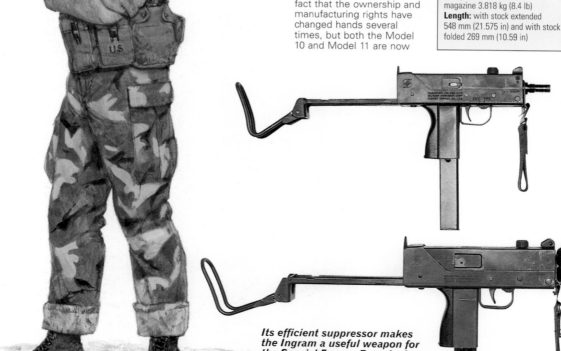

***The Ingram Model 11 (top) is chambered for 9-mm Short (0.380 ACP), while the Model 10 (below), fitted with a suppressor, can be chambered for either 9-mm Parabellum or 0.45 ACP. Both weapons are relatively well balanced due to the bolt enveloping the breech.***

***Its efficient suppressor makes the Ingram a useful weapon for the Special Forces. By reducing the escaping gas to subsonic speed and eliminating flash, the position of the firer can remain a mystery to the target, until hopefully it is too late.***

# Ruger Rifles

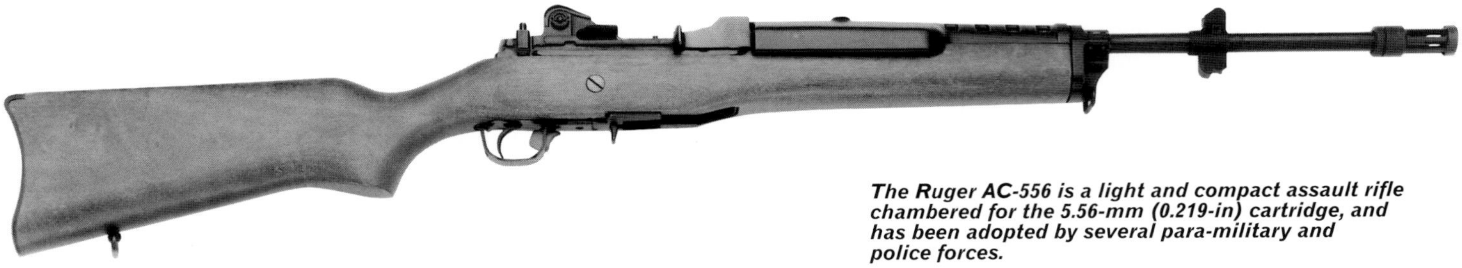

*The Ruger AC-556 is a light and compact assault rifle chambered for the 5.56-mm (0.219-in) cartridge, and has been adopted by several para-military and police forces.*

Storm, Ruger & Co., Inc of Southport in the American state of Connecticut is a comparative newcomer by the standards of most other well-established arms manufacturers. It has, however, pursued a steady course of enlarging its range of small arms to suit a whole host of civil, police, security/para-military and military applications in weapons types ranging from revolvers to assault rifles via semi-automatic pistols and shotguns. The hallmarks of Ruger weapons are the use of the best available materials and excellence of manufacture in combination with superb finish.

One of the simplest of the weapons for police, para-military and military use is the **Ruger Model 77** rifle, a weapon based closely on the German Gewehr 98 bolt-action rifle. The variant that has seen limited military use is the **Model 77V**, the 'varmint' rifle used for sniping. This is generally chambered for the NATO standard 7.62-mm (0.3-in) x 51 cartridge, of which five are accommodated in the integral magazine, although it can be delivered in forms chambered for other cartridges, and has a manually operated safety on the rear of the bolt. The 4.08-kg (9-lb) weapon entered production in 1968, and has an overall length of 1118 mm (44 in) including a 610-mm (24-in) barrel. The Model 77V has a heavy barrel and no 'iron' sights, invariably being used with a telescopic sight.

*The Mini-14 and its developments can accept various sizes of magazine, and incorporate on the upper part of their bodies Ruger's patented mounting for the high-accuracy installation of a telescopic sight.*

## Well-proved action

Developed in the early 1970s and placed in production just before the middle of the decade, the **Mini-14** is, as its name suggests, a development of the gas-operating system embodied in the M14 (and therefore the M1 Garand from which this was developed), but scaled down to fire the 5.56-mm (0.219-in) x 45 M193 NATO cartridge. The objective was to create a sturdy yet light rifle, and the required weight reduction was achieved by the use of high-tensile steels that permitted many of the components to be made less bulky than they would have been if less strong materials had been used.

The weapon was intended primarily as a hunting rifle, but was readily accepted by police and para-military services because of its useful round, light weight and its 5-, 20- and even 30-round magazines. This led the manufacturer to create a dedicated military version as the **K-Mini/14-20GB** with a bayonet fixing attachment, flash suppressor at the muzzle, heat-resistant glassfibre hand guard and, in a more specialised model, a pistol grip and a folding stock. Still further development of the same basic concept led to the **AC-556**, which was created specifically for the para-military and military roles with a selective-fire mechanism providing an automatic fire capability at a cyclic rate of 750 rounds per minute.

In an effort to widen its customer base and thereby generate additional sales, Ruger in 1987 introduced the Mini-30, which is is essence the Mini-14 re-calibred for the Soviet 7.62-mm (0.3-in) x 39 M1943 cartridge. This offers better capabilities for the hunting role than the American M193 cartridge, and the fact that the weapon was aimed at the hunting market was indicated by the provision of only a five-round magazine. with a weight of 3.26 kg (7.2 lb) and an overall length of 948 mm (37.33 in). The Mini-30 semi-automatic rifle has been adopted by some police forces. The weapon is reliable and, with a telescopic sight attached on Ruger's patented sight mount, more accurate than most rifles of this type.

*Although the British soldier in the foreground is armed with a standard military rifle, the officer of the Royal Ulster Constabulary by the Land Rover is armed with a Mini-14 variant.*

**SPECIFICATIONS**

**Ruger AC-556**
**Calibre:** 5.56-mm (0.219-in)
**Length overall:** 946 mm (37.25 in)
**Length of barrel:** 470 mm (18.5 in)
**Weight:** 2.9 kg (6.4 lb)
**Muzzle velocity:** not available
**Rate of fire, cyclic:** 750 rounds per minute
**Feed:** 5-, 20- and 30-round straight box magazine

**Ruger Mini-30**
**Calibre:** 7.62-mm (0.3-in)
**Length overall:** 948 mm (37.33 in)
**Length of barrel:** 470 mm (18.5 in)
**Weight:** 3.26 kg (7.2 lb)
**Muzzle velocity:** not available
**Feed:** 5-round box magazine

# AKSU Sub-machine gun

*The AKSU, otherwise known as the AKS-74U, is the sub-machine gun development of the AKS-74, and was created as a weapon to arm the personnel of armoured vehicles as well as other specialised and second-line troops.*

Just as the major armies of the West switched from the full-calibre 7.62-mm (0.3-in) cartridge to the smaller 5.56-mm (0.219-in) cartridge better suited to the shorter-range engagements that had been recognised as typical of modern infantry combat, the USSR switched from its 7.62-mm (0.3-in) x 39 M1943 cartridge to the 5.45-mm (0.215-in) x 39 M1974 cartridge; this was both lighter and lower-powered than its predecessor. This required the development and introduction of a new series of weapons chambered for the smaller cartridge. As they were content with the basic performance and capabilities of their current Kalashnikov assault rifle in its AK-47 standard and product-improved AKM forms, they opted for the simplest course, namely the scaling down of the basic Kalashnikov concept to chamber the new round.

The result was the **AK-74** and folding-stock **AKS-74** that were adopted in 1974. The weapons have the same gas-operated action and rotary bolt as the AKM, and though sighted to 1000 m (1,095 yards), they are typically used only at ranges considerably shorter than this. The AK-74 and AKS-74 have been produced in very large numbers for the Soviet forces and the armies of the USSR's allies and adherents, both within and outside of the Warsaw Pact organisation, and in combat have revealed themselves to be formidable rivals to the American M16 series of assault rifles. The Soviet arms are slightly less accurate than the M16, but provide somewhat better reliability and robustness and well as the capacity for easier battlefield cleaning and maintenance.

## Weapon development

Though happy with the AK-74 and AKS-74 for their infantry, the Soviets appreciated that specialised troops, such as tank crews, signallers and artillery crews, as well as second-line troops, needed a more compact weapon. This led to the development of the **AKSU**, otherwise known as the **AKS-74U**. This is generally regarded more as a sub-machine gun than as a short assault rifle, and is known to those armed with it as the 'spitter'. Like its longer half-brother, the AKSU is reliable and easy to maintain, but is not notably accurate and therefore suited more to the requirements of troops than to those of security and police organisations.

There have also been a large number of other developments based on the Kalashnikov gas-operated action with a rotary two-lug bolt. The **AK-101**, for example, was designed in an effort to boost international sales and is basically a development of the AK-47 to chamber the 5.56-mm x 45 NATO cartridge. This results in a weapon 943 mm (37.125 in) long with its butt extended and 700 mm (27.56 in) long with the butt folded. The weapon has a 415-mm (16.34-in) barrel and a weight of 3.4 kg (7.5 lb), and fires from a 30-round magazine at a cyclic rate of 600 rounds per minute.

The same basic desire to expand the market for Russian small arms has led to other developments, such as the **AK-103** that is in effect the AK-47 chambered for the 7.62-mm x 39 NATO cartridge but also incorporating a number of improvements suggested by operational experience as well as the availability of better materials and manufacturing techniques. The **AK-102**, **AK-104** and **AK-105** are variants of the same basic compact design chambered for the 5.56-mm x 45, 7.62-mm x 39 and 5.45-mm x 39 cartridges respectively, all fired from a 30-round magazine, and their data includes an empty weight of 3 kg (6.61 lb) and length of 824 mm (32.44 in) with the stock extended and 586 mm (23.07 in) with the stock folded. The barrel is 314 mm (12.36 in) long and the cyclic rate of fire is 600 rounds per minute.

The 5.45-mm **AK-107** and 5.56-mm **AK-108** are more advanced in basic concept as they work on the basis of a balanced operating system with two pistons operating in opposite directions (one driving the bolt carrier and the other a compensating mass) so that the weapons' centres of gravity are not altered as they fire. This greatly improves accuracy and reduces muzzle climb.

### SPECIFICATION

**AKS-74U**
**Calibre:** 5.45-mm (0.215-in)
**Length overall:** 735 mm (28.94 in) with the stock extended and 490 mm (12.29 in) with the stock folded
**Length of barrel:** 210 mm (8.27 in)
**Weight:** empty 2.71 kg (5.97lb)
**Muzzle velocity:** not available
**Rate of fire, cyclic:** not available
**Feed:** 20- or 30-round curved box magazine

**AK-107 and AK-108**
**Calibre:** 5.56-mm (0.219-in)
**Length overall:** 943 mm (37.13 in) with the stock extended and 700 mm (27.56 in) with the stock folded
**Length of barrel:** 415 mm (16.34 in)
**Weight:** 3.4 kg (7.5 lb)
**Muzzle velocity:** not available
**Rate of fire, cyclic:** 850 rounds per minute for the AK-107 and 900 rounds per minute for the AK-108
**Feed:** 30-round curved box magazine

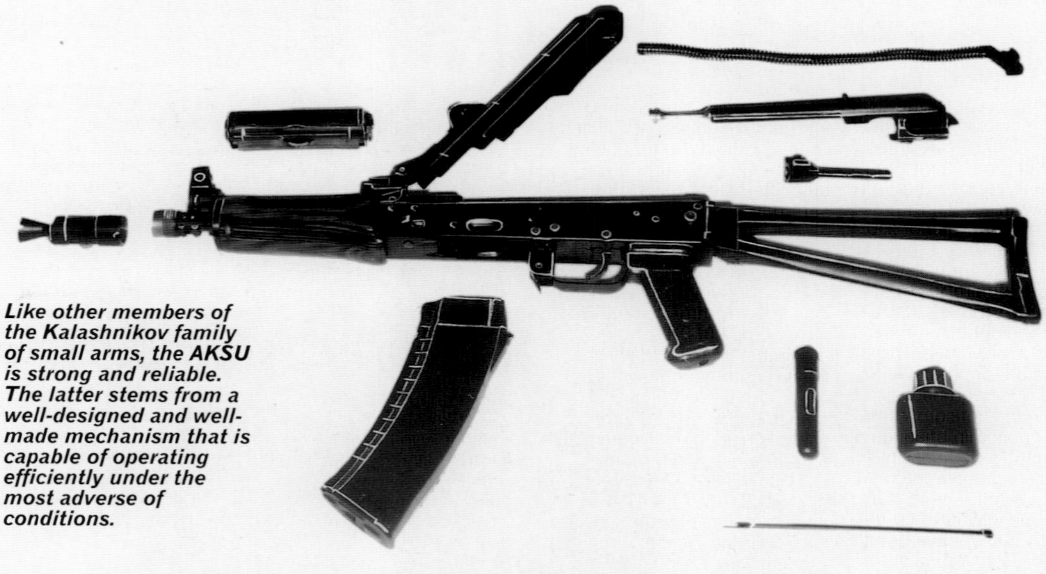

*Like other members of the Kalashnikov family of small arms, the AKSU is strong and reliable. The latter stems from a well-designed and well-made mechanism that is capable of operating efficiently under the most adverse of conditions.*

# Rifles

**In the 100 years from the end of the 19th century, the rifle was transformed from a long-range and highly accurate killing instrument, firing a high-powered cartridge, into a medium-range weapon capable of some accuracy but designed more for the generation of suppressive fire. Developed via the sub-machine gun, such assault rifles often fire only an intermediate-power round.**

*The current British service rifle is the L85, also known as the SA80. This fires the 5.56-mm NATO round, and although it has revealed problems of serviceability and maintenance, it is basically an excellent weapon with a good optical sight.*

When the British won the Battle of Omdurman against the Sudanese dervishes in 1898, it was partially as a result of their use of the new 0.303-in (7.7-mm) rifle, which shot down Sudanese spearmen at the unprecedentedly great range of 915 m (1,000 yards) and more. The lesson was underlined a year later at the opposite end of the continent – although this time the boot was on the other foot. In 1899 the British suffered a series of unexpected defeats against the volunteer riflemen of the Boer republics. Once again, attacks were broken up at long range by magazine-loading bolt-action rifles.

The British army learned to manoeuvre in small units, up-and-coming officers like Sir Douglas Haig pressing for more machine-guns to supplement rifle firepower, and Major Baden-Powell urging the adoption of an automatic rifle after his experiences with the Scots Guards in South Africa. In the event, the army was not allowed to buy the machine-guns it wanted, so when war with Germany began in 1914 British soldiers were reliant more than ever on the rifles of their long-service regulars, a high proportion of whom had worked to win the marksman's badge and the extra pay that went with it. Germany's first-line soldiers discovered between August and December 1914 that the rifle power of the British Expeditionary Force was truly formidable.

## Shorter combat range

With the onset of winter, the rival front-line troops dug in, beginning four years of trench warfare on the Western Front. This ended the dominance of the rifle. In the confines of the trenches, or fighting from shell hole to shell hole, 'bombs' (hand grenades) were better than bullets. In 1914 the rifle companies that made up the infantry battalions of every Western army had been armed with rifles. During World War I they evolved into far more complex units mixing grenades (hand- and rifle-launched), machine-guns (light and then sub-machine guns), and even mortars. Although the majority of the infantry company's men still carried rifles, many were there primarily to carry ammunition for the machine-guns and other weapons. The infantry tactics of 1916-17 (fire and manoeuvre co-operation of 'rifle groups' and 'gun groups') have not really changed since then.

Most armies of World War II issued their infantrymen with rifles little changed from those of 1914-18. Though the experience of the trenches was not repeated on anything like the same scale, the ranges at which soldiers fought each other hardly varied from those of World War I, namely a few hundred yards. The Americans introduced a self-loading rifle as its standard infantry weapon on the eve of the war. The Germans and Soviets used small numbers of similar

*In all of its forms, the Lee-Enfield bolt-action rifle in 0.303-in (7.7-mm) calibre served the British army with distinction through two world wars. Seen here in the European fighting typical of the period late in World War II, these are Rifle No. 1 Mk III* weapons.*

*The German equivalent of the Lee-Enfield was the Mauser Gewehr 98 in 7.92-mm (0.312-in) calibre. Another bolt-action rifle, in this instance fed from a five- rather than 10-round magazine, the rifle was accurate, very sturdy and wholly safe to use.*

weapons, but neither provided superiority in the struggle on the Eastern Front. Here, both sides made extensive use of sub-machine guns, pre-war anxieties about excessive ammunition expenditure by automatic weapons giving way to the reality of the battlefield. Volume of fire was often more important than individual accuracy, suppressing the enemy's fire so that the troops could close the position and storm it with grenades and sub-machine guns.

Both the Germans and Soviets worked on combining the best features of the sub-machine gun and rifle, the former being limited by its use of pistol ammunition and the latter by being too powerful. The answer was an intermediate-power cartridge for use in the 'assault rifle', as the Germans christened their new infantry weapon. This was handier for close ranges but able to shoot with reasonable accuracy out to the 300/500-m zone at which most infantry combats took place.

The Sturmgewehr 44 and its Soviet conceptual successor, the AK-47, were designed to fire intermediate-power cartridges, but the post-war West German army adopted the G3 assault rifle, firing a full-power 7.62-mm x 51 cartridge. So too did the most successful European rifle of the post-war period, the Belgian FAL. Neither weapon is really controllable in automatic fire, and some users adapted their weapons for single-shot only. The most successful American rifle design of all time began life as a full-power 7.62-mm weapon: Eugene Stoner's AR-10 Armalite. This was the ancestor of the AR-15, now the M16. To make it lighter, the AR-10 was reworked to fire a 0.223-in round. This evolved into the 5.56-mm NATO standard rifle bullet that tends to tumble and cause terrible injuries, if not death. When the Soviets adopted a smaller-calibre version of the AK-47 in the 1970s, their 5.45-mm bullet was observed to have an even greater chance of tumbling; this was not a ballistic accident but cold calculation.

*Following the point man with an M1 carbine are three US infantrymen with M1 rifles.*

*The standard US personal weapon of the Vietnam War was the M16 assault rifle.*

### Infantryman's friend

In the space of 100 years the infantryman's weapon has evolved from a long-range precision killing instrument to something closer to a sub-machine gun. Though professional soldiers have voiced fears that such rifles demand too much ammunition, 20th century history teaches that it is cheaper to spend bullets rather than manpower in capturing a position.

## WEIGHT: A CRITICAL FACTOR

**The infantryman has always entered battle weighed down by equipment. In the days of linear tactical dispositions and only limited movement, this was not a factor of overriding significance. In more modern times, though, the infantryman has become increasingly burdened by the impedimenta of modern warfare, and at the same time been expected to move farther and faster even when he is delivered onto the battlefield by a vehicle such as an armoured personnel carrier. Thus the reduction of equipment volume and weight have become increasingly important. The well-established German G3 rifle of 7.62-mm (0.3-in) calibre weighs 4.25 kg (9.37 lb), and a loaded 20-round magazine weighs 0.625 or 0.753 kg (1.38 or 1.68 lb) depending on whether it is of steel or aluminium construction: thus the rifle and 200 rounds can weigh up to 11.78 kg (25.97 lb). More modern rifles are smaller, less heavy and fire lighter ammunition: the 5.56-mm (0.219-in) French FA MAS, for example, weighs 3.38 kg (7.45 lb) and its loaded 25-round magazine 0.425 kg (0.94 lb), so the rifle and 200 rounds turn the scales at a more manageable 6.78 kg (14.95 lb).**

*Infantry rifles of the 1950s, firing a powerful full-calibre round, are exemplified by the Belgian FN FAL and its host of licensed derivatives such as the British L1, which weighs 11.68 kg (25.75 lb) complete with ten 20-round magazines.*

# Mannlicher Modell 1895 Rifle

***The Mannlicher Modell 1895 was the standard service rifle of the Austro-Hungarian army and fired a 6.5-mm (0.256-in) cartridge. It was a sound and strong weapon with a five-round box magazine and a straight-pull bolt action. The projection under the muzzle is a cleaning rod.***

By the early 1890s the Austro-Hungarian army was using a number of types of rifle based on the bolt action designed by Ferdinand von Mannlicher. This employed a straight-pull bolt action of two-piece construction, and the first of the type was taken into service as early as 1884. There followed a number of models with various modifications, all of them firing the old black-powder propellant, and it was 1890 before the first 'smokeless' model appeared. It was not until 1895 that the design was finally 'frozen' and it was thus that the **Mannlicher Modell 1895**, also known as the **8-mm Repetier Gewehr Modell 1895** (8-mm repeating rifle model 1895), became the standard rifle of the Austro-Hungarian army.

The Modell 1895 was a sound and straightforward weapon that proved reliable in service. Like so many other rifles of the period, the Modell 1895 was rather long but the straight-pull bolt action appears to have produced few problems. It fired the 8-mm (0.315-in) Modell 1890 round-nosed cartridge that was the first Austro-Hungarian round with smokeless propellant, and these were introduced into the five-round integral box magazine by a cartridge clip and a charger guide on the receiver, in itself something of an innovation for the time.

## Standard rifle

It was the Modell 1895 that the Austro-Hungarian armies carried when they went to war in 1914. By then the rifles had been joined by a carbine variant known as the **Modell 1895 8-mm Repetier-Stutzen-Gewehr** and issued to troops such as engineers, drivers, signallers and gunners. For once the usual proliferation of carbine types did not occur in the Austro-Hungarian armies, and the Stutzen became a familiar sight throughout Central Europe, during World War I and after it as the Modell 1895 rifle and carbine became virtual fixtures for many armies. One of the first to adopt the Modell 1895 was Bulgaria. After 1918 the type was taken over by Italy in war reparations and the rifle became one of the standard Italian weapons. Others went to Greece and Yugoslavia, and of course once the Austro-Hungarian Empire had been split up after 1918, both Austria and Hungary retained their familiar weapons.

Both the Modell 1895 and the Stutzen are now collector's pieces but for a very long period they were the standard service weapons for much of Central Europe. They were sound if unspectacular weapons that provided good service for over half a century.

***Right: Recruited from a variety of ethnic groups, the Austro-Hungarian army proved to be a fragile one. As World War I dragged on, the empire had to rely on the sort of hapless conscripts epitomised by the Good Soldier Svejk.***

***Left: Austro-Hungarian troops outside Jaroslav carry their Mannlicher Modell 1895s. This rifle used a straight-pull bolt action and was known as the Repetier-Gewehr from its use of a five-round box magazine compared with earlier Mannlicher rifles such as the Modell 1890.***

**SPECIFICATION**

| | |
|---|---|
| **Repetier-Gewehr Modell 1895** | **Weight:** 3.78 kg (8.3 lb) |
| **Calibre:** 8-mm (0.315-in) | **Muzzle velocity:** 619 m (2,031 ft) per second |
| **Length overall:** 1270 mm (50 in) | **Magazine:** 5-round box |
| **Length of barrel:** 765 mm (30.1 in) | |

# Fusil FN-Mauser mle 1889 Rifle

***The Belgian mle 1889 was a Mauser design built under licence, and had a distinctive muzzle surround and a pronounced curve to the front of the five-round magazine. It was produced at the FN plant at Herstal and remained the standard Belgian service rifle until World War II.***

The Belgian **Fusil FN-Mauser mle 1889** was something of an international weapon, for although it was designed in Belgium its action was a direct copy of the Mauser bolt action. It was accepted as the standard Belgian service rifle in 1889 and although some of the rifles came from the Belgian state arsenal, most were produced by an entirely new concern established specifically to manufacture the Model 1889. The Fabrique Nationale, now more commonly known as FN, is one of the largest arms manufacturing establishments in the world.

## Matched rifle/carbine

As was then usual, the mle 1889 was accompanied in production by a carbine variant, the **Carabine FN-Mauser mle 1889**, some of which were intended to be used in conjunction with a sword-like bayonet known as a 'Yatagan'; most of these were issued to fortress troops and others to Gendarmerie units. In its rifle form the mle 1889 was a very well-made weapon with some unusual features. One was that over its entire length the barrel was encased in a metal tube. This was intended to ensure that the barrel would not come into contact with any of the woodwork, which was prone to warping and could thus impair accuracy. While this feature had some advantages, such as the ability to mount the sights on the tube and not on the barrel, it was rather expensive to manufacture and under some conditions rust could accumulate between the barrel and the tube. But this was a long-term condition and during World War I caused few problems.

## Long service

When it entered service, the mle 1889 was set for a long life, for it remained in use until 1940, and even after that date the type was taken in German garrison use. Some examples were manufactured for export to Abyssinia and a few nations in South America, but generally speaking the mle 1889 was manufactured for the Belgian

Belgian troops armed with mle 1889 FN-Mauser rifles set up a roadblock outside Louvain in a vain attempt to arrest the onrush of the German armies through Belgium during August 1914.

army. When the Germans overran much of Belgium in 1914 the requirements of the remaining Belgian forces were met by switching production to Hopkins & Allen in the USA. For much of the war the small Belgian army was stationed on the far left of the Allied trench lines along the River Lys, when conditions were not suitable for large-scale troop movements, and accordingly the Belgian positions remained static for much of World War II.

### Distinctive magazine

The mle 1889 may be distinguished from other Mauser weapons by the magazine, which had a distinctive bulge on its forward edge. This bulge accommodated the hinge of the magazine platform that fed the rounds upwards into the bolt mechanism under the control of a leaf spring. The box magazine held five rounds fed into the box from a charger clip, and unlike the practice in later Mauser magazines, the rounds were held in a vertical stack. (The later versions used a 'staggered' arrangement.) Another recognition point was the barrel jacket, which extended to some way behind the muzzle. The usual Mauser cleaning rod was present and a long bayonet could be fitted.

**SPECIFICATION**

**Fusil FN-Mauser mle 1889**
**Calibre:** 7.65-mm (0.301-in)
**Length overall:** 1295 mm (51 in)
**Length of barrel:** 780 mm (30.6 in)
**Weight:** 4.01 kg (8.8 lb)
**Muzzle velocity:** 610 m (2,001 ft) per second
**Magazine:** 5-round box

# Ross Rifles

The Canadian Ross rifle (this is a Mk 2) was an excellent target rifle, but less successful in service, as mud and dirt tended to clog the straight-pull bolt action. Although they used the weapon in France, the Canadians later exchanged it for the Lee-Enfield No. 1 Mk III, and the Ross rifles were then used for training.

The first Ross rifle appeared during 1896 and was produced, like the later models, at Sir Charles Ross's own arms factory in Quebec, Canada. Ross was a keen marksman of the old 'Bisley School', and longed for what he considered to be the ideal service rifle: one that would provide consistent accuracy. In pursuit of this ideal he concentrated on items such as barrels and sighting systems as opposed to the more mundane aspects of design that are essential to the true service rifle. Thus although his products were superb target weapons, they revealed themselves to be less than ideal under the rough-and-tumble of service conditions.

### Long-range accuracy

The number of types of Ross rifle runs to well over a dozen. Many of the types produced were often minor modifications of the preceding model and to list them all would be unhelpful. The main service model was known to the Canadian army as the **Rifle, Ross, Mk 3** and may be taken as typical. It was a long-barrel rifle to provide accurate long-range fire, and used an unusual straight-pull bolt system allied to a box magazine holding five rounds. In common with other Commonwealth armies of the day, the Canadian army adopted the British 0.303-in (7.7-mm) cartridge, and this led to the British army taking numbers of Ross rifles in 1914-15.

The Canadian army adopted the Ross after about 1905, and the first Canadian troops to travel to France in 1914 were equipped with these. It was not long before the Ross rifles were found wanting in the muddy conditions typical of the Western Front's trench warfare, for their bolt actions clogged with remarkable ease once even a small amount of debris had entered the system. In his search for accuracy Ross had overlooked that service rifles need to be tolerant of rough conditions, and the Ross rifle required dedicated maintenance and care in handling. The bolt action frequently jammed and the resultant clearing revealed another nasty drawback to the design: the bolt had to be put together in a very precise manner, and if it was re-assembled in the wrong way after cleaning or repair it could still fire the rifle even though the locking lugs that held the bolt in place were not engaged. As the Ross used a straight-pull unit, the bolt could fly back and hit the firer in the face. Thus the Ross soon fell from grace and was replaced by the British No. 1 Mk III. Quite apart from the bolt problems, the length of the Ross rifle was too great for ease of use in the trenches.

### Special roles

The Ross was not completely withdrawn from service use. Fitted with a telescopic sight it was used very successfully as a sniping rifle, a role in which its accuracy was most prized. Trained snipers could also provide the weapon with the extra care it required. To this day the Ross is still a much-prized target rifle. Many were used during World War II by various British second-line units, including the Home Guard, but the Ross never overcame the reputation for problems that it gained during its introduction to the trenches during 1914 and 1915.

*After the Ross rifle was withdrawn from first-line service, some were used for training and some were issued to British armed trawler crews, providing them with at least limited defence against German aircraft and U-boats operating in the North Sea; they were better than nothing.*

**SPECIFICATION**

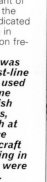

**Rifle, Ross, Mk 3**
**Calibre:** 7.7-mm (0.303-in)
**Length overall:** 1285 mm (50.6 in)
**Length of barrel:** 765 mm (30.1 in)
**Weight:** 4.48 kg (9.875 lb)
**Muzzle velocity:** 792 m (2,600 ft) per second
**Magazine:** 5-round box

# Fusil Lebel mle 1886 Rifle

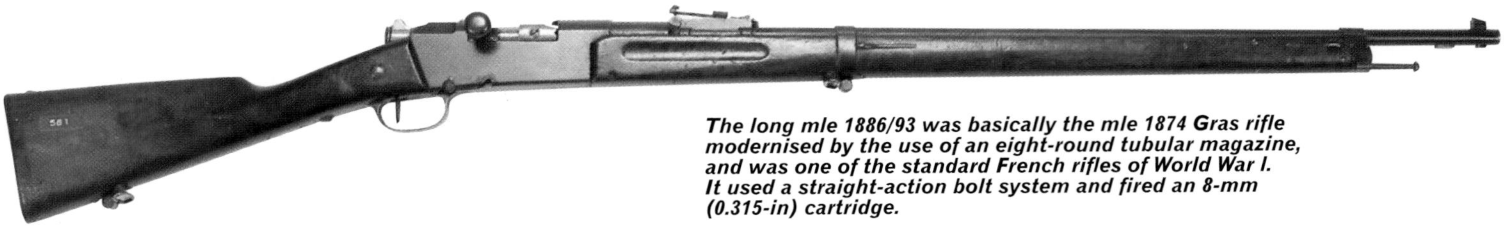

***The long mle 1886/93 was basically the mle 1874 Gras rifle modernised by the use of an eight-round tubular magazine, and was one of the standard French rifles of World War I. It used a straight-action bolt system and fired an 8-mm (0.315-in) cartridge.***

By 1886 the French army was in a position to introduce a new 'small' cartridge with a calibre of 8-mm (0.315-in) to fire the new completely smokeless propellant developed by Paul Vielle. With the new cartridge came a new rifle, the **Fusil mle 1886**, usually known as the **Lebel** after the officer who led the commission that recommended the adoption of the new rifle and round.

The Lebel was for its time only a tentative improvement of the existing Gras mle 1874. The mle 1886 rifle did indeed have the ability to fire the new 8-mm cartridge, but the bolt action of the Gras design was retained and, in place of the by-then accepted and practical box magazine, a tubular magazine in which the rounds were loaded nose-to-tail. This magazine was located under the fore-stock and contained eight rounds. It was still possible to load single rounds directly into the chamber and, as loading the tubular magazine was a somewhat slow process, the full loading was usually kept for use only when large amounts of fire were required.

***Left: A French Zouave is seen at Vincennes in 1917 with a mle 1886/93 fitted with the Epée-baionette mle 1886. This converted the rifle into a pike for close combat, where it was to prove very effective.***

***Below: Taken during the manoeuvres in July 1914, this photograph gives an indication of the French frontal attack tactics that were so costly in World War I's early battles.***

### Updated variant

The original mle 1886 underwent a major modification programme in 1893 and the designation was accordingly changed to **mle 1886/93**. Another revision came in 1898 when the ammunition was updated, but in this instance the designation remained unaltered.

The original mle 1896 has one major claim to fame, for it was the first service rifle to fire smokeless propellant cartridges. For a short while the French army was thus ahead of all its contemporaries, but this advantage did not last long once the 'secret' of the propellant became widely known. Within a few years all other major nations had converted to the new propellant and had also adopted the new 'small-calibre' type of cartridge, and thus the Lebel soon lost its early lead. In fact it then assumed something of a back place in rifle development as a result of its anachronistic tubular magazine. One of the major disadvantages of such a magazine was the relatively long loading time that has already been mentioned; another was the safety aspect, for as the rounds lay nose-to-tail in the magazine there was always the chance that a sudden jolt would cause the nose of one round to hit the primer of the round in front with dire results.

### Declining service

Thus there was a gradual move away from the Lebel towards the Berthier rifles, but in 1914 the Lebel remained in service in large numbers, and it was still standard issue to most front-line units. It served throughout World War I and was still in large-scale use in World War II.

The Lebel could mount a long cruciform bayonet, and was by all accounts a pleasant rifle to handle and aim. The loading was awkward, however, and there was always the chance of a magazine explosion when it was least expected. Another drawback was the two-piece bolt which took a degree of maintenance and was prone to clogging with dirt and dust at the earliest opportunity. A 5.5-mm (0.216-in) training version was produced in small numbers.

**SPECIFICATION**

| | |
|---|---|
| **Fusil Lebel mle 1886/93** | **Weight:** 4.245 kg (9.35 lb) |
| **Calibre:** 8-mm (0.315-in) | **Muzzle velocity:** 725 m (2,379 ft) per second |
| **Length overall:** 1303 mm (51.3 in) | **Feed:** 8-round tubular magazine |
| **Length of barrel:** 798 mm (31.4 in) | |

# Fusil Berthier mle 1907 Rifle

Soon after the Lebel had been adopted for service, it was appreciated that the design had several drawbacks, of which the most important was the use of a tubular magazine. By the time this had been realised the Lebel was in large-scale production so there was little chance of any immediate changeover to a new design. Instead there began a slow and gradual process of introducing a new rifle design known generally as the **Berthier**. This began in 1890 with the introduction of a cavalry carbine and gradually as new requirements arose new Berthier weapons were introduced.

This culminated in 1907 with the adoption of a **Fusil mle 1907** for use in France's colonial empire, especially Indo-China. The Berthier rifle was typical of the Berthier series in as much as it was a long, slender weapon with a box magazine but a bolt action based on that already in use on the Lebel. While the change-over to the box magazine was a belated but good move, the Berthier magazine could hold only three rounds, a poor capacity in comparison with those of rifles already in use elsewhere and therefore something of a disadvantage to the firer.

### Better than the Lebel

The mle 1907 was widely used by French troops serving in the colonies, and more were issued to colonial levies. Some were even issued to troops on the mainland of France, but in 1914 the Lebel was still the standard rifle. The situation was changed by 1915, for by then the French forces were expanding rapidly in numbers, and weapons were in short supply. The Berthier was therefore pushed into mass production, the mle 1907 being used as the baseline model. Some changes had to be made to the finer design points (especially to the bolt and sights) and the resulting weapon became the **mle 1907/15**. It was soon in service alongside the Lebel,

***Usually known as the Berthier rifle, the mle 1907 was a rifle version of the mle 1890 et 1892 carbine. This example is a mle 1916 modified from the original to take a five-round box magazine. This rifle was used by many armies after 1918 and was still in widespread service in 1939.***

was used by the French armed forces throughout World War I, and was still in widespread use in 1939.

The mle 1907/15 still retained the three-round box magazine, however, and this was clearly insufficient for the requirements of 1915. Accordingly the basic design was altered so that a five-round box could be used, and this variant was later placed into production as the **mle 1916**; it could be distinguished by the box magazine protruding from under the fore-stock, whereas on the mle 1907/15 the magazine was flush with the woodwork. The mle 1916 even had the facility to use a charging clip for loading the five rounds, a feature lacking on the mle 1907/15, into which each round had to be loaded individually and therefore slowly.

The mle 1907/15 and mle 1916 soon became popular rifles. They both had a very attractive appearance, for even under wartime production conditions the graceful shape of the long fore-stock was retained. In service the Berthiers were rather long for use in trench-warfare conditions, but they were easy to handle when firing, and were usually preferred to the Lebel. The mle 1907/15 was manufactured in large quantities, and was even once put in production by Remington in the USA, but only for French use as the US Army never used the type. The final development of the type occurred in 1934, when mle 1907/15 weapons were modified to fire the 7.5-mm (0.295-in) round developed for light machine-guns. The designation for the revised weapon with a five-round magazine was mle **1907/15 M34**.

| SPECIFICATION | |
|---|---|
| **Fusil Berthier mle 1907/15** | **Weight:** 3.8 kg (8.38 lb) |
| **Calibre:** 8-mm (0.315-in) | **Muzzle velocity:** 725 m (2,379 ft) per second |
| **Length overall:** 1306 mm (51.4 in) | **Feed:** 3-round box magazine |
| **Length of barrel:** 797 mm (31.4 in) | |

# Fucile modello 91 Rifle

***This Mannlicher-Carcano carbine is the 6.5-mm (0.256-in) Moschetto modello 91 per cavalleria. As it was meant for use by cavalry, it had a fixed but folding bayonet and the magazine held six rounds. In fact many of these weapons were used by other special troops, such as gunners and signallers.***

The Italian service rifle of World War I was the **Fucile modello 91**, and was of a type known as the **Mannlicher-Carcano**. This was developed at Turin Arsenal between 1890 and 1891, and in overall terms was an amalgamation of the Mauser bolt action from the Belgian/German mle 1889, the box magazine arrangement of the Mannlicher system, and a new bolt-sleeve safety device produced by one Salvatore Carcano. The Italians thought highly of the resulting weapon and adopted it in 1892; it remained the standard Italian service rifle until World War II.

No one else seemed to share the Italians' enthusiasm, for the only sales made outside Italy before World War I were to Japan, and this batch was made to accommodate the Japanese 6.5-mm (0.256-in) cartridge, which was dimensionally different from that in Italian use. In service the modello 91 proved sound enough, but the amalgamation of diverse features in the bolt and magazine areas meant that the design was rather more complicated than it might have been, and in the field the modello 91 required considerable attention, especially in Italy's African colonial territories; in particular, the straight-pull bolt action was prone to jamming when dirty.

## Family of variants

The modello 91 spawned a whole group of carbine types that were produced in variants for use by cavalry, special troops (including gunners and engineers) and others. While these carbines were handy and easy to carry, they suffered from the usual shortcomings inherent in short-barrel weapons, even though the cartridge used was less powerful than many others then in use elsewhere. Some of these carbines were provided with spike bayonets, whereas the modello 91 rifle used a knife-type bayonet.

As the modello 91 was used only by the Italians during World War I, its service use was confined to the border campaigns against Austro-Hungarian troops, coming to a climax with the Battle of Caporetto in 1917. During this action the Italians lost heavily and the resulting withdrawals led to some British divisions being diverted from the Western Front to stabilise matters.

The outcome of Caporetto was not due entirely to the performance of the modello 91, which was much the same as that of many of its contemporaries, but even at the time it was generally accepted that the Italian 6.5-mm cartridge was rather under- powered and the bullet it fired generally lacking in striking power. But these points were marginal, for the modello 91 handled and fired quite well. The small cartridge produced less recoil than was common among other designs, although the carbine versions kicked as nastily as other types, and the general lack of protrusions and items that could catch on things made the modello 91 a good weapon to use when moving across rough country. But even now the overall impression left by the modello 91 is that it was a rather more complicated weapon than others of the time, and despite the Italians' understandable enthusiasm for a national product it was among the 'also rans' in the World War I rifle stakes.

***Troops of the Italian 35th Division march through Salonika during August 1916, carrying their Mannlicher-Carcano modello 91 rifles at the trail. Known as the Fucile modello 91, this rifle was still in service in 1940. It differed from the standard Mannlicher rifle only in detail.***

| SPECIFICATION | |
|---|---|
| **Fucile modello 91** | **Weight:** 3.8 kg (8.4 lb) |
| **Calibre:** 6.5-mm (0.256-in) | **Muzzle velocity:** 630 m (2,067 ft) per second |
| **Length overall:** 1285 mm (50.6 in) | **Feed:** 6-round box magazine |
| **Length of barrel:** 780 mm (30.7 in) | |

# Mauser Gewehr 1898 Rifle

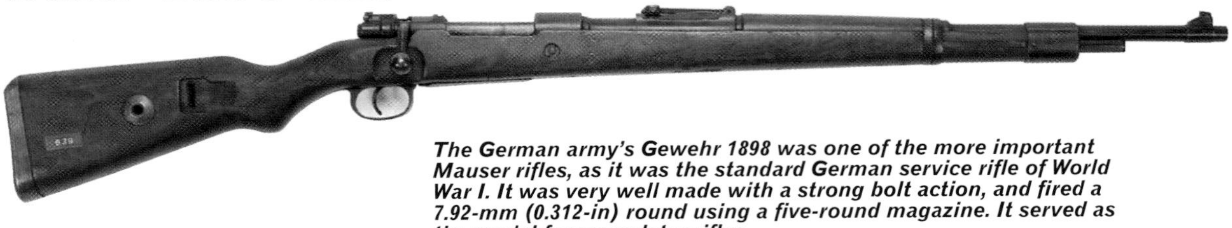

***The German army's Gewehr 1898 was one of the more important Mauser rifles, as it was the standard German service rifle of World War I. It was very well made with a strong bolt action, and fired a 7.92-mm (0.312-in) round using a five-round magazine. It served as the model for many later rifles.***

The first Mauser rifle approved for German army service was the **Mauser Modell 1888**. This used a Mauser bolt action that has remained virtually unaltered to this day, but in concert with a rather dated 8-mm (0.315-in) cartridge. An updated requirement and a series of trials then led to the adoption of a new 7.92-mm (0.312-in) cartridge with a much improved propellant to fire a more effective bullet, and the new rifle to fire this improved cartridge became known as the **Gewehr 1898** or **Gew 98** (Rifle Model 1898).

The new rifle was destined to become one of the most widely used and successful weapons of its type ever created, and it was produced in very large numbers. Many later rifles could trace their origins back to the Gewehr 1898, which came to be seen as the 'classic' Mauser rifle, handsome and rather long, but well-balanced and with everything excellently designed and in general nicely made. The term 'in general' is used advisedly, for once World War I had got into its stride, the previously high standard of rifle manufacture had to be relaxed, as indeed was the standard for virtually every type of weapon, and some comparatively rough specimens were therefore issued to the troops from the middle years of the war. But most Gew 98 rifles were very well-made, with good-quality wooden furniture that was emphasised by the use of a pistol-type grip behind the trigger as an aid to holding and aiming the rifle.

The original rear sight was a very elaborate affair with sliding ramps and other niceties, and needed both training and experience for effective use especially in long-range firing. However, some later versions of the rifle were completed with simpler sights that reduced manufacturing time and cost, trimmed the need for training, and were in any case more than adequate for the type of short-range firing that was characteristic of the trench warfare.

## Safe locking

The bolt action retained Mauser front-lug locking systems, with the addition of an extra lug to make the number up to three for added safety with the new and more powerful cartridge. The bolt used a straight-pull action which was (and indeed still is) rather awkward to use quickly and smoothly, but offered few problems in service. The magazine was an integral box, and this accommodated five rounds loaded from above by means of a charger clip.

While the Gewehr 1898 was produced primarily for the German armed forces, it was also the starting point for a multitude of rifle designs that spread all over the world. Spain was an early user of the basic Mauser action, and versions produced in that country differed little from the Gewehr 1898. The output of Mauser models from Germany and Spain was considerable, and rifles from these two sources were soon encountered all over the world in nations as far apart as China and Costa Rica.

## Great reliability

Over the years the Mauser action has accrued and retained an enviable reputation for reliability, strength and accuracy, and the arguments rage even today as to whether or not the Gewehr 1898 and its various cousins were the finest service rifles of their time. Many state that they were, but there are several other contenders to the title. What is certain is that during the years between 1914 and 1918 the Gewehr 1898 served the German army well. Front-line soldiers had to take good care of the weapons, but this usually meant no more than keeping the bolt area covered with a cloth at all times when the rifle was not in use.

Some versions, such as sniper models, appeared with special sights, including various forms of optical sight, and the weapon still has the claim to fame that it was one of the very first, if not the first, anti-tank weapon. This came about by the chance discovery that the armour of the first British tanks could be penetrated by the simple expedient of reversing the bullets used in the Gewehr 1898 before they were fired: the blunt end simply punched a hole through the armour before the bullet could warp.

**SPECIFICATION**

**Mauser Gewehr 1898**
**Calibre:** 7.92-mm (0.312-in)
**Length overall:** 1250 mm (49.2 in)
**Length of barrel:** 740 mm (29.1 in)
**Weight:** 4.2 kg (9.26 lb)
**Muzzle velocity:** 640 m (2,100 ft) per second
**Feed:** 5-round box magazine

***Years of trench warfare radically altered the appearance of the German soldier. Carrying the Gewehr 1898K shortened weapon, he wears the distinctive 'coal scuttle' helmet. Note the wire-cutters tucked into the belt.***

***Not all the time spent out of the trenches was passed in rest. Here three 'Frontschwein' are engaged in rifle practice with their Gewehr 1898s.***

# Mosin-Nagant Model 1891 Rifle

***Part of the Russian contingent is seen at Salonika in Greece during July 1916. This was the last year in which the Russian army could sustain combat; the Herculean offensive launched by General Brusilov dealt a savage blow to Austria-Hungary but could not save the tottering Tsarist empire.***

By a time in the late 1880s the Russian army was in the process of converting its massive forces from the use of the obsolete Berdan rifle. The army carried out a series of investigations in which it was attracted by a number of rifles produced by the Belgian Nagant brothers, but it also had on its doorstep a design produced by Sergei Mosin, a Tsarist officer. The planners decided to amalgamate the best features of the two designs, resulting in the **Mosin-Nagant** rifle which was introduced into service in 1891; its full Russian title was **Russkaya 3-lineinaye Vintovka obrazets 1891g** (Russian 3-line rifle model 1891).

The term '3-line' in the designation denotes that the calibre was gauged in an old Russian linear measurement known as a line, equal to 2.54 mm (0.1 in). This was later changed in 1908 when a new cartridge was introduced and the calibre became 7.62 mm (0.3 in). The original sights were calibrated in the equally old arshins (1 arshin equals 0.71 m or 27.95 in), but these too were changed to metres after 1908.

Overall the Model 1891 was a sound and rugged rifle design, but one that had a few unusual features. One was the five-round magazine, for with the system employed the top cartridge was always kept free of magazine spring pressure for the bolt-loading process, which had the advantage that feeding jams were less frequent than they might otherwise have been. But this was balanced by the introduction of some complexity in the mechanism. The two-piece bolt was also generally judged to be more complicated than was really necessary, though it gave little enough trouble in use. One other unusual feature was that the rifle was issued with a long bayonet with a screwdriver point that could be used to dismantle parts of the rifle. This bayonet was of the socket type, and during World War I it was a virtual fixture on the rifle at all times.

***These Russian troops are armed with Mosin-Nagant Model 1891 rifles, all with the long spike bayonet that was such a fixture that the sights were usually adjusted permanently to compensate for their weight. The bayonets used the ancient socket method of fixing.***

## Carbine versions

The Model 1891 was generally a weapon that could take hard knocks and was generally undemanding of care and attention. A Dragoon Rifle Model 1891 carbine version was produced for use by cavalry and the ubiquitous Russian mounted infantry, but this variant was only slightly shorter than the rifle and much longer than other carbines produced at the time; a genuine **Carbine Model 1910** variant was produced in 1910.

The main problem for the Russians was that they had selected a good service rifle, but there were never enough of the type. The weapon's production facilities were overstretched, and had to make the rifles virtually by hand as the concept of mass production was far from Russian thoughts before 1914. When extra Russian army units were formed from the reserves in 1914, very often there were no rifles with which to arm them.

The Model 1891 played its part in the revolutions of 1917 and was again in action during the civil war that followed in 1918. Between the wars the Model 1891 was replaced in production by the shorter **Model 1891/30**, and it was with this that the Red Army was armed in World War II, though some Model 1891s survived after 1941.

**SPECIFICATION**

| | |
|---|---|
| **Mosin-Nagant Model 1891** | **Weight:** 4.37 kg (9.62 lb) |
| **Calibre:** 7.62-mm (0.3-in) | **Muzzle velocity:** 810 m (2,657 ft) per second |
| **Length overall:** 1305 mm (51.4 in) | **Feed:** 5-round box magazine |
| **Length of barrel:** 802 mm (31.6 in) | |

# Rifle No. 3 Mk I Rifle

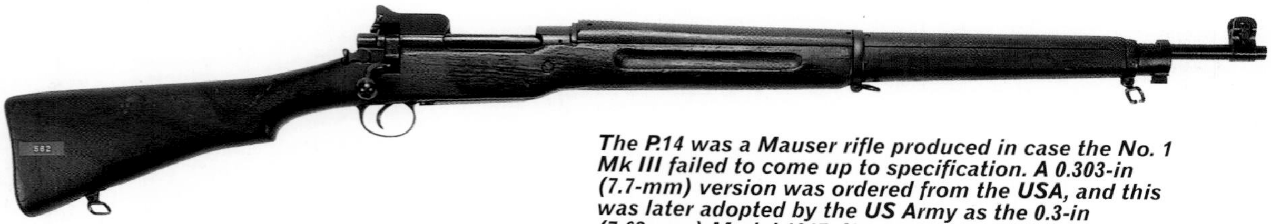

***The P.14 was a Mauser rifle produced in case the No. 1 Mk III failed to come up to specification. A 0.303-in (7.7-mm) version was ordered from the USA, and this was later adopted by the US Army as the 0.3-in (7.62-mm) Model 1917. It was an accurate weapon.***

Despite its eventual success, when first introduced the No. 1 Mk III rifle was deemed by some military thinkers to lack the features required. In case the new SMLE did not meet requirements a 'back-up' design was put forward, one chambered for a new 7-mm (0.276-in) cartridge and employing a Mauser bolt action. Being only a back-up design at first, this rifle did not appear until 1913 under the general title **P.13**. At the time the design was taken no further and work on the new 7-mm cartridge ceased. Thus things were in abeyance just as World War I began in 1914, and by then the P.13 had become the **P.14**.

In 1915 the overall shortage of rifles for the expanding British and Commonwealth armies was such that at one point rifles were being ordered from places as far away as Japan. It was accordingly decided that the P.14 could be ordered from the United States, but chambered for the standard 0.303-in (7.7-mm) cartridge. Several firms, including Winchester and Remington, became involved in production of the P.14, which was known to the British army as the **Rifle No. 3 Mk I**, and the results were shipped eastward across the Atlantic.

## Poor service rifle

When they arrived the new rifles were hurriedly issued and rushed into combat. The type did not fare very well, for it was a product of what became known as the Bisley School of rifle thought. To the Bisley School long-range accuracy was the touchstone of all combat rifle worth. Soldiers were expected to hit man-sized targets at ranges of over 915 m (1,000 yards), and if a rifle could not attain these standards it was reviled. It was exactly this factor that drew so much criticism to the SMLE when it was first issued in 1907, for the SMLE was never a perfect target rifle. With the No. 3, the Bisley School had been given full rein and the result was not unlike that of the ill-fated Canadian Ross rifle. The No. 3 was quite simply not a good service rifle: it was long and awkward to use under combat conditions, encumbered by a long bayonet it was ill-balanced and even less handy, and the bolt action took considerable maintenance. It was withdrawn from service when enough No. 1 Mk III rifles were to hand.

The No. 3 Mk I did have one saving grace: it was as accurate as the Bisley School had intended. Thus the No. 3 was used mainly for the sniping role, in which it was very successful.

The No. 3 Mk I had one more task to perform in World War I, and that came in 1917 when the Americans entered the war, and were even more desperate for service rifles than the British. As the production lines were still producing No. 3, they were changed to make the same rifle chambered for the American 0.3-in (7.62-mm) cartridge. Thus the No. 3 became the **Rifle M1917**, known to most Americans as the **'Enfield'**. In American hands the M1917 (or **P.17** to some) fared no better than it had with the British, and in 1919 the entire output was placed into store, only to be dragged out again in 1940 and sold to the United Kingdom to arm the new Home Guard.

**SPECIFICATION**

| | |
|---|---|
| **Rifle No. 3 Mk I** | **Weight:** 4.35 kg (9.6 lb) |
| **Calibre:** 0.303-in (7.7-mm) | **Muzzle velocity:** 762 m (2,500 ft) per second |
| **Length overall:** 1175 mm (46.2 in) | **Feed:** 5-round box magazine |
| **Length of barrel:** 660 mm (26 in) | |

# Rifle No. 1 Mks III & III* rifle

*The No. 1 Mk III rifle was often known as the SMLE (Short Magazine Lee-Enfield) and was one of the best service rifles of World War I. It could be fired at a rapid rate of over 15 shots per minute, as the bolt action was easy to operate and the magazine could be quickly loaded.*

Late in the 19th century the British army adopted the magazine and bolt system developed by the American engineer James Lee, and through a long process of 'in-house' improvements and trials this led to a series of what were known as Lee-Enfield rifles, the Enfield part of the name coming from the Royal Small Arms Factory at Enfield Lock, Middlesex.

This series led in 1907 to a new design known as the **Short Magazine Lee-Enfield (SMLE)**, a rifle with a length between those of a normal rifle and a carbine, for the SMLE was another of the weapons intended for use by all arms from infantry to cavalry. The SMLE had a rough introduction to service, but improvements and some modifications overcame these and by 1914, when the SMLE went to France with the British Expeditionary Force, it was called the **Rifle No. 1 Mk III**.

This is another candidate for the accolade 'best service rifle of the time'. It was a fully-stocked weapon with a snub-shaped fitting at the muzzle to accommodate a long bayonet. The action was of the turn-bolt variety and used rear locking lugs as opposed to the frontlocking lugs of the Mauser system. In theory this meant that the Lee system was less safe than that of the Mauser, but in service it caused no problems at all, and the smooth action of the Lee-Enfield mechanism made the British rifle easy and extremely fast to use.

*Australian troops move up into the line near Fricourt in October 1918, carrying the No. 1 Mk IIIs that their descendants were to carry throughout World War II; Australian production of this rifle did not end until 1955 at the Lithgow arsenal.*

## Large magazine

The detachable box magazine in front of the trigger group held 10 rounds, which was twice the capacity of many contemporary rifles. There was also a cut-out device that held all the rounds in the magazine while single rounds were fed into the chamber by hand; this arrangement was supposed to retain the magazine rounds for use only when really needed.

The main sights were of the ramp type and calibrated to well over 1,000 yards (915 m), and on the left-hand side of the rifle stock was a peculiar long-range sight that was used in the generation of really long-range fire to cover an area: it was used only under careful volley-fire control.

While the No. 1 Mk III was an excellent service rifle, it was expensive and time-consuming to make, for virtually everything had to be machined or made by hand. So when trench warfare became the norm and an ever increasing number of rifles was needed, some production shortcuts were made – including the removal of the magazine cut-out and long-range sights.

***Left:** This relaxed scene indicates the Entente Cordiale that was in place in March 1918. The picture was taken well behind the lines, for the No. 1 Mk III* lacks the usual wrappings that would have kept it clean in the dirt and mud of the trenches.*

## Simplified rifle

The result was the **Rifle No. 1 Mk III***, which may be regarded as the standard British rifle of World War I. It was produced in very substantial numbers not only in the UK but also in India and Australia, where it remained in production until 1955. It was a sturdy and sound rifle that was easily able to withstand the rigours of trench fighting. All manner of devices were invented to increase its utility, ranging fromperiscopic sights to grenade-launcher devices. In the hands of a fully-trained soldier it was capable of high rates of fire: a rate of 15 rounds per minute was accepted as the norm but trained soldiers could produce far more. At Mons in 1914 the Germans thought they were up against machine-guns at some stages, but it was simply the massed rapid fire produced by the superbly trained soldiers of the BEF using the No. 1 Mk III to full advantage.

***Left:** Two well-laden British soldiers are seen in action holding the south bank of the River Aisne during the battle of May 1918, in the aftermath of the series of German breakthroughs that started during March of that year. The rifle is a No. 1 Mk III*.*

**SPECIFICATION**

**Rifle No. 1 Mk III***
**Calibre:** 0.303-in (7.7-mm)
**Length overall:** 1133 mm (44.6 in)
**Length of barrel:** 640 mm (25.2 in)
**Weight:** 3.93 kg (8.656 lb)
**Muzzle velocity:** 634 m (2,080 ft) per second
**Feed:** 10-round box magazine

# Springfield Model 1903 rifle

***Above: The American M1903 Springfield was a Mauser-based rifle first introduced in 1903 and still in service during the Korean War. It was an excellent weapon and this is the original version, shown with a bayonet from the earlier Krag-Jorgensen Model 1896 service rifle.***

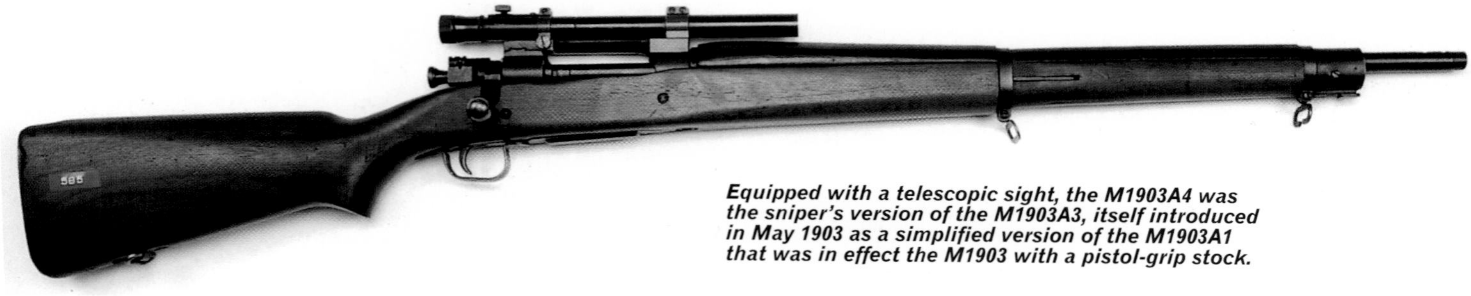

***Equipped with a telescopic sight, the M1903A4 was the sniper's version of the M1903A3, itself introduced in May 1903 as a simplified version of the M1903A1 that was in effect the M1903 with a pistol-grip stock.***

At the beginning of the 20th century the men of the US army had as their standard rifle a weapon known as the Krag-Jorgensen, which had been standardised for service in 1892. However, it was at about this time that the Americans realised, in the light of the rapid development of the rifle and its ammunition during the later part of the 19th century, that the Krag-Jorgensen left a lot to be desired. The US Army therefore decided to adopt a better rifle. It cast around for ideas and was soon impressed sufficiently with the basic Mauser system to negotiate a licence to manufacture Mauser-based rifles in the USA.

## Improved round

In the US the Mauser system was modified to produce a rifle built around a new American cartridge known as the Cartridge, Ball, Caliber .30 in M1903. This had a blunt nose, but when the Germans introduced their *Spitzer* sharp-nosed bullet with better all-round performance, the Americans were quick to follow suit and the rifle was accordingly modified to what was to be its classic form. In fact the rifle was ready in 1903, and was first manufactured at the Springfield Arsenal in Illinois, from which it took its generally accepted name of the **Springfield** rifle.

In appearance this was obviously a Mauser but the length was something new. The rifle was officially the **Magazine Rifle, Caliber .30, Model of 1903**, but this was usually abbreviated to **Model 1903** or simply **M1903**. It differed from most of its contemporaries by being of interim length between the period's full-length rifle and carbine, for it was intended as the service rifle for all arms from cavalry to infantry. This compromise between lengths resulted in an extremely attractive and well-balanced rifle that was, and still is, a joy to handle.

## Turn-down bolt action

The bolt action was of the turn-down design with a well-placed bolt handle that was easy to operate rapidly when required; the overall fine standard of finish and detail design made the weapon extremely accurate, and the M1903 and its later versions are still much prized as target rifles.

The original Model 1903 was the rifle the US army took to France in 1917, but it was soon succeeded on the production lines by variants including the **M1903 Mk 1**. This was basically a model 1903 adapted to accommodate the ill-fated Pedersen Device, a gadget that was supposed to turn the bolt action rifle into a form of automatic assault rifle by removing the bolt and replacing it with a new receiver firing special 0.3-in (7.62-mm) pistol ammunition fed from an overhead magazine; the rounds were fired using the normal rifle barrel. Although the device was issued, it was produced too late for widespread issue and was held in reserve for the expected offensives of 1919. After World War I it was totally withdrawn from use, the Mk 1 rifles being converted back to the normal Model 1903 bolt-action standard.

## Later variants

After 1918 the Model 1903 was further modified into various forms, usually with a view to easier production, and it was still in US Army service as a sniper rifle as late as the Korean War. By any standards it is still regarded as one of the best service rifles of its period, and quite apart from its continuing use as a target rifle, the type is now valued as a collector's item.

***The Springfield Model 1903 rifle was well made and totally reliable when maintained properly, and in the hands of a skilled marksman it was extremely accurate out to a tactically long range.***

***The first contingent of American troops to arrive in England in 1917 is seen here with their M1903 Springfields piled. These are probably men from the famous 'Rainbow Division' formed from all the states of the Union and the first to be sent to Europe.***

**SPECIFICATION**

**Rifle M1903**
**Calibre:** 0.3-in (7.62-mm)
**Length overall:** 1097 mm (43.2 in)
**Length of barrel:** 610 mm (24 in)
**Weight:** 3.94 kg (8.69 lb)
**Muzzle velocity:** 853 m (2,800 ft) per second
**Feed:** 5-round integral box magazine

# Lebel and Berthier Rifles

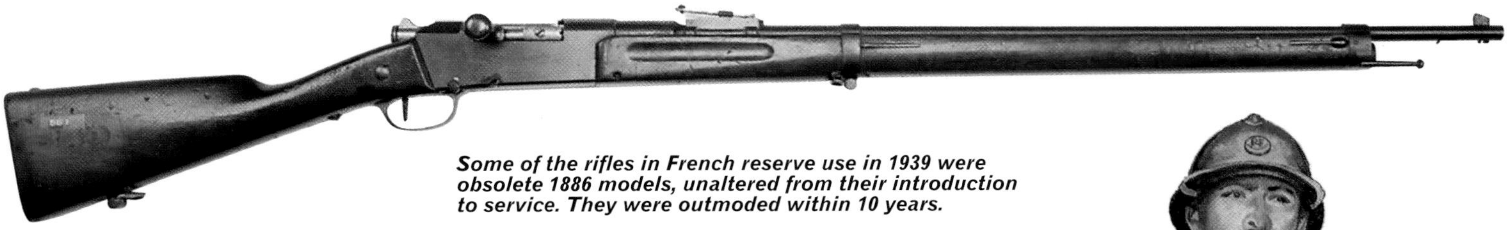

***Some of the rifles in French reserve use in 1939 were obsolete 1886 models, unaltered from their introduction to service. They were outmoded within 10 years.***

In 1939 the French army was equipped with an almost bewildering array of rifles, for the French appear to have adopted a policy of never throwing anything away. Some of the personal weapons could trace their origins back to the mle 1866 Chassepot rifle. One of them, the **Fusil Gras mle 1874**, was a single-shot weapon but still in use with some French second-line and colonial units at the time of the German invasion of 1940.

The original Lebel rifle, the **Fusil d'infanterie mle 1886**, was updated in 1893 to produce the **Fusil mle 1886/93**. It was with this Lebel rifle that the French army fought World War I, but another weapon also in use at that time was a Berthier carbine, the **Mousqueton mle 1890** (and similar **mle 1892**), a version of the original mle 1886 revised with the Mannlicher magazine system. On the Berthier the magazine was of the orthodox box type loaded from a clip, but on the Lebel it was a tubular magazine holding more rounds loaded singly.

## Berthier rifle

The first Berthier rifle was the **Fusil mle 1907**, but in 1915 this weapon for colonial troops was largely replaced by the **Fusil d'infanterie mle 07/15**. With the introduction of the mle 07/15 the older Lebel rifles gradually faded in importance as production concentrated on the Berthiers, but the Lebels were never replaced in service. They just soldiered on, and were still used in 1939.

The original Berthier magazine system held only three rounds, but it was soon realised that this was not enough and the **Fusil d'infanterie mle 1916** had a 5-round magazine. To complicate matters further there were carbine or other short versions of all the models mentioned above, and to complicate matters still more the French sold or gave away masses of all of these weapons in the inter-war years to many nations who promptly applied their own designations. Thus Lebel and Berthier rifles turned up not only in all the French colonies but in nations such as Greece, Yugoslavia, Romania and other Balkan states.

In 1934 the French decided to attempt to make some sense out of their varied rifle and carbine arsenal by adopting a new calibre. Up to this time the normal French calibre had been 8-mm (0.315-in), but in 1934 the 7.5-mm (0.295-in) calibre was adopted.

That same year the French started to modify the old Berthier rifles to the new calibre and at the same time introduced a new magazine (still holding only five rounds) and several other changes along with the new barrel. This 'new' version was the **Fusil d'infanterie mle 07/15 M34**, but the change went so slowly that in 1939 only a small proportion of the available stocks had been converted, ensuring that all the other models were still in use.

## German service

After the French capitulation of June 1940, the Germans found themselves with masses of all the various French rifles. Some they could use as they were, and many of these were issued to garrison and second-line formations. Others were stockpiled only to be dragged out in 1945 to arm Volkssturm and other such units. No doubt the Germans found that the variety of French rifle and carbine types was too much, even for their assorted stocks, but as they never had enough rifles to arm their ever-growing forces the French weapons were no doubt handy.

Few of the old French rifles are to be encountered today other than in the hands of museums and collectors.

**SPECIFICATION**

| Fusil mle 1886/93 | Fusil mle 1907/15 M34 |
|---|---|
| **Calibre:** 8-mm (0.315-in) | **Calibre:** 7.5-mm (0.295-in) |
| **Length overall:** 1303 mm (51.3 in) | **Length overall:** 1084 mm (42.7 in) |
| **Length of barrel:** 798 mm (31.4 in) | **Length of barrel:** 579 mm (22.8 in) |
| **Weight:** 4.245 kg (9.35 lb) | **Weight:** 3.56 kg (7.85 lb) |
| **Muzzle velocity:** 725 m (2,380 ft) per second | **Muzzle velocity:** 823 m (2,700 ft) per second |
| **Feed:** 8-round tubular magazine | **Feed:** 5-round box magazine |

***This Moslem Spahi of the 1st Moroccan Spahi Regiment of the Vichy colonial army is armed with the old Lebel rifle. Note the long bayonet in the man's belt.***

# Fusil MAS36 Rifle

In the period following World War I the French army decided to adopt a new standard service cartridge in 7.5-mm (0.295-in) calibre. The new cartridge was adopted in 1924, but following some low-priority and therefore lengthy trials, it was found that the new cartridge was unsafe under certain circumstances and thus had to be modified in 1929. In that year the French decided to adopt a new rifle to fire the new round, but it was not until 1932 that a prototype was ready. Then followed a series of further trials that went on at a slow pace until 1936, when the new rifle was accepted for service.

The new rifle was the **Fusil MAS36** (MAS for Manufacture d'Armes de Saint Etienne). This used a much-modified Mauser action which was so arranged that the bolt handle had to be angled forward quite sharply. The box magazine held only five rounds. The MAS36 had the odd distinction of being the last bolt-action service rifle to be adopted for military service anywhere (all later new weapons using some form of self-loading action) and in some other ways the MAS36 was anachronistic. In typical French style the weapon had no safety catch, and the overall appearance of the design belied its year of introduction, for it looked a much older design than it was.

## Very slow progress

Production of the new rifle was so slow that a modification programme to convert some of the old rifles for the new cartridge had to be undertaken. This lack of urgency was typical of the period for the nation seemed to suffer from an internal lethargy that could be traced back to the nation's exertions of World War I. Thus by 1939 only a relatively few French army units were equipped with the MAS36, and these were mainly front-line troops. The MAS36 could have had little effect on the events of May and June 1940, but many of the troops who left France at that time took their MAS36s with them and for a while it

**SPECIFICATION**

| Fusil MAS36 | |
|---|---|
| **Calibre:** 7.5-mm (0.295-in) | **Weight:** 3.67 kg (8.09 lb) |
| **Length overall:** 1019 mm (40.1 in) | **Muzzle velocity:** 823 m (2,700 ft) per second |
| **Length of barrel:** 574 mm (22.6 in) | **Feed:** 5-round box magazine |

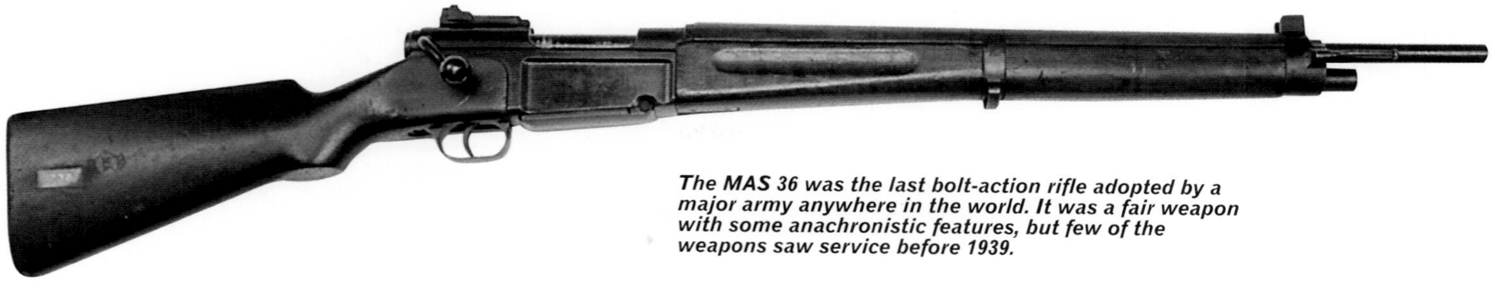

***The MAS 36 was the last bolt-action rifle adopted by a major army anywhere in the world. It was a fair weapon with some anachronistic features, but few of the weapons saw service before 1939.***

remained the favoured weapon of the Free French forces in exile. The Germans also took over numbers of MAS36s for service, with the designation **Gewehr 242(f),** by their own garrison units based in occupied France.

One odd variation of the basic MAS36 was a version known as the **MAS36 CR39**. This was a short-barrel version intended for paratroop use, and had an aluminium butt that could be folded forward alongside the body to save stowage space. Only a relative few were ever made, and even fewer appear to have been issued for service use.

When World War II ended, the new French army once more took the MAS36 into use and retained it for many years, using it in action in North Africa and Indo-China. Many are still retained for use as ceremonial parade weapons and the type is still used by the forces and police authorities of many colonial or ex-colonial states.

# Rifle Types 38 & 99

***The Type 99 rifle was a monopod-fitted version of the Type 38 employing the new 7.7-mm (0.303-in) calibre cartridge. The Japanese design drew on current Mauser and Mannlicher features, and first appeared in 1905.***

The **Rifle Type 38** was adopted for Imperial Japanese service in 1905, and was a development of two earlier rifles selected by a commission headed by one Colonel Arisaka, who gave his name to a whole family of Japanese service rifles. The Type 38 used a mixture of design points and principles taken from contemporary Mauser and Mannlicher designs, mixed with a few Japanese innovations. The result was a sound enough rifle in 6.5-mm (0.256-in) calibre. This relatively small calibre, coupled with a cartridge of modest power, produced a rifle with a small recoil that exactly suited the slight Japanese.

This fact was further aided by the Type 38 rifle being rather long: when the rifle was used with a bayonet, as it usually was in action, this gave the Japanese soldier a considerable reach advantage for close-in warfare, but it also made the Type 38 a rather awkward rifle to handle. As well as being used by all the Japanese armed forces, the Type 38 was exported to nations such as Thailand, and was also used by several of the warring factions then prevalent in China. At one point during World War I the Type 38 was even purchased as a training weapon by the British army.

A shorter version, the **Carbine Type 38**, was widely used, and there was a version with a folding butt for use by airborne troops. There was also a version of the Type 38 known as the **Sniper's Rifle Type 97** which, apart from provision for a telescopic sight, had a revised bolt handle.

## New calibre

During the 1930s the Japanese gradually adopted a new service cartridge of 7.7-mm (0.303-in) calibre, and the Type 38 was revised as the **Rifle Type 99**. The Type 99 had several new features, including a sight that was supposed to be effective for firing at aircraft, and a folding monopod to assist accuracy. A special paratroop model that could be broken down into two halves was devised, but proved to be unreliable and was replaced by a 'take-down' version known as the **Parachutist's Rifle Type 2**. Not many were made.

Once the Pacific war was under way, from 1942 the production standards of Japanese rifles and carbines deteriorated rapidly; any items that could be left off were deleted, and simplifications were introduced onto the production lines. But overall standards went down to the point where some of the late production examples were virtually lethal to the user, many of them being constructed from very low-quality materials, for the simple reason that the Allied air and sea blockade denied the Japanese the use of anything better.

## Dire straits

By the end the arsenals were reduced to producing primitive single-shot weapons firing 8-mm (0.315-in) pistol cartridges, and even black-powder weapons. There was even a proposal to use bows firing explosive arrows. It was all a long way from the days when the Type 38 was one of the most widely used service rifles in the Orient.

***Japanese infantry during the assault on the Yenanyaung oilfields in Burma. The great length of the Arisaka type rifle, especially with bayonet attached, is obvious. This made the weapon awkward to handle, but also gave the generally short-statured Japanese soldier an effective reach in close combat.***

**SPECIFICATION**

**Rifle Type 38**
**Calibre:** 6.5-mm (0.256-in)
**Length overall:** 1275 mm (50.2 in)
**Length of barrel:** 797.5 mm (31.4 in)
**Weight:** 4.2 kg (9.25 lb)
**Muzzle velocity:** 731 m (2,400 ft) per second
**Feed:** 5-round box magazine

# Gewehr 98 and Karabiner 98k Rifles

***The Karabiner 98k was a slightly shortened version of the Gewehr 98, which served Germany in World War I and, although supposedly a carbine, it was as long as many rifles of the period.***

The 7.92-mm (0.312-in) **Gewehr 98** was the rifle with which the German army fought through World War I. It was a Mauser rifle first produced in 1898, but based on a design dating back to 1888.

In service the Mauser action proved sturdy and reliable, but in the years following 1918 the German army carried out a great deal of operational analysis that revealed, among other things, that the Gew 98 was too long and bulky for front-line use. As an immediate result the surviving Gew 98s were modified to **Karabiner 98b** standard. *Karabiner* is the German for carbine, but there was nothing of the carbine in the Karabiner 98b with a length unchanged from that of the Gew 98. The only changes were to the bolt handle, the sling swivels and the ability to use improved ammunition. To confuse matters further the original Gew 98 markings were retained.

***Digging in during the early stages of the war. The length of the Mauser-designed Kar 98k is obvious, making it difficult to handle in confined spaces. Given the short combat ranges typical of World War II, the Kar 98k's long-range capability was largely superfluous.***

***German soldiers train for combat, armed with Kar 98k rifles. The photograph was probably taken between the wars, as indicated by the mix of old and new pattern helmets being worn at the same time.***

## Shortened model

The Kar 98b was still in service with the German army in 1939 (and remained so throughout World War II), but by then the standard rifle was a slightly shorter version of the basic Mauser known as the **Karabiner 98k**. This was slightly shorter than the original Gew 98 but was still long for a carbine, despite the letter suffix 'k' standing for *kurz* (short). This rifle was based on a commercial Mauser model known as the **Standard** and widely produced throughout the inter-war years in countries such as Czechoslovakia, Belgium and China. The German version was placed in production in 1935 and thereafter made in very large numbers.

## Worsening standards

At first the standard of production was excellent, but once World War II had started the overall finish and standards fell to the extent that by the end of the war the wooden furniture was often laminated or of an inferior material, and items such as bayonet lugs were omitted. All manner of extras were evolved by the gadget-minded Germans for the Kar 98k, including grenade-launching devices, periscopic sights and folding butts for weapons used by airborne troops. There were also variations for sniper use, some with small telescopic sights mounted half way along the forestock and others with larger telescopes mounted over the bolt action.

Despite all the innovations by the Germans during World War II, the Kar 98k was still in production as the war ended, looking not all that different overall from the original Gew 98 except for the rough finish resulting from wartime shortages of labour and materials. By this time the Germans had to hand a whole array of Mauser rifles drawn from nearly all the armies of Europe, and most of them were used to equip one arm or another of the services by 1945. Some of these Mausers, most of which were very similar to the Gew 98 or Kar 98k, and were kept in production on Belgian and Czechoslovak lines for German use after 1939-40. Away to the east the Chinese armies were mainly equipped with the Mauser Standard rifles virtually identical to the Kar 98k.

There will always be arguments as to whether or not the Mauser rifles were better service rifles than the Lee-Enfield, M1903 Springfield and M1 Garand, but although the Mausers lacked some of the overall appeal of the Allied rifles they provided the German forces with long and reliable service. Very few remain in use, but many are still prized as collector's pieces and match rifles.

### SPECIFICATION

**Gewehr 98**
**Calibre:** 7.92-mm (0.312-in)
**Length overall:** 1250 mm (49.2 in)
**Length of barrel:** 740 mm (29.1 in)
**Weight:** 4.2 kg (9.26 lb)
**Muzzle velocity:** 640 m (2,100 ft) per second
**Feed:** 5-round box magazine

**Karabiner 98k**
**Calibre:** 7.92-mm (0.312-in)
**Length overall:** 1107 mm (43.6 in)
**Length of barrel:** 600 mm (23.6 in)
**Weight:** 3.9 kg (8.6 lb)
**Muzzle velocity:** 755 m (2,477 ft) per second
**Feed:** 5-round box magazine

# Maschinenpistole 43 and Sturmgewehr 44 Rifles

Despite the orders of Adolf Hitler, the German army was so determined to develop and use the gas-operated assault rifle that had been developed by Louis Schmeisser to fire the new 7.92-mm (0.312-in) Polte *kurz* (short) cartridge that it hid the experimental work under a new name. Originally the new rifle/cartridge combination was the **Maschinenkarabiner 42(H)** (the H was for Haenel, the developer and manufacturer), but to distract attention once Hitler had issued his ill-advised order it was changed to **Maschinenpistole 43**, or **MP 43**.

With the weapon in this form, the army went ahead from the development to the production stage, and the first examples were rushed to the Eastern Front, where they soon proved to be invaluable.

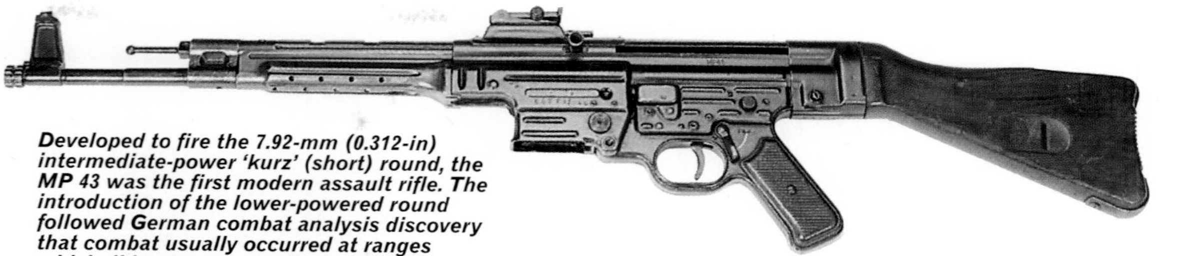

***Developed to fire the 7.92-mm (0.312-in) intermediate-power 'kurz' (short) round, the MP 43 was the first modern assault rifle. The introduction of the lower-powered round followed German combat analysis discovery that combat usually occurred at ranges which did not require high-power bullets.***

## Earliest assault rifle

The MP 43 was the first of what are today termed assault rifles. It could fire single shots for selective fire in defence, and yet was capable of producing automatic fire for shock effect in the attack or for close-quarter combat. It was able to do this by firing a relatively low-powered round that was adequate for most combat ranges but which could still be handled comfortably when the weapon was producing automatic fire. Tactically this had a tremendous effect on the way the infantryman could fight, as he was no longer dependent on supporting fire from machine-guns, being able to take his own personal support fire with him. This made German infantry units far more powerful because of the quantum increase in firepower that they could produce by comparison with that of units equipped with bolt-action rifles.

Once the importance of this increase in firepower had been fully realised, the MP 43 became a priority weapon and urgent requests were made for more and still more for the front-line troops. Initial supplies went mainly to elite units, but most went to the Eastern Front where they were most needed.

Unusually for wartime Germany, priority was given to production rather than development, and the only major change to the design was the **MP 43/1**, which had fittings for a grenade-launching cup on the muzzle. In 1944, for a reason undiscovered, the designation of the weapon was changed to **MP 44**, and late in the same year, after Hitler lifted his opposition to the weapon, a more forceful but also more accurate designation was bestowed on the weapon, which thereupon became known as the **Sturmgewehr 44**, which was generally abbreviated as **StG 44**. There were few if any production alterations to the design. Final production of the StG 44 was undertaken by Erma and Mauser as well as Haenel, and these major companies drew on the efforts of at least seven sub-contractors producing parts and assemblies.

***The Waffen SS were among the first troops to acquire the MP 43, and many were used in the battle of the Ardennes. The first combat use was probably on the Eastern Front, however, where the weapon was an immediate success.***

## Irrelevant accessories

Some accessories were produced for the MP 43 series. One was an infra-red night sight known as *Vampir*, but one of the oddest items ever to be produced for any weapon was the *Krummlauf* curved barrel that could direct bullets around corners. Apparently this device was developed for the clearing of tank-killing infantry squads from armoured vehicles, but it was a bizarre device that never worked properly and yet managed to absorb a great deal of development potential at a time when this could have been directed towards more rewarding things. The curved barrels were intended to direct fire at angles of between 30° and 45°, and special periscopic mirror sights were devised to aim their fire. Few were actually produced and even fewer were used operationally.

After the war large numbers of MP 43s were used by several nations such as Czechoslovakia, and were also used during some of the early Arab-Israeli conflicts.

**SPECIFICATION**

**StG 44**
**Calibre:** 7.92-mm (0.312-in)
**Length overall:** 940 mm (37 in)
**Length of barrel:** 419 mm (16.5 in)
**Weight:** 5.22 kg (11.5 lb)
**Muzzle velocity:** 650 m (2,132 ft) per second
**Rate of fire, cyclic:** 500 rounds per minute
**Feed:** 30-round box magazine

***Above: German troops seen late in the war on the Eastern Front illustrate the superb quality of German military equipment. In addition to the revolutionary Sturmgewehr being carried by the soldier third from the left, they are also equipped with the MG42 and the Panther tank.***

# Gewehr 41(W) & Gewehr 43 Rifles

***Developed from the Gewehr 41(W) with the Tokarev gas operating system, the Gewehr 43 was fitted with a telescopic sight mount and was a good sniper's rifle.***

The German army maintained an overall 'quality control' section that constantly sought ways to increase efficiency, and by 1940 this section had discovered the need for a self-loading rifle.

A specification was duly issued to industry, and Walther and Mauser each put forward designs that proved to be remarkably similar. Both used a method of operation known as the Bang system after its Danish designer, in which gases trapped around the muzzle are used to drive back a piston to carry out the reloading cycle. Troop trials soon proved that the Mauser design was unsuitable for service use and it was withdrawn, leaving the field free for the Walther design which became the 7.92-mm (0.312-in) **Gewehr 41(W)**.

Unfortunately for the Germans, once the Gewehr 41(W) reached front-line service, mainly on the Eastern Front, it proved to be somewhat less than a success. The Bang system proved to be too complex for reliable operation under service conditions, and the weapon was also too heavy for comfortable use as it was generally unhandy. The Gewehr 41(W) also proved to be difficult to manufacture and, as if all this was not enough, in action the weapon proved to be difficult and time-consuming to load. But for a while it was the only self-loading rifle the Germans had and it was kept in production to the extent of tens of thousands.

Most of the Gewehr 41(W)s were used on the Eastern Front, and it was there that the Germans encountered the Soviet Tokarev automatic rifle. This used a gas-operated system that tapped off gases from the barrel to operate the mechanism, and once they had investigated this system the Germans realised that they could adapt it to suit the Gewehr 41(W). The result was the **Gewehr 43**, which used the Tokarev system virtually unchanged.

### Swift production exit

Once the Gewehr 43 was in production, manufacture of the Gewehr 41(W) promptly ceased. The Gewehr 43 was much easier to make, and it was soon being churned out in large numbers. Front-line troops greatly appreciated the ease with which it could be loaded compared with the earlier rifle, and it became a popular weapon. All manner of production short-cuts were introduced into the design, including the use of wood laminates and even plastics for the furniture, and in 1944 an even simpler design known as the **Karabiner 43** was introduced, the Karabiner designation being adopted although the overall length was reduced by only some 50 mm (2 in).

Both the Gewehr 41(W) and the later Gewehr 43 used the standard German 7.92-mm cartridge, and were in no way related to the assault rifle programme that involved the 7.92-mm *kurz* cartridge. The retention of the rifle cartridge enabled the Gewehr 43 to be used as a very effective sniper rifle, and all examples had a telescopic sight mount. The Gewehr 43 was so good in the sniper role that many were retained in service with the Czechoslovak army for many years after World War II.

**SPECIFICATION**

| Gewehr 41(W) | Gewehr 43 |
|---|---|
| **Calibre:** 7.92-mm (0.312-in) | **Calibre:** 7.92-mm (0.312-in) |
| **Length overall:** 1124 mm (44.25 in) | **Length overall:** 1117 mm (44 in) |
| **Length of barrel:** 546 mm (21.5 in) | **Length of barrel:** 549 mm (21.61 in) |
| **Weight:** 5.03 kg (11.09 lb) | **Weight:** 4.4 kg (9.7 lb) |
| **Muzzle velocity:** 776 m (2,546 ft) per second | **Muzzle velocity:** 776 m (2,546 ft) per second |
| **Magazine:** 10-round box | **Magazine:** 10-round box |

# Fallschirmjägergewehr 42 Rifle

***The FG 42, seen here in the form of an early model, was an attempt to arm the German airborne arm with a rifle capable of providing full-power MG performance.***

By 1942 the Luftwaffe was encroaching on the preserves of the German army to an alarming extent for no other reason than petty wrangling, and when the army decided to adopt a self-loading rifle, the Luftwaffe decided that it too had to have such a weapon.

Instead of following the path followed by the army with its adoption of the *kurz* round, the Luftwaffe decided instead to retain the standard 7.92-mm (0.312-in) rifle cartridge and asked Rheinmetall to design a weapon to arm the Luftwaffe's parachute troops, the *Fallschirmjäger*.

Rheinmetall accordingly designed and produced one of the more remarkable small arms designs of World War II. This was the **Fallschirmjägergewehr 42** or **FG 42**, a weapon that somehow managed to compress the action required to produce automatic fire into a volume little larger than that of a conventional bolt action.

The FG 42 was certainly an eye-catching weapon, for the first examples had a sloping pistol grip, an oddly shaped plastic butt and a prominent bipod on the forestock. To cap it all there was a large muzzle attachment and provision for mounting a spike bayonet. The ammunition feed was from a side-mounted box magazine on the left, and the mechanism was gas-operated. All in all, the FG 42 was a complex weapon, but was not innovative as it was an amalgam of several existing systems.

### Difficult manufacture

Needless to say the Luftwaffe took to the FG 42 avidly and asked for more. It did not get them, for it soon transpired that the novelties of the FG 42 had to be paid for in a very complex and costly manufacturing process. In an attempt to speed production, some simplification was introduced. A simpler wooden butt was used and the pistol grip was replaced by a more orthodox component. The bipod was moved forward to the muzzle, and other shortcuts were introduced. Even so, by the end of the war only about 7,000 had been made.

It was after the war that the FG 42 made its biggest mark, for many of its design features were incorporated into later designs. Perhaps the most important of these was the compact gas-operated mechanism which could fire from a closed bolt position for single-shot fire and from an open bolt for automatic fire.

The FG 42 was a highly advanced design for its day, and its other advanced features included the 'straight line' layout from butt to muzzle. But for all this the FG 42 was too difficult to produce, and even by 1945 there were still some bugs to be ironed out. For all that, the FG 42 was a truly remarkable design achievement in overall terms.

***A drill book photograph of the FG 42 being fired in the prone position with its bipod folded. The FG 42 was a precursor of the modern-concept assault rifle.***

**SPECIFICATION**

| FG 42 | |
|---|---|
| **Calibre:** 7.92-mm (0.312-in) | **Weight:** 4.53 kg (9.99 lb) |
| **Length overall:** 940 mm (37 in) | **Muzzle velocity:** 761 m (2,500 ft) per second |
| **Length of barrel:** 502 mm (19.76 in) | **Rate of fire, cyclic:** 750-800 rpm |
| | **Magazine:** 20-round box |

# Tokarev Rifle

***The SVT40 was an early Soviet self-loading rifle, usually issued to NCOs and marksmen. A most influential weapon, it lent features to the German MP 43, and was the start of a chain leading to the modern AK range.***

Over the years the Soviets revealed a considerable talent for innovatory small arms design, and thus they were early in the move toward self-loading rifles. The first of these was the **Avtomaticheskaya Vintovka Simonova** designed by S. G. Simonov for introduction in 1936 (and thus known also as the **AVS36**). Although many were made and issued, the AVS was not a great success for it produced a prodigious muzzle blast and recoil, and it was all too easy for dust and dirt to get into the complex mechanism. The AVS thus had only a short service life.

The **Samozariadnyia Vintovka Tokareva** (**SVT38**) that replaced the AVS in 1938 was designed by F. V. Tokarev, and was initially not much of an improvement on the AVS. It was a gas-operated weapon, like the AVS, but in order to keep the rifle light the mechanism was far too flimsy for the stresses and strains of prolonged use. While the combination of a gas-operated system and a locking block cammed downwards into a recess in the receiver base proved basically sound, it gave rise to frequent troubles, mainly because parts broke. Thus the SVT38 was removed from production during 1940 and replaced by the much better **SVT40** in which the basic mechanism was retained but everything made more robust.

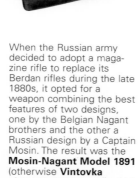

***Marines of the Soviet Northern Fleet in defensive positions, probably on exercise near Murmansk. The nearest man has a PPSh-41 sub-machine gun, and the others have Tokarev SVT40 rifles.***

## Continued problems

Even so, the SVT40 had a fierce recoil and considerable muzzle blast. To offset these effects, the SVT40 was fitted with a muzzle brake, initially with six ports but eventually with two. Theses muzzle brakes were of doubtful efficiency.

In order to get the best from the SVT40 the weapon was usually issued only to NCOs or carefully trained soldiers who could use their rapid fire potential to good effect. Some were fitted with telescopic sights for sniper use. A few weapons were converted to produce fully automatic fire as the **AVT40**, but this conversion was not a great success. There was also a carbine version, but this probably suffered excessively from the heavy recoil problem and only a few were made.

## Germans impressed

When the Germans invaded the USSR in 1941 they soon encountered the SVT38 and the SVT40. Any they could capture they promptly used under the designation **Selbstlade-gewehr 258(r)** and **Selbstladegewehr 259(r)**, but once the basic gas-operated mechanism had been examined it was incorporated into the Gewehr 43.

Soviet production of the SVT40 continued almost until the end of the war. Although there were never enough produced to meet demand, the SVT40 had a considerable influence on future Soviet small arms development leading to the AK-47 series. It also made a considerable impact on Soviet infantry tactics for the SVT40 demonstrated the importance of increased firepower for the infantry, a factor later emphasized by the introduction of the German MP 43 on the Eastern Front.

**SPECIFICATION**

| | |
|---|---|
| **Tokarev SVT40** | **Weight:** 3.89 kg (8.58 lb) |
| **Calibre:** 7.62-mm (0.3-in) | **Muzzle velocity:** 830 m (2,723 ft) per second |
| **Length overall:** 1222 mm (48.1 in) | **Magazine:** 10-round box |
| **Length of barrel:** 625 mm (24.6 in) | |

# Mosin-Nagant Rifle

***A Model 1938 Mosin-Nagant carbine. This variant, like the Model 1930, was simplified for ease of manufacture and was issued to the cavalry. Many were captured by Germany in the early war years.***

***A Red Army private at about the time of the 'Winter War' with Finland in the winter of 1940. He is armed with the Model 1930 variant of the Mosin-Nagant, a dragoon-length version of the rifle.***

When the Russian army decided to adopt a magazine rifle to replace its Berdan rifles during the late 1880s, it opted for a weapon combining the best features of two designs, one by the Belgian Nagant brothers and the other a Russian design by a Captain Mosin. The result was the **Mosin-Nagant Model 1891** (otherwise **Vintovka obrazets 1891g**) with which the Tsarist army fought its last battles up to 1917. The Model 1891 was then adopted by the new Red Army, and the rifle remained in use for many years.

The Model 1891 fired a 7.62-mm (0.3-in) cartridge and was a sound but generally unremarkable design. The bolt action was rather complicated and the ammunition feed used a holding device that offered only one round under spring tension to the bolt for reloading. But for all this it was a sound enough weapon, although rather long. This was mainly to increase the reach of the rifle when fitted with the long socket bayonet, which was almost a permanent fixture in action. The bayonet had a cruciform point that was used to dismantle the weapon.

## Metric updating

The original Model 1891s had their sights marked in arshins, an archaic Russian measurement equivalent to 0.71 m (27.95 in), but after 1918 these sights were metricated. In 1930 there began a modernisation programme, and all new rifles were produced to the new **Model 1891/30** standard, which was slightly shorter than the original and had several design alterations to ease production. It was the Model 1891/30 that was the main Red Army service rifle of World War II.

## Carbine variants

The Mosin-Nagant weapons were also produced in carbine form. The first of these was the **Model 1910**, followed much later by the **Model 1938** equivalent to the Model 1891/30. In 1944 there appeared the **Model 1944**, but this was only a Model 1938 with a permanently fixed folding bayonet.

The Mosin-Nagant rifles were also used by the Finns (**m/27** shortened Model 1891, **m/28/30** with altered sights, and re-stocked **m/39**), the Poles (**karabin wz 91/98/25**) and also by the Germans, who issued captured weapons to their own second-line garrison and militia units. Most of these were Model 1891/30s redesignated **Gewehr 254(r)**, but by 1945 even Model 1891s were being issued under the designation **Gewehr 252(r)**.

With the introduction of the automatic rifle in the years after World War II, the surviving Mosin-Nagant rifle soon disappeared from Red Army service.

**SPECIFICATION**

| | |
|---|---|
| **Model 1891/30 rifle** | **Model 1938 carbine** |
| **Calibre:** 7.62-mm (0.3-in) | **Calibre:** 7.62-mm (0.3-in) |
| **Length overall:** 1232 mm (48.5 in) | **Length overall:** 1016 mm (40 in) |
| **Length of barrel:** 729 mm (28.7 in) | **Length of barrel:** 508 mm (20 in) |
| **Weight:** 4 kg (8.8 lb) | **Weight:** 3.47 kg (7.6 lb) |
| **Muzzle velocity:** 811 m (2,660 ft) per second | **Muzzle velocity:** 766 m (2,514 ft) per second |
| **Magazine:** 5-round box | **Magazine:** 5-round box |

# Rifle No. 4 Mk I

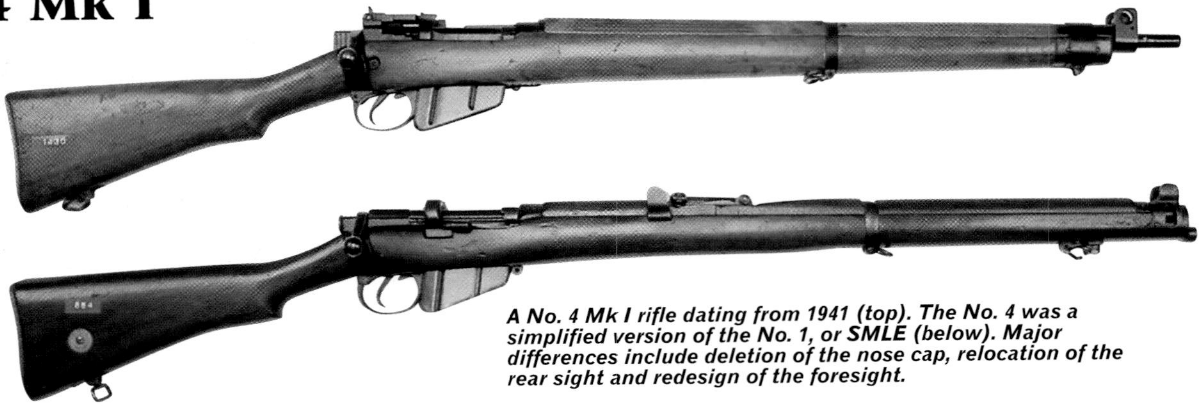

*A No. 4 Mk I rifle dating from 1941 (top). The No. 4 was a simplified version of the No. 1, or SMLE (below). Major differences include deletion of the nose cap, relocation of the rear sight and redesign of the foresight.*

Although the Lee-Enfield No. 1 Mk III rifle performed sterling service throughout World War I, it was an expensive and time-consuming weapon to produce as every example had to be made virtually by hand. In the years after 1919, consideration was therefore given to a version of the basic design that could be mass-produced, and in 1931 a trial series of a rifle known as the No. 1 Mk VI was produced. This was accepted as suitable for service, but at the time there were no funds to launch production, so it was not until November 1939 that the go-ahead was given for what was then redesignated the **Rifle No. 4 Mk I**.

The No. 4 Mk I was designed from the outset for mass production, and differed from the original No. 1 Mk III in several respects: the No. 4 Mk I had a much heavier barrel that improved overall accuracy; the muzzle protruded from the forestock by an easily discernible amount and provided the No. 4 Mk I with a definite recognition point; and the sights were moved back to a position over the receiver, which made them easier to use and also provided a longer sighting base, again an aid to accuracy.

## Unpopular bayonet

There were numerous other small changes, most of them introduced to assist production, but for the soldier the biggest change was to the muzzle. Here, a different fitting was introduced for a new bayonet, which was a light and simple spike with no grip or anything like it, so depriving the soldier of one of his favourite front-line tools. The spike bayonet was not liked but, being simple and easy to produce, it was retained in use for many years.

## Alongside the No. 1

The first No. 4 Mk Is were issued late in 1940, and thereafter the type supplemented the No. 1 Mk III. But during World War II the No. 1 Mk III was never entirely replaced. This was not for lack of production effort, for the No. 4 Mk I was churned out in very large numbers by numerous small arms production facilities all over the UK and even in the USA. These 'American' rifles were made at the Stevens-Savage plant in Long Branch and were known as the **No. 4 Mk I*** as they differed in the manner in which the bolt could be removed for cleaning. These American examples also differed in other small details, introduced mostly to assist production on US tooling and by American methods.

*Above: Carrying No. 1 rifles with bayonets fixed, New Zealand infantry fight their way into a building during the fighting for Cassino in 1943-44.*

*Right: In the ruins of the Norman city of Caen, British infantry had to be especially careful as the debris made excellent sniper cover. This man carries a No. 4 rifle.*

*Men of a Gurkha regiment are briefed by an officer before a foray in the jungles of Burma. The men are carrying No. 4 rifles, which were on the large side for the comparatively small stature of the Gurkhas, and also relatively unwieldy for jungle fighting.*

In service the No. 4 Mk I proved itself an excellent weapon, to the extent that many now regard the design as one of the finest of all service rifles of the bolt-action era. It was capable of withstanding even the roughest handling, and could deliver accurate fire for prolonged periods. It was relatively easy to strip and keep clean using the 'pull-through' carried inside the butt trap along with an oil bottle and a few pieces of the famous 'four by two' cleaning rag.

Special sniper's versions of the No. 4 were also produced. These used various types of telescopic sight over the receiver, as well as a special butt plate. The rifles were usually selected from production examples and were virtually rebuilt and restocked before issue with the revised designation **Rifle No. 4 Mark I(T)**.

The No. 4 Mk I is still in limited service around the world. Many current service examples have been revised with new 7.62-mm (0.3-in) barrels, and others have been converted to match or hunting rifles.

**SPECIFICATION**

| | |
|---|---|
| **Rifle No. 4 Mk I** | **Weight:** 4.14 kg (9.125 lb) |
| **Calibre:** 0.303-in (7.7-mm) | **Muzzle velocity:** 751 m (2,465 ft) per second |
| **Length overall:** 1129 mm (44.4 in) | **Magazine:** 10-round box |
| **Length of barrel:** 640 mm (25.2 in) | |

# Rifle No. 5 Mk I

By 1943 the British and Commonwealth armies fighting in the jungles of Burma and other Far Eastern areas began to question the suitability of the No. 1 and No. 4 Lee-Enfield rifles, which were too long and awkward. A shortened No. 4 was requested, and by September 1944 approval had been given for the **Rifle No. 5 Mk I**. This was virtually the No. 4 Mk I with a much shortened barrel, the fore-stock modified to accommodate the new barrel, and the sights changed to reflect the decreased-range performance of the shorter barrel.

## Flash hider

Two other modifications were also introduced, both of them associated with the short barrel: these were a conical muzzle attachment that was meant to act as a flash hider, and a rubber pad on the butt. Both had to be introduced as the shortening of the barrel gave rise to two unwanted side effects: the prodigious muzzle flash produced by firing a normal rifle cartridge in a short barrel, and the ferocious recoil resulting from the same unfortunate factor.

In a normal long rifle barrel most of the flash produced on firing is contained within the barrel and so are some of the recoil forces. In a shortened barrel a good proportion of the propellant gases are still 'unused' as the bullet leaves the muzzle, hence the added recoil.

## Lack of enthusiasm

The soldiers did not like the new weapon one bit, but they had to admit that in jungle warfare the No. 5 Mk I was a much handier weapon to carry and use. They also welcomed the reintroduction of a blade-type bayonet that fitted onto a lug under the muzzle attachment. In fact, following on from the first production order for 100,000 rifles made in 1944 it was thought that the No. 5 Mk I would become the standard service rifle of the years following World War II, despite the recoil and flash factors. But this did not happen.

The No. 5 Mk I had one built-in problem, quite apart from the flash and recoil, and that problem was never eradicated. For a reason that was never discovered the weapon was inaccurate. Even after a long period of 'zeroing', the accuracy would gradually 'wander' and be lost. All manner of modifications to the stocking of the weapon were tried, but the inaccuracy was never eliminated and the true cause was never discovered. Thus the No. 5 was not accepted as the standard service rifle, the No. 4 Mk I being retained until the Belgian FN was adopted in the 1950s. Most of the No. 5 rifles were retained for use by specialist units such as those operating in the Far East and Africa, and some are still in use in those areas by various armies.

***Developed specifically for jungle operations, the No. 5 rifle was not an unqualified success as it had a vicious recoil. It saw action in Kenya and Malaya (shown here), as well as at the end of World War II.***

**SPECIFICATION**

| | |
|---|---|
| **Rifle No. 5 Mk I** | **Weight:** 3.25 kg (7.15 lb) |
| **Calibre:** 0.303-in (7.7-mm) | **Muzzle velocity:** about 730 m (2,400 ft) per second |
| **Length overall:** 1003 mm (39.5 in) | **Magazine:** 10-round box |
| **Length of barrel:** 476 mm (18.75 in) | |

# Rifle, Caliber .30, Model 1903

In 1903 the US Army decided to replace its existing Krag-Jorgensen rifles and adopted a rifle based on the Mauser system. This rifle, officially known as the **US Magazine Rifle, Caliber .30, Model of 1903** (or **M1903**) was first produced at the famous Springfield Arsenal and has thus become almost exclusively known as the **Springfield**. It was produced as a weapon for use by infantry and cavalry, and was thus much shorter than most contemporary rifles, but it was a well-balanced and attractive rifle that soon proved itself to be a fine service weapon.

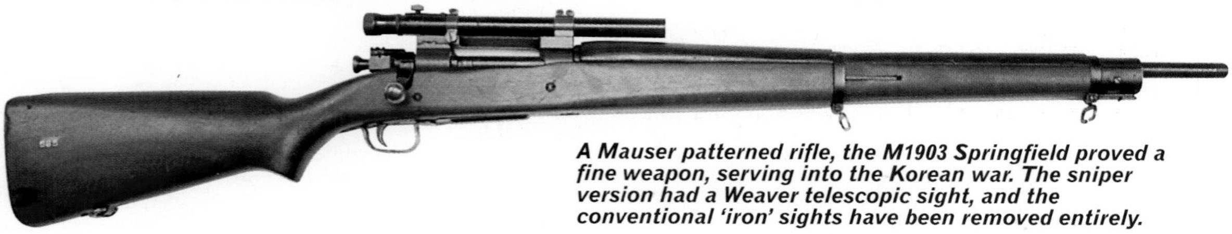

***A Mauser patterned rifle, the M1903 Springfield proved a fine weapon, serving into the Korean war. The sniper version had a Weaver telescopic sight, and the conventional 'iron' sights have been removed entirely.***

## Updated ammunition

Soon after the M1903 had entered production the original blunt-nosed ammunition was replaced by newer 'pointed' ammunition that is now generally known as the .30-06 (thirty-ought six) as it was a 0.3-in (7.62-mm) round introduced in 1906. This remained the standard US service cartridge for many years. The M1903 served throughout World War I, and in 1929 the design was modified to **M1903A1** standard by the introduction of a form of pistol grip to assist aiming. The **M1903A2** was produced as a sub-calibre weapon inserted into the barrels of coastal guns for low-cost training purposes.

When the USA entered World War II in 1941 the new M1 Garand rifle was not available in the numbers required, so the M1903 was placed back into large-scale production, this time as the **M1903A3**. This version was modified to suit modern mass-production methods, but it was still a well-made rifle. Some parts were stampings rather than machined units, but the main change was movement of the sights from over the barrel to a position over the bolt action.

## Sniper's model

The only other service version was the **M1903A4**. This was a sniper's version fitted with a Weaver telescopic sight without conventional 'iron' sights. The M1903A4 was still in service during the Korean War of the 1950s.

The M1903 was used by several Allied armies during World War II. Many of the US troops who landed in Normandy on D-Day in June 1944 were still equipped with the Springfield. In 1940 some were sent to the UK to equip Home Guard units, and the type was even placed back into production to a British order, only for the order to be taken over for the use of US forces.

The M1903 and its variants may still be met today with a few smaller armed forces. But many are also retained as target or hunting rifles, for the M1903 Springfield is still regarded as one of the classic rifles of all time. It is even now a rifle that is a delight to handle and fire, and many are now owned by weapon collectors for those reasons alone.

***The accuracy of the M1903 made it a popular weapon with sharpshooters, and in positions where a single well-aimed shot can be decisive, the small box magazine of five rounds was no handicap.***

**SPECIFICATION**

| | |
|---|---|
| **M1903A1** | **Weight:** 4.1 kg (9 lb) |
| **Calibre:** 7.62-mm (0.3-in) | **Muzzle velocity:** 855 m (2,805 ft) per second |
| **Length overall:** 1105 mm (43.5 in) | **Magazine:** 5-round box |
| **Length of barrel:** 610 mm (24 in) | |

# Rifle, Caliber .30, M1 (Garand)

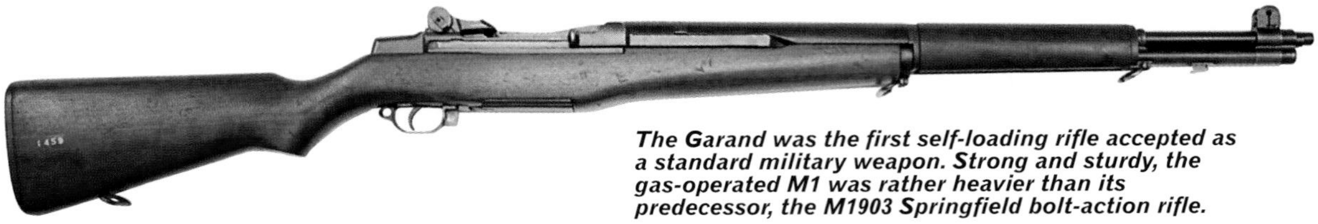

*The Garand was the first self-loading rifle accepted as a standard military weapon. Strong and sturdy, the gas-operated M1 was rather heavier than its predecessor, the M1903 Springfield bolt-action rifle.*

One of the main distinctions of the **Rifle, Caliber .30, M1**, almost universally known as the **Garand**, is that it was the first self-loading rifle to be accepted for military service. That acceptance happened during 1932, but there followed a distinct gap before the rifle entered service. This interval resulted from the fact that it took some time for the production facilities to tool up for the complex manufacturing processes demanded by the design. The rifle was created by John C. Garand, who spent a great deal of time developing the design. This had the useful benefit that once the weapon had entered production, it was found to require very few alterations. As a result, the last M1 to be completed looked very much like the first weapon of the series.

## Gold-plated rifle

As already mentioned, the M1 was a complicated and expensive weapon to manufacture, largely as a result of the numerous machining operations that were needed on many of the weapon's components. But in overall terms the Garand was a strong weapon, and in action proved to be sturdy. On the other side of the coin, however, the Garand was somewhat heavier than comparable bolt-action rifles.

The M1 was a gas-operated weapon. Thus gases were tapped off from the barrel near the muzzle to drive back a piston that in turn worked the operating system through the cycle of unlocking and driving back the bolt. The spent cartridge case was extracted and ejected as the bolt mechanism moved to the rear until checked and driven forward once more by the main spring to lift and chamber a fresh round before reaching its forward position and being locked once more, allowing the firer to pull the trigger once again.

When the USA entered World War II at the beginning of December 1941, most of the American regular forces were equipped with the M1. However, the rapid increase of numbers of men in uniform meant that the old M1903 Springfield rifle had to be placed back into production as a quick increase in the flow of M1s from the lines was virtually impossible for reason largely of the tooling problems. But gradually the manufacturing rate was built up, and some 5.5 million of these rifles had been made by the end of the war. Even so, production of the M1 was resumed during the Korean War of the early 1950s.

*Garand-armed infantrymen of the US 4th Armored Division are seen in action in the Ardennes during the drive to relieve Bastogne and the trapped 101st Airborne Division at the end of 1944 and start of 1945.*

## Genuine war winner

For the American forces the M1 Garand was a war-winning weapon whose strong construction earned the gratitude of many. But the rifle did possess one significant operational fault, namely its ammunition feed. Firstly, ammunition was fed into the rifle in eight-round clips, and the loading system was so arranged that it was possible to load only the full eight rounds or nothing. Secondly, after the last round had been fired, the empty clip was ejected from the receiver with a definite and pronounced sound that advertised to any nearby enemy that the firer's rifle was empty. This problem was not eliminated from the M1 until 1957, when the US Army introduced the M14 rifle which was virtually a reworked M1 Garand with an increased ammunition capacity.

Many sub-variants of the M1 were produced but few actually saw service as the basic M1 proved to be more than adequate for most purposes. There were two special sniper versions, the **M1C** and the **M1D**, both produced in modest numbers during 1944. Each had extras such as a muzzle flash cone and butt plates.

## German service

The Germans used as many M1 rifles as they could capture with the designation **Selbstladegewehr 251(a)**, and the Japanese produced their own copy, the 7.7-mm (0.303-in) **Rifle Type 5**, of which only prototypes had been completed by the time the war ended.

Post-war the M1 went on for many years as the standard US service rifle, and some were to be found in the hands of National Guard and other such units until recent times. Several nations continue to use the M1, and many designers have used the basic action as the basis for their own products: many Beretta rifles from Italy use the Garand system, as does the US 5.56-mm (0.22-in) Ruger Mini-14.

*A GI runs for cover as he comes under fire on Okinawa. The self-loading Garand gave US infantrymen a rate of fire advantage over opponents armed with bolt-action weapons.*

**SPECIFICATION**

**Rifle M1**
**Calibre:** 7.62-mm (0.3-in)
**Length overall:** 1.107 m (43.6 in)
**Length of barrel:** 609 mm (24 in)
**Weight:** 4.313 kg (9.5 lb)
**Muzzle velocity:** 855 m (2,805 ft) per second
**Magazine:** 8-round box

# Carbine, Caliber .30, M1, M1A1, M2 and M3

***Originally produced by Winchester, the lightweight M1 carbine was eventually manufactured by more than 10 companies in numbers exceeding six million.***

The traditional personal weapon of second-line troops and specialists such as machine-gunners has generally been the pistol. However, when the US Army considered the equipment of such soldiers during 1940 it made a request for some form of carbine that could be easily handled and also readily stowed in the vehicles that were often used by such troops.

The result was a competition in which several manufacturers submitted proposals for a weapon that was likely to be ordered in large and therefore lucrative numbers. The winning design was that offered by the Winchester company, and this was standardised for service as the **Carbine, Caliber .30, M1**.

## Intermediate power

The M1 carbine was based on the use of an unusual gas-operated system and was designed round a special cartridge that was intermediate in power between a pistol cartridge and a rifle cartridge.

The system works by tapping propellant gases from the underside of the barrel through a very small hole to pass into a sealed cylinder and so impinge on the head of a piston-like operating slide that moves back and thus starts the process of unlocking the bolt, extracting the spent case, compressing the return spring, chambering a fresh round and finally locking the bolt once more.

From the start the M1 carbine was an immediate success with the troops to whom it was issued. It was light and easy to handle, and this led to the situation in which the employment of the new weapon soon spread from the second-echelon troops who were supposed to be issued with the carbine, to front-line troops such as officers and weapon teams.

In order to speed its introduction into service the M1 had been created as a single-shot weapon, and there was also a special variant with a folding stock known as the **M1A1**. This was produced for use by airborne units.

Later during World War II, a capability for automatic fire was added to create the variant known as the **M2**, which had a cyclic rate of about 750 to 775 rounds per minute; the weapon used a curved box magazine holding 30 rounds that could also be used on the M1.

***A US Marine, member of a machine-gun crew in the Pacific, clutches his M1 carbine and also the ammunition belt for a Browning 7.62-mm (0.3-in) machine-gun while waiting for his partner to hurl a hand grenade.***

The **M3** was a special night-fighting version with a large infra-red night sight, but only about 2,100 of these weapons were made. The M3 proved to be the one version of the M1 carbine series that was not produced in quantity, for by the time the war ended the production total had reached 6,332 million examples of all versions, making the series the most prolific personal weapon family of the World War II period.

For all its handiness, the M1 carbine series had one major drawback, and that was the cartridge round which it had been designed. Being an intermediate-power type, the cartridge was characterised by a general lack of stopping power, even at close ranges. Being a carbine the M1 also lacked range, and was effective only to 100 m (110 yards) or so. But these drawbacks were more than offset by the overall handiness of the weapon. The M1 and its derivatives were easy to stow in vehicles or aircraft, and the M1A1 with its folding butt was even smaller. The weapon handled well in action and, after enough had been captured in the later stages of the European war, was deemed good enough for German use as the **Selbstladekarabiner 455(a)**.

## Rapid disappearance

But for all its mass production and war-time success, the M1 is now little used by armed forces anywhere. Many police forces retain the type, mainly because the low-powered cartridge offers a greater possibility of causing 'collateral damage' to bystanders and others, than more powerful cartridges, especially in operations in urban areas. Typical of these police operators was the Royal Ulster Constabulary, which used the Carbine M1 as a counter to the far more powerful Armalites typically used by the nationalist terrorists of the Irish Republican Army and their rival loyalist terrorists.

Another part of the M1 story is the current lack of adoption of the M1's intermediate-power cartridge. During the war years these cartridges were churned out in millions but now the cartridge is little used and has not been adopted for any other major weapon.

***Front-line troops soon found that the easily handled M1 carbine was much less of a burden than a rifle when slogging through the surf or the jungle, and it began appearing with front-line US Marine Corps units.***

**SPECIFICATION**

| | |
|---|---|
| **Carbine M1** | **Weight:** 2.36 kg (5.2 lb) |
| **Calibre:** 7.62-mm (0.3-in) | **Muzzle velocity:** 600 m (1,970 ft) per second |
| **Length overall:** 904 mm (35.6 in) | **Magazine:** 15- or 30-round box |
| **Length of barrel:** 457 mm (18 in) | |

# CETME Modelo 58 Assault rifle

*The core of the Mauser team which designed the German Sturmgewehr 45 decamped to Spain after the war and developed a new assault rifle based on the StG 45's layout. The Modelo 58 is made of low-grade steel and built with the emphasis on cheapness and reliability rather than looks.*

The **CETME Modelo 58** has a long history stretching back to the German Sturmgewehr 45 (StG 45) of World War II. This was an attempt by Mauser designers to produce a low-cost assault rifle incorporating a novel system using rollers and cams to lock the bolt at the instant of firing. After World War II's end the nucleus of the StG 45 design team moved to Spain and established a design team under the aegis of the Centro de Estudios Tecnicos do Materiales Especiales (CETME), outside Madrid.

With CETME the roller locking system was gradually perfected. The resulting assault rifle looked nothing like the StG 45 starting point, but the original low-cost manufacturing target was met. The assault rifle produced by CETME was made from low-grade steels and much of it was stamped and shaped using sheet steel. An automatic-fire capability was featured, and in overall terms the weapon was simple and basic.

*The Spanish army adopted the CETME as its standard rifle in 1958, initially buying the Modelo B, chambered for a unique, light, 7.62-mm (0.3-in) round. In 1964 Spain decided to adopt the more powerful 7.62-mm NATO cartridge, and CETME modified their design accordingly to make the Modelo C.*

## Initial German sale

It was 1956 before the first sales were made to West Germany. This involved a batch of only 400 rifles, but the Germans decided that some modifications to the rifle were needed to enable the weapon to meet their requirements. By a series of licence agreements (between a CETME licensed production offshoot in the Netherlands and Heckler & Koch) the CETME rifle became the Heckler & Koch G3, although the Spanish appear to have gained little from the deal.

In 1958 the Spanish army decided to adopt the CETME rifle in a form known as the **Modelo B**, and this became the Modelo 58. The Modelo 58 fired a special cartridge outwardly identical to the standard NATO 7.62-mm (0.3-in) cartridge but using a lighter bullet and propellant charge. This made the rifle much easier to fire (as a result of the reduced recoil) but also made the cartridge non-standard as far as other NATO cartridge users were concerned. In 1964 the Spanish adopted the NATO cartridge in place of their own less powerful product, and rifles adapted or produced to fire the NATO round became the **Modelo C**.

The Modelo 58 has since been produced in several versions, some with bipods, some with semi-automatic mechanisms and others with folding butts, and there has even been a sniper version fitted with a telescopic sight. The latest version is the **Modelo L** chambered in 5.56 mm (0.219 in), but the basic Model 58 is still available from CETME.

| SPECIFICATION | |
|---|---|
| **Modelo C** | **Muzzle velocity:** 780 m (2,559 ft) per second |
| **Calibre:** 7.62-mm (0.3-in) | **Rate of fire, cyclic:** 600 rounds per minute |
| **Length overall:** 1016 m (40 in) | **Feed:** 20-round straight box |
| **Length of barrel:** 450 mm (17.7 in) | |
| **Weight:** 4.49 kg (9.9 lb) | |

# SIG Assault rifles

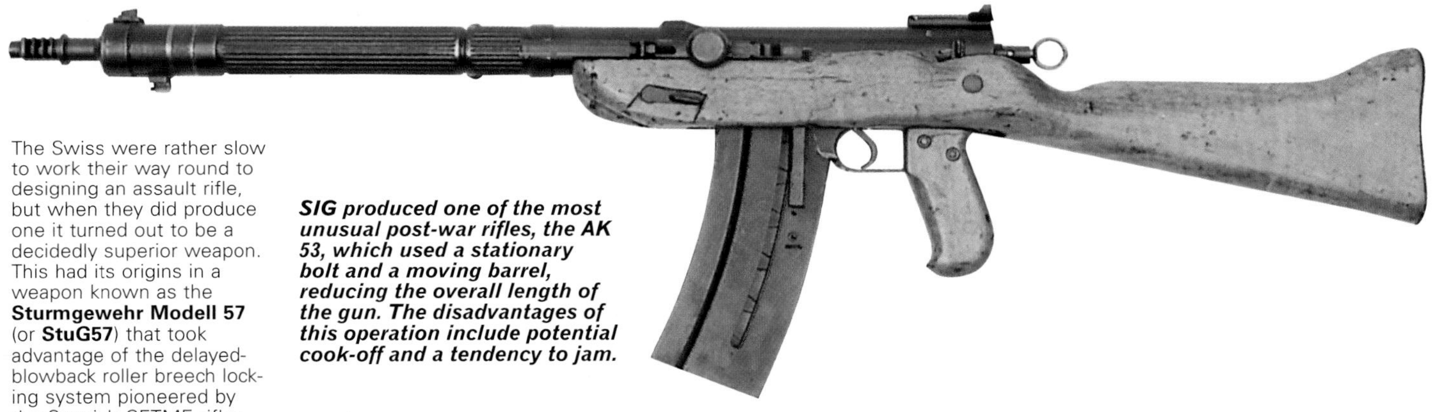

*SIG produced one of the most unusual post-war rifles, the AK 53, which used a stationary bolt and a moving barrel, reducing the overall length of the gun. The disadvantages of this operation include potential cook-off and a tendency to jam.*

The Swiss were rather slow to work their way round to designing an assault rifle, but when they did produce one it turned out to be a decidedly superior weapon. This had its origins in a weapon known as the **Sturmgewehr Modell 57** (or **StuG57**) that took advantage of the delayed-blowback roller breech locking system pioneered by the Spanish CETME rifles. This rifle was produced by SIG for the Swiss army calibred for the national 7.5-mm (0.295-in) rifle cartridge, and even carried over the fluted chamber of the CETME rifle.

## First-class handling

At first sight the StuG57 looked odd and awkward. In use it was quite the opposite. As always, the high standard of SIG manufacture made it a good weapon to handle, and Swiss soldiers liked the integral bipod and grenade launcher. The use of the Swiss cartridge limited sales, so SIG went one stage further and developed the **SG510** series of rifles to fire more internationally accepted cartridges. In many ways the SG510 was identical to the StuG57 and carried over the extremely high standards of workmanship which, in their turn, meant that although the weapon was a soldier's dream, it was very expensive. As a result sales were few. The Swiss army purchased the larger batches, but some went to African and South American nations.

## Numerous variants

This was not for want of trying on the part of the SIG designers. They produced several versions. The first was the **SG510-1** chambered for the 7.62-mm (0.3-in) NATO cartridge. The **SG510-2** was a lighter version of the SG510-1. The **SG510-3** was produced to fire the Soviet 7.62-mm short cartridge used on the AK-47. The **SG510-4** was another 7.62-mm NATO round model, and there was also a single-shot only sporting version known as the **SG-AMT** which was sold in large numbers to Swiss target-shooters.

The SG510-3 and SG510-4 had some extra features. One was an indicator on the magazine to show how many rounds were left and another was a folding winter trigger. The bipod (folding up over the barrel) was retained, and both had provision for optical sights for night vision or sniping.

The StuG57 and SG510 can still be found hanging on the walls of many Swiss army reservists, and numbers of the SG510 are still in use in Bolivia and Chile.

| SPECIFICATION | |
|---|---|
| **SG510-4** | **Muzzle velocity:** 790 m (2,592 ft) per second |
| **Calibre:** 7.62-mm (0.3-in) | **Rate of fire, cyclic:** 600 rounds per minute |
| **Length overall:** 1016 m (40 in) | **Feed:** 20-round straight box |
| **Length of barrel:** 505 mm (19.8 in) | |
| **Weight:** 4.45 kg (9.81 lb) | |

# Beretta BM59
## Rifle

***The BM59 is based on the US M1 Garand self-loading rifle, which Beretta was producing under licence when NATO adopted the 7.62-mm x 51 cartridge. Beretta modified the M1 design to accept the new round.***

In 1945 Beretta started the licensed manufacture of the American M1 Garand semi-automatic rifle for the Italian armed forces, and by 1961 had made about 100,000, some for export to Denmark and Indonesia. The introduction of the NATO 7.62-mm (0.3-in) cartridge meant that these rifles would have to be replaced as they fired the American World War II 0.3-in round, for a mere rechambering of the existing Garand rifles would have meant that the Italian armed forces would have been saddled with a rifle of outdated design for years to come.

### 'Breathed on' Garand

The Beretta designers had for some time before 1961 been contemplating a revision of the basic Garand design to produce a selective-fire weapon using as much as possible of the existing mechanism. The result was the **Beretta BM59**, which was the Garand at heart but modified to provide the required automatic-fire feature. It fired the NATO standard 7.62-mm cartridge, of which 20 were carried in a detachable box magazine replacing the old eight-round magazine. Some other slight alterations were introduced, but basically the BM59 was a 'breathed-on' Garand.

### Special-role variants

Almost as as soon as the BM59 was placed in production for the Italian armed forces a number of variants began to appear. The basic model was the **BM59 Mk 1**, issued to most of the Italian army. Then came the **BM59 Mk 2** with a pistol grip and a light bipod. The next two variants were virtually identical: the **BM59 Mk 3 Paracudisti** for use by airborne units had a removable grenade launcher at the muzzle, while the **BM59 Mk 3 Alpini** model for mountain troops had a fixed grenade launcher. These two versions both had folding skeleton butts and light bipods. On the **BM59 Mark 4** the bipod was much more robust, for this version was intended as a squad fire-support weapon. The Mk 4 also had a heavier barrel and a butt strap to allow it to be used for its fire-support role.

The BM59 proved to be an excellent modification of an existing design and it is still in use by the Italian armed forces. It was built at one time under licence in Morocco and Indonesia, and Nigeria planned to produce the BM59 as well, though the Biafran War put paid to that project.

The two drawbacks to the BM59 compared with many contemporary designs are its weight and the need for extensive machining during manufacture. For all that the BM59 is a very robust and reliable weapon that still has some service life left to run.

**SPECIFICATION**

**BM59 Mk 1**
**Calibre:** 7.62-mm (0.3-in)
**Length overall:** 1095 m (43.1 in)
**Length of barrel:** 490 mm (19.3 in)
**Weight:** unloaded 4.6 kg (10.14 lb)
**Muzzle velocity:** 823 m (2,700 ft) per second
**Rate of fire, cyclic:** 750 rounds per minute
**Feed:** 20-round curved box

# Fusil Automatique Modèle 49 Rifle

***The FN mle 49 is the ancestor of the FN FAL, designed before the war by Dieudonné Saive, who escaped to the UK when the Germans overran Belgium. While in England, Saive continued to develop his designs, and after the war the mle 49 was sold to Egypt and Latin America.***

***Weapons produced to a high standard often lose potential sales to cheaper weapons, but FN managed to sell its mle 49 to several different armies, offering it in many calibres. This Egyptian carries the 7.92-mm (0.312-in) model.***

Made by the Fabrique Nationale d'Armes de Guerre organisation based at Herstal in Belgium, the **Fusil Automatique Modèle 49** was known by several other names: to some it was the **Saive**, to others the **SAFN (Saive Automatique, FN)** and to more as the **ABL (Arme Belgique Legère)**. The weapon was actually designed before World War II, but the arrival of the war led to the temporary shelving of the project, ready for it to be revived as soon as peace had arrived once more. The weapon was designed by one D. J. Saive, who moved to the UK when the Germans arrived in Belgium during May 1940 and spent the rest of World War II working on small arms designs for the British. In 1945 he offered his pre-war design to the British army, which tested it but then turned down the offer.

### Return to Belgium

Once the new rifle's design had been returned to Belgium, the weapon entered production by FN, and much of the company's growing prosperity from the late 1940s started with the good sales record of the new rifle.

### Sound design

By whatever name it was called, the Modèle 49 was in basic design a gas-operated self-loading rifle. The locking of the bolt was achieved by the operation of cams in the sides of the receiver, which caused the bolt to tilt into the locked position at just the correct instant. This action was notably strong, and could therefore absorb a great deal of hard use, but it also meant that the rifle's entire mechanism had to be very carefully machined out of high-quality materials.

The combination of high-grade materials and the use of extensive machining rendered the weapon rather expensive to manufacture, but when the Modèle 49 was placed on the open market in 1949 it sold surprisingly well. This was the result partially of the fact that the Modèle 49 was offered in a variety of calibres, ranging from 7-mm (0.275-in) and 7.65-mm (0.301-in), which were both well established calibres on the continent of Europe, to 7.92-mm (0.312-in) which was then widely used as a legacy of the German control of most of Europe in World War II, and the American 0.3-in (7.62-mm). In all these well-established calibres, the Modèle 49 was firing full-power rifle cartridges.

The Modèle 49 was sold not only in Europe but also to Venezuela and Colombia in South America and to Indonesia in South-East Asia. One of the largest sales was made to Egypt, where the Modèle 49 remained in use for some time.

But perhaps the most important impact made by the ABL was that it was used as the design starting point for the FN FAL (Fusil Automatique Legère), destined to be one of the most important rifles within NATO and elsewhere for the following decades.

**SPECIFICATION**

**Fusil Automatique Modèle 49**
**Calibres:** 7-mm (0.275-in), 7.65-mm (0.301-in), 7.92-mm (0.312-in) and 0.3-in (7.62-mm)
**Length overall:** 1116 m (43.94 in)
**Length of barrel:** 590 mm (23.2 in)
**Weight:** 4.31 kg (9.5 lb)
**Muzzle velocity:** dependent on cartridge fired
**Feed:** 10-round box

# EM-2 Assault rifle

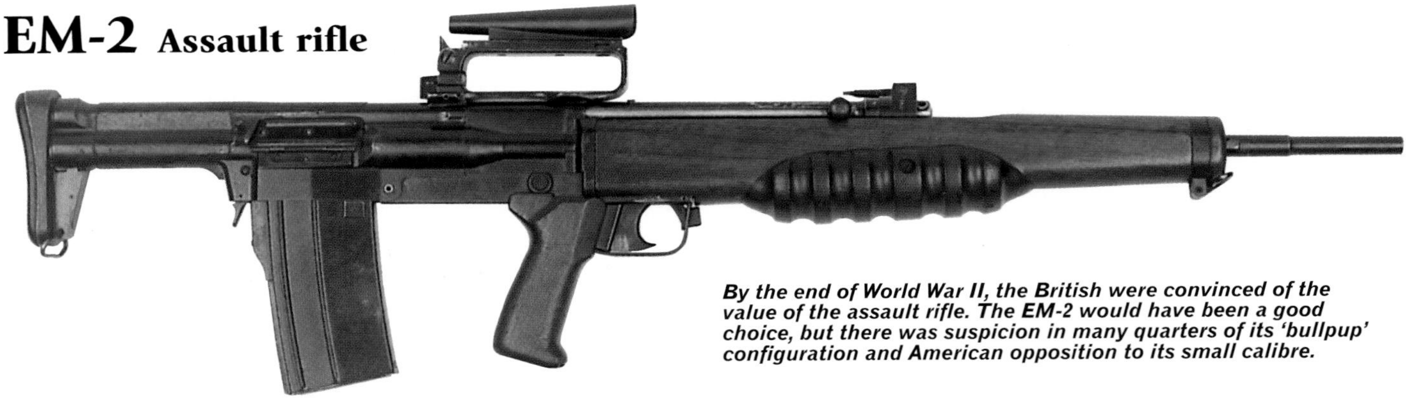

***By the end of World War II, the British were convinced of the value of the assault rifle. The EM-2 would have been a good choice, but there was suspicion in many quarters of its 'bullpup' configuration and American opposition to its small calibre.***

The **EM-2** story is one of political considerations taking precedence over military requirements, for although the EM-2 was an excellent weapon it was not accepted for service.

The British army learned some hard lessons during World War II, one being that its time-honoured 0.303-in (7.7-mm) cartridge was outdated, was too powerful and used cordite, which had been overtaken by more efficient propellants. After 1945, therefore, the army initiated a series of trials to find something better and came up with a short-cased cartridge known as the 0.28-in (actually 7-mm/ 0.276-in) type. A rifle was devised to fire the new round, though the first attempt, known as the **EM-1**, was not fully developed as it was deemed too complicated.

## 'Bullpup' layout

Then a new design team came up with the **EM-2**. For its day the EM-2 (Enfield Model 2) was a novelty, for it used a 'bullpup' layout with the magazine behind the trigger group. This made the weapon short and handy without reducing the barrel length, the receiver being in the butt. Gas operation was used and the weapon fired from a closed breech. A selective-fire mechanism was introduced, and there was something then completely new, a permanently fixed optical sight.

The EM-2 proved very reliable in trials, and in 1951 it was announced that the EM-2 would be adopted by the army as the Rifle, Automatic, 7-mm No. 9 Mk 1. All seemed well until politics intruded. The Americans announced that they did not consider the British round powerful enough, and since the newly formed NATO alliance was supposed to introduce ruthless standardisation, a conference was held to determine that all new weapon and ammunition development should cease until a new NATO round was determined. This emerged as the American-designed 0.3-in (7.62-mm) cartridge.

There was no way the EM-2 could be usefully engineered to accommodate this more powerful round, so the decision to adopt the EM-2 was reversed and the British army instead took the Belgian FN FAL in a self-loading form as the L1.

For a short while the EM-2 was retained as a research tool to determine an 'optimum' cartridge, despite the NATO decision, but that project was eventually terminated. A few rifles were rechambered to accommodate some odd rounds (one was even chambered for the low-powered 0.3-in cartridge of the American Carbine M1) but gradually the extant EM-2 weapons were relegated to museums where some still remain today as examples of yet another intriguing small arms 'might have been'.

### SPECIFICATION

**EM-2**
**Calibre:** 7-mm (0.276-in)
**Length overall:** 889 mm (35 in) and 1092 mm (43 in) with bayonet
**Length of barrel:** 622 mm (24.49 in)
**Weight:** 4.78 m (10.54 lb) loaded with sling
**Muzzle velocity:** 771 m (2,530 ft) per second
**Rate of fire, cyclic:** 600-650 rpm
**Feed:** 20-round box magazine

# Samonabiject Puska vz 52

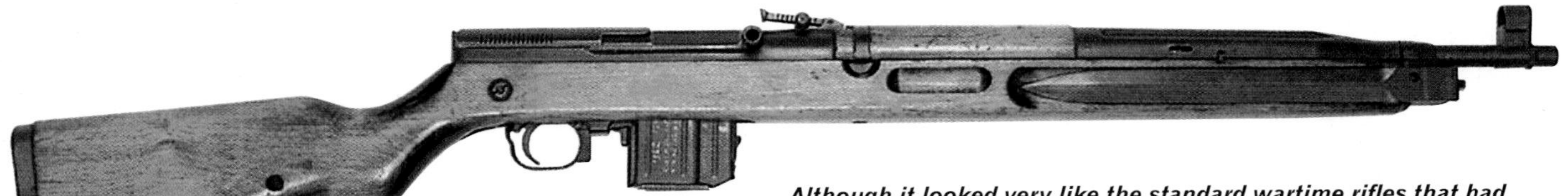

***Although it looked very like the standard wartime rifles that had preceded it, the vz 52 was in fact an early example of what would come to be known as the assault rifle, firing a low-powered 7.62-mm rifle round.***

For a few years after the end of World War II Czechoslovakia was a completely independent nation and for a while returned to the importance of the pre-war days when its armament industry was one of the leaders in Europe.

## World War II

The Czech armaments industry had been heavily used by the Germans during World War II. Experienced small arms designers were available, together with extensive facilities.

One of the first major small-arms developed during the early post-war period was a 7.62-mm (0.30-in) self-loading rifle known as the **Samonabiject Puska vz 52** (vz for *vzor* or model) that followed many of the design trends initiated by late war German automatic rifles.

## New cartridge

The Czechs also developed a new short assault rifle cartridge (also known as the vz 52) based on German *kurz* cartridge experience for use in the new rifle. The lower-powered cartridges evolved after German combat analysis showed that standard rifle rounds, accurate to a thousand metres or more, were far too powerful for most infantry combat, which rarely took place at ranges of more than 300 m (984 ft), and which often were fought at less than 100 m (328 ft).

## Czech individuality

As always the Czechs followed their own design paths and the vz 52 rifle had some unusual features, not the least of which was a method of tipping the bolt to lock the mechanism.

There was also a permanently-fixed bayonet, and the 10-round box magazine was filled using chargers. The gas-operated mechanism used a gas piston system wrapped around the barrel. Hardly innovative was the trigger mechanism, which was a direct lift of that used on the American MI (Garand) rifle.

Overall the vz 52 was rather heavy but this made it easy to fire as recoil was limited. Even so the vz 52 took up quite a lot of manufacturing potential, and was really too complex a weapon for the period.

Only the Czech army took the vz 52 into service for a while, and when other better weapons came along (such as the vz 58 assault rifle) the vz 52s were withdrawn and sold on the international arms markets.

## Warpac conversion

By the time the vz 52s were deleted the Czechs had been drawn into the Soviet sphere of influence. The Czech 7.62-mm vz 52 cartridge had nothing in common with the Soviet equivalent, although both had been designed from the same starting point. The Soviet military authorities were very strict regarding standardisation throughout the armies under their control, and the Czechs were thus forced to abandon their cartridge and convert to the Soviet equivalent.

Since the Czech and Soviet short cartridges were far from interchangeable, this meant the vz 52 rifles had to be modified accordingly, and late vz 52s with alterations to use the Soviet ammunition were known as the vz 52/57.

## Export vz 52s

Many of the VZ-52s were placed into storage by the Czechs. Large numbers were exported to Soviet and Third World client states, notably to Cuba and Egypt, and many of those were passed on to guerrillas.

### SPECIFICATION

**vz 52**
**Calibre:** 7.62-mm (0.30-in)
**Weights:** empty 4.281 kg (9.44 lb), loaded 4.5 kg (9.92 lb)
**Lengths:** overall, bayonet folded 1.003 m (39.49 in); overall, bayonet extended 1.204 m (47.4 in); barrel 523 mm (20.6 in)
**Muzzle velocity:** about 744 m (2,441 ft) per second
**Feed:** 10-round box

# Fusil Mitrailleur Modèle 49 (MAS 49) Rifle

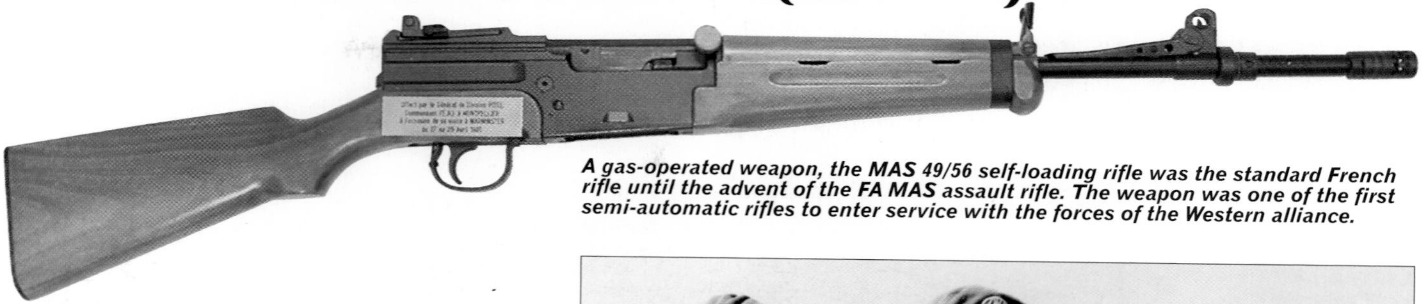

*A gas-operated weapon, the MAS 49/56 self-loading rifle was the standard French rifle until the advent of the FA MAS assault rifle. The weapon was one of the first semi-automatic rifles to enter service with the forces of the Western alliance.*

*Above: Legionnaires of the 2nd REP are seen with a MAT 49 sub-machine gun (left) and a MAS 49/56 rifle (right). The rifle fired the standard 7.5-mm (0.295-in) x 54 ball cartridge, and there were also armour-piercing and tracer rounds.*

Designed by the Manufacture d'Armes de St Etienne, the **Fusil Mitrailleur Modèle 49 (MAS 49)** was one of the first semi-automatic rifles to enter service after World War II. Although it resembles the MAS 36 bolt-action rifle, it was not created as an automatic version of the earlier weapon but as a completely new design. At over 4.5 kg (10 lb) it is no lightweight, but its strength proved itself invaluable in the French campaigns in Indo-China and Algeria during the 1950s and 1960s. In French service the MAS 49 was replaced by the FA MAS assault rifle from 1979.

## Gas operation

The MAS 49 was based on work in the earlier part of the 20th century on direct-impingement operating systems. Prototypes were produced in the 1920s and 1930s, and a few examples of the MAS 44 type were made after the Germans had been driven from France in 1944, primarily for service trials. The MAS 49 is thus a gas-operated weapon, but uses no cylinder or piston. In this system propellant gas is tapped off from the barrel and ducted into a tube that directs it to the face of the bolt carrier where it expands and forces back the carrier. The system has often been eschewed because it can produce excessive fouling, but the MAS 49 did not suffered unduly from the problem. The breech is locked in the same simple manner as on the Fabrique Nationale mle 49, simply by tilting the breech block.

*Left: French soldiers cautiously approach a possible 'freedom fighter' in one of their African colonies. The man in the foreground has a MAS 49/56 rifle.*

## New magazine

Though the MAS 49 was derived from the MAS 44, it differed from its predecessor in having a detachable rather than integral box magazine. This magazine holds 10 rounds and can be replaced when empty, but there are stripper clip guides machined into the front of the bolt carrier, and this provision allows two five-round clips to be loaded straight into the magazine. Somewhat unusually, the MAS 49 also has an integral grenade launcher, with a dedicated sight fitted on the left-hand side.

The MAS 49 was modified in 1956 to produce the **MAS 49/56**, which is the variant that was generally supplanted by the FA MAS. The MAS 49/56 is easily distinguished from the earlier weapon: the wooden fore-stock is much shorter and the barrel has a combined muzzle-brake/grenade-launcher with raised fore-sight. The length of the whole weapon was reduced by 90 mm (3.54 in) and that of the barrel by 60 mm (2.36 in), and provision was made for the mounting of a spike bayonet. Like the MAS 49, the MAS 49/56 has a mounting rail machined into the left-hand side of the receiver for an APX L mle 1953 telescopic sight with x3.85 magnification. The standard sights, calibrated to a range of 1200 m (1,315 yards), comprise a hooded front sight on the front stock band and an aperture rear sight above the receiver.

*Left: A French infantry patrol on the move, the weapons evident including the MAS 49, complete with a rifle grenade, carried by the point man.*

## Obsolete cartridge

The French obstinately stuck with the obsolete 7.5-mm x 54 mle 1929 cartridge, but a few MAS 49/56 assault rifles were experimentally modified to fire the NATO standard 7.62-mm (0.3-in) cartridge. Armour-piercing ammunition was also produced, but this proved very unkind to the barrels of the weapons that fired it.

**SPECIFICATION**

**MAS 49/56**
**Calibre:** 7.5-mm (0.295-in)
**Length overall:** 1010 mm (39.8 in)
**Length of barrel:** 521 mm (20.5 in)
**Weights:** 3.9 kg (8.6 lb) empty and 4.34 kg (9.52 lb) loaded
**Muzzle velocity:** 817 m (2,680 ft) per second
**Feed:** 10-round box magazine

# Rifle M14

The rifle that was eventually to be the standard American service rifle for most of the late 1950s and 1960s had a simple origin but a most convoluted development period. When the American military planners virtually imposed their 7.62-mm (0.3-in) cartridge upon their NATO partners, they had to find their own rifle to fire it, and quickly.

For various reasons it was decided simply to update the existing M1 Garand rifle design to fire the new ammunition, and also to add a selective-fire mechanism. Unfortunately these innovations proved difficult to achieve, for the evolution from the M1 had to progress through a number of intermediate 'T' trials models.

## Two models planned

Eventually, in 1957, it was announced that a model known as the **T44** had been approved for production as the **Rifle M14**. A planned heavy-barrel version, the M15, did not materialise. The assembly lines began to hum, at one time involving four different manufacturing centres.

## Updated Garand

The M14 was basically the M1 Garand semi-automatic rifle updated to take a new 20-round box magazine and selective-fire mechanism. The M14 was long and rather heavy, but well made, involving a great deal of machining and handling during manufacture at a time when other weapon designers were moving away from such methods. But the Americans could afford it and the soldiers liked the weapon. In service there were few problems, but the selective-fire system that had needed so much development time was usually altered so that automatic fire could not be produced: the US Army had soon discovered that prolonged bursts overheated the barrel and that ammunition was in any event wasted firing non-productive bursts.

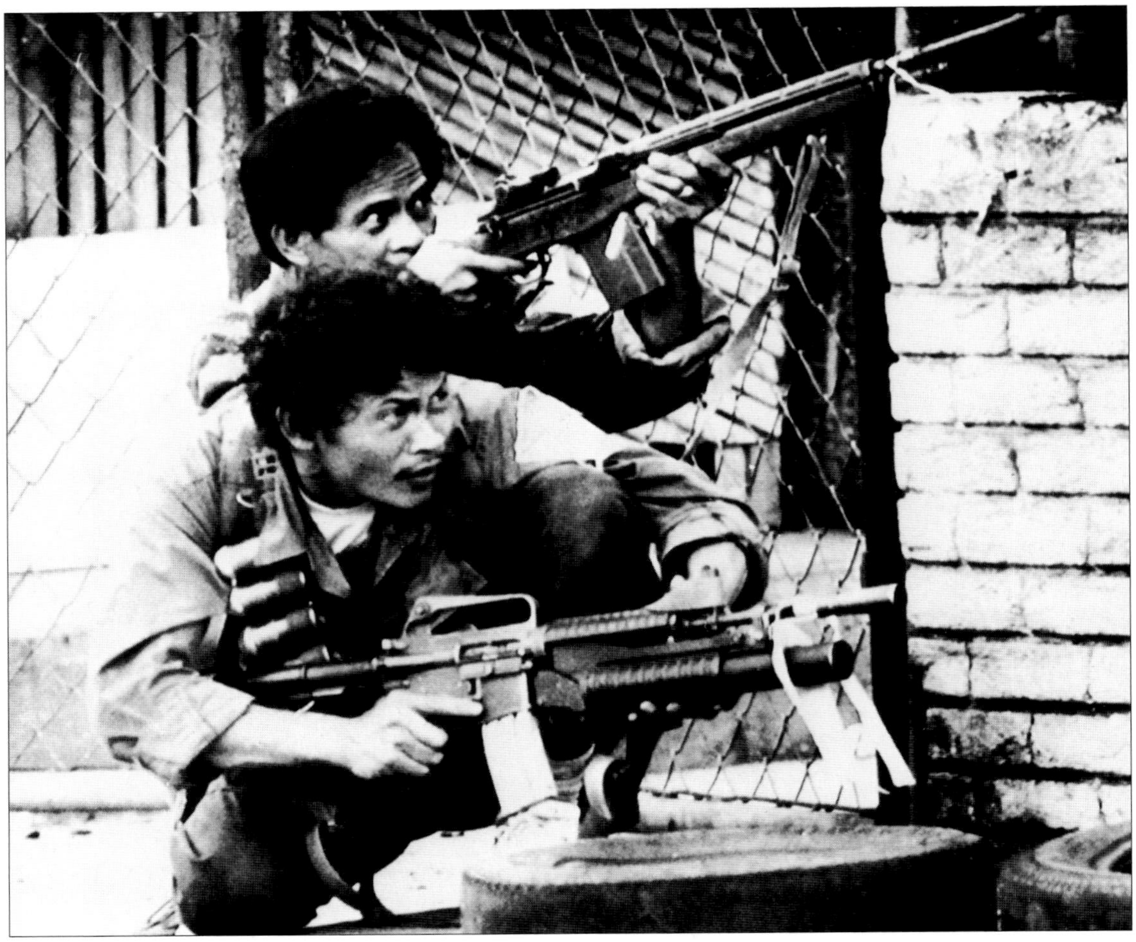

***Rebel Filipino soldiers fire on loyalist forces during the last days of the Marcos regime. Note the spent case being ejected from the M14 (higher weapon).***

***Once NATO had adopted the American-developed 7.62-mm (0.3-in) cartridge, most NATO countries opted for a variant of the Belgian FAL rifle. As now, the USA was still in thrall to the 'not invented here' syndrome and wanted an American rifle, developed from the M1 as the recalibred M14 with a larger magazine.***

## Major production

Production of the basic M14 ceased in 1964, by which time 1,380,346 had been made. In 1968 a new version, the **M14A1**, was introduced. This had a pistol grip, a bipod and some other changes. It was intended as a squad fire-support weapon producing automatic bursts but the bursts had to be short as the barrel could not be changed when hot. Also produced were experimental folding butt versions and the **M21** sniper model.

The M14 is no longer used by first-line US forces, surviving last with the National Guard and other reserve formations. As the M14 was replaced by the M16, many were passed to nations such as Israel, where they stayed in service until replaced by the Galil assault rifle.

### SPECIFICATION

**Rifle M14**
**Calibre:** 7.62-mm (0.3-in)
**Length overall:** 1120 mm (44.0 in)
**Length of barrel:** 559 mm (22.0 in)
**Weight:** 3.88 kg (8.55 lb)
**Muzzle velocity:** 853 m (2,798 ft) per second
**Rate of fire, cyclic:** (M14A1) 700-750 rounds per minute
**Feed:** 20-round straight box

***The M14A1 was created as the squad fire-support variant of the M14 rifle with an automatic action, bipod and a combination of pistol and fore grips.***

# Stoner 63 System

Eugene Stoner was one of the most influential and innovative weapon designers of the1950s and 1960s, and his hand can still be discerned in many small arms types in use today. His innovatory thinking was such that at one point Stoner was involved in developing a modular weapon system that not surprisingly became known as the **Stoner 63 System**.

Produced not long after Stoner had left Armalite Inc in the late 1950s, the Stoner 63 System was based on 17 modular units that could be arranged and assembled in ways that allowed the creation of a whole series of small arms. The basis for the system was the rotary lock mechanism first used on the AR-10 rifle and later on the AR-15/M16 rifle. However, the Stoner 63 System used a different method of gas operation based on a long-travel piston.

***Seen mounted on a tripod for evaluation by the US Marine Corps, this is the medium machine-gun variant of the Stoner 63 System.***

***The light machine-gun variant of the Stoner 63 System, normally fitted with a bipod, is seen here in its belt-fed form with an open box of disintegrating metal-linked ammunition.***

## Kits of components

The only components common to all weapons in the system were the receiver, bolt and piston, return spring and trigger mechanism. To these core elements could be added, such as buttstocks, feed devices, various barrels and items including bipod or even tripod mountings to produce the weapon types required in any of the many possible tactical situations in which an operator might find himself involved.

Originally the Stoner 63 System was developed to use the 7.62-mm (0.3-in) NATO cartridge, but when it became clear that the 5.56-mm (0.219-mm) calibre was destined to overtake this, Stoner revised the system to accommodate the lighter round. This change had the benefit of making many of the components considerably lighter, and as a result the weapons themselves were also lighter, with obvious tactical advantages.

The basic weapon was a carbine with a folding butt. and then came an assault rifle; magazine- and belt-fed light machine-guns using bipods were next, while the addition of a heavy barrel, belt feed and tripod finally produced a medium machine-gun. It was even possible to produce a solenoid-fired machine-gun for co-axial use in AFVs.

## Stoner pedigree

Given its provenance and also its manifest overall advantages, the Stoner 63 System attracted a great deal of attention. The system was put into small-scale production by Cadillac Gage, the company under whose aegis Stoner had developed the project. Plans were made with a Dutch firm for licensed production, but military interest was not so forthcoming. The US Marines carried out a series of trials, and more trials were carried out in Israel. The system performed well throughout all these trials, but no large-scale procurement resulted. Exactly why this happened is not easy to determine, but the main reason was perhaps the fact that for a set of components to be produced to perform so many roles, a number of the parts had to be something of a compromise and thus less successful than a purpose-built design. The Stoner System gradually faded from the scene and is no longer offered.

***US Navy SEAL (SEa-Air-Land) special forces teams used the Stoner 63 System weapons in the Vietnam War. This is a belt-fed light machine-gun with 100-round plastic ammunition boxes.***

| SPECIFICATION | |
|---|---|
| **Stoner 63 System assault rifle** | **Muzzle velocity:** about 1000 m (3,280 ft) per second |
| **Calibre:** 5.56-mm (0.219-in) | **Rate of fire, cyclic:** 660 rounds per minute |
| **Length overall:** 1022 mm (40.23 in) | **Feed:** 30-round curved box |
| **Length of barrel:** 508 mm (20.0 in) | |
| **Weight loaded:** 4.39 kg (9.68 lb) | |

***This is the fixed-stock assault rifle member of the Stoner 63 Weapon family. The magazine is a 30-round unit, and at the muzzle is a combined flash suppressor and grenade launcher.***

# Armalite AR-10 Assault rifle

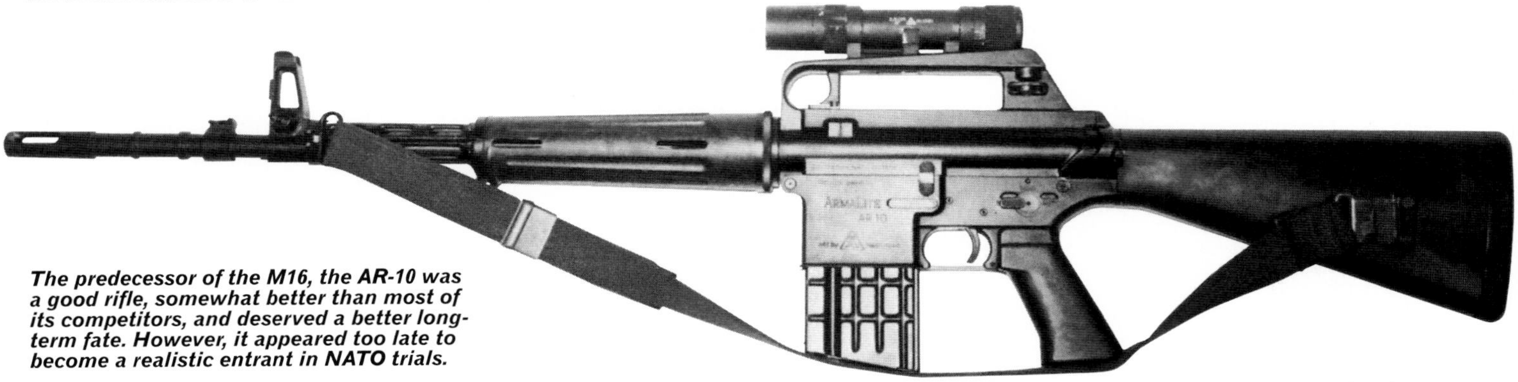

***The predecessor of the M16, the AR-10 was a good rifle, somewhat better than most of its competitors, and deserved a better long-term fate. However, it appeared too late to become a realistic entrant in NATO trials.***

In 1954 the newly formed Armalite Division of the Fairchild Engine & Airplane Company started the development of an assault rifle firing the World War II 7.62-mm (0.3-in) rifle cartridge. By 1955 Eugene Stoner had joined the company and development had switched towards using the new 7.62-mm NATO cartridge, though the Armalite team, greatly influenced by Stoner, was not restricted to using established small arms design conventions. The team thus evolved an innovative 'all-in-line' configuration with the sights above the weapon, but perhaps the concept's most important contribution to small arms design was the reintroduction of the rotary-bolt locking system that has now become virtually standard on assault rifle designs throughout the world.

## Lightweight rifle

The new rifle emerged during 1955 as the **Armalite AR-10**. This made great use of aluminium in its construction, and steel was used only for the barrel, bolt and bolt carrier. This made the weapon light, or perhaps too light as its tendency to 'rear' when fired automatically meant that a muzzle compensator had to be fitted to overcome this failing. The cocking lever was on top of the receiver, protected by a carrying handle that also carried the rear sight. Originally it was planned that there would be sub-machine gun and light machine-gun variants of the basic AR-10, but only prototypes of these variants were produced.

The Armalite team found that marketing its product was rather more difficult than designing it. Tooling up for production was slow, and sales were not helped by the fact that the NATO nations had already made their various new rifle decisions by the time the AR-10 appeared. The Dutch seemed to offer hope of sales, and arrangements were made with a Dutch company, NWM, for licensed production of the AR-10, but that project finally came to nothing despite a great deal of preparatory work.

This was a pity, for the AR-10 was really far better than any weapon then in NATO use and far more advanced than most. It was simple, easy to handle and had much potential. Some sales were made, by far the largest to Sudan, Portugal bought 1,500 examples and other batches went to Burma and Nicaragua, some via the Dutch NWM.

Perhaps the greatest importance of the AR-10, whose production ended in 1961, was that it paved the way for the AR-15 (M-16).

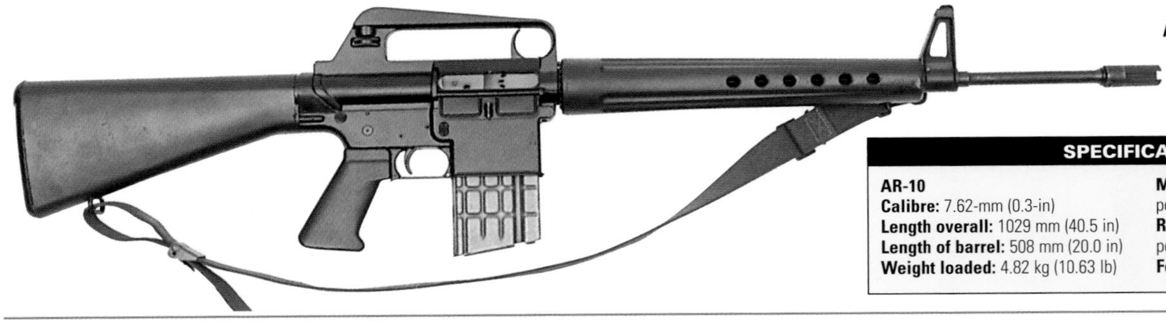

***The innovative AR-10 made extensive use of aluminium alloy for most of its metal parts, exceptions being the steel barrel, bolt and bolt carrier. Light weight also meant a muzzle-climb tendency, however.***

**SPECIFICATION**

**AR-10**
**Calibre:** 7.62-mm (0.3-in)
**Length overall:** 1029 mm (40.5 in)
**Length of barrel:** 508 mm (20.0 in)
**Weight loaded:** 4.82 kg (10.63 lb)
**Muzzle velocity:** 845 m (2,772 ft) per second
**Rate of fire, cyclic:** 700 rounds per minute
**Feed:** 20-round straight box

# Valmet/Sako Rk.60 and Rk.62 Assault rifles

Although it was not a member of the Warsaw Pact, its proximity to the USSR meant that despite its neutrality Finland inevitably had to go along with the Soviet way of doing things in some matters through most of the 20th century's second half. Thus, when it decided to adopt a new service rifle in the late 1950s, the Finnish army not surprisingly opted for the Soviet AK-47 assault rifle and its ammunition, and Finland therefore negotiated a manufacturing licence for both. Once the AK-47 design was in their hands, Finnish small arms designers at the Valmet company made changes to create the **Valmet m/60** rifle, later redesignated as the **Rk.60**.

## AK-47 origins

Its AK-47 origins can readily be discerned in the Rk.60, but the reworking of the basic design resulted in a much better all-round weapon. The Rk.60 has no wood in its construction, the wooden furniture of the AK-47 being replaced by plastics or metal tubing. The tubular butt of the Rk.60 is thus easier to produce and is also more robust as well as carrying the cleaning tools and equipment. The pistol grip and forestock are cast from hard plastic, while the trigger is left virtually unguarded to allow the wearing of gloves.

Other changes from the AK-47 include slightly altered sights, a three-pronged flash hider at the muzzle, and a revised bayonet mounting bracket to accommodate the Finnish bayonet. Internally the mechanism of the AK-47 is left virtually unchanged apart from the introduction of a few manufacturing expedients, and the curved magazine and its housing are also unaltered to allow.

***The Rk.62 is an improved finnish development of the Soviet AK-47 optimised for Finnish manufacturing capabilities and operating conditions.***

use of AK-47 magazines.

The later **m/62** or **Rk.62** is virtually the same as the Rk.60 apart from a few extra cooling holes in the forestock and the introduction of a vestigial trigger guard. Export variants were also created in 5.56-mm (0.219-in) calibre.

### Improved variants

After Valmet's merger with Sako, the small arms team created modernised variants of the Rk.62 as the **Rk.76** and **Rk.95TP**. The former has a stamped rather than machined receiver, much reducing weight, and the option of four buttstocks (fixed wooden, fixed plastic, fixed tubular and folding tubular in the **Rk.76W**, **Rk.76P**, **Rk.76T** and **Rk.76TP** respectively). Also known as the **Sako Rk.75**, the latter has a machined receiver but a folding skeleton buttstock, new handguards and an improved flash hider.

***The m/60 was in effect the production prototype of the m/62 that became better known as the Rk.62. This appears to be a non-standard example with a trigger guard.***

***The large trigger guard of the Rk.62 was designed to allow the weapon's use in winter conditions by a soldier wearing gloves.***

**SPECIFICATION**

| | |
|---|---|
| **Rk.62** | **Weight loaded:** 4.7 kg (10.36 lb) |
| **Calibre:** 7.62-mm (0.3-in) | **Muzzle velocity:** 719 m (2,359 ft) per second |
| **Lengths:** overall 914 mm (36.0 in) and barrel 420 mm (16.54 in) | **Rate of fire, cyclic:** 650 rpm |
| | **Feed:** 30-round curved box |

# Samozaryadnyi Karabin Simonova (SKS) Rifle

The semi-automatic rifle known as the **SKS** (**Samozaryadnyi Karabin Simonova obrazets 1945g**, or Simonov self-loading carbine type 1945) was designed in World War II, but was not placed in production until some time after this war's end. The designer was Sergei Gavrilovich Simonov, who was responsible for many important Soviet small arms, but in the SKS Simonov decided to play things safe and thus created what was in fact a relatively uninspired design.

The SKS was the first weapon designed to use the new Soviet 7.62-mm (0.3-in) cartridge derived from the German 7.92-mm (0.312-in) *kurz* (short) round of World War II.

The SKS was based on the use of a gas-operated mechanism with a simple tipping bolt locking system. So conservative was the overall design that the SKS even outwardly resembled a conventional bolt-action rifle, complete with extensive wooden furniture. A fixed folding bayonet was fitted under the muzzle and the box magazine could hardly be seen: it held only 10 rounds and was fixed to the receiver. Loading was by chargers or insertion of single rounds; to unload, the magazine was hinged downward, allowing the rounds to fall free. In typical Soviet fashion the SKS was very strongly built, so much so that many Western observers derided it as being far too heavy for the relatively light cartridge it fired. Despite this, the SKS was well able to withstand the many knocks and rough treatment likely to be encountered during service use, and the SKS was the standard rifle of the Warsaw Pact nations for years until the arrival in adequate numbers of the AK-47 assault rifle and the later AKM firing a smaller-calibre round.

### Phased out of service

By the mid-1980s the SKS was no longer in Warsaw Pact service other than as a ceremonial weapon for parades or 'honour guards'. However, it may somewhat improbably still be encountered elsewhere as enormous numbers were produced, not only in the USSR but in East Germany and Yugoslavia where it was known as the **Karabiner-S** and **m/59** respectively; a variant of the m/59 was produced as the **m/59/66** with a spigot-type grenade launcher attached permanently to the muzzle. The communist Chinese have produced a slightly revised version of the SKS known as the **Type 56** with a spike rather than blade bayonet.

With so many SKS rifles produced, it is not surprising that many remained in use throughout the Middle and Far East until recent times. Large numbers of the weapon were encountered by US and South Vietnamese forces during the Vietnam conflict, and from there many passed into the hands of irregular forces. Being simple and robust weapons, they are easy to use after a minimum of training, and the SKS will be around for many years to come.

**SPECIFICATION**

| | |
|---|---|
| **SKS** | **Weight empty:** 3.85 kg (8.49 lb) |
| **Calibre:** 7.62-mm (0.3-in) | **Muzzle velocity:** 735 m (2,411 ft) per second |
| **Length overall:** 1021 mm (40.2 in) | |
| **Length of barrel:** 521 mm (20.5 in) | **Feed:** 20-round integral box |

***The SKS almost has the appearance of a bolt-action rifle, but is in fact a gas-operated self-loading weapon with a 20-round integral magazine.***

***The Type 65 is the Chinese-made SMS, and while many of the weapons are virtually indistinguishable from the Soviet version, this has a spike bayonet.***

# Development of the assault rifle

The AK-47 is the most successful military rifle since World War II, and probably the most widely manufactured rifle of all time. Here East German border guards, carrying AK-47s, are on lookout patrol.

**Proving immune to tactical change but keeping apace with technology, the assault rifle remains a vitally important core weapon for infantryman, commando and guerrilla alike.**

After analysis in 1939-40, the German army established that most firefights took place at comparatively short ranges, around 400 metres (1,312 ft) – not the 800-1000 metres (2,625-3,281 ft) for which weapons like the Kar 98K were designed. The 7.92-mm K (0.31-in) short round was therefore developed by Polte for this short range combat. With a muzzle velocity (MV) of 650 metres (2,133 ft) per second it was more powerful than 9-mm (0.35-in) sub-machine gun ammunition, with a MV of 365 m (1,198 ft) per second. The ammunition was more compact and ideal for automatic weapons – the ground had been prepared for the development of the post-war assault rifle.

## New order

The army issued a specification to Haenel and Walther for a new machine-carbine. The two resulting gas operated designs were remarkably similar, using the same straight line butt and barrel arrangement, pistol grip and curved 30-round box magazine. The Haenel designed weapon was known as the Maschinkarabiner 42 (H) or MKb42(H) and the Walther as the MKb42(W). Both were designed to be manufactured quickly and cheaply using plastic and stamped and die-cast metal components.

The MKb42(H),designed by Louis Schmeisser, was 940-mm (37-in) long, weighed 4.9 kg (10.81 lb) and had a cyclic rate of fire of 500 rpm. About 8,000 were produced for troop trials on the Eastern Front where they were very successful.

Despite the success of the MKb42(H), Hitler decided that further development of assault rifles should be halted. Fortunately for the soldiers in the field, the German army and Haenel changed the designation of the improved MKb42(H) to MP 43 and so for documentation purposes made the weapon a Maschinenpistole or sub-machine gun. In this guise it went into mass production. Further modifications to the weapon, including the facility to launch rifle grenades produced the MP 44. This weapon had the same length and rate of fire as the MKb42(H) and weighed 5.22 kg (11.5 lb). It was now back in favour with Hitler who in late 1944 gave it the designation Sturmgewehr 44 (StG44) – Storm/Assault Rifle 44. The StG44 would form the basis of the AK-47 family of assault rifles developed in the Soviet Bloc after

Above: Near Duc Pho City, Vietnam, June 1967, US soldiers patrol to find North Vietnamese units, both carrying M16s. The soldier in the foreground has additional 0.3-in (7.62-mm) ammunition belts for the section M60 machine-gun.

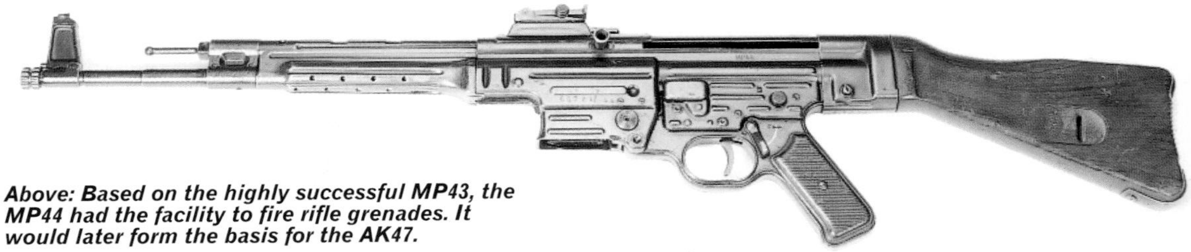

Above: Based on the highly successful MP43, the MP44 had the facility to fire rifle grenades. It would later form the basis for the AK47.

Right: A signature weapon of the Vietnam War and the US GI, the M16 has proved to be a highly popular jungle warfare weapon, because of its light weight and minimal recoil. Both of which helped to greatly incease the weapon's accuracy.

the war. It was used by East German border guards and subsequently appeared in Africa with liberation movements.

The StG44 was fitted with the GwZf 4-fach telescopic sight and also in early 1945 the futuristic Zielgerät 1229 'Vampir' infra-red night sight. Its most unusual development was the Krummlauf – 'Curved Track' which could be bolted to the muzzle and allowed the weapon to be fired around 30° curves. Though bullets were slightly distorted by the curved barrel and its life was relatively short, a system of vents reduced the gas pressure when it had exited from the weapon's main barrel.

***Royal Marines head inshore in a landing craft during an amphibious warfare exercise. The soldier in front is carrying an SA80, while the others are carrying the Light Support Weapon (LSW).***

## Kalashnikov

The AK-47 assault rifle in all its numerous versions is probably the most widely used weapon in the world. The original assault rifle designed by Mikhail Kalashnikov at the end of World War II entered service with the Soviet Army in 1951. It fired a 7.62- x 39-mm (0.3- x 1.5-in) 122 grain round. The effective range of both the AK-47 and the modernised AKM version is 400 metres (1,312 ft). The AK family of assault rifles are well designed, easy to use, even by unskilled men, and have very few working parts. They were used by the Rhodesian SAS and US Special Forces in Southeast Asia because they were not 'signature' weapons when they fired, lacking the distinctive sound of the M16. In cross border raids the AK was easy to replenish from captured ammunition. However, at one stage in the Vietnam War the US were producing 'sterile' 7.62- x 39-mm ammunition with no stamping on the base of the cartridge cases for their special forces. AK weapons were produced throughout the Warsaw Pact countries and also in China and North Korea.

## Early M16

In the West the Colt AR-15, which became the M16 when it was adopted by the US army in Vietnam in 1964, was an equally innovative weapon. It was made from alloys and plastic and fired a 0.22-in (5.56-mm) round and so was much lighter than the big 0.3-in rifles like the M14. The weapon currently in service is the M16A1/2, which has a manual bolt closing device on the right side of the receiver which allows extra pressure to be applied if there is dirt in the chamber or a cartridge case jams. The M16A2 has a heavier barrel and a case deflector that allows left handed firers to handle the weapon. The M16A3 is an A2 with a telescopic sight fitted in the place of the handle. The 0.22-in M193 round pioneered by the M16 is now widely used in assault rifles, albeit in the x45 NATO configuration.

***Left: This Alpine soldier is armed with a French FA MAS rifle, one of the smallest and most compact of the modern assault rifles. The carrying handle contains the sight and the cocking lever is just underneath.***

***Below: The overall length of an SA80 assault rifle is dramatically reduced by the bullpup layout – placing the magazine behind the pistol grip. The telescopic sight magnifies to a factor of four, giving a clear view of the target.***

***Members of elite Warsaw Pact paratroop formations and special forces had the option of carrying a conventional AK with wooden stock or the 'paratroop' version with a detachable, folding metal stock.***

# Steyr AUG
## Assault rifle

The 'Star Wars' look of the **AUG (Armee Universal Gewehr**, or army universal rifle) is one of the most striking of all modern assault rifles. But it has been around for a surprisingly long time: it first entered service with the Austrian army in 1977.

### Bull-pup design

Manufactured by the old-established Steyr concern, the AUG is a 'bull-pup' design, with the trigger group forward of the magazine. This makes for a compact, handy weapon. The thoroughly modern appearance is enhanced by the liberal use of nylonite and other non-metallic materials in the rifle's construction.

The only metal parts are the barrel and the receiver with the internal mechanism; even the receiver is an aluminium casting. All the materials are very high quality. The magazine is made from tough clear plastic – this has the advantage that a soldier can see at a glance how many rounds the magazine contains.

Steyr AUG-A1

The original AUG assault rifle has proven extremely tough in operational service: in tests, one example remained fireable even after being repeatedly run over by a 10-tonne truck! The only damage it received was a crack in the plastic receiver cover.

Steyr AUG-P

The police version of the AUG has a shorter barrel than the assault rifle, and is usually supplied in black plastic. Most law enforcement examples are semi-automatic, capable of single-shot fire only.

### Weapon system

The Steyr AUG is the heart of a modular weapon system. By changing the barrel, working parts or magazine, it can be converted to a sub-machine gun, a carbine, a specialist sniper rifle, or a light machine-gun. By changing the fittings on the receiver the AUG can be fitted with a wide range of night sights or sighting telescopes, but the usual sight is a simple optical telescope with a graticule calibrated for normal combat ranges.

Stripping the AUG for cleaning is rapid and simple, and cleaning is facilitated by the use of a chromed barrel interior. Repairs can be easily effected by changing an entire module.

Full production of the AUG began in 1978, and since that date Steyr has been kept busy supplying the Austrian army, various Middle Eastern, African and South American armed forces, as well as the armed forces of Australia, New Zealand and Ireland.

The AUG is also in the armouries of special forces all over the world, and has been used by the British SAS and the German GSG-9 hostage rescue units.

The AUG weapon is popular with law enforcement agencies in a number of countries, and has been a commercial success in the US.

**SPECIFICATION**

**Steyr AUG (assault rifle)**
**Calibre:** 5.56 mm (0.22 in)
**Length:** 790 mm (31 in)
**Length of barrel:** 508 mm (20 in)
**Weight loaded:** 4.09 kg (9 lb)
**Magazine:** 30-round box
**Rate of fire, cyclic:** 650 rpm

***Left:* The *AUG* has been exported to a number of nations around the world, including the Malaysian armed forces.**

***Above:* In spite of its space-age appearance, the *AUG* has been in service with the Austrian army for nearly 25 years.**

# FN FAL
## Assault rifle

*Dutch Marines on exercise in Norway aim their FALs. The rifle's popularity is a reflection of its ability to be used in any climate and terrain.*

Produced by the famous Belgian arms maker of Fabrique Nationale, the origins of the **Fusil Automatique Legère** or **FN FAL** (light automatic rifle), date back to 1948. Originally intended to fire the wartime German 7.92 mm x 33 kurz (short) cartridge, the design was recast following NATO ammunition standardisation. The FAL was chambered for the new NATO standard 7.62-mm x 51 cartridge.

### Combat classic

The resulting rifle was a classic, being tough, reliable, battle-worthy and accurate at combat ranges. In its long career it has been used by more than 90 armies, and has been licence produced in countries as diverse as Britain, Israel, Canada, Mexico, India and South Africa. Many of these overseas production models differ in detail from the original FAL but the overall appearance is the same.

The FAL is a sturdy weapon which uses many of the manufacturing methods of a bygone era. High-grade materials are used throughout, extensively machined to fine tolerances. The gas-operated action uses a gas regulation system that taps off propellant gases from above the barrel to operate a piston. This in turn pushes back the bolt action for unlocking the breech. The unlocking system has a delay action built in for increased safety. Automatic fire is possible on most models of the rifle.

FAL models are many and various. Most have solid wooden or nylonite butts and other furniture but some models, usually issued to airborne forces, have particularly sturdy folding butts. Overall toughness is a feature of the FAL weapon, and the rifle has proved itself well able to withstand the rigours of service life from the deserts and jungles to the high Arctic.

### Britain's L1A1

One production version of the FAL that deserves further mention is the British **L1A1**. The L1A1 was adopted by the British armed forces only after a lengthy series of trials and modifications that resulted in the elimination of the automatic fire feature. There are some other differences as well, but the L1A1 itself has been adopted by many other nations, including India where the type remained in production until the 1990s. The Australians also adopted the type and even produced a shorter version, the **L1A1-F1**, to suit the stature of the New Guinea troops.

Both the FAL and the L1A1 rifles are equipped to fire rifle grenades, but these are now little used. Bayonets can also be fitted and some versions of the FAL have heavy barrels and bipods to enable them to be used as light machine-guns. Night sights are another optional fitting.

Although the 7.62-mm (0.3-in) FAL is no longer in full-scale production as a military weapon, it can still be found in military service and in reserve all over the world. However, the trend since the 1980s has been towards lighter calibre, and most major armies have re-equipped with weapons of 5.56-mm (0.22-in) calibre.

| SPECIFICATION | |
|---|---|
| **FN FAL** | **Magazine:** 20-round box |
| **Calibre:** 7.62 mm (0.3 in) | **Rate of fire:** 30-40 rpm (single shot) or 650-700 rpm (FAL, cyclic) |
| **Length:** 1143 mm (45 in) | **Muzzle velocity:** 838 m (2,750 ft) per second |
| **Barrel length:** 554 mm (21¾ in) | |
| **Weight loaded:** 5 kg (11 lb) | |

*Although most FALs are capable of automatic fire, only those fitted with heavy barrels and bipods are really controllable. This heavy barrelled version (top), together with the folding-stocked para rifle, were captured by the British in the Falklands.*

# FN FAL, L1 and FNC Assault rifles

Produced by Fabrique Nationale in Belgium, the **FN FAL** (Fusil Automatique Légère, or light automatic rifle) was originally produced in 1948. The prototypes fired the German 7.92-mm (0.312-in) *kurz* (short) cartridge, but later attempts at NATO standardisation meant that the FAL was revised for the standard 7.62-mm (0.3-in) cartridge. The rifle was then widely adopted not only throughout NATO but by many other nations, and has been licence-produced by nations as diverse as South Africa and Mexico. Many of these overseas production models differ in detail from the original FAL but the overall appearance is the same.

The FAL is a sturdy weapon based on the use of high-grade materials and extensive machining. The action is gas-operated via a gas regulator that taps propellant gases from above the barrel to operate a piston that pushes back the bolt action for unlocking the breech. The unlocking system has a delay action built in for increased safety. Automatic fire is possible on most models by use of a selector mechanism located near the trigger group.

***Top: The L1A1, once the standard British infantry weapon and lacking automatic fire capability.***
***Centre: Short-barrel FAL.***
***Bottom: Argentine FAL with folding butt and, like the FAL, capable of automatic fire.***

The FAL models are many and varied. Most have solid wooden or nylonite butts and other furniture, but some models (usually issued to airborne forces) have folding butts. An overall sturdiness is a feature of the FAL.

## British model

One version of the FAL that deserves further mention is the British **L1A1**. This was adopted by the British forces only after a lengthy series of trials and modifications that resulted in the elimination of the automatic fire feature and the introduction of some other differences. The L1A1 has been adopted by many other nations, including India, for licensed production. Australia also adopted the type and even produced a shorter version, the **L1A1-F1**, to suit the stature of the New Guinea troops.

Both the FAL and the L1A1 are equipped to fire rifle grenades. A bayonet can also be fitted, and some versions of the FAL have heavy barrels and bipods to enable them to be used as light machine-guns. Night sights are another optional fitting.

The trend in assault rifle design is now toward the 5.56-mm (0.219-in) calibre, and a new model in this calibre is now in production as the **FN Carbine**.

The FNC first appeared in 1978, and has since been adopted by Belgium, Indonesia and Sweden, the latter two making the weapon under licence as the **Bofors AK-5** and **Pindad SS1**. The FNC is based on a rotary bolt, and is a light weapon through the use of features such as a stamped steel upper receiver, aluminium alloy lower receiver, plastic pistol grip and fore end, and plastic-coated steel folding buttstock; a fixed buttstock is optional. The FNC fires in single-shot, three-round burst and full-automatic modes.

### SPECIFICATION

**FNC**
**Calibre:** 5.56-mm (0.219-in)
**Length overall:** 997 mm (39.25 in)
**Length of barrel:** 449 mm (17.68 in)
**Weight empty:** 4.06 kg (8.95 lb)
**Muzzle velocity:** not available
**Rate of fire, cyclic:** about 650 rounds per minute
**Magazine:** 30-round curved box

***The FNC drew its inspiration from weapons such as the AK-47, M16 and Galil, and is a gas-operated weapon with a rotary bolt. This is the standard weapon with the folding buttstock, and there is also a shortened Para model for the use of airborne troops.***

***Australian infantry with their version of the L1A1 manufactured locally at Lithgow in New South Wales. The Australians also produced a short version called the L1A1-F1 for use by local troops in New Guinea. They also use the M16A1.***

# FA MAS Assault rifle

For some years after World War II the French armaments industry lagged in the design of small arms, but with the **FA MAS**, or in full the **Fusil d'Assaut de la Manufacture d'Armes St Etienne**, it has made up that leeway with a vengeance. The FA MAS is a thoroughly modern and effective assault rifle, and yet another example of the overall compactness that can be achieved by using the 'bullpup' layout that was initially unorthodox but has now became virtually standard. This 'bullpup' layout located the trigger group in front of the magazine, allowing the weapon to be made very short in overall terms. Even by the standards of this abbreviated concept, the FA MAS is very short and handy, and must be one of the smallest in-service assault rifle designs of all.

## Small but capable

Developed from 1972, the **FA MAS F1** baseline model was accepted in 1978 as the standard service rifle for the French armed forces, thus ensuring a lengthy production run at St Etienne for many years.

The first FA MAS F1 rifles were issued to some paratroop and specialist units, and the type was initially used in combat by French troops in Chad and the Lebanon in 1983.

The FA MAS F1 is easy to spot, for in appearance it is quite unlike any other assault rifle. It fires the American 5.56-mm (0.219-in) M193 cartridge and over the top of the receiver there is a long handle that doubles as the base for both the rear and fore sight units. The buttstock is prominent and chunky, and from the front of the weapon's main bulk there protrudes a short length of barrel with a grenade-launching attachment.

## Three fire options

There is provision for a small bayonet, and folding bipod legs are provided as standard. The fire selector has three positions: single-shot, three-round burst, and automatic. The mechanism to control this last feature is housed in the buttstock along with the rest of the rather complex trigger mechanism. The FA MAS F1's operating system is of the delayed blowback type. Use is made of plastics where possible and no particular attention is paid to detail finish: for instance, the steel barrel is not chromed.

Despite its unusual appearance, the FA MAS F1 is comfortable to handle and fire, and presents no particular problems in use. Great attention was given to features such as grenade sights and generally easy sighting. The weapon has proved easy to handle and training costs have been reduced by the use of a version employing a small sparklet gas cylinder to propel inert pellets for target training: this version is otherwise identical to the full service version.

Developed via the **FAS MAS F2** interim model, the latest variant is the **FA MAS G2** with the bipod replaced by a sling swivel (though a bipod can still be attached), the grenade launcher removed, the trigger guard extended to cover the whole grip and the magazine housing modified to accept NATO-standard as well as FA MAS magazines.

***The French 5.56-mm (0.219-in) FA MAS F1 is one of the smallest and most compact of modern assault rifles. The magazine has been removed, but note that the carrying handle contains the sights and that the cocking lever is just underneath; note also the folded bipod legs.***

***Although the rifle grenade has fallen from favour as a battlefield weapon, it still retains a limited utility for tasks such as persuading the skippers of small vessels to halt and undergo a search by naval or coast guard forces.***

***This FA MAS F1 is fitted with a TN21 night sighting infra-red spotlight under the muzzle. This equipment has a useful range of 150 m (165 yards), and the soldier picks up the IR reflections in the night vision binoculars held over his eyes. This equipment is in service with the French army.***

**SPECIFICATION**

**FA MAS F1**
**Calibre:** 5.56-mm (0.219-in)
**Length overall:** 757 mm (29.8 in)
**Length of barrel:** 488 mm (19.21 in)
**Weight loaded:** 4.59 kg (10.12 lb) with sling
**Muzzle velocity:** 960 m (3,150 ft) per second
**Rate of fire, cyclic:** 1,000 rounds per minute
**Magazine:** 25-round straight box

# Heckler & Koch G3 Assault rifle

The **Heckler & Koch G3** assault rifle is a development of the CETME design created in Spain by a team largely of German small arms designers, and was adopted by the West German Bundeswehr during 1959. In many ways the G3 has proved to be one of the most successful of all the post-war German weapon designs, and it has been manufactured in Germany not only for that nation's forces but in several other countries desirous of manufacturing their own weapons under licence. Within a total of 13 countries that have made the G3, these nations include Greece, Mexico, Norway, Pakistan, Portugal, Saudi Arabia and Turkey. The G3 has served with the armed forces of some 60 countries in all.

## Low-cost manufacture

Although the maker would not like it to be said, the G3 can be regarded as virtually the nearest that small arms designers have come to the concept of the 'use-and-throw-away' rifle. Despite the cost the G3 is a weapon designed from the outset for mass production using as much simple machinery as possible and thus reducing the need for expensive machining tools and operations. On the basis of the CETME design Heckler & Koch developed the design so that cheap and easily produced materials such as plastics and pressed steel were used wherever possible. The locking roller system developed by CETME was retained to provide a form of delayed blow-back operation after the weapon has been fired.

***Above: The Heckler & Koch HK 21 is the 7.62-mm (0.3-in) light machine-gun version of the basic G3. This version uses a belt feed which can be altered to take a 20-round box magazine if required. This weapon has been produced in Portugal and has been widely sold in Africa.***

***Below: Using the same basic layout as the G3, this 5.56-mm (0.219-in) version is known as the HK 33. It can take a 20- or 40-round magazine, and exists in several versions, including a special sniper's rifle and a version with a telescopic folding butt. Most versions can fire rifle grenades.***

The G3 possesses a general resemblance to the FN FAL in its overall configuration, but there are many differences between the two weapons. The G3 is a whole generation ahead of the FAL, and this significant fact is reflected not only in the G3's general construction and materials but also in the development of the whole family of variants based on the basic G3 assault rifle. There are carbine versions, some with barrels so short they could qualify as sub-machine guns, sniper variants, light machine-gun versions with bipods and heavy barrels, and so on. There is also a version for use with airborne or other such troops: this is the **G3A4**, which has a butt that telescopes onto either side of the receiver.

| SPECIFICATION | |
|---|---|
| **Heckler & Koch G3A3** | **Muzzle velocity:** 780-800 m (2,560-2,625 ft) per second |
| **Calibre:** 7.62-mm (0.3-in) | **Rate of fire, cyclic:** 500-600 rounds per minute |
| **Length overall:** 1025 mm (40.35 in) | **Feed:** 20-round box magazine |
| **Length of barrel:** 450 mm (17.7 in) | |
| **Weight:** loaded 5.025 kg (11.08 lb) | |

## Special features

For all its overall simplicity, the G3 nonetheless possesses some unusual features. One is the bolt, which was designed so that it locks with the bulk of its mass forward and over the chamber to act as an extra mass to move when unlocking. Stripping is very simple and there are only a very few moving parts. With very few changes the basic G3 can be produced with a calibre of 5.56 mm (0.219 in), and this version is manufactured as the **HK 33**.

The success of the G3 can be seen in the number of nations that have adopted the type. The G3 was prominent in the overthrow of the Shah of Iran's regime by the Moslem fundamentalist revolution of 1979, and was also one of the weapons obtained despite sanctions by Rhodesia when defying the world by a unilateral declaration of independence before the war that led to the creation of Zimbabwe. Some nations find it profitable to produce the G3 under licence for export rather than the use of their own forces, and in this category were France and the United Kingdom.

***Carrying the launcher for a rocket-propelled anti-tank weapon with the pack on his back, this German soldier has a variant of the G3 with a telescoping butt as his personal weapon.***

## Popular weapon

In many ways the G3 can be regarded as one of the most important of all modern assault rifles, but it uses the over-powerful NATO 7.62-mm (0.3-in) x 51 cartridge, in common with other designs such as the FAL. Despite this it remains a popular assault rifle and one that will remain in service for some considerable number of years to come.

# Heckler & Koch HK 53 Assault rifle

The **Heckler & Koch HK 53** is a highly capable weapon that falls in classification terms into the borderland between the sub-machine gun and the assault rifle, most commentators placing it on the assault rifle side of the border because of the cartridge it fires.

The HK 53 is one of a series of weapons derived from the operating system that was first adopted by the manufacturer for the 7.62-mm (0.3-in) G3 assault rifle. This delayed-blowback action is based on a two-part bolt comprising a bolt head and a heavier bolt body behind it. The bolt head carries two vertically aligned rollers: when the weapon is ready to fire, these rollers are driven out into recesses in the barrel extension by a wedge-shaped extension of the bolt body, which pushes forward during the chambering of the cartridge to drive the rollers outward. When the cartridge is fired, the gas pressure in the barrel tries to force the bolt head backward, but the movement is limited until the rollers are driven inward by the shaping of the recess walls. The inward movement of the rollers is further checked by the wedge-shaped extension of the bolt body, backed by the return spring. As the rollers are forced inward, the bolt body is accelerated to the rear as the rollers push the wedge-shaped extension rearward: so the bolt body moves swiftly as the bolt head is still checked and so withstands the gas pressure. By the time the rollers have been driven fully inward, the buller has departed from the muzzle and the two parts of the bolt move backward together under the force of the residual gas pressure. There follow the extraction and ejection as the return spring is compressed, and then the bolt is driven forward to chamber a fresh round and become locked as the rollers are driven outward once more.

***The HK 53 is a cross between an SMG and a rifle, being fractionally larger than the MP5 but firing the powerful 5.56-mm NATO round. This can lead to control difficulties, requiring experienced hands to allow the weapon to be used to good effect.***

## Selective fire

If the fire selector lever is set for 'auto', pressure on the trigger releases the hammer to fire the weapon, but if the selector lever is set for 'single shot', the presence of a disconnector makes it necessary to release the pressure on the trigger between shots. This means that the weapon fires from a close breech, which leads to a greater consistency of operation on the one hand, but also to the possibility of a round 'cooking off' if the chamber is hot from previous burst firing.

***The very rare firing port variant of the HK53 is designed to be used from within an armoured vehicle. The foresight is removed, and a bag is fitted to prevent spent cartridges from bouncing dangerously around the inside of the APC.***

## Related models

The HK 53 is closely related to the **HK 33** developed from the mid-1960s for production from 1968 as a scaled-down version of the G3 rifle. The HK 33 was developed for the then-new 5.56-mm x 45 (actual 0.223-in) Remington cartridge, and was exported to countries such as Chile, Malaysia and Thailand. Since 1999 the HK 33 has also been made under licence in Turkey. The HK 33 is still in German production, and has served as the basis for developments such as the G41 assault rifle and HK 53 compact assault rifle, which is known to its manufacturer as a sub-machine gun.

The HK 53 is an ultra-compact version of the HK 33, which can be categorised as a compact (short) assault rifle by the fact that its fires the intermediate rifle round. The HK 53 was developed in the mid-1970s.

The HK 33 is a selective-fire rifle. The receiver is of stamped steel, and the HK 33 is available with either a fixed plastic butt (HK 33A2) or retractable metal butt (HK 33A3). A carbine version of the HK33 is also available as the HK 33k with a shorter barrel and similar fixed or retractable butts as the HK 33kA2 and HK 33kA3 respectively. The HK 33 variants are available with different trigger units, with or without a three-round burst mode.

The HK 53 is internally similar to the HK 33 but cannot fire rifle grenades, or carry an under-barrel 40-mm grenade launcher, or be equipped with a bayonet. The weapon features a long, four-pronged flash hider. Both the HK 33 and HK 53 use 25-, 30- and 40-round box magazines, but the last has now been out of production for some considerable time.

***The emphasis in the creation of modern battlefield weapons such as the HK 33 and HK 53 series is on the reduction of weapon weight and size. Also important is maximising firepower flexibility by the introduction of larger magazines and more comprehensive firing options.***

### SPECIFICATION

**Heckler & Koch HK 53**
**Calibre:** 5.56-mm (0.219-in)
**Length overall:** 780 mm (30.71 in) with the butt extended and 565 mm (23.23 in) with the butt retracted
**Length of barrel:** 211 mm (8.31 in)
**Weight:** empty 3 kg (6.61 lb)
**Muzzle velocity:** not available
**Rate of fire, cyclic:** 750 rounds per minute
**Feed:** 25-, 30- or 40-round curved box magazine

# Heckler & Koch G36 Assault rifle

In the late 1960s Heckler & Koch launched development of the G11 rifle after the West German army had decided to replace its G3 rifle with a lighter weapon offering a considerably greater hit probability. The company's initial studies led to the concept of a small-calibre rifle firing caseless ammunition (created by Dynamit Nobel) for a high rate of fire and, to provide sufficient stopping power despite the use of a small-calibre bullet, a three-round burst capability and a large-capacity magazine.

The G11 was of notably advanced concept and, in its official evaluation from the late 1980s, proved an excellent weapon. But then the whole programme was cancelled for economic and NATO standardisation reasons.

***The G36 reflects the state of the art production for assault rifles, and is a thoroughly workmanlike and reliable weapon offering light weight, adequate magazine capacity, a good rate of fire, accuracy and imponderables such as 'user friendliness'.***

### Second-line rifle

While the G11 was envisaged as the personal weapon of first-line German forces, a G41 rifle was planned as the equivalent for second-line units. This G41 was developed in the early 1980s from the HK-33E assault rifle, and the cancellation of the G11 sealed the fate of the G41 for German service. The G41 was in effect a further development of the G3 rifle based on the same roller-delayed blowback action but chambered for 5.56-mm (0.219-in) ammunition.

### Current weapon

The **G36** assault rifle was created at the **HK-50** project in the early 1990s, and in 1999 the weapon was adopted by the German army as successor to the G3. The G36 differs from earlier Heckler & Koch assault rifles in having a gas-operated operating system with a rotating bolt locking into the barrel extension. The receiver is made from steel-reinforced plastic, the trigger unit is contained inside the plastic pistol grip and there are variants with or without a three-burst fire capability. The charging handle is attached to the top of the bolt carrier and can be hinged to the left or right.

The G36 is fed from a polymer magazine with translucent walls, and this magazine has inbuilt clips to connect magazines one to another for faster reloading. The plastic buttstock folds to the side. Above the receiver is a large carrying handle with built-in sights. The standard G36 has dual sights: an x3.5 compact scope is coupled to an x1 'red-dot' sight for faster short-range target acquisition. The **G36E** export and **G36K** carbine versions have only one sight, an x1.5 scope. The G36 has NATO-standard muzzle brake for launching rifle grenades, and can be equipped with a bayonet or 40-mm (1.57-in) grenade launcher.

There is also a somewhat smaller **G36C** close assault model created for the use of special forces and the like.

**SPECIFICATION**

**Heckler & Koch G36**
**Calibre:** 5.56-mm (0.219-in)
**Length overall:** 998 mm (39.3 in) with the buttstock extended
**Length of barrel:** 480 mm (18.9 in)
**Weight empty:** 3.6 kg (7.94 lb)
**Muzzle velocity:** not available
**Rate of fire:** 750 rounds per minute
**Magazine:** 30-round curved box

# Galil & R4

## Assault rifles

The exact provenance of the Israeli **Galil** assault rifle is more than a trifle clouded, for although it is claimed that the design was created as an indigenous Israeli effort, there are some obvious likenesses to the Finnish Valmet assault rifles that were produced in a variety of models and calibres. Things are made more confused by the fact that the Valmet rifles were themselves modelled on the Soviet AK-47 in its original form with a machined rather than stamped steel receiver unit. Though it would be an over-simplification to state that the Galil is a direct derivative of the AK-47, there are certainly some resemblances in operation (the usual rotating bolt) and general layout, but these are now common to many designs. The situation is further complicated by the fact that the Galil was initially manufactured on tooling supplied by Valmet and with Valmet's type of manufacturing documentation.

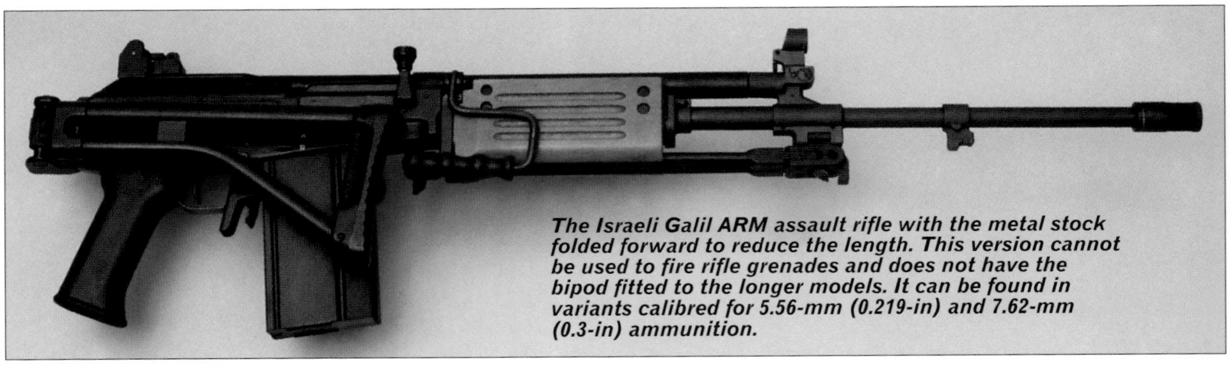

***The Israeli Galil ARM assault rifle with the metal stock folded forward to reduce the length. This version cannot be used to fire rifle grenades and does not have the bipod fitted to the longer models. It can be found in variants calibred for 5.56-mm (0.219-in) and 7.62-mm (0.3-in) ammunition.***

The Galil assault rifle has been produced in both 5.56- and 7.62-mm (0.219- and 0.3-in) calibres, and is now one of the most widely used weapons issued to the various Israeli armed forces. It is produced in three forms: one is known as the **Galil ARM**, which has a bipod and a carrying handle and is the all-purpose weapon; another is the **Galil AR**, which lacks the bipod and handle; and the third is the **Galil SAR**, which has a shorter barrel and no bipod or carrying handle. All three have folding stocks. The bipod on the ARM can be used as a barbed wire cutter, and all three versions have a bottle cap opener fitted as standard to prevent soldiers using other parts of the weapon as bottle openers (e.g. the magazine lips). A fixture over the muzzle acts as a rifle grenade launcher.

### Three magazine sizes

In its full ARM version the Galil can be used as a form of light machine-gun, and 35- and 50-round magazines are produced; there is also a special 10-round magazine used to contain the special cartridges for launching rifle grenades. As usual a bayonet can be fitted.

The Galil has proved to be very effective in action and has attracted a great deal of overseas attention. Some have been exported and the design has also been copied – the Swedish 5.56-mm **FFV 890C** is obviously based on the Galil.

One nation that negotiated a licence for local production was South Africa, which then manufactured a version known as the **R4**, which is the standard rifle for the front-line units of the South African defence forces. The

**SPECIFICATION**

**Galil ARM (5.56-mm)**
**Calibre:** 5.56-mm (0.22-in)
**Length overall:** 979 mm (38.54 in)
**Length of barrel:** 460 mm (18.1 in)
**Weight loaded:** 4.62 kg (10.19 lb) with 35-round magazine
**Muzzle velocity:** 980 m (3,215 ft) per second
**Rate of fire, cyclic:** 650 rpm
**Magazine:** 35- or 50-round boxes

R4 is produced in 5.56-mm calibre and differs in some details from the original, the changes resulting mainly from operational experience in the South African and Namibian bush. The R4 has also been exported to a number of countries.

*Key features of the Galil ARM include a straight-through design, the gas system above the barrel, an inbuilt bipod folding into the underside of the fore grip and the location of the magazine forward of the trigger group.*

| SPECIFICATION | |
|---|---|
| **Galil ARM (7.62-mm)** | **Weight loaded:** 4.67 kg (10.30 lb) |
| **Calibre:** 7.62-mm (0.3-in) | **Muzzle velocity:** 850 m (2,790 ft) per second |
| **Length:** 1050 mm (41.34 in) | **Rate of fire, cyclic:** 650 rpm |
| **Length of barrel:** 533 mm (20.98 in) | **Magazine:** 20-round curved box |

# Beretta AR70 & AR90 Assault rifles

*This Beretta AR70 assault rifle, fitted with a 20-round magazine reveals the weapon's clean overall lines and good finish. It is used by some Italian anti-guerrilla special units and has been sold in Jordan and Malaysia, but large-scale sales have not been made.*

The **AR70** was developed by Beretta of Italy following a series of manufacturer's in-house trials involving several types of assault rifle designs, and from these evolved a gas-operated design using the rotary-bolt locking principle but in a very simple form. To provide increased safety, Beretta decided to strengthen the locking system with extra metal around the chamber area. The result is a functional and well-made weapon that can be stripped down into its few operating parts with ease.

## Normal options

There are three production versions of the AR70: one is the AR70 proper, which has a nylonite stock and furniture; the **SC70** with a folding buttstock constructed from shaped steel tubing; and the **SC70 Short** that is a version of the SC70 with a shorter barrel for the soldiers of special forces units. While the AR70 and SC70 can fire 40-mm (1.57-in) rifle grenades, the SC70 Short lacks this capability.

The AR70 is as good as any assault rifle on the market, and is notable for the high standard of care that is taken in its manufacture, which is a hallmark of Beretta small arms design and manufacture.

For some reason the AR 70 series has yet to make any large impact on the market for small arms. Modest numbers have been adopted by the Italian special forces, and some weapons have also been exported to Jordan and Malaysia, but in none of these cases have the numbers involved been large. This is rendered even more odd when it is realised that the care in design and construction is such that the weapons of the AR70 series are notably accurate – accurate enough for a telescopic sight to be fitted to standard production versions if required.

In the early 1980s the Italian army's requirement for a new 5.56-mm rifle was met by the **AR90** derivative of the AR70. Entering service in the 1990s, this has a carrying handle and fixed sight above the receiver. The standard model has a longer barrel and fixed buttstock, but there are also long- and short-barrel models with a folding buttstocks, and there is provision for a bipod on every model.

*The AR70 has several equipment options, including the fitting of night sights, a bayonet or a MECAR rifle grenade launcher. The butt can easily be removed and replaced with a skeleton butt to convert the rifle to SC70 standard.*

*The Beretta AR70 in service in the Malaysian jungles; note the applied camouflage paint scheme. The AR70 weighs only 4.15 kg loaded with 30 rounds and is thus a fairly handy weapon for the small-statured men of Asian armies to handle.*

| SPECIFICATION | |
|---|---|
| **AR70** | **Weight loaded:** 4.15 kg (9.15 lb) |
| **Calibre:** 5.56-mm (0.22-in) | **Muzzle velocity:** 950 m (3,115 ft) per second |
| **Length overall:** 955 mm (37.6 in) | **Rate of fire, cyclic:** 650 rpm |
| **Length of barrel:** 450 mm (17.72 in) | **Magazine:** 30-round curved box |

# ST Kinetics assault rifles Singapore 5.56-mm rifle series

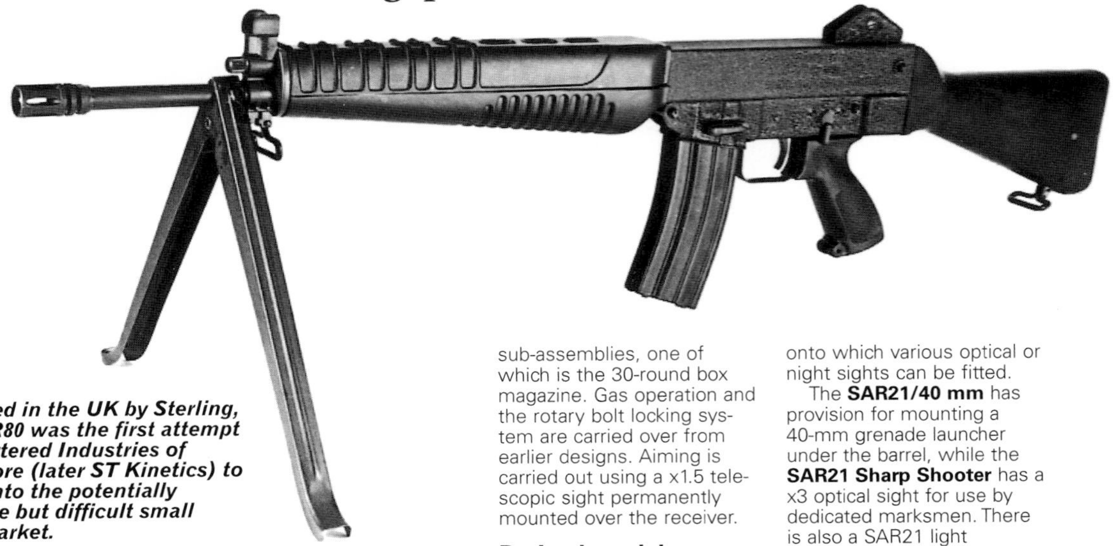

***Designed in the UK by Sterling, the SAR80 was the first attempt by Chartered Industries of Singapore (later ST Kinetics) to break into the potentially lucrative but difficult small arms market.***

The first assault rifle produced by Chartered Industries of Singapore (now Singapore Technologies Kinetics, or ST Kinetics) was the 5.56-mm (0.219-in) **SAR80** designed in the UK under contract for the Singaporean company by Sterling. The first prototypes appeared in 1978.

The design emphasis was on ease of production with a gas-operated system, with a rotary bolt, based around that of the American M16. The M16 had been manufactured under licence in Singapore for the local armed forces. Although ordered in quantity, the SAR80 did not completely supplant the M16 in local use. Despite intensive marketing no sales of the SAR80, other than those for local use, resulted.

### Steady evolution

The Singaporean company's next foray into the small arms market involved the 5.56-mm **SR88** and the subsequent **SR88A**. This could be regarded in design terms as an enhanced export model based around the SAR80 with numerous detail design changes. There was also a shortened carbine model. Once again there were no export sales so the SR88A, the final offering, was withdrawn.

Its successor seems certain to attract far more sales interest. It is the 5.56-mm **SAR21**, designed from about 1995 onwards in the light of the company's intention of producing a rifle which could replace all the rifles then in service with the Singapore armed forces. It was first demonstrated publicly during 1999 and is now in series production. The SAR21 has a bullpup layout, with the magazine behind the trigger group, to ensure a compact and handy weapon. Great use is made throughout the design of composite materials and plastics for enhanced handling ergonomics.

Construction is modular to assist maintenance, the rifle stripping down into only five sub-assemblies, one of which is the 30-round box magazine. Gas operation and the rotary bolt locking system are carried over from earlier designs. Aiming is carried out using a x1.5 telescopic sight permanently mounted over the receiver.

### Derived models

The SAR21 assault rifle is only one of a series of variants. One is the **SAR21 P-Rail**, an assault rifle model with the usual sight replaced by a length of Picatinny Rail onto which various optical or night sights can be fitted.

The **SAR21/40 mm** has provision for mounting a 40-mm grenade launcher under the barrel, while the **SAR21 Sharp Shooter** has a x3 optical sight for use by dedicated marksmen. There is also a SAR21 light machine-gun with a heavy barrel, bipod and automatic fire only – all other models can be fired as single shot when required. The weapon's cyclic rate of fire is 450-650 rounds per minute.

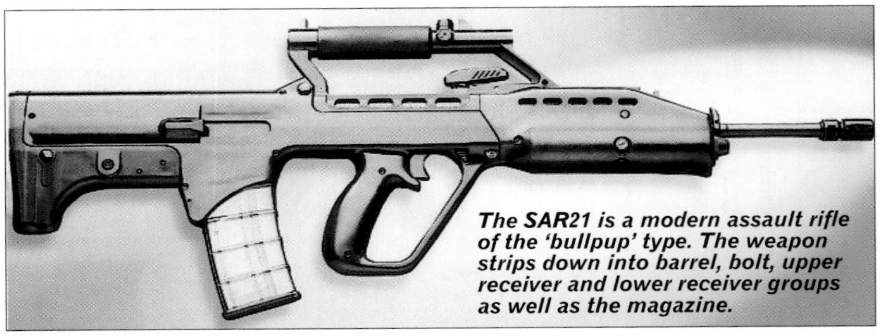

***The SAR21 is a modern assault rifle of the 'bullpup' type. The weapon strips down into barrel, bolt, upper receiver and lower receiver groups as well as the magazine.***

**SPECIFICATION**

**SAR80**
**Calibre:** 5.56 mm (0.219 in)
**Length:** 970 mm (38.19 in)
**Length of barrel:** 459 mm (18.07 in)
**Weight:** empty 3.7 kg (8.16 lb)
**Magazine capacity:** 30 rounds
**Rate of fire:** 600-800 rpm

**SPECIFICATION**

**SR88A**
**Calibre:** 5.56 mm (0.219 in)
**Length:** 960 mm (37.8 in)
**Length of barrel:** 460 mm (18.11 in)
**Weight:** empty 3.68 kg (8.11 lb)
**Magazine capacity:** 30 rounds
**Rate of fire:** 700-900 rpm

**SPECIFICATION**

**SAR21**
**Calibre:** 5.56 mm (0.219 in)
**Length:** 805 mm (2 ft 7.7 in)
**Length of barrel:** 508 mm (31.69 in)
**Weight:** empty 3.82 kg (8.42 lb)
**Magazine capacity:** 30 rounds
**Rate of fire:** 450-650 rpm

# CETME Model L/LC

## Spanish 5.56-mm assault rifles

Production of the 5.56-mm (0.219-in) assault rifles generally known as the **CETME** family ended under another manufacturer's designation, that of Santa Barbara (now owned by General Dynamics) at the Oviedo arsenal. The rifle had design origins dating back to 1945 as it employed a German delayed-blowback locking system based on gas operation and rollers moving outward into slots in the receiver walls at the instant of firing. This system was used in Spain for a series of 7.62-mm and 7.92-mm (0.3-in and 0.312-in) CETME rifles (and in Germany by Heckler & Koch) before Spanish attentions turned to producing a 5.56-mm rifle.

CETME stood for Compañia de Estudios Técnicos de Materiales Especiales, the name of a design bureau that modified the 7.62-mm rifle designs into a lighter, handier and more compact 5.56-mm assault rifle. Two models resulted –

**SPECIFICATION**

**Model L**
**Calibre:** 5.56 mm (0.219 in)
**Length:** 925 mm (36.42 in)
**Barrel length:** 400 mm (15.75 in)
**Weight:** empty 3.4 kg (7.5 lb)
**Magazine capacity:** 30 rounds
**Rate of fire:** 600-750 rpm

***Two versions of the CETME 5.56-mm selective fire assault rifle were built: a standard model with a fixed butt stock (the Model L) and a short-barrelled version with a telescopic stock (Model LC). A 20-round magazine was originally fitted.***

the **Model L** with a fixed butt stock and the **Model LC** with a telescopic butt stock. The Model LC was also slightly shorter overall with the butt stock extended and the barrel was shorter, resulting in a higher cyclic rate of fire.

### Spanish production

Production of these weapons for service with the Spanish armed forces took place between 1986 and 1991, and a key feature of the basic design was the extensive use in much of the weapons' exteriors on the basis of various composite material mouldings. Early production models were supplied with a 20-round box magazine, but this was later altered to allow M16 pattern 30-round magazines to be employed. The 30-round magazine then became standard, although a 10-round box was occasionally seen.

Another production change was to the sights. These were altered from the original four-position sight graduated up to 400 m (440 yards), to a far simpler flip-over sight assembly graduated only for 200 m (220 yards) and 400 m. Another change was to the fire-control lever: the rifle was originally produced with a three-round burst limiter device in addition to the usual safe, single shot and fully automatic selections, but this was omitted from late-production weapons after experience had revealed that the limiter was unnecessary.

The CETME 5.56-mm rifles were sold only to the Spanish armed forces. In service the rifles proved to be somewhat prone to damage, requiring care and maintenance. The only complete answer was a replacement rifle, so in mid-1998 it was revealed that the replacement would be the Heckler & Koch G36. The forecast requirement was then for about 115,000 rifles, and so a factory is being constructed in Spain in order to carry out licensed manufacture.

***The Model LC is readily distinguishable from its Model L half-brother by its telescopic butt. Though mainly successful, the Model L series has revealed a tendency toward damage.***

**SPECIFICATION**

**Model LC**
**Calibre:** 5.56-mm (0.219 in)
**Length:** 860 or 665 mm (33.86 or 26.18 in)
**Barrel length:** 320 mm (12.6 in)
**Weight:** empty 3.4 kg (7.5 lb)
**Magazine capacity:** 30 rounds
**Rate of fire:** 650-800 rpm

# SIG SG550 Assault rifle

***This SG550 (Stgw 90) assault rifle reveals the facility for the carriage on the weapon of three plastic magazines to provide a large quantity of ready-use ammunition.***

The **SG550** series of 5.56-mm (0.219-in) assault rifles was developed to meet a Swiss army requirement for an assault rifle to replace the service's 7.5-mm (0.295-in) Sturmgewehr 57 (Stgw 57, otherwise the SG510-4). The two basic SIG models originally involved were the **SG550** and **SG551**. The Swiss army designation for the SG550 is **Sturmgewehr 90** (**Stgw 90**), while the SG551, also in Swiss army service, is shorter and lacks the fittings for a bipod. Both models were accepted for service during 1984, and remain in production.

A number of related models have since appeared. The **SG550 SP** and **SG551 SP** are semi-automatic sporting rifles for the large Swiss target rifle market. A **SG551 SWAT**, virtually identical to the SG551, is intended mainly for special forces or special law enforcement agencies, and has provision for the installation of optical sights and, under the barrel, a 40-mm grenade launcher. The **SG550 Sniper** rifle is a specialised semi-automatic rifle with a longer barrel, a telescopic sight and numerous other associated refinements. This variant is also used by the Jordanian police. By contrast the **SG552 Commando**, launched during mid-1998, is a much lighter and more compact model, also with a folding butt stock, intended for issue to special forces. It has provision for a number of alternative optical sights.

### High specification

The SG550 series is one where superlatives can be liberally lavished. The overall standard of construction and ease of handling are excellent. As is usual these days, extensive use is made of plastics-based materials to save weight wherever possible. The method of operation is the usual gas-operated rotary-locking bolt.

Noticeable on all models is the attention to design detail in features such as the translucent plastic magazines that allow the magazine contents remaining to be instantly assessed. The 20- or 30-round magazines also have studs and lugs on the sides to allow a number of magazines to be clipped together in such a way that as one magazine is emptied the firer can pull the assembly out, shifting its sideways and then pushing in one of the still-loaded magazines. The provision of 60 or possibly even 90 ready-use rounds has obvious tactical advantages. A five-round magazine containing rifle grenade-launching cartridges is also available.

The butt stock can be folded to the right hand side of the receiver to reduce carrying or stowage length. It is claimed that the balance of the rifle with the stock folded is such that firing with reasonable accuracy at combat ranges is possible. The sights are particularly easy to utilise and have luminous spot facilities for night firing. A telescopic sight mounting is provided, as is a three-round burst limiter.

**SPECIFICATION**

**SG550**
**Calibre:** 5.56 mm (0.219 in)
**Length:** 998 mm (39.29 in)
**Barrel length:** 528 mm (20.47 in)
**Weight:** empty 4.1 kg (9.04 lb)
**Magazine capacity:** 20 or 30 rounds
**Rate of fire:** 700 rpm

**SPECIFICATION**

**SG551**
**Calibre:** 5.56 mm (0.219 in)
**Length:** 827 mm (32.56 in)
**Barrel length:** 372 mm (14.65 in)
**Weight:** empty 3.4 kg (7.5 lb)
**Magazine capacity:** 20 or 30 rounds
**Rate of fire:** 700 rpm

***The SG550 Sniper retains the 20- or 30-round magazine of the basic model but has a number of different features, including an adjustable stock and telescopic sight, to optimise the weapon for improved accuracy at longer ranges.***

# Kalashnikov AK-47 Assault rifle

The **Avtomat Kalashnikova AK-47** is one of the most successful and widely used small arms ever produced. It is used all over the world, and even after more than half a century variants of the type are still in production in one form or another in many countries.

The first AK-47 was designed around a short 7.62-mm (0.3-in) calibre cartridge that owed much to the German 7.92-mm (0.31-in) *kurz* round. The Red Army was often on the receiving end of the German assault rifle family (the MP 43, MP 44 and StuG 44) and asked for their own counter. The result was the 7.62-mm x 39 cartridge and the AK-47. The designer was Mikhail Kalashnikov and the rifle is universally known by his name.

The first experimental examples were issued for service during 1947, though the weapon did not enter wide scale service until the 1950s. The AK-47 gradually became the standard weapon of the Warsaw Pact. The production lines were huge, but such was the demand that most Warsaw Pact nations set up their own production facilities. From this sprang the large numbers of AK-47 sub-variants that continue to delight the gun research buff to this day.

## Reliable quality

The basic AK-47 is a sound and well-made weapon that carried over few of the mass production expedients employed by its German wartime equivalents. The AK-47 receiver is machined, and good-quality steel is used throughout with wooden furniture as standard. The result is a weapon that can absorb any amount of hard use and mishandling.

As there are few moving parts and stripping is very simple, maintenance is also simple and can be accomplished with even a minimum of training.

Numerous variants of the basic AK-47 emerged over the years, one of the most common was a version with a folding butt.

All these different versions used the same mechanism, a simple rotary bolt that was cammed into corresponding grooves in the receiver by bolt cams. Operation is by gas tapped from the barrel via a gas port.

### Original AK-47

One of the most popular variants of the Kalashnikov, fitted with a folding metal buttstock.

### Modernized AKM

Identifiable by different muzzle brake attachment and hand-grip on forestock

### Chinese Type 56

The Chinese version of the AK-47 with its own integral bayonet seen folded under the forestock.

## World manufacture

AK-47s were produced in China, Poland and East Germany and the operating system was copied by several countries, emerging as the Finnish Valmet and the Israeli Galil.

For all its success, it was finally admitted during the late 1950s that production of the AK-47 involved too much use of manufacturing facilities. A redesign produced the **Avtomat Kalashnikova Moderniziro-vannyi** or **AKM**, which outwardly resembles the earlier design but is generally revised to facilitate production.

The most obvious external change is to the receiver, which is formed from a steel stamping in place of the former machined equivalent, but internally the locking system has been revised to make it simpler. There are numerous other differences but the overall changes are in manufacturing methods.

The AKM did not immediately take the place of the AK-47, being used more as a supplement to numbers. The other Warsaw Pact production lines gradually switched to the AKM, some nations (such as Hungary) even going so far as to modify the basic design to produce their own version, which often differs in many ways from the original (the Hungarian **AKM-63** even looks different but retains the basic mechanism of the AKM). A version with a folding steel butt is known as the **AKMS**.

***Built in larger numbers than any other firearm in history, the Kalashnikov assault rifle has been used in virtually every conflict fought in the second half of the 20th Century.***

## Huge numbers

More than 50 million AK-47s and variants have been produced, and the AK-47 and AKM will remain in service until well into the 21st century, if not beyond. This longevity must be partially attributed to widespread availability and the numbers produced, but the basic fact is that the AK-47 and AKM are both sound and tough weapons that are easy to use and simple to maintain.

***AK-47s, AKMs and local variants of the design were made in almost every country of the Warsaw Pact. This East German infantryman would have been armed with the MPiKM version, made in the GDR.***

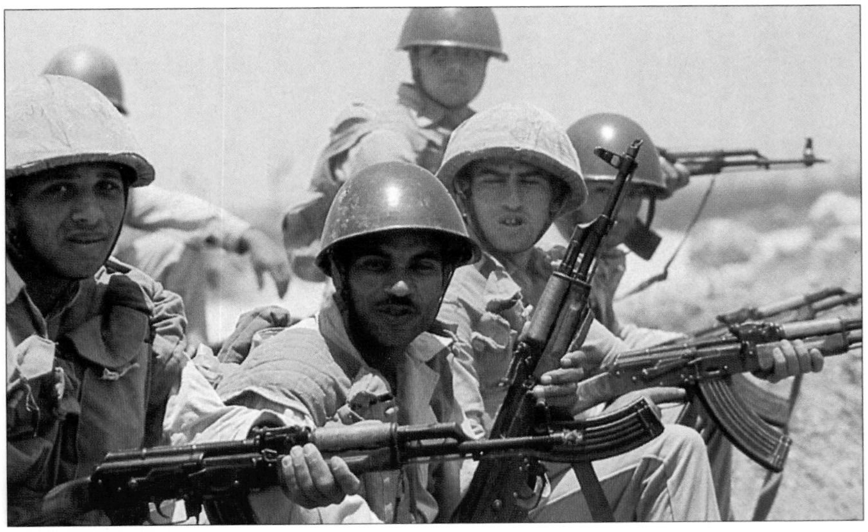

***Egyptian troops are pictured here during the 1973 Yom Kippur War. Their weapons are AKMs with the characteristic angled muzzle attachment and the handgrip grooved into the stock. The AKM was the standard Egyptian rifle for over 20 years.***

**SPECIFICATION**

| AK-47 | AKM |
|---|---|
| **Calibre:** 7.62 mm (0.3 in) | **Calibre:** 7.62 mm (0.3 in) |
| **Length:** 869 mm (34.21 in) | **Length:** 876 mm (34.49 in) |
| **Length of barrel:** 414 mm (16.30 in) | **Length of barrel:** 414 mm (16.30 in) |
| **Weight loaded:** 5.13 kg (11.31 lb) | **Weight loaded:** 3.98 kg (8.77 lb) |
| **Magazine:** 30-round box | **Magazine:** 30-round box |
| **Rate of fire:** cyclic, 600 rpm | **Rate of fire:** cyclic, 600 rpm |
| **Muzzle velocity:** 710 m (2,330 ft) per second | **Muzzle velocity:** 710 m (2,330ft) per second |

# Kalashnikov AK-74 Assault rifle

*Left:* ***A Soviet rifleman circa 1988, dressed in leaf pattern camouflage, with a gas mask and NBC oversmock. He is armed with a standard AK-74 rifle, which by this time had replaced the AK-47 in front line Soviet military units.***

***An AK-74 (top), with an AK-47 for comparison beneath. The AK-74 has a skeleton butt, but note the prominent muzzle brake and the brown plastic magazine. Note also the size difference between the two cartridges.***

The Soviet Union was surprisingly slow in following the Western adoption of small-calibre cartridges for its future weapon designs. Perhaps the huge numbers of AK-47s and AKMs already in service made such a change a low priority, so it was not until the early 1970s that any intimation of a new Warsaw Pact cartridge was given. In time it emerged that the new cartridge had a calibre of 5.45 x 39 mm and the first examples of a new weapon to fire it were noted.

In time the weapon emerged as the **AK-74**, which entered full-scale production to meet the requirements of the Red Army; as with earlier designs, variants were manufactured in other Warsaw Pact countries.

The AK-74 is basically an AKM revised to suit the new cartridge. It is almost identical to the AKM in appearance, weight and overall dimensions. Some changes, such as a plastic magazine, have been introduced and there is a prominent muzzle brake. There are versions with the usual wooden stock and with a folding metal stock.

One matter relating to the AK-74 that deserves special mention is the bullet used. To gain maximum effect from the high-velocity 5.45-mm (0.215-in) calibre bullet, the designers have adopted a design that is very effective but outlawed by international convention, for the steel-cored projectile has a hollow tip and the centre of gravity far to the rear. This has the effect that when the nose strikes a target it deforms, allowing the weight towards the rear to maintain the forward impetus and so tumble the bullet. In this way the small-calibre bullet can have an effect on a target far in excess of its cross sectional area. Some high-velocity projectiles can display this nasty effect, but on some, such as the M193 5.56-mm (0.219-in) cartridge, it is an unintended by-product. On the Soviet 5.45-mm the effect has been deliberately designed into the projectile.

## New Kalashnikovs

The end of the Soviet era has seen cosmetic modification of the Kalashnikov design, and it is being sold for export under 'Series 100' designations. The **AK101** fires the 5.56 x 45 NATO rounds, while the **AK 102** is a short-barrelled variant. The **AK103** fires the original 7.62 x 39 cartridge used by the AK-47, while the **AK105** is a short barrelled update of the AK-74 firing the high-velocity 5.45 x 39 round.

***The AK-74's combat debut came in Afghanistan, where captured examples soon fell into the hands of the Mujahideen. Since then, it has been used in conflicts from Chechnya to the Congo.***

**SPECIFICATION**

**AK-74**
**Calibre:** 5.45 mm (0.215 in)
**Length:** 930 mm (36.61 in)
**Length of barrel:** 400 mm (15.75 in)
**Weight unloaded:** 3.6 kg (7.94 lb)
**Magazine:** 30-round box
**Rate of fire:** 650 rpm
**Muzzle velocity:** 900 m (2,955 ft) per second

# Armalite AR-15/M16

## Assault rifle

The **M16** assault rifle was created by the noted designer Eugene Stoner. Derived from the Armalite AR-10, a revolutionary full-power battle rifle developed in the mid-1950s, the new design emerged as a 5.56-mm (0.22-in) calibre weapon known as the **Armalite AR 15**.

The AR-15 was submitted for a competition to decide the new standard rifle for the US armed forces. Before the competition was decided, the British army took a batch of 10,000, making it one of the first customers to purchase significant quantities of the new design. The US Air Force bought soon afterwards in 1961.

### Standard rifle

The AR-15 was selected by the US Army to become its new standard rifle, the M16. Production was then switched to the Colt Firearms Company, which took out a production and sales contract with Armalite.

The M16 became the **M16A1** in 1966 with the addition of a bolt closure device, fitted as the result of experience in Vietnam. There had been a number of problems encountered during initial fielding, especially in combat situations, but better training, preventive maintenance, and several design changes resulted in the weapon that has become the standard issue rifle of the US Army.

Since then more than three million M16s have been manufactured, and the rifle has been widely issued and sold to nations all around the world. Numerous developments have been produced and tried, including a light machine-gun variant with a heavy barrel and a bipod, and short-barrel versions for special forces.

### Operation

The M16 is a gas-operated weapon that uses a rotary bolt locking system. A carrying handle over the receiver also acts as the rear-sight base, and nylonite is used for all the furniture. The plastic gave it something of the feeling of a toy to soldiers accustomed to the heavy wood of previous generation weapons like the M14, but the M16 was far from a toy. The use of 5.56-mm ammunition meant that the soldier could carry more rounds than before, and the reduced power of the rounds meant that for the first time ordinary soldiers could be issued with a fully automatic weapon.

### M16A2

In the 1980s a product-improved version of the rifle was introduced. The most obvious change is the redesigned handguard with a tougher round contour which provides a better grip. Less obvious is the heavier barrel with a 1 in 7 twist to fire NATO-standard SS109-type (M855) ammunition which is also fired from the M249 Squad Automatic Weapon (SAW). This increases the range and penetration.

The M16A2 will also shoot the older M193 ammunition designed for a 1 in 12 twist. It also incorporates a burst control device that limits automatic fire to three-round bursts, which increases accuracy while greatly reducing wasteful ammunition expenditure.

***Above: The rifle used to develop the US Army's 'Land Warrior' infantry system for the 21st century is the M4 carbine version of the M16 assault rifle.***

***Right: M16-armed troopers from the 101st Airborne in combat near Dak To during Operation Hawthorne, which took place during the Vietnam War in 1966.***

### M4/M4A1

The M4/M4A1 5.56-mm Carbine is a carbine variant of the M16A2. It is designed to provide heavyweight firepower to individual soldiers working in close quarters and confined spaces.

The M4 Carbine shares most (over 80 per cent) of its parts with the M16A2. The M4 Carbine has replaced 45-cal submachine guns and some pistols with troops such as armour crews and special operations forces.

**SPECIFICATION**

**M16A2 Assault rifle**
**Calibre:** 5.56 mm (0.22 in)
**Length:** 1006 mm (39.63 in)
**Barrel length:** 508 mm (20 in)
Weight:, loaded: 3.99 kg (8.79 lb)
**Range:** maximum 3600 m (11,811 ft); effective 550 m (1,804 ft); normal combat range less than 200 m (656 ft)
Muzzle velocity: 853 m (2,800 ft) per second
**Rate of fire:** 800 rounds per minute cyclic; 45 rounds per minute semi-auto; 90 rounds per minute burst fire
**Magazine capacity:** 30 rounds

***The original M16 became famous as an icon of the Vietnam War. The standard rifle was used by tens of thousands of infantrymen, but the short-barrelled, sliding-stocked Colt Commando was used primarily by special operations forces.***

# Armalite AR-15/M16

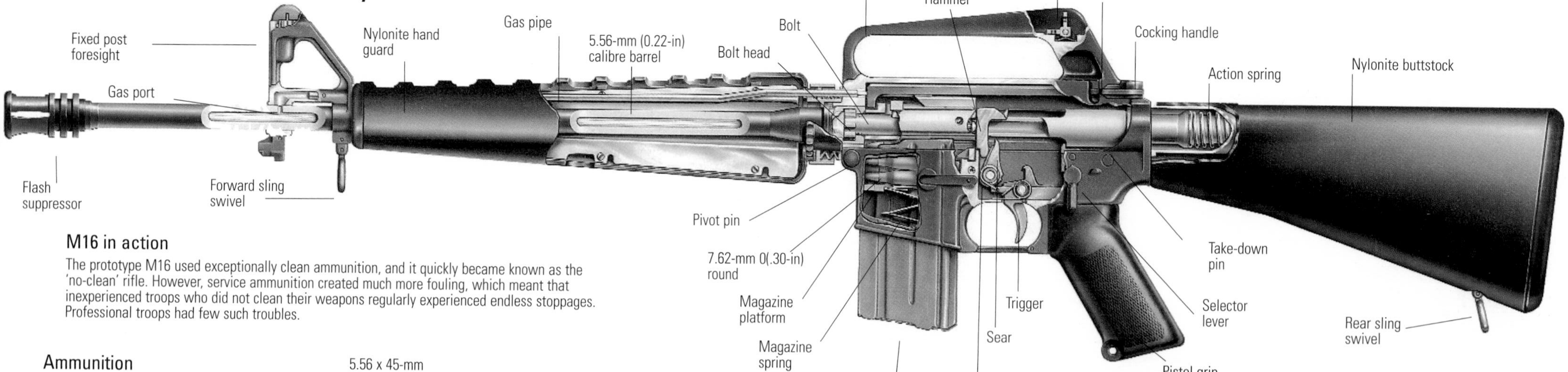


## M16 in action

The prototype M16 used exceptionally clean ammunition, and it quickly became known as the 'no-clean' rifle. However, service ammunition created much more fouling, which meant that inexperienced troops who did not clean their weapons regularly experienced endless stoppages. Professional troops had few such troubles.

## Ammunition

The main advantage of adopting a smaller-calibre rifle like the M16 (ammunition and magazine at right) is that any soldier so armed can carry twice as much ammunition as one equipped with a full-power 7.62-mm (0.30-in) rifle.

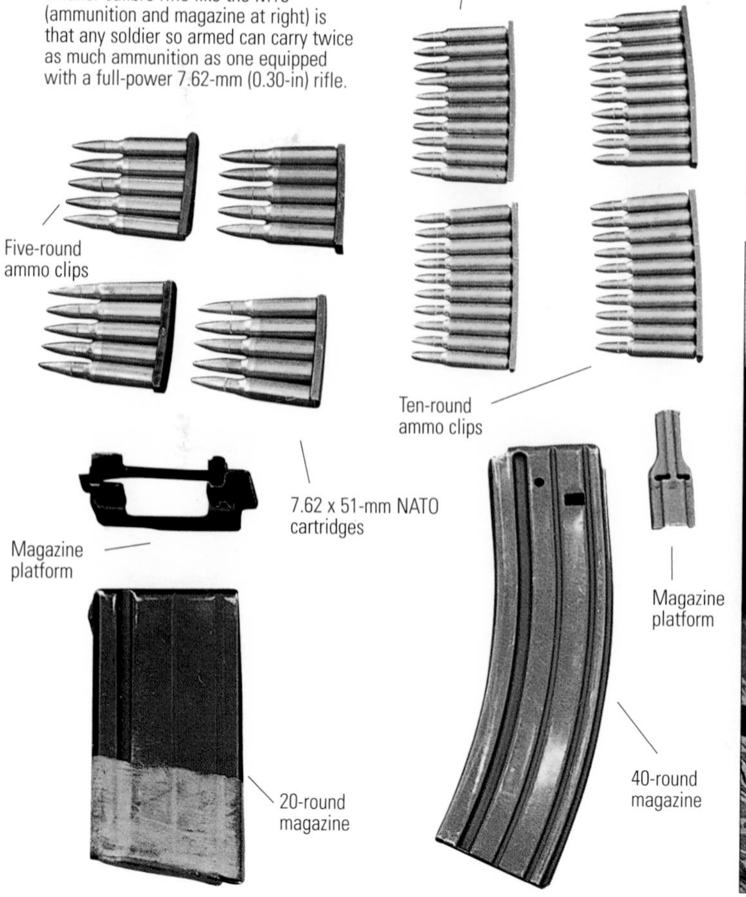


***Right:** The **AR-15** (far right) was developed from the **AR-10** rifle of the 1950s (near right). The **AR-10**, chambered for the 7.62-mm **NATO** round, was one of the first rifles to make extensive use of plastic and aluminium parts.*

***Below:** By releasing the take-down pin and swivelling the fore-end on the pivot pin, the working parts of the M16 rifle become easy to extract at any time for cleaning, maintenance or repair.*

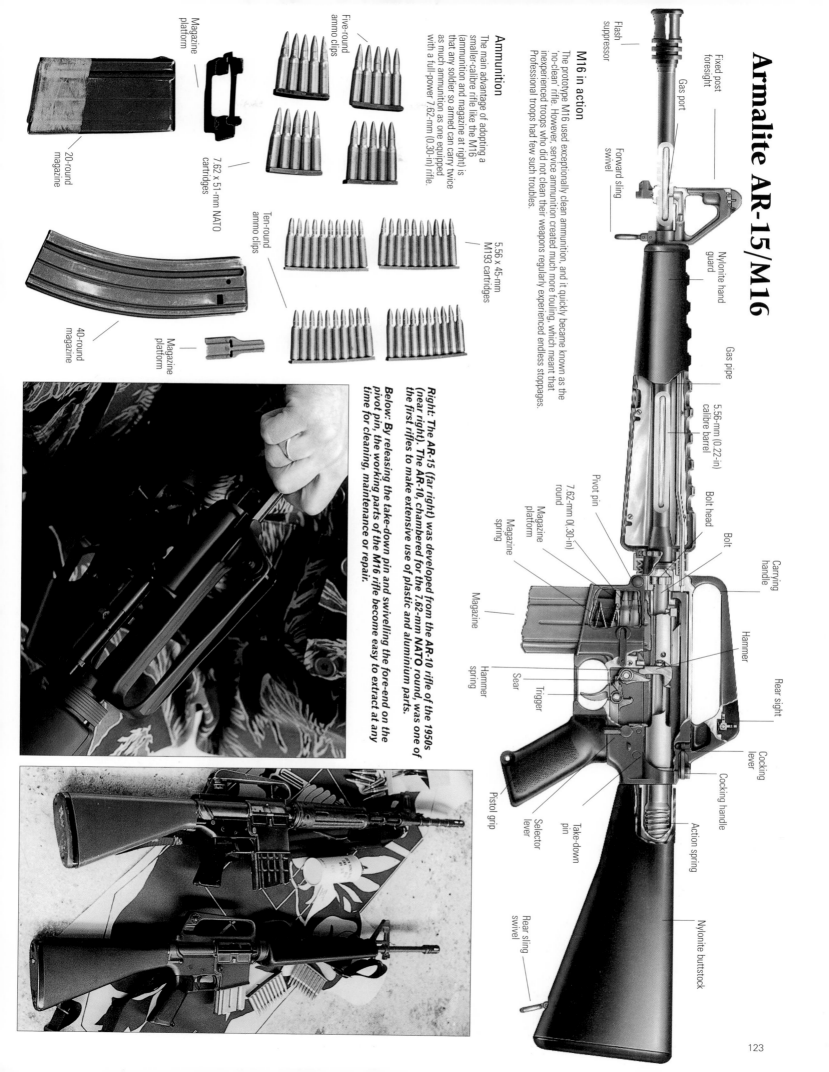

# SA80 British Army rifle

Above: The ergonomic nature of the SA80 suits the weapon well to the demands of modern warfare by aiding fast movement and prone firing.

The British army's standard rifle is the **SA80**, more formally known as the **L85A1** in its initial form. This is accurate and in theory is easy to maintain, and is a pleasure to shoot. Its light recoil allows the soldier to keep the weapon on target with the minimum of problems, and a special optical sight gives the soldier a clear view even in poor light. The most striking feature of the SA80 is its compactness. The 'bullpup' layout means that the magazine is located behind the trigger group, which opens the way to the inclusion of a relatively long barrel into a weapon of small overall dimensions. The barrel of the SA80 is only a little shorter than that of the SLR (Self-Loading Rifle) it has replaced, but the complete weapon is 30 per cent shorter. As a result, the SA80 is easy to handle, especially in confined spaces such as an APC.

The compact size of the SA80 is important for the British soldier: thus the SA80 is ideal for troops entering action in the Warrior infantry fighting vehicle, which was used for the movement of British infantry in the course of Operation Desert Storm.

The SA80 also works well in house-to-house fighting, and its sling arrangement has proved popular; the SA80 can be slung across the chest, the back or to one side to leave the soldier's hands free, but still ensure that the weapon can still be brought into action without undue delay, simply by unclipping the sling at the top.

Because of its 'bullpup' design, the SA80 ejects its empty cases from a port opposite the firer's face, so it can only be fired right-handed mode.

## SUSAT sight

The SA80 is one of the first combat rifles to be issued with a telescopic sight as a standard fitting. This SUSAT (Sight Unit, Small Arms, Trilux) gives x4 magnification and comes with a comfortable rubber eyepiece through which the soldier sees a pointer (dark in daylight, illuminated by the radioactive Trilux lamp in poor light) that he places over the target.

A selector lever set at R (Repetition) provides the soldier with a single-shot capability, while the A (Automatic) setting provides for continuous fire as long as the trigger is pulled and there are rounds in the magazine.

The SA80 fires a 5.56-mm (0.22-in) round that is light enough for each man to carry eight 30-round magazines plus an ammunition bandolier. Light as it is, the bullet is effective at up to 500 m (1,640 ft), although in practice small arms fire is rarely used at ranges over 300 m (984 ft). A strong wind can affect the flight of the bullet, however, and at long ranges the soldier needs to adjust his aim to compensate for this factor.

The SA80 replaces three weapons in the infantry armoury: the SLR, the 9-mm Sterling sub-machine gun and the 7.62-mm (0.31-in) General Purpose Machine-Gun. To take the GPMG's place there is another version of the SA80 which has a heavy barrel and a bipod. Known as the **Light Support Weapon**, this **L86A1** is otherwise virtually identical to the SA80, so the soldier only needs to be familiar with one weapon instead of three.

The SA80 assault rifle has proved far from popular in service, and first-line use has uncovered a number of problems. Much of the SA80's mechanism was therefore redesigned by Heckler & Koch to create the **L85A2** version. This is more reliable than the L85A1, but there have been complaints that reliability is still poor under dusty, high-temperature conditions.

Left: The small size of the SA80 is an advantage for troops who typically ride into battle in the confined troop compartment of armoured personnel carriers.

Above: Shown here, infantryman carrying the SA80 on patrol. This rifle has become a signature weapon of the Northern Ireland conflict.

Left: A problem faced by the designers of small arms is the need to make weapons usable under all conditions, including those typical of high-technology battlefields where NBC protection may be worn.

| SPECIFICATION | |
|---|---|
| **L85A1 (SA80)**<br>**Calibre:** 5.56 mm (0.22 in) x 45 mm NATO<br>**Length:** 85 mm (30.91 in)<br>**Length of barrel:** 518 mm (20.39 in)<br>**Weight:** 3.80 kg (8.38 lb) without magazine and optical sight<br>**Weight loaded:** 4.98 kg (10.98 lb) | **Magazine:** 30-round detachable box<br>**Rate of fire, cyclic:** 610-775 rounds per minute<br>**Muzzle velocity:** 940 m (287 ft) per second<br>**Range:** 300 m (984 ft) typical and 500 m (545 yards) effective |

# Armalite AR-18 Paramilitary rifle

Once the Armalite concern had cleared its design desks of the AR-15, with production under way by Colt Firearms of the M16 series, it decided to look to the future for new products. With the 5.56-mm (0.22-in) round well established, Armalite decided that what was needed was a notably simple and therefore reliable and easily produced weapon that could fire this cartridge. While the AR-15 was a sound weapon, it was not easy to produce without sophisticated machine tools, and throughout much of the world these machine tools were not available. Thus the need for a weapon which could be simply produced by Third World nations was recognised, and a drastic revision of the AR-15 design was undertaken.

The result was the **Armalite AR-18**, which is very basically an AR-15 adapted for manufacture by the now-familiar production expedients of pressed steel, plastics and castings. For all these expedients the AR-18 is a sound design that is easy to produce, maintain and use. In general appearance and layout the AR-18 is similar to the AR-15, but the stamped steel receiver gives it a bulkier outline. The plastic butt is designed to fold alongside the receiver for stowage or firing from the hip.

## Completed design

Once the AR-18 design was complete, Armalite attempted to find purchasers, but with the AK-47 and the M16A1 flooding the world's markets, there were few takers. An arrangement to produce the AR-18 in Japan fell through and for some years the design was in abeyance. Then the Sterling Armaments Company of the UK took out a licence, undertaking some production and at one time moving production to Singapore. Some sales were then made locally, but what was more important was that the local defence industry took the design as the basis for its own weapon designs, the AR-18 now living on disguised in many forms and under various labels.

**SPECIFICATION**

**Calibre:** 5.56 mm (0.22 in)
**Length:** 940 mm (37 in) extended or 737 mm (29 in) folded
**Weight loaded:** 3.48 kg (7.67 lb) with 20-round magazine
**Magazine:** 20-, 30- and 40-round detachable box
**Rate of fire:** 800 rpm cyclic
**Muzzle velocity:** 1000 m (3,280 ft) per second

***This AR-18 was originally manufactured in Japan but was captured from the IRA in Belfast. It is the standard production model with a folding butt.***

# Ruger Mini-14 Paramilitary and special forces rifle

When it was first produced in 1973, the **Ruger Mini-14** marked a significant turn away from the mass production methods introduced during World War II, towards the fine finish and attention to detail that was formerly the hallmark of the gunsmith's art. The Mini-14 is an unashamed example of how guns used to be made before the concepts of steel stampings and die-cast alloys came upon the scene.

## Variant

From a design viewpoint, the Mini-14 is a 5.56-mm (0.22-in) version of the 0.3-in (7.62-mm) Garand M1 service rifle of World War II. By adopting the Garand action, Ruger managed to combine a sound and well-engineered design with the ammunition of a new technology. Allied to craftsmanship and a deliberate appeal to those who look for that something extra in a weapon, the result is a remarkable little rifle.

In appearance the Mini-14 has the characteristics of a previous age. The materials used are all high quality and in an age where plastics have now taken over, the furniture is all manufactured from high-grade walnut. But visual appeal has not been allowed to take precedence over functional safety, for the Mini-14 has been carefully engineered to prevent dust and debris entering the action. Some degree of visual appeal has been allowed to affect the finish, for the weapon has been carefully blued all over, and there is even a stainless steel version that sells very well in the Middle East.

## Export

The Mini-14 has not yet been adopted by any major armed forces but it has been sold to such establishments as police forces, personal bodyguard units and to many special forces who prefer a well-engineered and balanced weapon to the usual 'tinny' modern products. To suit the requirements of some armed forces Ruger later developed a special version that should appeal to many soldiers. This is the **Mini-14/20GB** with a bayonet lug. Police forces have been catered for by the introduction of the **AC-566** with glass fibre furniture, and another innovation is the **AC556GF** with a folding stock and a shorter barrel. The two versatile AC-556 designs can be used to either fire on single shot or full automatic for bursts, whereas the standard Mini-14 is limited solely to single-shot operation.

***Key features of the Mini-14 and its relatives, including the military adapted Mini-14/20GB with optional stainless steel furniture, include high-quality manufacture based on the use of the best possible materials.***

***The AC556GF selective fire weapon is a variant of the Mini-14 intended mainly for police and paramilitary use, and features a folding stock and rear pistol grip.***

**SPECIFICATION**

**Mini-14**
**Calibre:** 5.56 mm (0.22 in)
**Length:** 946 mm (37.24 in) overall
**Weight loaded:** 3.1 kg (6.8 lb) with 20-round magazine
**Magazine:** 5-, 20- or 30-round detachable box
**Rate of fire:** 40 rpm
**Muzzle velocity:** 1005 m (3,300 ft) per second

***The appearance of the basic Mini-14 is immediately redolent of the American M1 rifle of World War II, of which it is a re-engineered and re-calibred derivative.***

# Sniper rifles

## From hunter to scout

**To the normal military headaches such as river crossings, mountains and the weather, the sniper can add further problems, increasing the normal friction to the point where the whole army machine seizes up.**

The popular image of a sniper is one man firing at a distant enemy from a carefully-concealed position. In modern mobile battles the sniper has little chance to exercise such skills. What role, therefore, is there for the sniper in such a war?

The short answer is that there will be times when battles will settle down to allow both sides to regroup and supply themselves in preparation for the next round. This takes time, and during this time the sniper can return to his task, which is little changed from that of old, i.e. being the big game hunter of the battlefield.

### Observation role

The sniper is not just a killer who can pick off his or her targets at long ranges. The sniper is also a highly-trained observer who can move across country in such a way as to avoid notice by an enemy and thus reach areas in which they are not expected. Once there they have to save their fire for the important target. For this to happen the sniper acts under strict control after careful preparation and planning.

### Two-man team

Snipers rarely operate alone. In general, each infantry battalion in any army has a team of about eight snipers, and these often operate in pairs. The idea is that one soldier concentrates on observation and location of targets, while the other sticks to the shooting. This is not a hard and fast rule, for there will be many occasions when the snipers will be operating primarily as observers and will use their weapons only if absolutely necessary or if a target of importance is detected.

*Inset: A key element in any sniper's equipment is his sight. The British Army's L96A1 rifle carries a x6 Schmidt & Bender telescopic sight. Counter-terrorist variants can carry a sight with a variable x2.5 to x10 magnification.*

*Above: Although bolt-action rifles have long been replaced by automatics on the battlefield, they are still favoured by snipers for their accuracy and their easy, reliable action.*

In the static conditions produced by the intervals in mobile warfare there is much snipers can do. They can infiltrate enemy positions observe movements and strengths, and they can disrupt and unsettle an enemy attempting to recuperate or carry out maintenance tasks. And if they remain within their own defended area the sniper can keep watch for an enemy carrying out exactly the same infiltration tactics

*The United States Marine Corps have always emphasised the importance of sniper skills. Introduced in the 1970s, the 7.62-mm (0.31-in) M40 sniper rifle is based on the commercial Remington 700, but each example is hand-built at the Rifle Team Equipment workshop at Quantico, Virginia.*

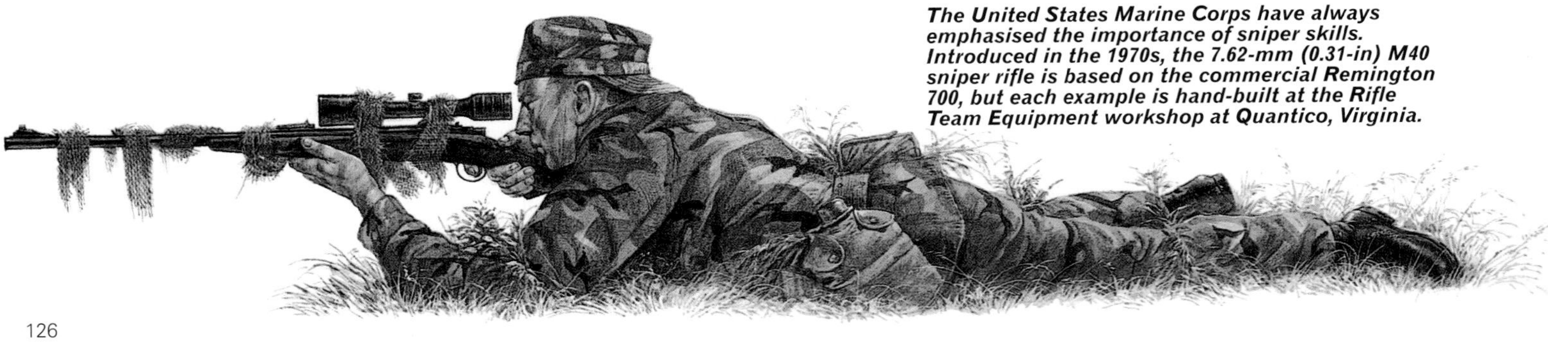

## SSG 69: UNCONVENTIONAL SNIPER

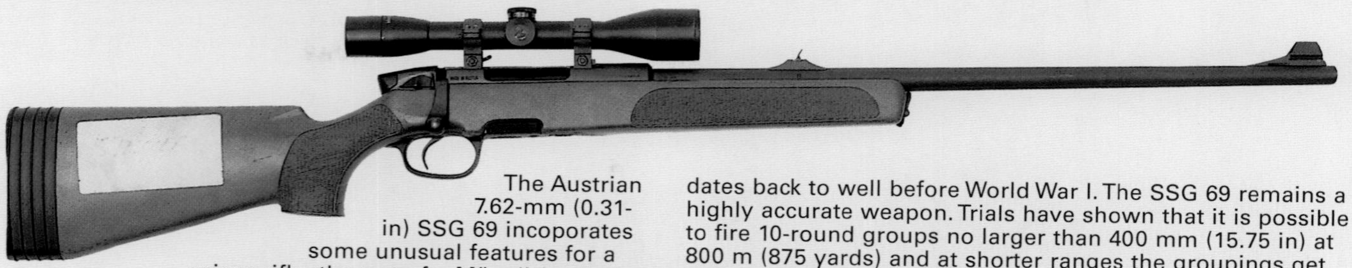

The Austrian 7.62-mm (0.31-in) SSG 69 incoporates some unusual features for a sniper rifle: the use of a Männlicher bolt action with a form of rear locking instead of the far more common forward-lug locking and the use of the five-round Männlicher rotary magazine, a design feature that dates back to well before World War I. The SSG 69 remains a highly accurate weapon. Trials have shown that it is possible to fire 10-round groups no larger than 400 mm (15.75 in) at 800 m (875 yards) and at shorter ranges the groupings get much tighter. Electro-optical sights may be added on a standard NATO mounting. As well as being operated by the Austrian army, the SSG 69 is used by a number of foreign police and military forces.

in return. They can also prevent enemy patrols from getting too close by anticipation of the enemy's likely approach paths and the establishment of an appropriate ambush point.

In more mobile conditions the sniper can still have an important battlefield role, Infantry do not constantly operate from the armoured confines of personnel carriers: to close with an enemy they have to leave their 'battle taxis'and fight on foot. They then become prone to all the battlefield hazards encountered by the foot soldiers of the past: machine-gun or other weapon fire can then pin them down, often from undetected fire positions.

### Sniping by stealth

Under such circumstances the sniper may infiltrate enemy positions before an advance gets under way. Using camouflage and stealth, small teams of snipers can work their way through the enemy lines to lie in wait until their colleagues make their move. They can then smooth the advance by detecting and knocking out weapon positions from the rear, probably with the old ploy of knocking out the weapon rather than its team.

In past conflicts, a heavy weapon such as a machine-gun or mortar was often taken out of action far more effectively by a single well-placed armour-piercing bullet than by the slower and more uncertain method of knocking out every member of the weapon team – this applies particularly to missile launchers. Some sniper teams will no doubt be detailed to infiltrate as far into the enemy rear as the artillery lines to create mayhem and general disruption.

Weapons will not be the only targets to be engaged. As always, enemy officers and NCOs will be prime targets of opportunity. Even though most officers, even senior ones, now wear the same uniforms and carry the same weapons as their men, their very actions and conduct generally give them away to a trained observer.

Snipers can also be used to knock out their opposite numbers. In many modern armies an advance screen of snipers is often laid out in front of defended positions for the sole purpose of disrupting and slowing enemy movements. These snipers have to be tackled, and the sniper will be used to deal with his counterpart. This is particularly true in wooded or close country where the number of positions in which an enemy can hide are many.

### Observation tactics

The role of the modern sniper is more that of a scout than of a hunter. The training which produces snipers necessarily produces excellent observers, men who can infiltrate and report back enemy positions and activities. Such information is invaluable to a commander who also knows that his observer has the capability to knock out important enemy weapons and men.

This offensive capability may be secondary to the observing function, and the trained sniper will rarely use his rifle to take out targets at ranges greater than 800 m (875 yards): there are usually too many imponderables involved and the sniper risks giving away his position.

Whatever weapon snipers carry, when they see a target they have to be able to hit it, first time and effectively. Even if the battle moves around, the sniper must remain, watching and waiting, still carefully concealed and with a definite objective in mind: to use his field and observational skills together with his skill-at-arms to achieve the maximum possible results.

***Above:** One of the most important skills needed by any sniper is the ability to blend into the background, and in this capacity local vegetation and netting are useful additions to camouflage kit*

***Right:** Sniper rifles like this Parker-Hale bolt-action weapon require careful maintenance for maximum efficiency. Care of his weapon and equipment is a vital task for any sharpshooter.*

*The successful marksman is a creature of nature and training. Nature must provide the right blend of physical and psychological raw materials, and training can then blend these with acquired skills such as accurate rifle shooting to create an effective long-range killer.*

# Marksmanship

**The sniper's task is to hit his target with a single shot. To do that, he must be a master of fieldcraft and a master of the art of marksmanship. He has to prepare two things before he sets out to do his job: himself and his weapon. His own preparations, which may have taken years of training, will tell him how to solve the first problem: which position should he take up from which to fire?**

The four basic firing positions are prone, sitting, kneeling and standing. Which of these is adopted depends on the individual circumstances, but the object is to take up the steadiest position in a location which provides both cover and a good field of fire.

There are five elements involved in taking up a shooting position.

## Natural point of aim

The first element is to ensure that the shooter has a natural point of aim. The secret to achieving this is to have used the weapon enough that it becomes an extension of the sniper's own body, enabling it to be pointed at the target without conscious thought. Snipers can test their abilities by raising the rifle to the shoulder, aiming at a target and then closing their eyes and relaxing for 10 seconds. If the rifle is still pointing at the target on reopening the eyes, then the marksman has found the natural point of aim.

## Bone support

A steady, reliable shooting position needs support from the bones, not from the muscles. When lying prone, the left hand is forward, palm up, just behind the front sling swivel. The wrist is straight and locked, the rifle lying across the relaxed palm of the hand; the left forearm and elbow are directly below the barrel.

If the elbow is not directly underneath the barrel, the arm muscles will have to work to hold the rifle and it will not be steady. The rifle butt is held firmly into the shoulder, the right arm and elbow out at an angle to help form the 'shoulder pocket' and to give balanced support.

## Right-hand grip

The right hand must hold the stock firmly, thumb over the top. The trigger finger should just touch the trigger, so that it can come straight back without itself touching the stock and perhaps spoiling the aim. The hold on the trigger should be firm – a loose grip may cause the trigger to be jerked at the last moment.

The point of contact between the thumb and the cheekbone is called the 'spot weld'. The cheek should be pressed firmly against the thumb so that head, arm, hand and weapon all act as a single unit, keeping the eye still in relation to the sight both before and after firing.

## Breathing

Breathing normally while aiming causes the chest to rise and fall, spoiling the shot. Instead, part of the breath should be released, and then held while aiming and firing. The breath should not be held for too long – more than 10 seconds causes muscular tension and involuntary movement.

## Squeezing the trigger

Control of the trigger is probably the single most important aspect of marksmanship. It is the key to firing the round without disturbing the way the weapon is lined up with the target.

The finger should touch the trigger somewhere between the tip and the second joint. The exact position is a matter of personal preference, depending on the size of the hand and the size of the rifle's stock. It is very difficult to hold a rifle perfectly still and, instead of trying, the sniper concentrates on getting perfect hand/eye co-ordination.

Unless the round is fired at the precise moment that the cross-hairs are over the target, it will probably miss. That may sound obvious, but it is actually all there is to say about marksmanship. The best shots are generally quick ones, where everything comes together straight away, and there is no time to drift off. But even so, it is most important not to snatch at the trigger. A good exercise is to balance a small coin on the muzzle and see how still it stays when squeezing off a dry shot.

The wind and other weather conditions can make a very great difference to where the bullet strikes the target, and also has an effect on the sniper unless he is lying in the prone position. The light affects how the target is seen. In general it seems that people shoot low on bright, clear days and high when it is gloomy and overcast.

### Slow and low

Damp, humid air is thicker than dry air, so will resist the passage of the bullet more when it is on its way to a target. This slowing down will cause it to drop faster than normal, so shots will strike low.

High temperature has the reverse effect. Hot air is thinner than cold air, so offers less resistance to the bullet, sending it high.

The rifle should not be left standing in the sun. One side getting hotter than the other will cause the barrel to warp – just by a fraction, but enough to throw a shot off by a long way at only moderate ranges.

Weather affects ammunition as well. A good sniper will keep his weapon and ammunition dry. Wet ammunition is colder than dry. Warmer ammunition works more efficiently than cold, making the round go high. If some is dry and some wet, the sniper will get different results from different rounds, so if he cannot keep his ammunition dry, he is better off making sure that it is all thoroughly wet and reduce the elevation when shooting.

***Right:** One of the keys to sniping is camouflage, using either natural items or man-made equipment such as paint and scrim netting to eliminate reflective areas of skin and to break up a man-like outline.*

## SHOOTING POSITIONS

The best shooting position is determined by a number of factors, including the nature of the position from which the man must fire and its relationship to the target area, and the requirements of supporting the rifle in the fashion that will make it most controllable and therefore accurate. Contrary to popular belief, the sniper is not necessarily a 'natural' marksman, but a man with certain intrinsic skills honed by a regime of intensive training and practice.

***Above left:** The prone firing position offers great steadiness of aim, and has obvious concealment advantages as only the firer's head and shoulders are facing the target.*

***Above:** The kneeling position creates a steady base for the arms and thus for the rifle. However, this is not a position that many can maintain for long before muscular tremors begin to make their effects felt.*

***Left:** The sitting position also provides the steadiness of the back, in this particular instance in combination with the bracing of the elbows on the spread knees to help make the rifle as steady as possible.*

# SSG 69 Sniper rifle

*The Steyr SSG 69 rifle uses a Kahles ZF69 telescopic sight graduated up to 800 m (875 yards) – this example is not fitted with the usual 'iron' sights. The SSG 69 uses an unusual five-round rotary magazine, but can also be fitted with a 10-round box magazine.*

**SSG 69** is the Austrian army's designation for the Steyr-Mannlicher sniper rifle the service adopted in 1969, the SSG prefix standing for *Scharfschützengewehr* (sharp-shooters' rifle). It has been widely adopted as both a military and police marksman's rifle and is available in numerous versions, from the 'Police' type with extra-heavy barrel and oversize match-type bolt handle to the latest sniper/sports rifle version, the **SSG P11**.

However, the fundamental design of the rifle dates back to the beginning of the 20th century: the bolt and magazine are little changed from a weapon made by Steyr for the Greek army, the Mannlicher-Schoenauer Model 1903. The bolt is manually operated, locked by six symmetrically positioned rear locking lugs.

## Rear locking lugs

Rear lock-up, pioneered so successfully on the famous Lee-Enfield, is theoretically dangerous as the whole length of the bolt – rather than just the bolt head – is placed under compressive stress during firing. Yet in practice neither the Mannlicher nor the Lee-Enfield has suffered notable problems and the benefit is appreciated by many shooters: the cartridges feed directly into the chamber without having to traverse space for forward-locking lugs. Loading is thus smoother and faster, aided by the spool magazine that feeds more consistently than a stacked, spring-loaded magazine. On the other hand, some shooters believe the multiple lug system to be less accurate, and it can make it harder to use re-loaded brass.

The barrel is 650 mm (26 in) long with a heavy contour and a target crown. The rifling consists of four lands and grooves, and the twist rate is one turn in 305 mm (12 in). The barrel is cold-forged, that is, the tube of metal that will form the barrel is placed over a mandrel (a steel bar with the rifling in raised relief) and a rotary hammer is used to forge the barrel both internally and externally. The hammering hardens the barrel internally and externally as it forms the rifling.

## Spiral-shaped barrel

This process was developed by Steyr and has since been employed by many other manufacturers. It gives the barrel a characteristic spiral appearance and there is a faintly discernible taper from breech to bore. The barrel is screwed into the receiver for 57 mm (2.24 in), which is farther than on most other rifles. Once the barrel is in place, a concentric press is used to apply considerable pressure round the join between barrel and receiver, which makes for a fantastic, rigid action, albeit making it next to impossible to change the barrel other than by returning it to the factory.

The bolt action of the SSG 69 is pleasantly smooth and even more so now it is teflon-coated. A cocking indicator is provided. The two-position safety is a sliding type safety catch on the right-hand side of the receiver. With the safety 'on', the bolt cannot be operated, which is a mixed blessing. However, the safety is at least silent, so there is no tell-tale 'click' when the firer is ready to take a shot. The safety can be operated whether or not the weapon is cocked.

The P11 is optionally available with a double trigger, which is really suitable only if the firer has small hands. The modular assembly of the rifle permits a change in trigger assembly very easily, although second assemblies are not cheap.

The standard magazine holds five rounds and is made of plastic with a transparent plate so that the firer can see how many rounds are inside it. Unlike most magazines with detachable floorplates, the rounds are directly on top of each other and are held securely so bullet tips cannot get damaged during firing. Also available is a 10-round magazine, but this protrudes from the weapon for some way.

The accuracy of the SSG 69 is typical of that of modern sniper rifles. At 100 yards a competent shot can group all five shots in less than 15 mm (0.6 in) when firing commercially manufactured ammunition such as Remington Winchester 168-grain type. Tighter groups are possible with hand-loaded cartridges.

*The Steyr SSG 69 rifle is the standard Austrian army sniper's rifle, and is used by mountain troops as it is possible for a single sniper to virtually seal a mountain pass against advancing troops for long periods. The SSG 69 is robust enough to survive in such conditions and retain its accuracy.*

**SPECIFICATION**

**SSG 69**
**Calibre:** 7.62-mm (0.3-in)
**Lengths:** overall 1140 mm (44.9 in), barrel 650 mm (25.6 in)
**Weight:** empty, with sight 4.6 kg (10.14 lb)
**Muzzle velocity:** 860 m (2,821 ft) per second
**Magazine capacity:** 5-round rotary or 10-round box

# FN Model 30-11 Sniper rifle

*The FN Model 30-11 can be fitted with a wide range of accessories. The large sight seen here is a standard NATO infra-red night vision sight, and the bipod fitted is that used on the FN MAG machine-gun.*

The **Fabrique Nationale Model 30** is an entirely conventional Mauser-action rifle used by the Belgian army and many other military forces and law enforcement agencies as a sniper rifle.

The connection between Mauser and FN dates back to 1891, when FN began to manufacture Mauser rifles under licence for the Belgian army. Subsequent production for export was eventually agreed with Mauser after the Belgian company cheerfully sold thousands of rifles to China and South America too, an action contrary to the spirit, if not the letter, of its agreement with Mauser. From 1897 to 1940 over half a million Mauser-action rifles were made in Belgium for delivery to armies all over the world. Manufacture was interrupted by the German occupation during World War II, and when it resumed in 1946, the vast quantities of war-surplus weapons then available made it difficult to sell new bolt-action weapons except to specialist markets, hence the company's production of sports/sniper rifles.

### Elderly but capable

The Model 30 was originally produced in 1930 and was itself derived from a Mauser type of 1898, slightly modified to become the Model 24. Production of the Model 30 resumed in 1950. The sniper rifle version is essentially a standard Gewehr 98 type of rifle made to a much higher standard than an issue weapon. The military sniper rifle is chambered for 7.62-mm (0.3-in) x 51-mm NATO ammunition and is intended to shoot the highest quality commercial rounds. Most of the rifles are sold with the five-round internal magazine, but a detachable 10-round box magazine is also made.

The **Model 30-11** features a heavy barrel and the Mauser forward-locking bolt action. This is considered by some shooters to be inherently the safest and most accurate action. The Model 30-11 has an adjustable stock with spacers so that the weapon can be tailored to the dimensions of the shooter. The standard sighting system is Fabrique Nationale's 28-mm telescope with x4 magnification plus aperture sights. Accessories include a bipod (the same as that of the world famous FN MAG 7.62-mm general-purpose machine gun), additional butt spacer plates, a sling and a carrying case. The scope mounts will accept NATO standard kit including IR night sights.

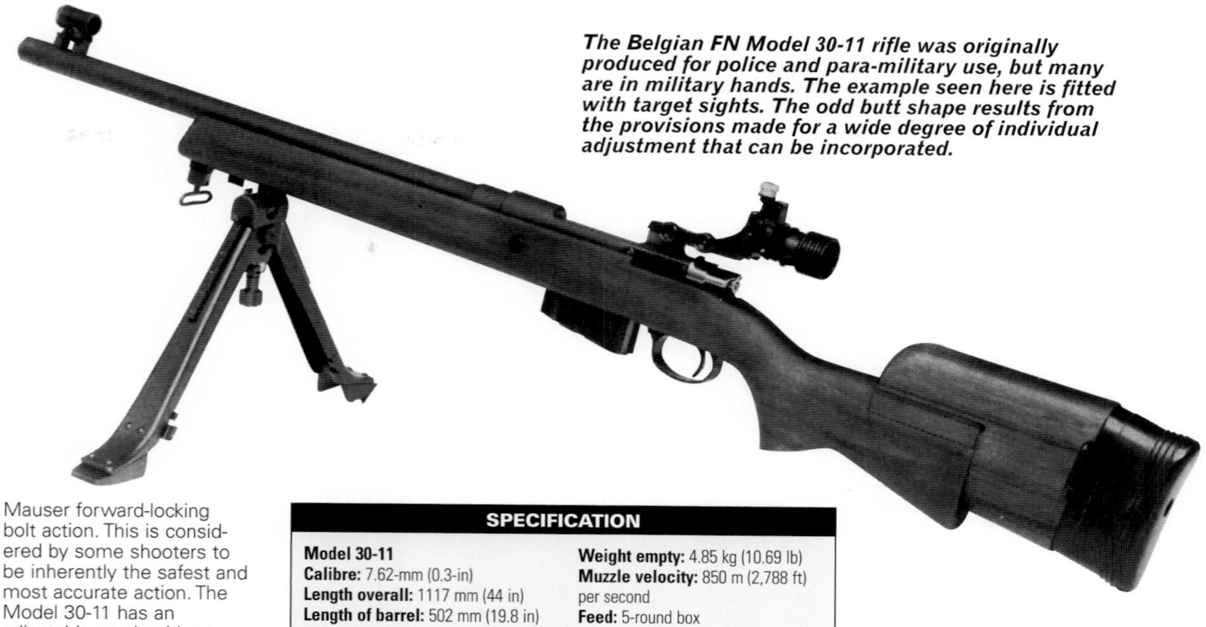

***The Belgian FN Model 30-11 rifle was originally produced for police and para-military use, but many are in military hands. The example seen here is fitted with target sights. The odd butt shape results from the provisions made for a wide degree of individual adjustment that can be incorporated.***

**SPECIFICATION**

**Model 30-11**
**Calibre:** 7.62-mm (0.3-in)
**Length overall:** 1117 mm (44 in)
**Length of barrel:** 502 mm (19.8 in)
**Weight empty:** 4.85 kg (10.69 lb)
**Muzzle velocity:** 850 m (2,788 ft) per second
**Feed:** 5-round box

# MAS FR-F1 & F2
## Sniper rifles

MAS (Manufacture d'Armes, St Etienne) is now part of the GIAT (Groupement Industrial des Armaments Terrestres) conglomerate. The MAS company has produced most of the French army's small arms from the 1920s, and its current sniper rifle is a development of the standard service rifle of the French army during World War II. The French army today issues sniper rifles much more widely than most Western armies. Instead of issuing a few sniper rifles to each infantry battalion, the French (like the former Soviet armies) have a dedicated sniper in each rifle section (or squad, in US terminology). A section comprises eight men armed with 5.56-mm (0.219-in) FA-MAS assault rifles, one AA-52 light machine-gun, and a sniper (FR-F1 or FR-F2).

### Well-proved concept

The **Fusil à Répétition F1** was developed in 1964 by the MAS bureau in general and designer Jean Fournier in particular, and manufacture began in 1966. Like the MAS 36 service rifle on which it is based, the F1 is chambered for the French army's standard 7.5-mm (0.295-in) x 54 cartridge, but is also available in 7.62-mm (0.3-in) x 51 NATO calibre. The F1 or **Tireur d'élite** has a free-floating barrel projecting from a half-length wooden stock and a distinctive pistol grip behind the trigger. A muzzle brake and bipod are fitted as standard. Wooden spacers can be used to adjust the length of the butt and cheek pieces can be added. The Model 1953 L.806 telescopic sight is the service issue scope, but its x3.8 magnification has been criticised as insufficiently powerful for sniping. On the other hand, some units in the French army, most notably the Foreign Legion, devote enormous effort to rifle shooting and their standard of accuracy is commendable. FR-F1s used by French law enforcement agencies use more powerful scopes such as the variable (x1.5 to x6) Zeiss Diavari and others.

The **FR-F2** was introduced in 1984 and is available only in 7.62-mm NATO, thus giving a French rifle section three types of non-interchangeable ammunition for their weapons The F2 features a stronger bipod mounted on a yoke ahead of the barrel. The barrel is encased in a plastic sleeve intended to reduce the 'mirage' effect generated by the heat of the barrel after repeated firing.

The F1 is also available to sports shooters in the **Tir Sportif** or **Type B** version, which is distinguishable by the absence of the bipod and an aperture sight positioned above the receiver on a bar mounting. This is for target shooting; a **Grande Chasse** hunting rifle was also manufactured with a telescopic sight.

***In this photograph the French sniper is using the telescopic sight of his FR-F1 as an observation aid, resting the barrel on a tree branch. He would never fire the weapon from such a stance, for accuracy would be minimal.***

**SPECIFICATION**

**FR-F1**
**Calibre:** 7.5-mm (0.295-in) or 7.62-mm (0.3-in)
**Length overall:** 1138 mm (44.8 in)
**Length of barrel:** 552 mm (21.73 in)
**Weight:** empty 5.42 kg (11.95 lb)
**Muzzle velocity:** 852 m (2,795 ft) per second
**Feed:** 10-round box

# Mauser SP 66 and SP 86 Sniper rifles

***This version of the SP 66, known as the Model 86 SR, is equipped with a set of target sights and a bipod for super-accurate competition shooting; the service version is basically the same weapon fitted with a telescopic sight but lacking the forward-located bipod.***

The Mauser-Werke at Oberndorf in West Germany can lay claim to a long and distinguished background and history in the design and production of manually operated (or bolt-action) rifles that are now known under the blanket name of Mauser.

The company's forward-locking bolt action is still widely used by designers, and Mauser-Werke has even introduced its own variations to the action, one of them being the relocation of the bolt handle from the rear of the bolt to the front. On most rifles this would be of little significance, but on a rifle for the highly specialised task of sniping it means that the firer can work the bolt action without having to move his head out of the way as the bolt itself can be made relatively short; it also means the barrel can be made correspondingly longer for enhanced accuracy. This has been done on a custom-built Mauser-Werke sniper's rifle known as the **SP 66**. The revised bolt action is just a single example of the level of care lavished on this weapon: others include a heavy barrel, a buttstock with a carefully contoured thumb aperture, provision for adjustable cheek and butt pads, and a special muzzle attachment. This last is so designed that, on firing, the great bulk of the resultant flash is directed away from the firer's line of sight, and the device also serves as a muzzle brake to reduce the recoil forces transmitted through the weapon to the firer. Both of these factors are important in allowing the firer to get off second and subsequent shots more accurately and more rapidly.

### Superb finish

The standard of finish throughout the production of the SP 66 is very high. Even such details as roughening all surfaces likely to be handled to prevent slipping have been carried out with meticulous care, and the trigger is extra wide to facilitate use with a gloved finger.

The sights have been selected with equal attention. There are no fixed sights and the standard telescopic sight is a Zeiss-Divari ZA with zoom capability from x1.5 to x6. Night sights can be fitted, though it is recommended that the manufacturer selects and calibrates them to an exact match for the rifle on which they are used. As is usual with such rifles the ammunition fired from the SP 66 is taken from carefully chosen batches of 7.62-mm (0.3-in) NATO rounds produced for sniper use.

The SP 66 has been a considerable success even though it is manufactured virtually to order only. It is in service with the West German armed forces and more have been sold to a further 12 or so nations, most of which are unwilling to divulge their names for security reasons.

The **SP 86** is a less expensive version of the SP 66 mainly for police use. The weapon has a new bolt, cold-forged barrel, nine-round magazine, combined flash suppresser and muzzle brake, and furniture of laminated wood with ventilation to eliminate warping.

**SPECIFICATION**

| | |
|---|---|
| **SP 66** | **Weight:** 6.25 kg (13.8 lb) |
| **Calibre:** 7.62-mm (0.3-in) | **Muzzle velocity:** about 860 m (2,821 ft) per second |
| **Length overall:** 1120 mm (44.1 in) | **Magazine:** 9-round box |
| **Length of barrel:** 680 mm (26.8 in) | |

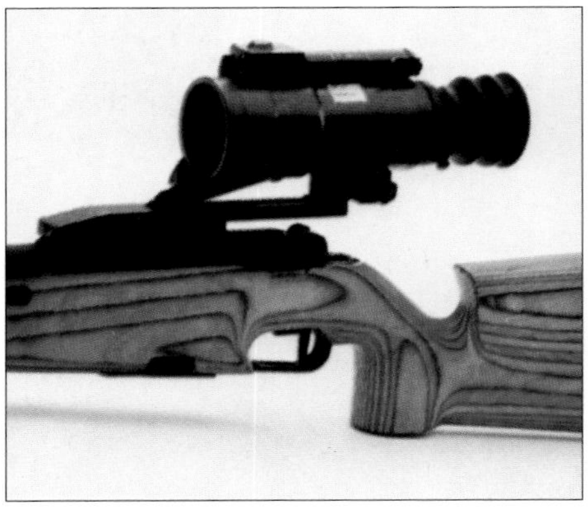

***This Mauser SP 86 is fitted with a night vision device. It is recommended that the manufacturer selects and calibrates the sights of each individual weapon.***

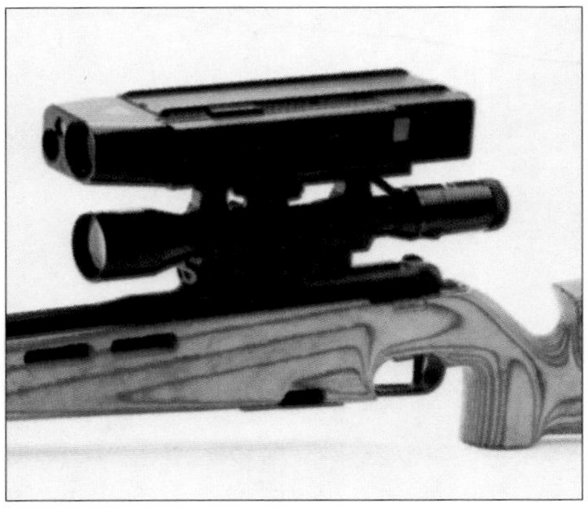

***Long-range accuracy depends on good ammunition, which Mauser selects from batches of NATO 7.62-mm cartridges. This Mauser is fitted with a laser rangefinder.***

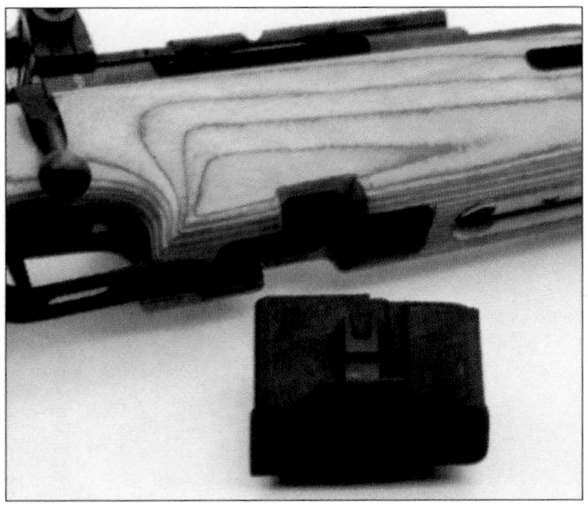

***A close-up of the double-row, detachable nine-round magazine of the Mauser SP 86, one of the improvements incorporated into this development of the SP 66.***

# Walther WA2000 Sniper rifle

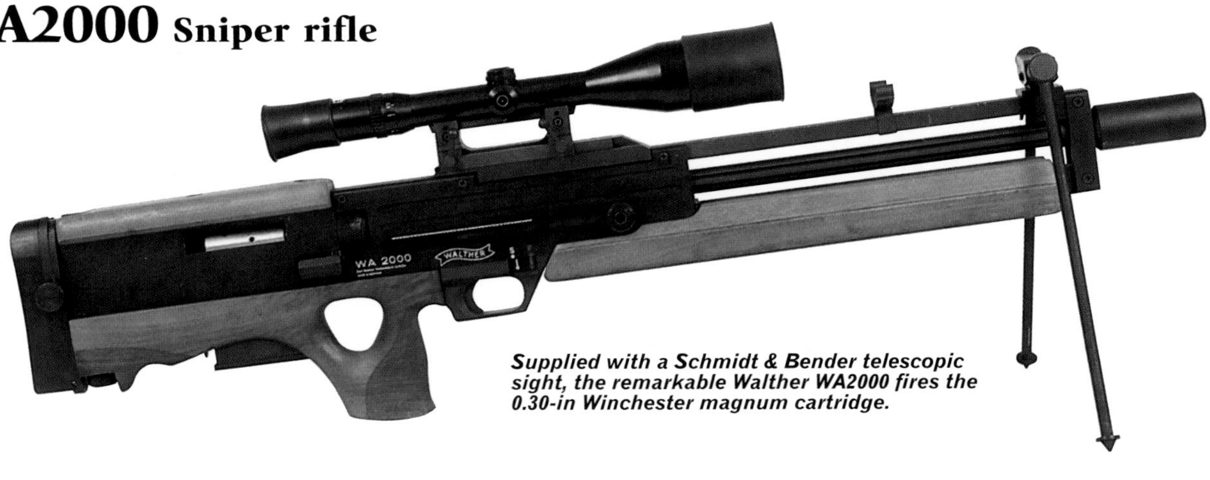


***Supplied with a Schmidt & Bender telescopic sight, the remarkable Walther WA2000 fires the 0.30-in Winchester magnum cartridge.***

With the **WA2000** from the Walther company of Germany, it would appear that small arms design is already in the 'Star Wars' era, for this weapon has a unique appearance more redolent of film concepts than standard small arms design. The rifle was created specifically for sniping, and the Walther approach was to put aside all known small arms design precepts, and thus to start from scratch after it had fully analysed the requirements.

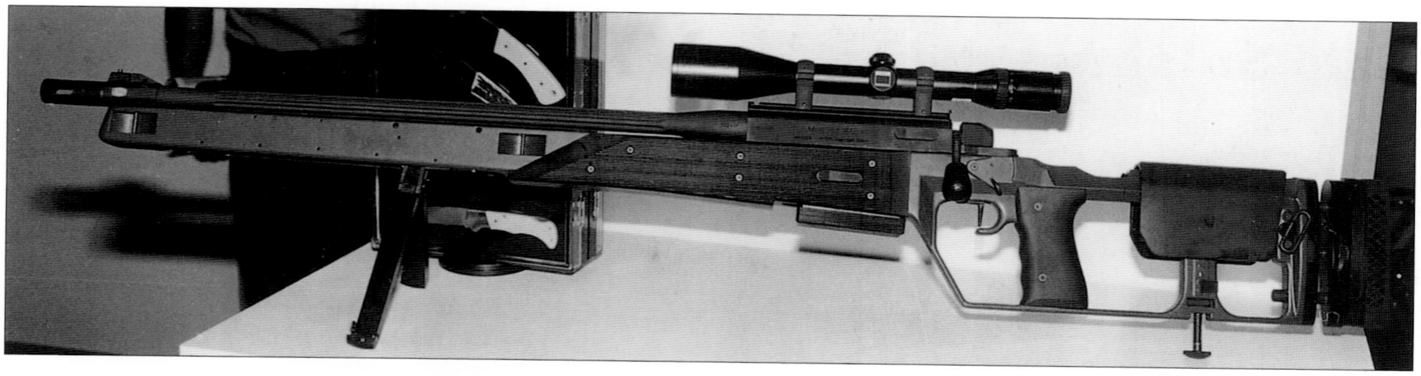

The most important part of any rifle design is the barrel. Walther decided to clamp the barrel at the front and rear to ensure that the torque imparted by a bullet passing through the bore would not lift the barrel away from the intended point of aim. The barrel is also fluted longitudinally over its entire length. This not only provides more cooling area but also reduces the vibrations imparted on firing, vibrations that can also cause a bullet to stray. The design team also opted for a gas-operated mechanism to reduce the need for bolt manipulation between shots and, to reduce recoil, the barrel is in direct line with the shoulder so that the muzzle is not thrown upward after every shot.

Thus the strange outline of the WA2000 begins to make sense, but there is more to come for the WA2000 is a 'bullpup' design with the gas-operated bolt mechanism behind the trigger group. This arrangement makes for a shorter and therefore more easily handled design without any need for reducing the barrel length. This does mean that the ejection port is close to the firer, so there are special left- and right-handed versions.

The overall standard of finish of the WA2000 is all that one would expect. The butt pad and cheek rests are adjustable, and there is a carefully-shaped pistol grip for added aiming stability. The normal telescopic sight is a Schmidt and Bender x2.5 to x10 zoom, but other types can be fitted.

Walther has decided that the best round for the sniping role is now the .300 (7.62-mm) Winchester Magnum cartridge, but while the WA2000 is chambered for this round others such as the 7.62-mm NATO or much favoured 7.5-mm (0.295-in) Swiss cartridge can be accommodated with the required alterations to the bolt and rifling.

***The WA2000 was created as a single-purpose rifle with a design that made no concessions to anything but accuracy and the ability of the firer to use the weapon effectively.***

**SPECIFICATION**

**WA2000**
**Calibre:** various
**Length overall:** 905 mm (35.63 in)
**Length of barrel:** 650 mm (25.59 in)
**Weight loaded:** 8.31 kg (18.32 lb)
**Muzzle velocity:** not available
**Magazine:** 6-round box

# Heckler & Koch Sniper rifles

***The MSG90 is a cheaper version of the PSG1, and notable features are the lighter barrel and buttstock, and the folding bipod arrangement under the forward end of the forestock.***

The range of Heckler & Koch rifles has now become so large that a weapon suitable for just about any application can apparently be selected from the array. Sniper's rifles have not been neglected, but in general most of the company's weapons for this highly specialised task are little more than standard designs. Such weapons are produced with a little extra care, the addition of a few accessories and the incorporation of a mounting for the telescopic sight that is an essential aid for accurate shooting at long range. This does not detract from the serviceability or efficiency of these weapons, and indeed many of them are altogether more suitable for typical field conditions than other designs that have been produced with emphasis on supreme accuracy rather than a practical serviceability.

Typical of these Heckler & Koch sniper weapons are the 7.62-mm (0.3-in) **G3 A3ZF** and **G3 SG/1**, both of which were produced for the West German police, the latter model with a light bipod. Good as these weapons are, there can be no dispute of the fact that they are basically only 'breathed on' versions of standard weapons originally designed with mass production rather than specialisation in mind.

Accordingly Heckler & Koch turned its attention in the mid-1980s to the design and production of a special design known as the **PSG1**. It is believed that before it embarked on the design of this weapon, the company solicited the input of potential special forces operators such as the GSG9 unit of Germany's border police, the Special Air Service Regiment of the UK and a number of Israeli counter-terrorist units.

The PSG1 is still based on the standard Heckler & Koch rotary lock mechanism, but in this instance combined with a semi-automatic operating system and a precision heavy barrel with bore characterised by polygonal rifling. The influence of the G3 can still be seen in the outlines of the receiver and also in the 5- or 20-round magazine housing (it is also possible to load single rounds manually), but the rest is entirely new. Forward of the magazine housing is a new forestock and the long barrel, while the buttstock has been reconfigured to the widely used all-adjustable form so that the weapon can be configured for the use of a specific firer.

## Precision aiming

The PSG1 was originally produced with a Hensoldt x6 telescopic sight adjustable in six settings for ranges between 100 m (110 yards) up to 600 m (655 yards), but later examples have claw fittings allowing them to accept a wide range of telescopic sight units. It has been stated that the weapon is extremely accurate, but for obvious reasons these claims are difficult to confirm independently.

For special purposes there has been mention of a precision-aiming tripod for this 7.62-mm round weapon, but its form (if any) is still unclear. It may well emerge that this tripod is an adaptation of one of the Heckler & Koch's machine-gun mountings (the butt used on the PSG1 is a much-modified HK-21 machine-gun component). The PSG1 is one of the most expensive of current sniper rifles, with a price in the order of $9,000 or more.

In 1990 there appeared the latest of Heckler & Koch's sniper rifles, the **MSG90**, a designation in which the letter prefixed stands for Militärisch Scharfshützen Gewehr (military marksman rifle) and the number suffix for the year of introduction. This was created as a cheaper derivative of the PSG1 in an effort to drum up greater sales, and is therefore based ultimately on the G3. The MSG90 has the trigger group of the PSG1 in combination with a lighter barrel and a smaller and lighter buttstock. This reduces the overall length to 1165 mm (45.87 in) and the weight to 6.4 kg (14.1 lb).

**SPECIFICATION**

**PSG1**
**Calibre:** 7.62-mm (0.3-in)
**Length overall:** 1208 mm (47.56 in)
**Length of barrel:** 650 mm (25.6 in)
**Weight empty:** 8.1 kg (17.85 lb)
**Muzzle velocity:** about 860 m (2,821 ft) per second
**Magazine:** 5- or 20-round straight box

# Galil Sniping Rifle Combat sniping rifle

Ever since Israel was formed in 1948, the role of the sniper within the Israeli armed forces has been an important one, and over the years snipers have usually been equipped with an array of weapons from all around the world. At one point attempts were made to produce sniper rifles locally, so for a period Israeli army snipers used an indigenous 7.62-mm (0.3-in) design known as the M26. This was virtually a hand-made weapon using design features from both the Soviet AKM and Belgian FAL rifles. However, for various reasons the M26 was deemed not fully satisfactory and work began on a sniping rifle based on the Israel Military Industries 7.62-mm Galil assault rifle, the standard Israeli service rifle.

The resultant **Galil Sniping Rifle** bears a resemblance to the original weapon, but it is virtually a new weapon. Almost every component has been redesigned and manufactured to very close tolerances. A new heavy barrel is fitted, as is an adjustable bipod. The solid butt (which can be folded forward to reduce carrying and stowage bulk) has an adjustable butt pad and cheek rest, while a Nimrod x6 telescopic sight is mounted on a bracket offset to the left of the receiver.

## New mechanism

The mechanism is now single-shot only, the original Galil 20-round magazine being retained. The barrel is fitted with a muzzle brake/compensator to reduce recoil and barrel jump on firing. A silencer can be fitted to the muzzle, but subsonic ammunition must then be used. As would be expected, various night sights can be fitted. The Sniping Rifle also retains its 'iron' combat sights.

The Galil Sniping Rifle is a very serviceable weapon that is far more suitable for the rigours of military life than many of the current crop of super-accurate models. Despite its basic design approach, it can still place group of rounds of less than 300-mm (11¾-in) diameter at a range of 600 m (1,969 ft), with the use of an integral bipod, which is more than adequate for most sniping purposes.

**SPECIFICATION**

**Galil Sniping Rifle**
**Calibre:** 7.62 mm (0.3 in)
**Lengths:** overall 1115 mm (44 in); barrel 508 mm (20 in)
**Weights:** 6.4 kg (14.1 lb) including bipod and sling
**Muzzle velocity:** 815 m (2,674 ft) per second
**Magazine capacity**: 20 rounds

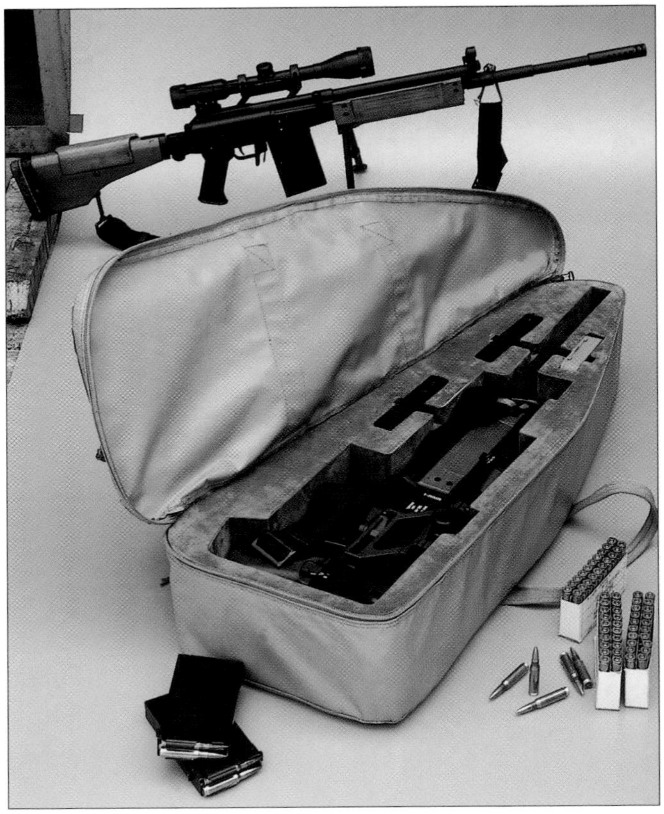

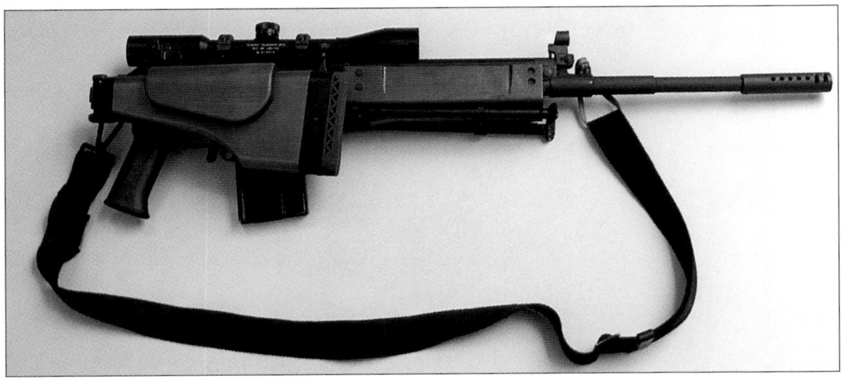

***Above:** When not in use the Galil Sniping Rifle is kept in a special case together with the telescopic sight, optical filters to reduce sun glare when using optical sights, a carrying and firing sling, two magazines and the all important cleaning kit.*

***Left:** The design of the Galil sniper rifle was shaped by the IDF's extensive battlefield experience, and it is perhaps not surprising that the gun is built more for reliability in combat than exceptional accuracy in ideal conditions.*

# Beretta Sniper Combat sniping rifle

**SPECIFICATION**

**Beretta Sniper**
**Calibre:** 7.62 mm (0.3 in)
**Lengths:** overall 1165 mm (46 in); barrel 586 mm (23 in)
**Weights:** 5.55 kg (12.23 lb); complete with sight and bipod 7.20 kg (15.87 lb)
**Muzzle velocity:** about 865 m (2,838 ft) per second
**Magazine capacity:** 5 rounds

When the market for high-precision sniper rifles expanded in the 1970s, virtually every major small-arms manufacturer started to design weapons that they thought would meet international requirements. Some of these designs have fared better than others on the market, but one that does appear to have been overlooked by many is the **Beretta Sniper** 7.62-mm (0.3-in) sniping rifle. This design appears to have been given no numerical designation. In addition to its military applications, the weapon is likely to be in use with some Italian paramilitary police units for specialist internal security duties.

## Orthodox design

Compared with many of the latest 'space-age' sniper rifle designs, the Beretta offering is almost completely orthodox but well up to the usual high standards of Beretta design and finish.

The Sniper uses a manual rotary bolt action allied to the usual heavy barrel, and one of its most prominent features is the large and unusually-shaped hole

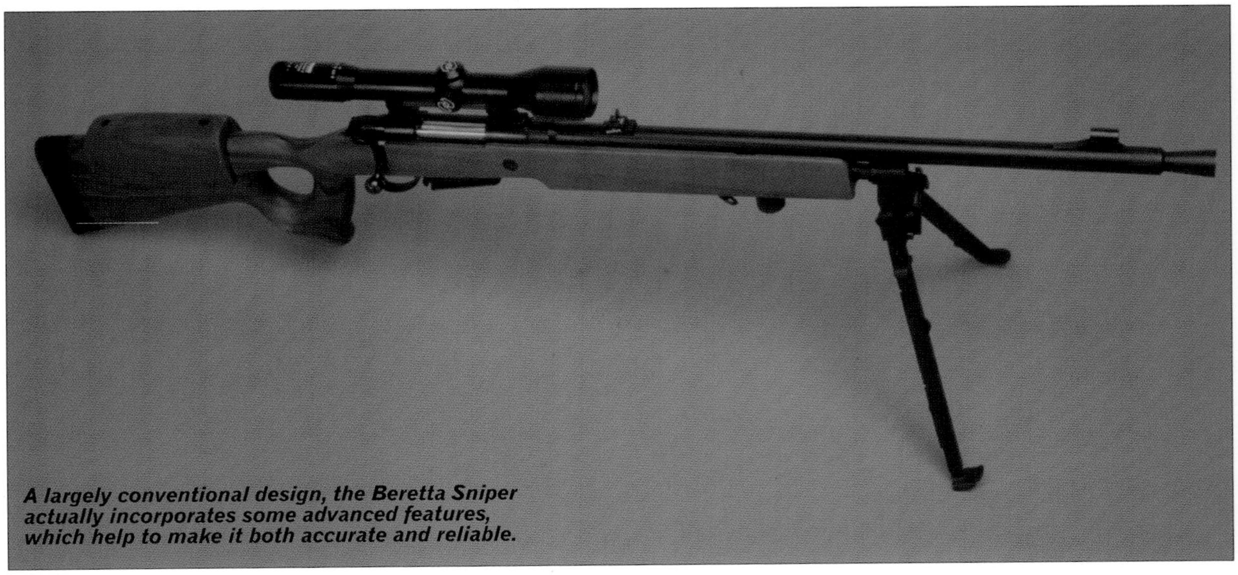

*A largely conventional design, the Beretta Sniper actually incorporates some advanced features, which help to make it both accurate and reliable.*

carved into the high-quality wooden stock that forms a prominent pistol grip for the trigger.

### Advanced features

Despite the overall conventional design there are one or two advanced features on the Sniper. The wooden forestock conceals a forward-pointing counterweight, under the free-floating barrel, that acts as a damper to reduce the normal barrel vibrations produced on firing. At the front end of the forestock is a location point for securing a light adjustable bipod to assist the sniper in keeping the rifle steady. The underside of the forestock contains a slot for an adjustable forward hand stop for the firer, and this forestop can also be used as the attachment point for a firing sling if one is required. The butt and cheek pads are adjustable and the muzzle has a flash hider as standard.

Unlike many of its modern counterparts, the Beretta Sniper is fully provided with a set of all-adjustable precision match sights, even though these would not normally be used for the sniping role. Over the receiver is a standard NATO optical or night sight mounting attachment, to accommodate virtually any military optical or electro-optical sighting system. The normal telescopic sight as recommended by Beretta is the widely-used Zeiss Diavari-Z with a zoom capability from x1.5 to x6, but other types can be fitted.

# SVD Dragunov Combat sniping rifle

Anyone familiar with accounts of the Great Patriotic War cannot but help note the emphasis given to sniping by the Soviet army. Post-war, that emphasis remained undiminished, and to carry out the sniping role the Soviets developed what is widely regarded as one of the best contemporary sniper rifles. This is the **SVD**, sometimes known as the **Dragunov**.

### Prized weapon

The SVD (**Samozariy-adnyia Vintokvka Dragunova**) first appeared in 1963, and ever since has been one of the most prized of infantry trophies. It is a semi-automatic weapon that uses the same operating principles as the AK-47 assault rifle, but allied to a revised gas-operated system. Unlike the AK-47, which uses the short 7.62-mm (0.3-in) x39 cartridge, the SVD fires the older 7.62-mm x54R rimmed cartridge, originally introduced during the 1890s for the Mosin-Nagant rifles. This remains a good round for the sniping role, and as it is still used on some Russian machine-guns, availability is no problem.

The SVD has a long barrel, but the weapon is so balanced that it handles well and recoil is not excessive. The weapon is normally fired using a sling rather than the bipod favoured elsewhere, and to assist aiming, a PSO-1 telescopic sight is provided. This is secured to the left-hand side of the receiver and has a magnification of x4. The PSO-1 has an unusual feature in that it incorporates an infra-red detector element to enable it to be used as a passive night sight, although it is normally used in conjunction with an independent infra-red target-illumination source. Basic combat sights are fitted for use if the optical sight becomes defective.

Perhaps the oddest feature for a sniper rifle is that the SVD is provided with a bayonet, the rationale for this remaining uncertain. A 10-round box magazine is also fitted.

### Long-range accuracy

Tests have demonstrated that the SVD can fire accurately to ranges of well over 800 m (2,625 ft). It is a pleasant weapon to handle and fire, despite the lengthy barrel. SVDs were provided to many Warsaw Pact and other nations and the weapon was used in Afghanistan, some ending up in the hands of the Mujahideen. It seems reasonable to assume that te SVD remains in use in Russia and with other former client states of the USSR. The Chinese produce a direct copy of the SVD and offer this version for export, quoting an effective range of 1000 m (621 ft).

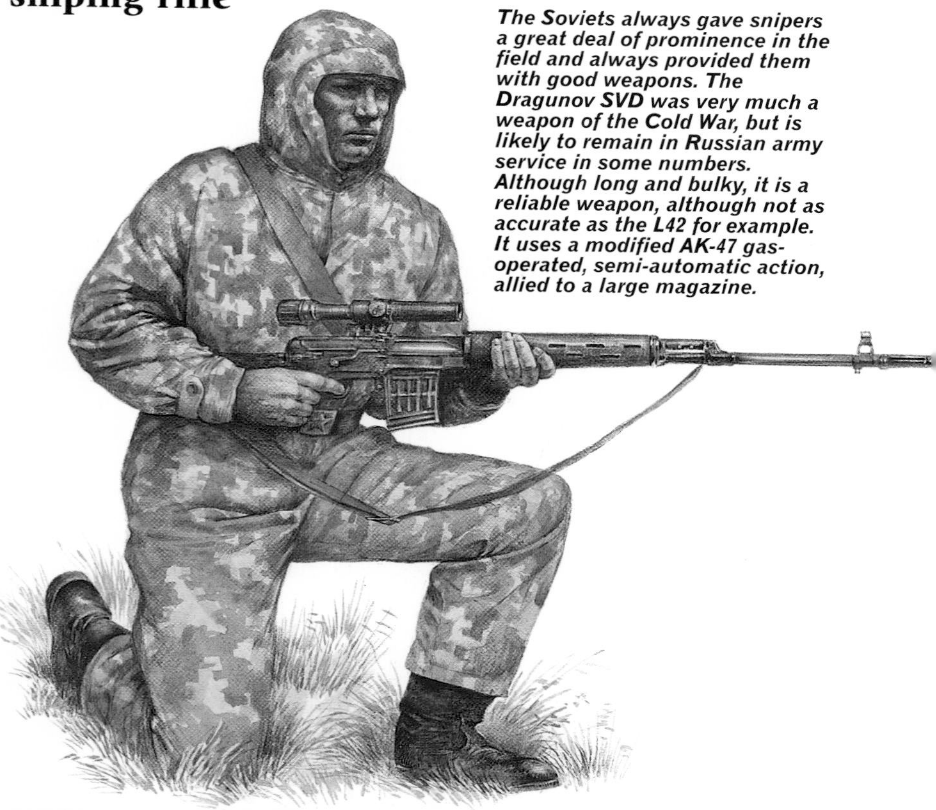

***The Soviets always gave snipers a great deal of prominence in the field and always provided them with good weapons. The Dragunov SVD was very much a weapon of the Cold War, but is likely to remain in Russian army service in some numbers. Although long and bulky, it is a reliable weapon, although not as accurate as the L42 for example. It uses a modified AK-47 gas-operated, semi-automatic action, allied to a large magazine.***

***The Dragunov uses a bolt system similar to that of the AK-47 and its derivatives, but it is modified to suit the different characteristics of the rimmed 7.62-mm X 54R cartridge. The mechanisms of the SVD and AK-47 are not interchangeable.***

**SPECIFICATION**

**SVD**
**Calibre:** 7.62 mm (0.3 in)
**Lengths**: overall, less bayonet, 1225 mm (48¼ in); barrel 547 mm (21½ in)
**Weight:** complete, unloaded 4.39 kg (9.67 lb)
**Muzzle velocity:** 830 m (2,723 ft) per second
**Magazine capacity:** 10 rounds

***If the long barrel of the Dragunov is not a decisive recognition point, then the distinctive cut-away butt certainly is. The SVD retains the AK-47's ability to withstand harsh treatment during combat operations in the field.***

# Rifle L42 Sniper rifle

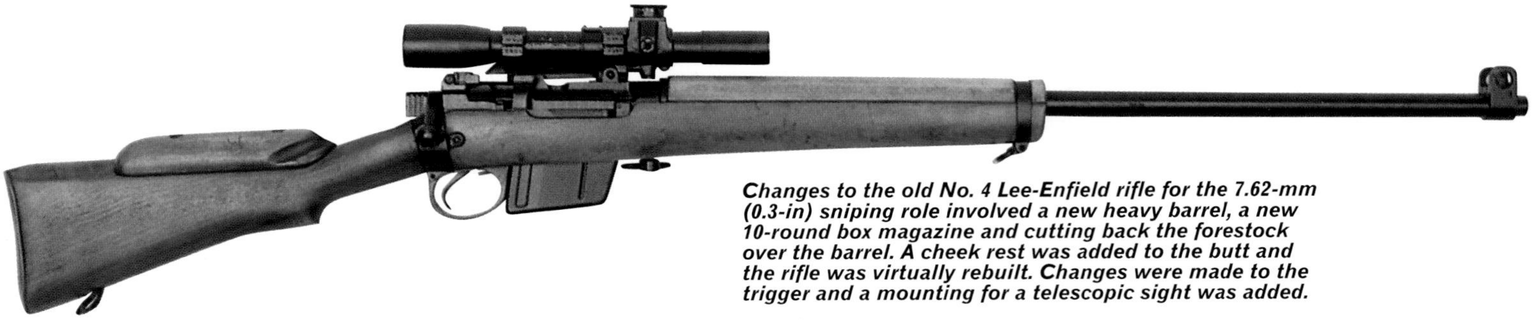

***Changes to the old No. 4 Lee-Enfield rifle for the 7.62-mm (0.3-in) sniping role involved a new heavy barrel, a new 10-round box magazine and cutting back the forestock over the barrel. A cheek rest was added to the butt and the rifle was virtually rebuilt. Changes were made to the trigger and a mounting for a telescopic sight was added.***

The Lee-Enfield rifle had a long career with the British army reaching back to the 1890s, and throughout that time the basic Lee-Enfield manual bolt mechanism remained little changed. The weapon remained in service as the **Rifle L42A1** recently supplanted by the Accuracy International L96 in the same 7.62-mm (0.3-in) calibre. These L42A1 weapons were used only for sniping, and were conversions of 0.303-in (7.7-mm) No. 4 Mk 1(T) or Mk 1*(T) rifles, as used during World War II. The conversion – or rebuilding – process involved the addition of a new barrel and magazine, some changes to the trigger mechanism and fixed sights, and alterations to the forestock. The World War II No. 32 Mk 3 telescopic sight (renamed the L1A1) and its mounting over the receiver were retained, and the result was a good, rugged and serviceable sniping rifle, used not only by the army but also by the Royal Marines.

In more modern terms the L42A1 was very much the product of a previous generation, but it could still give excellent first-shot results at ranges over 800 m (875 yards), although this depends very much on the skill of the firer and the type of ammunition used. The ammunition was normally selected from special 'Green Spot' high-accuracy ammunition produced at the Royal Ordnance facility at Radway Green.

The rifle itself was also the subject of a great deal of care, calibration and attention. When not in use it was stowed and transported in a special chest containing not only the rifle but the optical sight, cleaning gear, firing sling and perhaps a few spares such as extra magazines: the L42A1 retained the 10-round magazine of the 0.303-in version but with a revised outline to accommodate the new rimless ammunition. The often-overlooked weapon record books were also kept in the chest.

The L42A1 was not the only 7.62-mm Lee-Enfield rifle still around. A special match-shooting version known as the **L39A1** was used for competitive use, and there are two other models, the **Envoy** and the **Enforcer.** The former may be regarded as a civilian match version of the L39A1, while the Enforcer is a custom-built L42A1 variant with a heavier barrel and revised butt outline, produced specifically for police use.

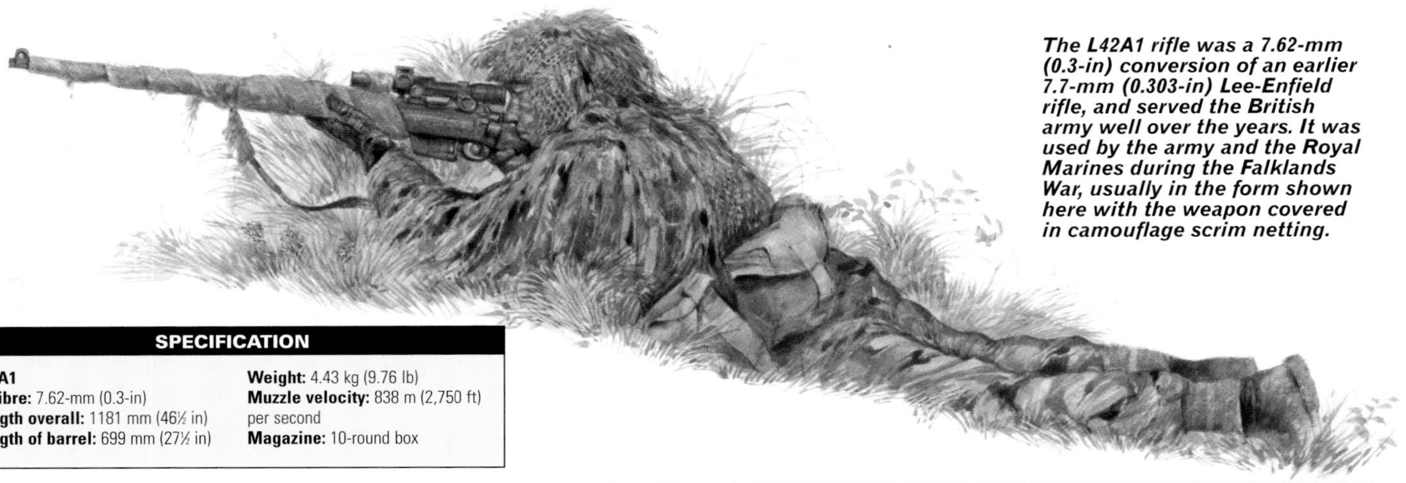

***The L42A1 rifle was a 7.62-mm (0.3-in) conversion of an earlier 7.7-mm (0.303-in) Lee-Enfield rifle, and served the British army well over the years. It was used by the army and the Royal Marines during the Falklands War, usually in the form shown here with the weapon covered in camouflage scrim netting.***

**SPECIFICATION**

**L42A1**
**Calibre:** 7.62-mm (0.3-in)
**Length overall:** 1181 mm (46½ in)
**Length of barrel:** 699 mm (27½ in)
**Weight:** 4.43 kg (9.76 lb)
**Muzzle velocity:** 838 m (2,750 ft) per second
**Magazine:** 10-round box

# Rifle L96

***The Model PM's Counter-Terrorist version has at its muzzle a spiral device not fitted to the Infantry model, which has a 10-round box magazine, 'iron' sights and sling swivels.***

After many years of faithful and effective service, the L42A1 sniper rifle, based on the Lee-Enfield bolt-action service rifle dating from the last decade of the 19th century and steadily upgraded in the half century following that time, has been replaced as the British army's standard sniping rifle by a purpose-designed weapon, the **Rifle L96A1** designed and manufactured by Accuracy International. Unlike its predecessor, the new weapon is not a conversion of a tried and trusted battle rifle, but is more akin to the special target weapons used in sporting events such as the Olympic Games and therefore optimised for great accuracy at longer ranges than would characterise modern battlefield combat.

In its No. 4 Mk 1(T) and L42A1 forms, the Lee-Enfield No. 4 rifle gave British snipers sterling service over the years, but these two weapons were originally straightforward conversions of standard rifles with few innovations for the sniper role. The L42A1 was a good weapon in terms of accuracy, but time had marched on and technological advances meant that something better could be provided. For some time the British army was denied the opportunity to procure replacement weapons by budgetary restrictions, but that changed in 1984 and the army could specify to all concerned what it wanted.

## Orthodox concept

It is interesting to note that of the three weapons finally selected for final trials none were of the super-accuracy 'space-age' type. All three were conventional designs, brought up to date by the use of modern materials and design niceties. The weapons were the Parker-Hale Model 85, a design from Interarms, and the Accuracy International Model PM designed by Malcolm Cooper, an Olympic gold medallist. All three of these weapons were subjected to extensive trials by the staff of the Small Arms School Corps at Warminster in Wiltshire, and although there was apparently little to choose between the three, in the end the Model PM was selected for service. In this decision the evaluation team was probably influenced to some extent by experience gained from use of the Model PM by the SAS, which had already obtained a few of the type.

Although the Model PM

*The art of sniping includes the ability of the firer to merge into his background and avoid the type of movement that will betray his presence. This sniper and his rifle are artfully draped to break up their outlines.*

appears to be an entirely orthodox design, in this case the appearances are deceptive. The Model PM is in effect little more than a heavy stainless steel 7.62-mm (0.3-in) barrel secured to a bolted aluminium chassis. The entire weapon consists of a bipod, stock, action and buttstock, all enclosed in plastic furniture provided for little reason other than to hold everything together and give it an acceptable appearance. Although the forestock appears to enclose the barrel, for instance, in fact it does not touch the free-floating barrel at any point.

### Forward-locking bolt

The Model PM uses a Tasco telescopic sight and has a forward-locking manual bolt action designed so that on withdrawal the bolt does not touch the firer's face. The light alloy bipod can be allied with a retractable monopod 'spike' under the butt that can be used to act as a holding platform for prolonged periods of use (i.e. the firer can aim the rifle at a selected area with the weight taken on the bipod and spike). An integral box magazine holds five rounds and the trigger assembly can be removed entirely for adjustment.

There are at least four versions of the Model PM. Two are the so-called **Counter-Terrorist** weapon already in army use, and the **Infantry** of which the first of 1,212 were delivered from 1986. The latter has a 6x42 non-zoom scope and match sights effective at ranges up to 900 m (985 yards). The other two variants are the **Moderated** with an integral sight and the single-shot **Long-Range** chambered for the 7-mm (0.275-in) Remington Magnum or 7.62-mm Winchester Magnum cartridges.

**SPECIFICATION**

**L96A1**
**Calibre:** 7.62-mm (0.3-in)
**Length overall:** 1124 mm (44.25 in)
**Length of barrel:** 654 mm (25.75 in)
**Weight:** 6.5 kg (14.33 lb)
**Muzzle velocity:** not available
**Magazine:** 10-round box

# Parker-Hale Model 82 Sniper rifle

*In service with the armed forces of Australia, Canada and New Zealand, the Parker-Hale Model 82 is intended to hit point targets at up to 400 m (440 yards) in good light, or up to the maximum range of any sights fitted.*

Parker-Hale Limited of Birmingham has for many years been manufacturing match rifles and their associated sights, and has also been long employed in the equally specialist task of designing and manufacturing sniping rifles. The company's best-known product to date is the 7.62-mm (0.3-in) **Parker-Hale Model 82**, also known as the **Parker-Hale 1200TX**. The Model 82 has been accepted for military and police service by several nations.

In appearance and design terms the Model 82 is an entirely conventional sniping weapon. It uses a manual bolt action very similar to that used on the classic Mauser Gewehr 98 rifle, allied to a heavy free-floating barrel; the barrel weighs 1.98 kg (4.365 lb) and is manufactured as a cold-forged unit of chrome molybdenum steel. An integral four-round magazine is provided. The trigger mechanism is an entirely self-contained unit that can be adjusted as required.

The Model 82 is available in a number of forms to suit any particular customer requirements. Thus an adjustable cheek pad may be provided if wanted and the butt lengths can be altered by adding or taking away butt pads of various thicknesses. The sights too are subject to several variations, but the Model 82 is one weapon that is normally supplied with 'iron' match-type sights. If an optical (telescopic) sight unit is fitted, the rear sight has to be removed to allow the same mounting block to be used. The forward mounting block is machined into the receiver. Various types of 'iron' foresight or optical night sights can be fitted.

### Military service

The Australian army uses the Model 82 fitted with a Kahles Helia ZF 69 telescopic sight. The Canadian army uses a version of the Model 82/1200TX altered to meet local requirements; this service knows the Model 82 as the **Rifle C3**.

**SPECIFICATION**

**Model 82**
**Calibre:** 7.62-mm (0.3 in)
**Length overall:** 1162 mm (45.7-in)
**Barrel length:** 660 mm (25.98 in)
**Weight empty:** 4.8 kg (10.58 lb)
**Muzzle velocity:** about 840 m (2,756 ft) per second
**Magazine:** 4-round box

New Zealand also uses the Model 82.

Parker-Hale produces a special training version of the Model 82 known as the **Model 83**. This single-shot rifle is fitted with match sights only and there is no provision for a telescopic sight. The weapon was accepted by the British Ministry of Defence as the **Cadet Training Rifle L81A1** in a form with a shortened buttstock and a shortened fore end.

The Model 82 was later updated to the **Model 85**. This introduced a butt outline that was considerably revised by comparison with that of the Model 82, a 10-round box magazine and a bipod (optional on the Model 82) was fitted as standard.

Weighing 5.7 kg (12.57 lb) with its sight, this Model 85 weapon was one of the rifles competitively tested by the British army to find its new sniper rifle, a competition won by Accuracy International. Parker-Hale then ceased the manufacture of rifles and in 1990 sold its rifle business (including the rights to its various designs) to the Gibbs Rifle Company of the USA, which placed the Model 85 in production under the Parker-Hale name.

*The Parker-Hale Model 82 was selected by the Canadian Armed Forces as their sniper rifle, and is seen here in winter camouflage. It uses a Mauser-type bolt action and is fitted with a four-round box magazine.*

# Rifle M21 Sniper rifle

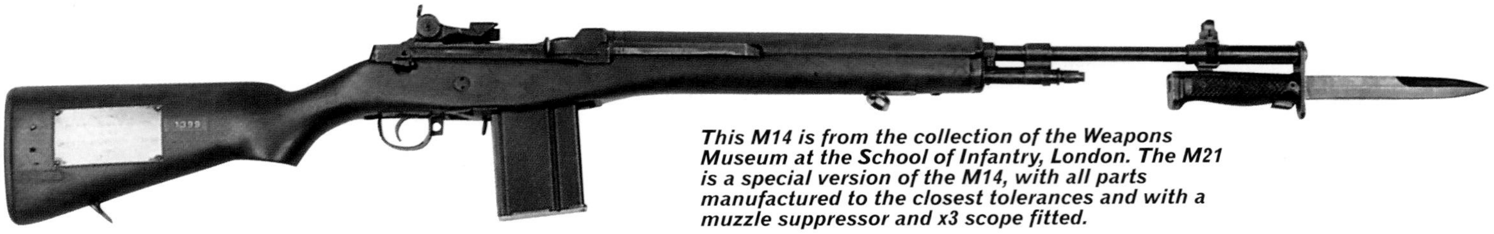

***This M14 is from the collection of the Weapons Museum at the School of Infantry, London. The M21 is a special version of the M14, with all parts manufactured to the closest tolerances and with a muzzle suppressor and x3 scope fitted.***

When the US armed forces made the move from the 7.62-mm (0.3-in) NATO cartridge to the smaller 5.56-mm (0.223-in) round during the late 1960s, they not surprisingly decided to retain the larger calibre for the sniping role. This was for the simple reason that the smaller round had been designed from the outset to impart its best performance at ranges much shorter than the usual sniping distances. This meant the retention of the current sniping rifle, at the time known as the **Rifle 7.62-mm M14 National Match (Accurized)**, but now known as the **Rifle M21**.

The M21 is a special version of the 7.62-mm M14, for many years the standard US service rifle. It retains the basic appearance and mechanism of the original, but some changes were introduced at the manufacturing stage.

## Attention to detail

For a start the barrels were selected so that only those with the closest manufacturing tolerances were used. These barrels were left without their usual chromium plating inside the bore, again to reduce the possibility of manufacturing inaccuracies. A new muzzle suppressor was fitted and reamed to the barrel to ensure correct alignment. The trigger mechanism was assembled by hand and adjusted to provide a crisp release action at a trigger pull of between 2 and 2.15 kg (4.41 and 4.74 lb), and a new walnut stock was fitted, this latter being impregnated with an epoxy resin and individually fitted to the stock using a fibreglass compound. The gas-operated mechanism was also the subject of attention such as hand polishing and hand fitting to ensure an operation that was as smooth as possible.

The fully automatic fire mode is retained on the M21, but the weapon is normally fired only in the semi-automatic (single-shot) mode.

The main change on assembly was the fitting of a x3 magnification telescopic sight. As well as the usual aiming cross-hairs, this uses a system of graticules that allows the user to judge accurately the range of a man-sized target and automatically set the angle of elevation. Using this sight the M21 can place 10 rounds within a 152-mm (6-in) circle at 300 m (330 yards).

One unusual piece of equipment that can be fitted to the M21 is a sound suppressor. This is not a silencer in the usually accepted sense of the word, but a series of baffles. The bullet suffers no penalty in velocity, helping to ensure a trajectory as flat as possible, but the baffles reduce the velocity of the gases produced on firing to a figure below the speed of sound. This produces a muffled report with none of the usual firing signatures, and its use makes the source of the sound (and thus the firer) that much more difficult to detect.

***Although many Israeli snipers use the Galil sniping rifle, some still retain the American M21, the 'accurized' version of the M14 rifle. They were observed in use during the early stages of the invasion of Lebanon, and many were used against the PLO in Beirut in August 1982.***

**SPECIFICATION**

**Rifle M21**
**Calibre:** 7.62-mm (0.3-in)
**Length overall:** 1120 mm (44.1 in)
**Length of barrel:** 559 mm (22 in)
**Weight loaded:** 5.55 kg (12.24 lb)
**Muzzle velocity:** 853 m (2,798 ft) per second
**Feed:** 20-round box magazine

# Barrett M82 & M95 Sniper rifles

In 1981, 26-year old Ronnie Barrett designed and made a 0.5-in (12.7-mm) semi-automatic rifle based on the Browning short-recoil operating system and firing the M33 round of the Browning M2 heavy machine-gun.

The prototype offered long range and considerable accuracy in conjunction with mild recoil forces, and caught the attention of the US military, which was looking for a weapon to penetrate thin-skinned vehicles following its losses to

***One of the first sniper rifles based on the M33 ball round developed for the Browning M2 heavy machine-gun was the Iver Johnson Model 500, a development of the multi-calibre Model 300.***

**SPECIFICATION**

**Barrett 'Light 50' M82A1**
**Calibre:** 0.5-in (12.7-mm)
**Length overall:** 1448 mm (57 in)
**Length of barrel:** 737 mm (29 in)
**Weight:** 12.9 kg (28.4 lb)
**Muzzle velocity:** 854 m (2,800 ft) per second
**Feed:** 11-round box magazine

terrorist attacks in Beirut, Lebanon. Some NATO armies also showed interest and the **M82A1** went into production as a military weapon.

During Operation 'Desert Storm' in 1991 the M82A1 won considerable approval when US ground troops used it successfully against APCs and high-value personnel. The US Marine Corps is a strong advocate of the M82A1 and has collaborated with Barrett on a programme of improvements. The latest refinements to the weapon include a removable carrying handle, improved bipod, lightened components and provision for the new day and night optics that the corps will soon be fielding.

### Ammunition

The standard armour-piercing incendiary ammunition is now complemented by the new Raufoss Mk 211 round with a zirconium penetrator to ignite flammable material after impact and explosion at the target.

The two primary variants of the M82 are the M82A1 manufactured between 1983 and 1992, and the **M82A2** that entered production in 1990 as a less cumbersome 'bullpup' development of the M82A1 with the action and magazine located to the rear of the trigger group to reduce overall length to 1409 mm (55.5 in) and weight to 12.24 kg (27 lb).

The latest variant of the Barrett 0.5-in sniper rifle, intended like its predecessors for the whole range of long-range roles including explosive ordnance disposal, is the **M95**. This is basically a bolt-action derivative of the M82A2 with an overall length of 1143 mm (45 in), weight of 11.2 kg (24.7 lb), five-round box magazine and the standard x10 telescopic sight for an effective range of some 1830 m (2,000 yards).

# Rifle M40 Sniper rifle

***The US Marine Corps adopted the Remington Model 700 in 1966 and had the weapon modified to meet its particular requirements. The M40A1 rifle differs from the M40 in having a heavier but shorter stainless steel barrel, a fibreglass stock and a powerful telescopic sight.***

The US Marine Corps has always been allowed its own equipment procurement system, for it has long been accepted by the American authorities that the corps' particular role in the prosecution of amphibious warfare requires the adoption and use of the specialised equipment to match. Thus when the selection of a new sniping rifle to replace the M1C and M1D weapons, both based on the M1 Garand rifle, came to be appreciated, the USMC went its own way with a weapon tailored to its own very exacting requirement.

### Sniper emphasis

For the US Marines Corps the sniper has always had a special role, often operating in advance of other ground units to gain information as well as acting as a long-range killer of commanders and other high-value troops. So when, in the course of the Vietnam War, the US Marine Corps contemplated weapons such as the US Army's M14 and M21 sniper rifles, it decided that its men needed something better than these adapted service rifles. The US Marine Corps could not find exactly what it wanted on the open market, but found that the design coming the closest to meeting its requirement was a commercial rifle, as the **Remington Model 700**. This was produced to custom order by Remington as the target-tuned Model 700 weapon with a heavy barrel and the Model 40XB target rifle action. The US Marine Corps decided to standardise this weapon, which therefore became the **Rifle M40** in 1966. The original order for 800 such rifles was later increased to 995 weapons based on the Model 700BDL commercial rifle with a one-piece wooden buttstock.

The M40 has a Mauser-type manual bolt action and a heavy barrel. It is normally fitted with a Redfield telescopic sight with a zoom magnification of from x3 to x9. A five-round magazine is fitted, and the M40 is an entirely conventional but high-quality design.

### On the battlefield

In service with the US Marines the M40 proved to be perfectly satisfactory, but battlefield experience gained with the basic design showed the Marines that something better could be produced. The US Marine Corps accordingly asked the Remington Arms Company to introduce a number of modifications. These included the replacement of the original barrel by a new stainless steel component, the replacement of the wooden furniture by fibreglass furniture (supplied by McMillan Brothers) and the introduction of a new sight. This Unertl telescopic sight was produced entirely to demanding US Marine Corps specification with a fixed x10 magnification. No 'iron' sights were fitted for use as an alternative to the telescopic sight.

With all these changes embodied the M40 became the **M40A1**, and this was produced only for the US Marine Corps at its workshops at Quantico, Virginia, on the basis of parts delivered by Remington (action), Winchester (magazine floorplate), McMillan Brothers and other civil contractors.

By all accounts the M40A1 is one of the most accurate 'conventional' sniping rifles ever produced, although exact figures are not available to confirm this assertion. The main reasons for this excellence are the combination provided by the heavy stainless steel barrel and the superb optical sight. The magnification of this sight is much more than usual on such devices, but despite this fact, and the possibility of the distortion that might have resulted, the sight produces a notably bright and clearer image for the firer. All the usual adjustments can be introduced to the sight.

### Magnificent accuracy

As always with a weapon of this type, the degree of accuracy is dependent on the performance of the ammunition selected and also, of course, on the skill of the firer. However, the US Marine Corps has traditionally spent a great deal of time and effort on the training of its snipers. But by all accounts the M40A1 is the rifle that 'everyone else wants'.

**SPECIFICATION**

| | |
|---|---|
| **Rifle M40A1** | **Weight:** 6.57 kg (14.48 lb) |
| **Calibre:** 7.62-mm (0.3-in) | **Muzzle velocity:** 777 m (2,549 ft) per second |
| **Length overall:** 1117 mm (44 in) | **Feed:** 5-round box magazine |
| **Length of barrel:** 610 mm (24 in) | |

***When the US Marine Corps decided to select its own sniping rifle it ordered numbers of commercial Remington Model 700 rifles, some still with 'iron' sights, as seen here. These became the M40 sniping rifle and many remained in use despite the introduction of the later M40A1. The weapon is used only by the US Marine Corps.***

# Machine-guns

**The machine-gun has dominated infantry operations since World War I. It has been developed in different roles in a host of calibres, and is still a key feature of the modern battlefield despite its prodigious hunger for ammunition in the sustained-fire role.**

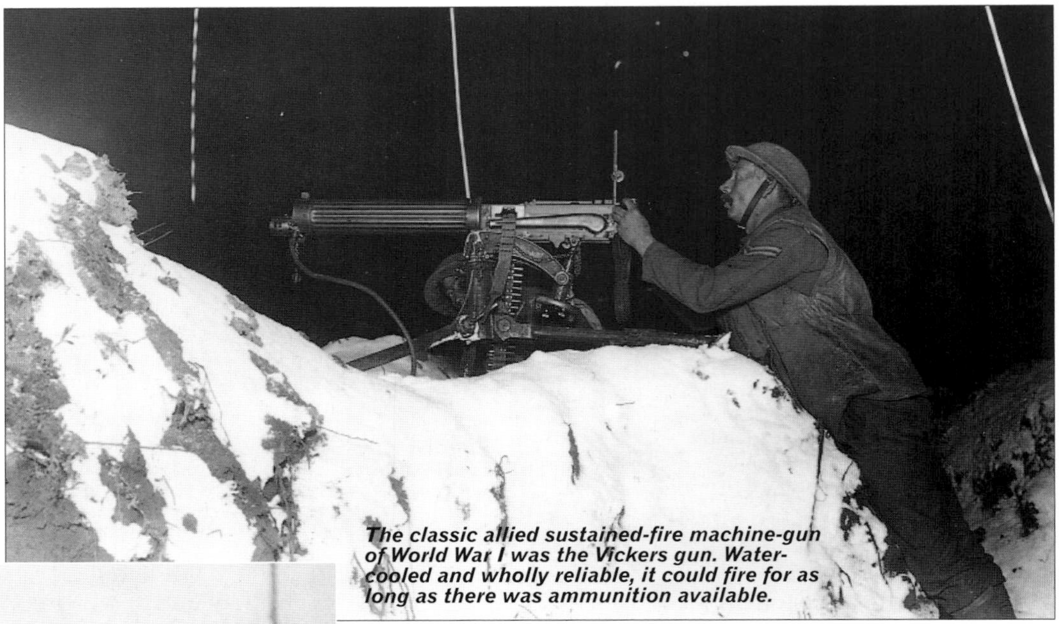

*The classic allied sustained-fire machine-gun of World War I was the Vickers gun. Water-cooled and wholly reliable, it could fire for as long as there was ammunition available.*

Since World War I the machine-gun has been the primary weapon of the infantry company. In modern armies the smallest tactical unit is the squad or section; since the 1930s this has tended to be divided into a 'gun group' (light machine-gun) and a 'rifle group' leap-frogging each other with one group firing to keep the enemy's heads down while the other moves forward.

*Above: The Germans pioneered the concept of the general-purpose machine-gun with their MG 34 (seen here) and cheaper-to-produce MG 42. Both were air-cooled, light, reliable and capable of very high rates of fire.*

*Right: The USSR retained the light machine-gun concept with the DP, fired from a bipod and fitted with a 47-round ammunition drum.*

## Gun classifications

Machine-guns have been known as 'light', 'medium' or 'heavy', but these World War I terms were blurred from the 1950s by weapons such as the general-purpose machine-gun and automatic rifle. The first 'modern' machine-gun was the creation of an American inventor, Hiram S. Maxim, who produced a recoil-operated weapon that could deliver up to 600 rpm just by pressing the button and keeping the ammunition belts flowing. The Vickers Maxim service weapon fired the British army's standard 0.303-in rifle cartridge and weighed 27 kg (60 lb). It was fired from a tripod, and the weapon and mounting could be carried by a team of men.

John M. Browning's contribution was even longer lasting. Browning used the gases produced at the instant of firing by the expansion of the propellant within the cartridge, and his gas operation has been the basis for many machine-guns.

## Machine-gun power

A fatal trinity of machine-guns, barbed wire and artillery led to bloody deadlock on the Western Front in 1914-18. Easily concealed and protected by concrete emplacements, tripod-mounted machine-guns were difficult to knock out with artillery fire; if only a few survived a preliminary bombardment they could shoot down any number of attackers the moment these went 'over the top'.

One answer to the tactical problems of trench warfare was to lighten the machine-gun so that it could be carried for use in defending captured ground against any counter-attack. The British

## MACHINE-GUN: BATTLEFIELD ACE

The adoption of a smaller-calibre cartridge – in the NATO armies the 5.56-mm (0.219-in) type in place of the previously standard 7.62-mm (0.3-in) type – had done much to alleviate the loads that have had to be carried by the typical infantryman. However, this factor also has a downside, for the smaller and therefore lighter ammunition has a shorter effective range and less stopping power. For the fire-support role, therefore, most armies still retain the full-calibre general-purpose machine-gun, such as the FN MAG, which can provide considerable power in the longer-range role. For shorter-range tasks there have appeared two types of 5.56-mm light machine-gun, as epitomised by the FN Minimi and the L86 LSW. Weapons such as the Minimi, with a changeable barrel and firing from a belt or a box magazine, are true light machine-guns, while the L86 exemplifies what is in effect only a light squad support weapon as it has a fixed barrel and can fire only from a box magazine.

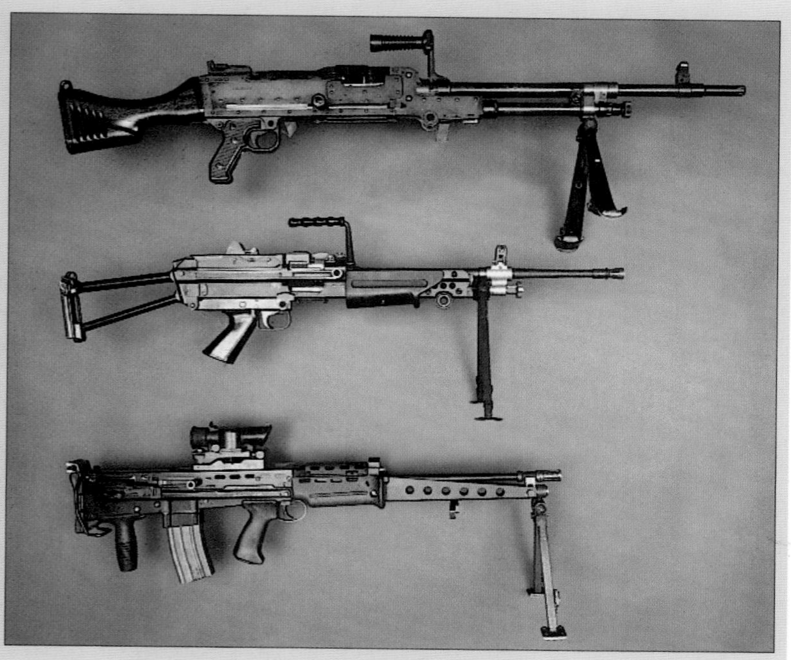

***From top to bottom, the FN MAG, FN Minimi and L86 Light Support Weapon revealed how the size (and by extension weight) of the machine-gun has been reduced by the smaller-calibre ammunition.***

army adopted the Lewis gun, the first truly successful light machine-gun. The Lewis gun could also be used by the new-look infantry companies to fight their way forward in the origins of modern 'fire and manoeuvre' tactics.

Between the wars the division between 'light', 'medium' and 'heavy' machine-guns became formalised. The successors of the Lewis gun, best exemplified by the British army's Bren gun, were air-cooled guns light enough to be carried by one man, with one or more other soldiers carrying additional ammunition in strips or box magazines carrying about 30 rounds. Medium machine-guns were often water-cooled and able to fire tens of thousands of rounds without a pause. Heavy machine-guns were similar but whereas the medium machine-guns fired rifle-calibre bullets, these were chambered for something bigger, typically a 0.5-in (12.7-mm) cartridge that provides an anti-aircraft and limited armour-piercing capability.

### German pioneering

The Allied armies of World War II used all three categories of machine-gun, as did the Italian and Japanese, but the Germans pioneered the concept of the 'general-purpose machine-gun'. Fed from a box magazine or a belt, and fitted with a bipod, the MG 34 was light enough to be operated by a small team of two or three men yet could also generate the sort of sustained fire normally the preserve of medium machine-guns, and mounted on a tripod with a box of spare barrels handy, it could lay down a hail of fire just like the much heavier medium gun. The MG 34 and later MG 42 so impressed the Allies that they followed suit after the war. Indeed, the US Army's M60 GPMG is closely based on the MG 42 design. The Belgian FN MAG is a far better weapon.

### Light machine-gun

As they adopted intermediate-calibre rifles (NATO 5.56-mm or Soviet 7.62-mm x 39 and then 5.45-mm), some armies adopted light machine-guns to avoid the logistic problems of two different ammunition calibres in an infantry platoon. Some, like the FN Minimi, have proved highly successful.

Toward the end of the 20th century the 'heavy' machine-gun made a reappearance, with 14.5-mm or 15-mm weapons on offer from Belgium and eastern Europe. Capable of accurate long-range fire and of penetrating light armour, they offer infantry companies the ability to ambush lightly equipped mechanised units.

***The standard general-purpose machine-gun of the US forces is the M60, a full-calibre weapon whose sustained-fire ammunition requirements are fully revealed in this Vietnam War photograph.***

***The Soviet counterpart to the classic Browning M2 heavy machine-gun is the 12.7-mm DShK. The weapon is used for anti-aircraft and local defence on many types of AFV, and has cooling rings on the barrel.***

# Schwarzlose Machine-guns

The first indigenous Austro-Hungarian machine-gun was designed by Andreas Schwarzlose in 1902, and was later manufactured at the Waffenfabrik Steyr. The first model was the **Schwarzlose Maschinengewehr Modell 07**, soon followed by the **MG Modell 08** and the definitive **MG Modell 12**, to which standard the two earlier models were later converted by the Austro-Hungarian armed forces. There was little to differentiate these models, for they all used an identical method of construction and the same operating method.

The Schwarzlose machine-guns were heavy belt-fed and water-cooled weapons working on an unusual principle, namely that known as delayed blowback, in which the recoil forces impinge to the rear upon a heavy breech block held in position (with the spent case still in the chamber) by a levered mechanism. Only after a short period of time has elapsed do these levers move sufficiently for the breech block to travel to the rear; this time is just long enough for the bullet to leave the muzzle and for the pressure in the barrel to fall to a safe figure. But the system means that the barrel length is limited: too long a barrel and the breech opens before the bullet has left the muzzle. The operating system is therefore a compromise between cartridge propellant strength, barrel length and the delayed-action lever timing.

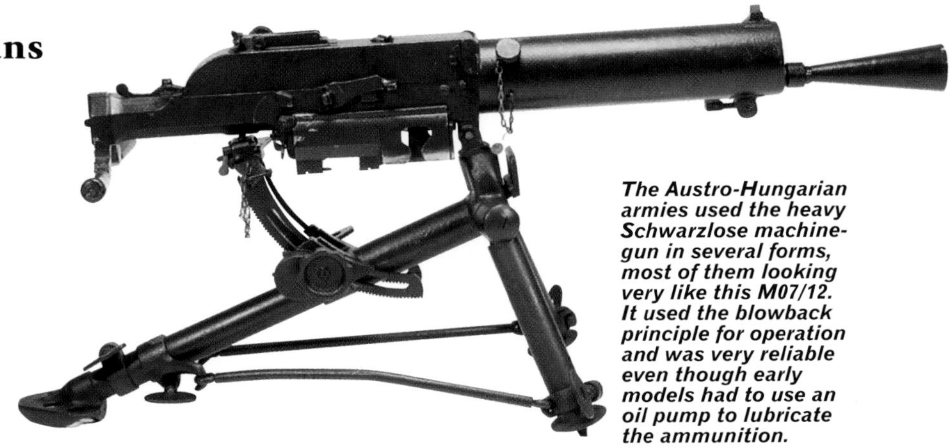

***The Austro-Hungarian armies used the heavy Schwarzlose machine-gun in several forms, most of them looking very like this M07/12. It used the blowback principle for operation and was very reliable even though early models had to use an oil pump to lubricate the ammunition.***

### Short barrel

In practice the Schwarzlose machine-guns worked well enough, but the barrel used was really too short for the standard Austro-Hungarian 8-mm (0.315-in) cartridge of the period, and this resulted in excessive muzzle flash. As a result a long tapering flash hider became standard, and this became one of the distinguishing features of the Schwarzlose. Another design feature of the series was the feed, which was among the first to use a drive sprocket to carry a cartridge into the system in a very precise manner. This added to the Schwarzlose's overall reliability.

***Another task undertaken by the Austro-Hungarian army's Schwarzlose machine-guns was protection of friendly troops from the close attention of low-flying warplanes.***

### Limited exports

Between 1914 and 1918 the main operators of the Schwarzlose were the Austro-Hungarian armies, but later in the war Italy had also become a major user, mainly of captured weapons. The Netherlands was another major buyer, but was a neutral during World War I. By 1914 nearly all the versions in use were the Modell 07/12, 08/12 and 12 models. The original two models used lubricated ammunition, but on the Modell 12 this feature was deleted. There was also a **Modell 07/16** intended for use on aircraft and featuring a rudimentary system of air cooling, but it was not a great success.

The Schwarzlose machine-guns were large and heavy weapons notable for the excellence of their manufacture. Indeed, they were so heavy and well made that few appear to have worn out, so many were still in service during 1945 in Italy and Hungary. The delayed-blowback system has not been widely copied.

**SPECIFICATION**

| | |
|---|---|
| **Schwarzlose Modell 07/12** | tripod 19.8 kg (43.65 lb) |
| **Calibre:** 8-mm (0.315-in) | **Muzzle velocity:** 620 m (2,034 ft) per second |
| **Length overall:** 1066 mm (42 in) | **Rate of fire, cyclic:** 400 rpm |
| **Length of barrel:** 526 mm (20.7 in) | **Feed:** 250-round fabric belt |
| **Weights:** gun 19.9 kg (43.87 lb); | |

# Madsen Machine-guns

The first Madsen machine-gun was produced in Denmark by the Dansk Industri Syndikat in 1904 and the last in 1950. The Madsen series was really a long string of near-identical models produced in a very wide array of calibres to suit the requirements of many worldwide customers.

Although it was not fully realised at the time that it was first produced, the **Madsen 8-mm Rekytgevaer M1903** was one of the very first light machine-guns, and even featured the world's first overhead box magazine.

The weapon used a unique operating principle that has been used in no other machine-gun design and which even for its time was expensive, complex and difficult to manufacture. This was the Peabody-Martini hinged block action, an action familiar on small-calibre match rifles. What Madsen did was to convert this essentially manually operated action to fully automatic operation. By using a combination of the recoil plus the movement of a plate on cams and levers, the action opened and closed the hinged block, but as this block had no integral bolt action (as with a normal breech block) a separate rammer and extractor mechanism had to be used. It was complicated, but the system had one major advantage: it worked very reliably under a wide range of conditions and with all sorts of ammunition, although rimmed ammunition such as the British 0.303-in (7.7-mm) was not so successful.

As well as being produced in many calibres for customers as far away as Thailand, the Madsen was also manufactured in a wide variety of forms. Having an air-cooled barrel, the Madsen was not ideally suited for the sustained-fire role, but various types of heavy tripod were produced. The more

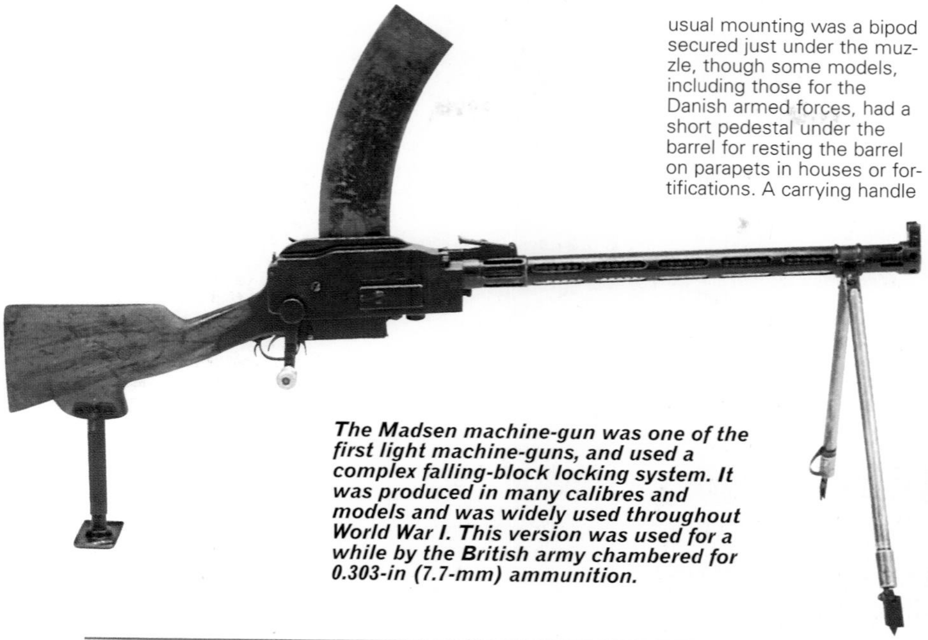

usual mounting was a bipod secured just under the muzzle, though some models, including those for the Danish armed forces, had a short pedestal under the barrel for resting the barrel on parapets in houses or fortifications. A carrying handle was often fitted. One feature that promoted the Madsen's reliability was its excellent manufacture using the best possible materials, which added to cost.

### Much unofficial use

During World War I the Madsen was not an official weapon used by any of the major protagonists, but all the same many Madsens appeared in nearly every continental army. The Madsen was one of the first weapons used by both sides for early experiments in aircraft armament, although it was soon passed over in favour of other weapons. It was also used in small numbers by German troops experimenting on the Eastern Front with their *Sturmtruppen* tactics, and more were used by some of the Central European armies, again in small numbers only. When the light machine-gun concept became more accepted the Madsen was investigated by many nations, and the British even attempted to use it in 0.303-in calibre. Unfortunately this cartridge was rimmed and it was one that did not work well in the Madsen mechanism; the guns were thus put by only to be issued again in 1940, to the new Home Guard.

***The Madsen machine-gun was one of the first light machine-guns, and used a complex falling-block locking system. It was produced in many calibres and models and was widely used throughout World War I. This version was used for a while by the British army chambered for 0.303-in (7.7-mm) ammunition.***

**SPECIFICATION**

**Rekytgevaer M1903**
**Calibre:** 8-mm (0.315-in)
**Length overall:** 1145 mm (45.1 in)
**Length of barrel:** 596 mm (23.46 in)
**Weight:** 10 kg (22.05 lb)
**Muzzle velocity:** 825 m (2,707 ft) per second
**Rate of fire, cyclic:** 450 rpm
**Feed:** 20-round box magazine

# Hotchkiss mle 1909 Machine-gun

In the years up to 1914 the French army was trained in the tenet that the attack (or the offensive) was the key to victory. The infantry and cavalry were trained to attack at all times, overcoming any opposition by the force of their onslaught and by their determination. In this optimistic scenario the machine-gun hardly featured, but at one point in the early 1900s it was thought that a light machine-gun would be useful for cavalry units, and might also be portable enough for attacking infantrymen to carry.

The result was the **Fusil-mitrailleur Hotchkiss mle 1909**, which used the basic gas-operated mechanism of the larger Hotchkiss machine-guns, though for some reason the ammunition feed was complicated further by inversion of the ammunition feed strip mechanism. When the weapon was introduced, the cavalry units did not take to it at all and it proved to be too heavy for infantry use, so the numbers produced were either relegated to use in fortifications or stockpiled. However, export sales of the mle 1909 were more encouraging for the weapon was adopted by the US Army, which knew it as the **Benét-Mercié Machine Rifle Model 1909**; it was used mainly by cavalry units.

***The Hotchkiss mle 1909 was used by the French, the British (as the Hotchkiss Mk 1) and also by the US Army, which knew the weapon as the Benét-Mercié.***

### Reprieved by the war

When World War I began the mle 1909 was once more taken from the stockpiles, and it was even adopted by the British army (as the **0.303-in Gun, Machine, Hotchkiss, Mk 1**) in an attempt to get more machine-guns into service. The mle 1909 was produced in the UK chambered for the British 0.303-in (7.7-mm) cartridge, and in British use many were fitted with a butt and a bipod in place of the original small tripod located under the centre of the gun body.

However, the mle 1909 was not destined to be used very much in the trenches: the ammunition feed was a constant source of trouble and gradually the Hotchkiss was diverted to other uses. The mle 1909 in its several forms became an aircraft gun and it formed the main armament of many of the early tanks such as the British 'Female' tanks with their wholly machine-gun armament, and the French Renault FT-17 light tank.

### Limited traverse

On the tanks the ammunition feed strips sometimes limited the traverse available inside the close confines of the tank mountings, so many guns, especially those of the British, were converted to use the three-round linked strips intended for use on the larger Hotchkiss mle 1914. Some of these guns were still in British army use in 1939, and more were later taken from the stockpiles for use as airfield defence weapons and for arming merchant shipping.

The mle 1909 was one of the first light machine-guns, but it had little impact at the time, although it was used in quite large numbers. Its main disadvantage was not so much a technical difficulty as a tactical problem, for the tactics involved in the trench warfare of the period and the lack of appreciation of the potential of the weapon never gave the mle 1909 a chance to shine. As a tank weapon it made its mark on history, but it was less successful as an aircraft gun, the feed strip mechanism proving a definite drawback in an open aircraft cockpit.

***A drummer of the 1/7th Lancashire Fusiliers demonstrates a Hotchkiss Mk 1 to US soldiers newly arrived in France during May 1918.***

**SPECIFICATION**

**Fusil-mitrailleur Hotchkiss mle 1909**
**Calibre:** 8-mm (0.315-in)
**Length overall:** 1190 m (46.85 in)
**Length of barrel:** 600 mm (23.6 in)
**Weight:** 11.7 kg (25.8 lb)
**Muzzle velocity:** 740 m (2,428 ft) per second
**Rate of fire, cyclic:** 500 rpm
**Feed:** 30-round metal strip

# Hotchkiss
## Medium machine-guns

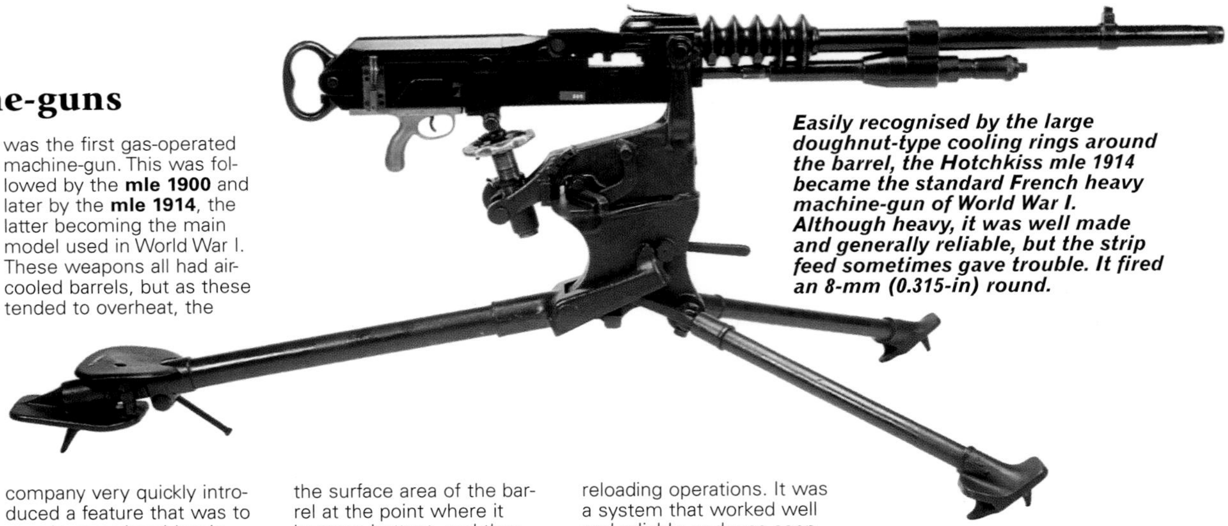

***Easily recognised by the large doughnut-type cooling rings around the barrel, the Hotchkiss mle 1914 became the standard French heavy machine-gun of World War I. Although heavy, it was well made and generally reliable, but the strip feed sometimes gave trouble. It fired an 8-mm (0.315-in) round.***

In the 1890s the only viable machine-guns were those produced by Maxim and Browning, both of whom wrapped their products in a tight wall of patents to prevent others enjoying the fruits of their inventions. Many armament concerns, including the French Hotchkiss company, were desperate to find a way of getting around the patent wall. Thus when it was approached by an Austrian inventor who described a novel method of gas operation to power a machine-gun, the invention was quickly purchased and developed by Hotchkiss.

### New concept

The first Hotchkiss machine-gun was the **Mitrailleuse Hotchkiss mle 1897**, and although this was hardly a viable service weapon, it was the first gas-operated machine-gun. This was followed by the **mle 1900** and later by the **mle 1914**, the latter becoming the main model used in World War I. These weapons all had air-cooled barrels, but as these tended to overheat, the company very quickly introduced a feature that was to remain as a virtual 'trademark' of the Hotchkiss machine-gun: this was an assembly of five prominent 'doughnut' collars around the end of the barrel close to the receiver. These rings (sometimes brass and sometimes steel) enlarged the surface area of the barrel at the point where it became hottest, and thus provided greater cooling.

### Gas-operated system

For automatic fire, gas was tapped off from the barrel and used to push back a piston to carry out all the various extracting and reloading operations. It was a system that worked well and reliably, and was soon used (in one form or another) by many other machine-gun designers.

The weapon had its first exposure to action during the Russo-Japanese War of 1904-05, in which it performed well enough though one feature did cause trouble. This was the ammunition feed, the Hotchkiss system being based on the feeding of the cartridges into the gun by means of metal strips; brass strips were used initially, but these were later replaced by steel strips. These strips carried only 24 or 30 rounds, which severely limited the amount of sustained fire that could be produced. On the mle 1914 this was partly overcome by redesigning the strip system to give three-round strips linked together to form a 249-round 'belt'. Even in this form the strips were prone to damage and any dirt on them tended to cause jams.

There were some variations on the basic design. Versions for use in fortifications had a downward Y-shaped muzzle attachment that was supposed to act as a flash hider, and several types of tripod were in use during World War I, including a mle 1897 mounting that had no provision for traverse or elevation.

The Hotchkiss machine-guns were used mainly by the French army in World War I, but in 1917 large numbers were handed over to the newly arrived American Expeditionary Force. Its divisions used the weapon until the war's end.

***French and British infantry at the Battle of the Aisne during 1918 in the follow-up to the Allied final offensive. The gun is a Hotchkiss mle 1900 mounted on the mle 1916 tripod, with ammunition boxes close to hand behind the gunner. To the left of the gun are two ammunition handlers ready to assist.***

| SPECIFICATION | |
|---|---|
| **Mitrailleuse Hotchkiss mle 1914** | **Muzzle velocity:** 725 m (2,379 ft) per second |
| **Calibre:** 8-mm (0.315-in) | **Rate of fire, cyclic:** 400-600 rpm |
| **Length overall:** 1270 mm (50 in) | **Feed:** 24- or 30-round strips, or 249-round strip in 3-round links |
| **Length of barrel:** 775 mm (30.5 in) | |
| **Weight:** gun 23.6 kg (52 lb) | |

# Chauchat Light machine-gun

Officially known as the **Fusil-Mitrailleur mle 1915**, the **Chauchat** or **CSRG** has one of the more unpleasant weapon production stories of World War I. The weapon was intended as a light machine-gun, and was created in 1914 by a commission of designers (MM. Chauchat, Suterre, Ribeyrolle and Gladiator, hence the CSRG name in these men's 'honour'). The result was a long and awkward weapon using the long-recoil mechanism in which the barrel and breech block move to the rear after firing, the barrel then being allowed to move forward while the bolt is held and released later to feed the next round. This mechanism works, but is rather complicated and the movement of so much mass inside the gun makes aiming difficult.

The Chauchat was apparently intended for ease of manufacture, but when the design was rushed into production in 1915 its manufacture was hived out to a large number of firms, some of whom had virtually no weapons-manufacturing experience. The result was a horror, for many manufacturers used the Chauchat simply as a means of making maximum profit and so used cheap and unsuitable materials that either wore out quickly or broke in action. Even when suitable materials were used, the service versions of the Chauchat were still bad: the weapon handled poorly and tended to jam at the slightest excuse. The half-moon magazine under the body did little to make the weapon easier to

***The Fusil-Mitrailleur mle 1915 or 'Chauchat' was one of the worst machine-guns ever made, and it was reviled by the soldiers who had to use it.***

carry, and the light bipod was so flimsy that it bent very easily. French soldiers detested the weapon, many later proclaiming that the manufacturers' greed for profits had caused the deaths of many French soldiers, as they no doubt had.

### Americans duped

Unfortunately, the manufacturers were not alone in their search for weapon production profits. When the Americans entered the war, some French politicians prevailed upon the US Army to adopt the Chauchat and the unsuspecting Americans agreed. They accepted over 16,000 Chauchats and a further 19,000 were ordered of a version chambered for the American 0.3-in (7.62-mm) cartridge; this model had a vertical box magazine instead of the French half-moon magazine.

Neither of these versions proved to be any better in American hands than they were in French hands. The Americans often simply cleared jams by throwing the jammed weapon away and taking up a rifle, especially when the rechambered weapons reached their ranks. The American cartridge was more powerful than the French 8-mm (0.315-in) round and made the gun components break even more readily.

### Speedily dumped

Eventually, existing production contracts were allowed to run their course but the resultant weapons were usually stockpiled to be dragged out and later dumped upon unsuspecting post-war markets. In France some parliamentary investigations were made into the Chauchat affair in an attempt to determine exactly how the production contracts were placed and where the profits ended, but by then so many parliamentarians and industrialists were involved that the whole affair fizzled out.

Most references state that the Chauchat in all its forms was one of the worst machine-guns of World War I in all aspects. From basic design to manufacture and the materials used, it was a disaster, but what now appears worse is the fact that the whole programme was not controlled at all. The result was that many soldiers suffered from having to use the weapon while others pocketed the profits their greed had generated.

***A French soldier fully attired in his* horizon bleu *uniform and greatcoat holds his Chauchat in the prescribed drill book manner for use in an assault.***

**SPECIFICATION**

| | |
|---|---|
| **Chauchat** | **Muzzle velocity:** 700 m (2,297 ft) per second |
| **Calibre:** 8-mm (0.315-in) | **Rate of fire:** 250-300 rounds per minute |
| **Length overall:** 1143 mm (45 in) | **Feed:** 20-round curved box |
| **Length of barrel:** 470 mm (18.5 in) | |
| **Weight:** 9.2 kg (20.3 lb) | |

# Mitrailleuse St Etienne mle 1907 Medium machine-gun

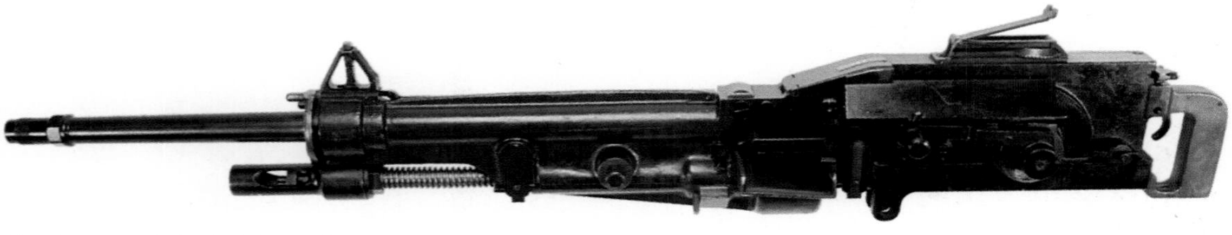

The Hotchkiss was a commercial design and the French military authorities wanted to have their own design of machine-gun to match. Unfortunately their efforts were not a success, and indeed were not helped by the fact that the gas-operated mechanism devised by Hotchkiss was protected by a long list of patents that were almost impossible to circumvent.

### Pig-headed design

Not deterred, the French attempted to produce a model known as the mle 1905 or Puteaux. It was so unsuccessful that it was withdrawn from use within two years, the basic design being used for another attempt that was known as the **Mitrailleuse mle 1907** or **Saint Etienne**, after the arsenal at which it was manufactured.

The designers decided to use a gas mechanism based on that of the Hotchkiss, but with the process reversed. Instead of tapped gases pushing back a piston, the Saint Etienne used a system in which the gases were tapped forward, where the piston compressed a spring. The compressed spring was then released to power the rest of the operation. This system worked, but only at the cost of complication and of the use of more pieces that could break or go wrong. Thus in practice the whole idea was simply not worth the trouble involved. The mle 1907 had an inherent source of ammunition and other jams, and the return spring that was supposed to do all the work got so hot that it either lost its tempering and ceased to operate or else simply broke. In the end the designers could do nothing more than leave the spring exposed to the elements, which aided cooling but also allowed dust and dirt to enter the workings and so produce more jams.

### Forced service

Despite all these inherent troubles, the mle 1907 guns were used during World War I for the simple reason that the French army became so desperate for weapons that it used anything it could obtain. The tribulations of the mle 1907 simply had to be borne, and as late as 1916 attempts were made to eradicate some of the more obvious faults. None of the modifications was of any use, and gradually the mle 1907s were phased out in favour of the far more reliable Hotchkiss guns. The mle 1907s were shunted off to the French colonies, where they were used to arm local levies and police units. Others were issued to fortress units.

All in all, the Saint Etienne was not a success; indeed, it even carried over the failings from other models. The mle 1905 Puteaux had already indicated the impracticality of some of the mle 1907's features, and the troublesome ammunition feed strip method of the Hotchkiss guns was adopted even when it was known that it should have been phased out in favour of a better method. The result was that in the dreadful conditions of the Western Front trenches the Saint Etienne often failed.

***The French mle 1907 was a state-produced machine-gun intended to improve upon the basic Hotchkiss designs. It was less successful, many being sent to the colonies or relegated to fortress use.***

***A St Etienne mle 1907 machine-gun team poses for a publicity photograph on one of the levels of the Eiffel Tower in an attempt to prove that Paris was able to defend itself against German air raids. The mle 1907 was no more successful in this role than it was in any other.***

**SPECIFICATION**

| | |
|---|---|
| **Mitrailleuse Saint Etienne mle 1907** | **Weight:** 25.4 kg (56 lb) |
| **Calibre:** 8-mm (0.315-in) | **Muzzle velocity:** 700 m (2,297 ft) per second |
| **Length overall:** 1180 mm (46.46 in) | **Rate of fire:** 400-600 rpm |
| **Length of barrel:** 710 mm (28 in) | **Feed:** 24- or 30-round metal strip |

# Maschinengewehr 08 Machine-gun

Contrary to general belief, the German army was not an avid proponent of the machine-gun when Hiram Maxim started to demonstrate his product around the European capitals in the 1890s. His gun aroused some interest but few sales, and the first made to the German army were actually bought with the private funds of Kaiser Wilhelm II. Thereafter things began to improve and gradually a licensing agreement was made between Maxim and the German army. From this agreement Maxim machine-guns were soon being produced by both commercial concerns and the Deutsche Waffen und Munitionsfabriken at Spandau, near Berlin. Several models preceded the 1908 appearance of the **sMG 08**, or **schwere Maschinengewehr 08**, as the first standard weapon. This fired the standard 7.92-mm (0.312-in) rifle cartridge of the day.

As a machine-gun the sMG 08 differed little from many other Maxim guns – the Maxim recoil-operated mechanism was used unchanged and manufacture was very solid. In service the **'Spandau'** proved to be very reliable under the most demanding battlefield conditions. Where the sMG 08 did differ from other machine-guns of the time was the mounting.

Even the early German Maxims used a type of mounting known as a *Schlitten* (sledge) that was intended to be dragged across country when folded and with the gun carried on top. As an alternative this mounting could be carried by two men as though it was a stretcher. The mounting, known as the Schlitten 08, provided a stable firing platform but was very heavy, to the extent that in 1916 an alternative tripod mounting known as the Dreifuss 16 was introduced.

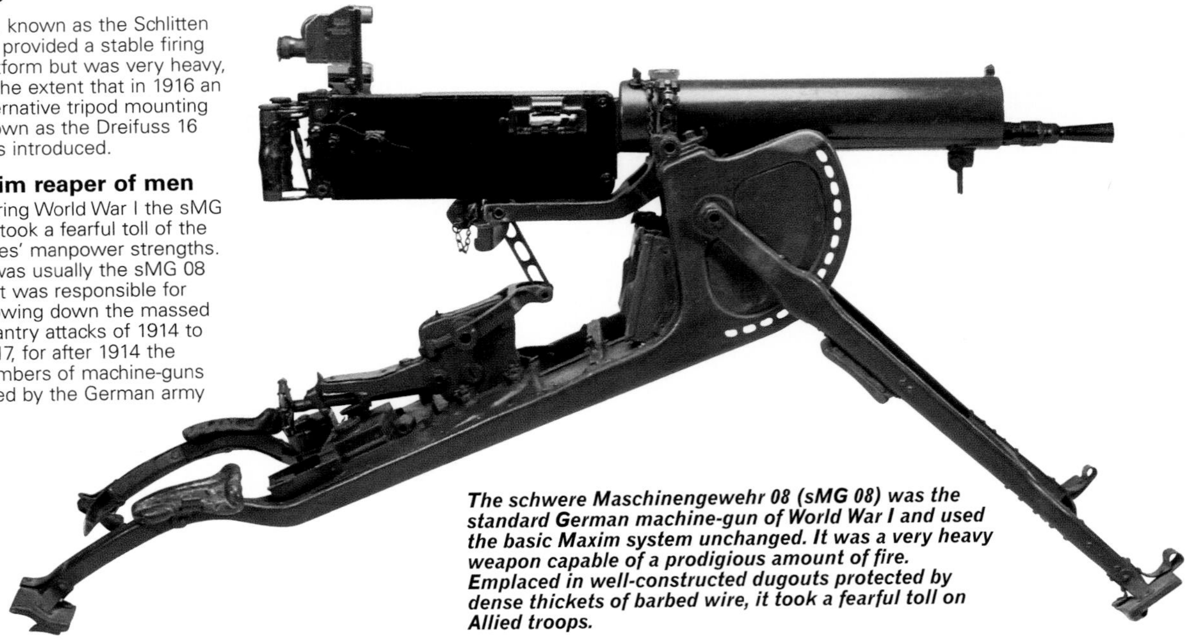

*The schwere Maschinengewehr 08 (sMG 08) was the standard German machine-gun of World War I and used the basic Maxim system unchanged. It was a very heavy weapon capable of a prodigious amount of fire. Emplaced in well-constructed dugouts protected by dense thickets of barbed wire, it took a fearful toll on Allied troops.*

## Grim reaper of men

During World War I the sMG 08 took a fearful toll of the Allies' manpower strengths. It was usually the sMG 08 that was responsible for mowing down the massed infantry attacks of 1914 to 1917, for after 1914 the numbers of machine-guns used by the German army increased greatly and, as probably the more important change, the Germans learned to use them in widely spaced pairings. Instead of simply placing a machine-gun to face directly across no man's land, the Germans learned to set up their machine-guns to fire on the flanks of advancing troops. This meant that the guns could enfilade and break up an infantry attack to much better effect and at the same time this tactical disposition provided the opportunity of more cover for the gun crews. The German machine-gunners were picked men who often maintained their guns in action to the last, and they were highly trained in all aspects of their task. They knew the sMG 08 backwards and were fully trained and equipped to carry out repairs in the front line should the need arise.

## Decisive firepower

At times the two/three-man crew of a single sMG 08 was responsible for breaking up and destroying the advance of entire Allied infantry battalions once the latter had left the shelter of their trenches. Thus the slaughter of Neuve Chapelle, Loos, the Somme and all the other costly infantry carnages of World War I's Western Front fighting can be traced to the sMG 08 machine-guns and their determined crews, aided by the shell-shattered terrain and its masses of barbed wire entanglements, which slowed the Allied advances and thereby offered the machine-gun crews more time in which to wreak their destruction.

After 1918 the sMG 08 was maintained in German service, and many were still in use for second-line tasks in 1939.

**SPECIFICATION**

**sMG 08**
**Calibre:** 7.92-mm (0.312-in)
**Lengths:** gun 1.175 m (46.26 in); barrel 719 mm (28.3 in)
**Weights:** gun complete with spares 62 kg (136.7 lb); sledge mount 37.65 kg (83.0 lb)
**Muzzle velocity:** 900 m (2,953 ft) per second
**Rate of fire, cyclic:** 300-450 rpm
**Feed:** 250-round fabric belt

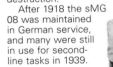

*Bulgarian machine-gun teams in action use Maxim Model 1908 machine-guns purchased from Vickers of the UK. This gun fired an 8-mm (0.315-in) cartridge and was very similar to the German sMG 08.*

*The heavy tripod-mounted guns in service in 1914 had to be broken down into several loads for prolonged marching. Here a Jäger (light infantryman) in 1914 service kit shoulders the burden of the sMG 08 gun.*

# Maschinengewehr 08/15 Machine-gun

*The MG 08/18 was the last of the World War I versions of the sMG 08 to see service. It used an air-cooled barrel without the usual large casing, and was an attempt to provide German troops with an air-cooled light machine-gun for more mobile tactical use.*

By 1915 the German army had come to appreciate that it had an acute need for a light machine-gun for front-line use. While the sMG 08 was an excellent heavy machine-gun, it was too heavy for rapid tactical moves and trials were held to determine what type of weapon would suffice. Among weapons tested was the Danish Madsen, as well as Bergmann and Dreyse light machine-guns, but the choice fell upon a lightened form of the sMG 08. This emerged as the **MG 08/15** and the first examples of the type were issued in 1916.

The MG 08/15 retained the basic mechanism and water-cooling system of the sMG 08, although the water jacket was smaller. Other changes were a thinning of the receiver walls, the elimination of some detail parts, the replacement of the heavy sledge mounting by a bipod, the addition of a pistol grip and butt and modification of the sights. However, by no stretch of the imagination could the MG 08/15 be called light, for it still weighed a hefty 18 kg (39.7 lb). But it was portable and could even be fired from a standing position with the weight taken by a sling. A shorter fabric belt was introduced to make handling easier, or a belt drum could be fitted to the side of the weapon to prevent feed belts dragging in the mud.

## No extra training

The choice of the basic sMG 08 mechanism meant that no additional training was required for use of the lighter weapon, and there was a fair degree of spares interchangeability. Late in the war the designers went one stage further and did away with the water-cooling jacket altogether to produce the **MG 08/18**. World War I ended before this version could be widely used, the few that were produced being issued to the more mobile units of the German army; few actually reached the front-line infantry.

There was one further variant of the MG 08/15. This was the **LMG 08/15**, in which the L denoted Luft (air). This version was one of several air-cooled machine-guns used in fixed mountings by the new German air arm, and was basically the MG 08/15 with its water jacket retained for strength but extensively perforated to allow air-cooling of the barrel. The gun was fired via a cable and its mechanism was synchronised with the propeller so that it would not fire when a propeller blade was in the line of fire. Ammunition was fed into the gun from a drum, and another spring-loaded drum was often used to draw in the used fabric belt and so prevent it from flapping in the slipstream.

Some of the early Maxim aircraft guns had been of the lightened sMG 08 type known as the **LMG 08**, but these passed out of use once the LMG 08/15 was established.

## Devastating capability

The ground-used MG 08/15 equipped front-line troops at company level and below, while the heavier sMG 08 was retained at battalion level or even deployed in special heavy machine-gun companies. The portability of the MG 08/15 enabled it to be used by the Sturmtruppen of 1917 and 1918, but it was never a genuinely handy weapon: in comparison with the period's other light machine-guns it was much larger and bulkier. But it remained every bit as reliable in action as its heavier counterpart, and the German troops were well trained in its use. Perhaps the most effective use was made of the MG 08/15 during the last stages of the 1918 campaign, when the retreating German army used small MG 08/15 teams to cover its withdrawals, single weapons sometimes holding up whole battalions and preventing the Allied cavalry from taking part in any action.

**SPECIFICATION**

**MG 08/15**
**Calibre:** 7.92-mm (0.312-in)
**Length overall:** 1398 mm (55 in)
**Length of barrel:** 719 mm (28.3 in)
**Weight:** 18 kg (39.7 lb)
**Muzzle velocity:** 900 m (2,953 ft) per second
**Rate of fire:** 450 rpm
**Feed:** 50-, 100- or 250-round fabric belt

# Pulemet Maksima obrazets 1910 Machine-gun

*Originally built by Vickers for the Russian army, the Maxim gun was soon being manufactured in the Imperial Arsenal at Tula, outside Moscow. It was to remain in quantity production until 1943.*

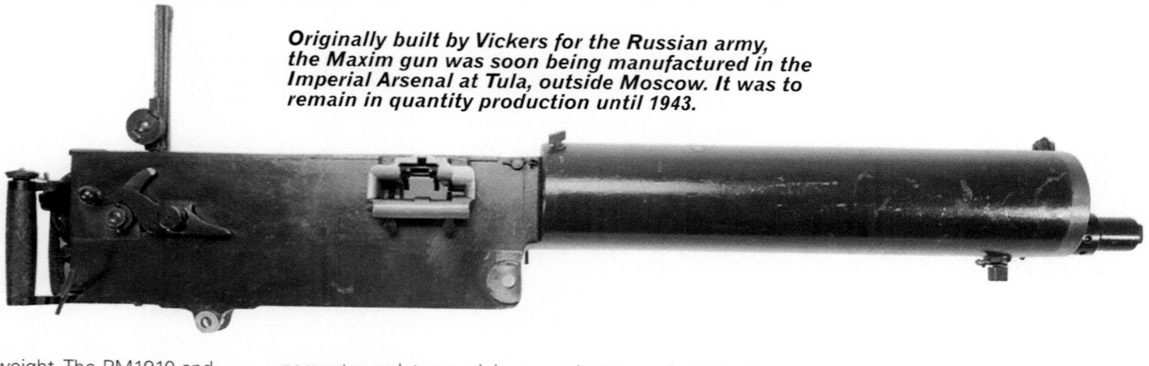

The first Maxim machine-guns for Russian service were ordered direct from Vickers in the early 1900s, but it was not long before the Russians were producing their own models at the state arsenal at Tula. The first Russian model was the **Pulemet Maksima obrazets 1905** (Maxim gun model 1905), which was a direct copy of the original Maxim gun but produced with a typical Russian flourish in the bronze water jacket. In 1910 this bronze jacket was replaced by a sheet steel jacket and this was known either as the **obrazets 1910** or **PM1910**.

## Great longevity

The PM1910 was destined to be the longest-produced version of all the many Maxim gun variants, for it remained in full-scale manufacture until 1943. Although there were several variants over the years, the basic PM1910 was a solid piece of equipment that served very well under even the most drastic conditions and all extremes of climate, a fact which suited the Russians very well considering their far-flung empire. This reliability had to be purchased at a cost, and that cost was weight. The PM1910 and anything to do with it were very heavy, so heavy in fact that the usual carriage resembled a small artillery field carriage. On this carriage, known as the Sokolov mounting, the gun was usually protected by a removable shield. The gun rested on a large turntable for traversing and was elevated by a large wheel-operated screw. The turntable was carried on two spoked steel wheels and the whole arrangement could be towed by hand using a U-shaped handle. On many of these early Sokolov mounts there were two side legs that could be extended forward to raise the entire equipment for firing over parapets; on later models these legs were omitted.

The weight of the PM1910 complete with the mounting was no less than 74 kg (163.1 lb). This meant that at least two men were required to drag the weapon – more if the ground was rough – a task for which drag ropes were provided. A special sledge mounting was available for winter service, and the weapon could also be carried on the widely available peasant carts used all over Russia.

As compensation for this weight penalty, the PM1910 could be kept firing for as long as belts were fed into the mechanism. It required next to no maintenance, which was just as well for the state of training in the Tsarist armies usually meant that no servicing (other than rudimentary cleaning) was provided.

## Limited change

The PM1910 was made in vast numbers until 1917, by which time production had spread to centres other than Tula. The only change made during World War I was the replacement of the original smooth water-cooling jacket by a corrugated jacket to increase the surface area and thus improve cooling. At times the heavy shields were left off to decrease the weight slightly. During World War I the amount of rough handling the PM1910 could absorb became legendary, so much so that the Germans used as many as they could capture, though only on the Eastern Front.

**SPECIFICATION**

**PM1910**
**Calibre:** 7.62-mm (0.3-in)
**Length overall:** 1107 mm (43.6 in)
**Length of barrel:** 720 mm (28.35 in)
**Weights:** gun 23.8 kg (52.47 lb); mounting with shield 45.2 kg (99.65 lb)
**Muzzle velocity:** 863 m (2,831 ft) per second
**Rate of fire, cyclic:** 520-600 rpm
**Feed:** 250-round fabric belt

# Lewis Machine-gun

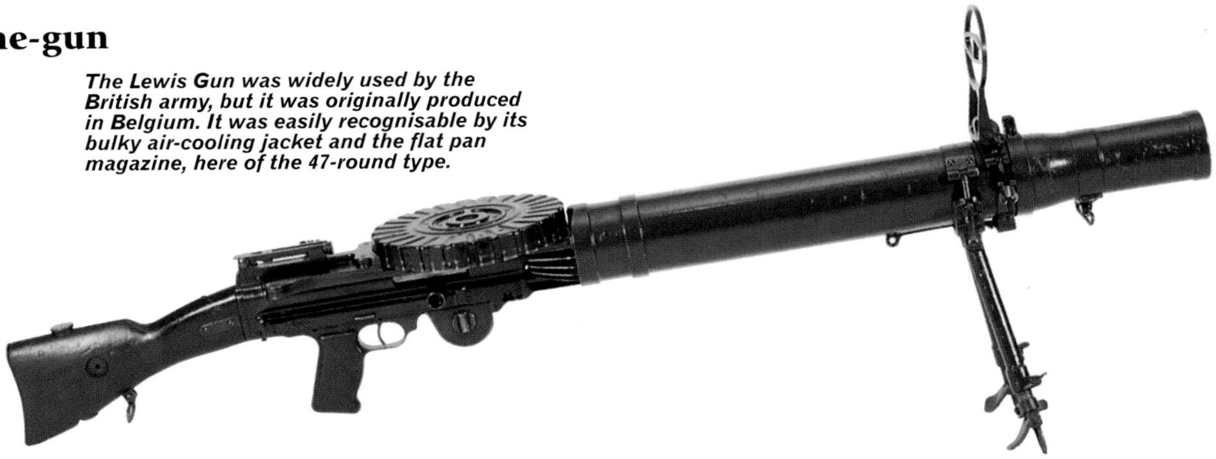

***The Lewis Gun was widely used by the British army, but it was originally produced in Belgium. It was easily recognisable by its bulky air-cooling jacket and the flat pan magazine, here of the 47-round type.***

The **Lewis** machine-gun, generally called just the **Lewis Gun**, was an international weapon, for though its origins were American, it was first produced and manufactured in Europe. Its inventor was an American, one Samuel Maclean, but the basic concept was developed further and 'sold' by Colonel Isaac Lewis, another American. The US military authorities were unenthusiastic about the new gun, so Lewis took the design to Belgium, where it was put into production for the Belgian army. That was in 1913, and in the following year production was switched to the UK, BSA (Birmingham Small Arms) taking over the programme.

## The British take over

The Lewis Gun was put into production at BSA as the **Lewis Gun Mk 1** for the British army for the simple reason that five or six Lewis Guns could be produced in the time it took to produce a single Vickers machine-gun. The fact that the Lewis was light and portable was secondary at that time, but once in service the Lewis proved to be a very popular front-line weapon with a host of mobile tactical uses. The Lewis Gun was one of the first of the true light machine-guns, and with its distinctive overhead drum magazine it was soon a common sight on the British-manned sector of the Western Front.

**SPECIFICATION**

| | |
|---|---|
| **Lewis Gun Mk 1** | **Muzzle velocity:** 744 m (2,441 ft) per second |
| **Calibre:** 0.303-in (7.7-mm) | **Rate of fire, cyclic:** 450-500 rpm |
| **Length overall:** 1250 mm (49.2 in) | **Feed:** 47- or 97-round overhead drum magazine |
| **Length of barrel:** 661 mm (26 in) | |
| **Weights:** 12.25 kg (27 lb) | |

***A Lewis Gun team in action shows the ready-filled ammunition pans still in their box. The fins of the air-cooling jacket can be seen under the ammunition pan on the gun; these fins were supposed to force air along the barrel, but were found to be superfluous.***

## Gas operation

The Lewis Gun was a gas-operated weapon, gas being tapped from the barrel on firing to push a piston to the rear; the piston pushed back the breech block and mechanism and compressed the coil spring under the gun that then returned everything to the start position. The mechanism was rather complex and took careful maintenance, but even then was still prone to jams and stoppages, some of them introduced by the overhead drum magazine, which was a constant cause of trouble, especially when only slightly damaged. The barrel was enclosed in a special air cooling jacket that was supposed to use a forced draught system of cooling, but experience showed that the jacket's efficiency had been over-rated and the gun worked quite well without it. Aircraft-mounted Lewis Guns had no jacket.

## Return to the USA

Only after large numbers of Lewis Guns had been produced in Europe did the USA finally realise the weapon's potential and order it into production for the US Army chambered in the American 0.3-in (7.62-mm) calibre.

Some Lewis Guns were used on the early tanks and more were used by naval vessels. A similar role cropped up again in World War II when stockpiled Lewis Guns were distributed for the defence of merchant shipping and for Home Defence in the hands of the Home Guard and Royal Air Force airfield defence units.

***A Lewis gunner fires his weapon as if it were a rifle, no doubt at some hastily presented target. Firing the Lewis Gun in this fashion was usually inaccurate, for the weight of the gun was too high for prolonged firing and the recoil soon shook the aim off the target.***

# Vickers Machine-gun

The UK was among the first to adopt the Maxim gun following demonstrations held in the country as early as 1887. A production line for various models was set up at Crayford in Kent by a company that came to be known as Vickers' Sons & Maxim Ltd, and from this factory Maxim guns went to the British armed forces and to those of many other countries. The Vickers engineers realised the virtues of the Maxim gun but considered that some weight savings could be made by a redesign, and by careful stress studies much of the mechanism was gradually lightened and the basic action inverted so that the toggle lock invented by Maxim could be made lighter.

***This Vickers gun is an American-made version mounted on the British Mk 4B tripod. It was the standard British machine-gun and was even used as the badge of the Machine-Gun Corps, a formation whose very creation underscores the importance of the machine-gun during World War I.***

## Slow acceptance

The result came to be known as the **Vickers Gun**. In relative terms it was not all that much lighter than a comparable Maxim machinegun, but the operating principles were much refined, making the weapon more efficient. It was approved for British army service in November 1912 as the **Gun, Machine, Vickers, 0.303-in, Mk 1**, and all production initially went to the British army, by which the machine-gun was still regarded with such suspicion that the rate of issue was only two such weapons per infantry battalion.

***A properly maintained Vickers machine-gun was a superb sustained-fire weapon that could be kept in action as soon as it was supplied with ammunition and barrel-cooling water. The weapon also had an indirect-fire capability.***

Once World War I started that allotment changed drastically. New production centres were soon opened, some of them in Royal Ordnance Factories, but the basic design was unchanged throughout its long production life even though there were detail changes.

## Special drills

Like most machine-guns of its period, the Vickers was subject to jams, most of them induced by the ammunition, and a series of drills was devised to clear the weapon rapidly. These drills took a bit of learning, and in time a new Machine Gun Corps was formed within the British army so that experience and skills could be confined within a relatively small body and not spread throughout all the regiments of the expanding armies. The Machine Gun Corps developed its own *esprit de corps*, and its cap badge was two crossed Vickers machine-guns.

## Total reliability

In action a Vickers could be kept firing for as long as ammunition could be fed into it. The water in the cooling jacket also had to be topped up, and after early experiences where steam from the jacket gave away the gun's position, a special condenser system (using a hose fed into a water can) was introduced to conceal the steam. After a while the water could be replaced in the jacket.

The Vickers machine-gun was usually mounted on a heavy tripod. Variations on the basic gun included air-cooled versions for use on aircraft, usually on fixed installations only. Many more variations were produced between the two world wars, and the Vickers is still in service with some armed forces to this day; it did not pass from British service until the 1970s.

The Vickers machine-gun was, in the opinion of many authorities, one of the best of all the World War I machine-guns, and would still be a very useful weapon today.

***Wearing hoods designed to offer protection against the effects of German poison gas, the two-man crew of this Vickers machine-gun keep watch for the German infantry attack that was often presaged by a gas barrage.***

**SPECIFICATION**

**Vickers Gun**
**Calibre:** 0.303-in (7.7-mm)
**Length overall:** 1156 mm (45.5 in)
**Length of barrel**: 721 mm (28.4 in)
**Weights:** gun 18.14 kg (40 lb); tripod 22.0 kg (48.5 lb)
**Muzzle velocity:** 744 m (2,440 ft) per second
**Rate of fire, cyclic:** 450-500 rpm
**Feed:** 250-round fabric belt

# Colt-Browning Model 1895 Machine-gun

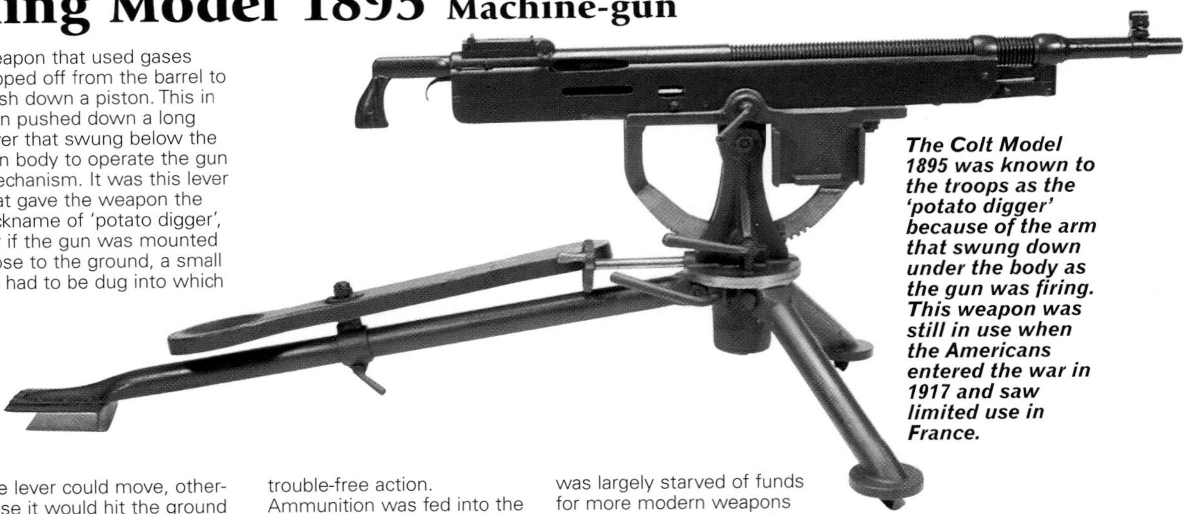

*The Colt Model 1895 was known to the troops as the 'potato digger' because of the arm that swung down under the body as the gun was firing. This weapon was still in use when the Americans entered the war in 1917 and saw limited use in France.*

John Moses Browning started design work on a machine-gun as early as 1889, at a time when the American forces were still using the hand-operated Gatling gun and Maxim had already patented his recoil-operated machine-gun.

Browning was thus directed towards a gas-operated mechanism, which he gradually refined to the point at which the Colt company built some prototypes, one of which was demonstrated to the US Navy. It was 1895 before the US Navy decided to purchase a batch chambered for the Krag-Jorgensen 0.3-in (7.62-mm) cartridge, but later this was altered to the .30-06 cartridge that was to remain in use for two world wars.

## 'Potato digger'

The **Colt-Browning Model 1895** was a gas-operated weapon that used gases tapped off from the barrel to push down a piston. This in turn pushed down a long lever that swung below the gun body to operate the gun mechanism. It was this lever that gave the weapon the nickname of 'potato digger', for if the gun was mounted close to the ground, a small pit had to be dug into which the lever could move, otherwise it would hit the ground and cause stoppages. This drawback was partially offset by the fact that, being based on a mechanical operation, the movements were very definite and precise, and so able to provide a smooth and trouble-free action. Ammunition was fed into the weapon in 300-round belts.

## Action in 1898

The Model 1895 first went into action with the US Marine Corps during the Cuban campaign of 1898. The US Army took over a few, and some sales were made to Belgium and Russia. By the time World War I started the Model 1895 was already obsolete, but since as the US Army was largely starved of funds for more modern weapons the Model 1895s were all that were available and were retained for training. Some did make the journey to France in 1917 and 1918 but few were used in action, the Americans instead taking over numbers of French and British machine-guns.

The Model 1895 did remain in production for a while during World War I: production was switched to the Marlin-Rockwell Corporation, which modified the weapon by designing out the lever action and replacing it by a more orthodox gas piston system. The result was known as the **Marlin Gun**. It resembled the Model 1895 but was much lighter and was a better weapon overall. Many were produced for the US Army's air element as aircraft weapons, and the weapon also became standard for tanks produced in America. In the event the war ended before many of the Marlin guns could reach the front in sizeable numbers, and the bulk of the production run was stockpiled, only to be sold to the United Kingdom for home defence in 1940.

The Belgian and Tsarist Russian armies used the Model 1895 machine-gun throughout World War I, some of the Russian weapons being prominent during the political upheavals of 1917. A few of the Russian Model 1895s were still in service as late as 1941.

*Despite its awkward underbody lever that swung down during firing, the Colt Model 1895 was selected as a weapon for early combat aircraft such as this Voisin. This was the result mainly of the weapon's relatively light weight and air-cooled barrel, but the type was not used for long.*

**SPECIFICATION**

| | |
|---|---|
| **Colt-Browning Model 1895** | tripod 29 kg (64 lb) |
| **Calibre:** 0.3-in (7.62-mm) | **Muzzle velocity:** 838 m (2,750 ft) per second |
| **Length overall:** 1200 m (47.25 in) | **Rate of fire, cyclic:** 400-500 rpm |
| **Length of barrel:** 720 mm (28.3 in) | **Feed:** 300-round belt |
| **Weights:** gun 16.78 kg (37 lb); | |

# Browning M1917 Machine-gun

Almost as soon as the Colt-Browning Model 1895 gas-operated machine-gun had entered production, Browning started work on a recoil-operated weapon. Unfortunately for Browning, at that time the American military authorities had no interest in the procurement of another type of machine-gun: they considered they had enough already, and anyway funds to purchase more were few and far apart. Thus virtually nothing happened until 1917, when the United States found itself at war and faced with committing its forces to combat with few modern weapons in general and even fewer serviceable machine-guns in particular.

In a very short space of time the 'new' Browning machine-gun was ordered into production in large numbers as the **Machine-Gun, Caliber .30, M1917**.

With a simple external examination the M1917 might seem to resemble other machine-guns of the time, especially the Vickers gun, but the M1917 was in fact quite different: it used a operating mechanism

*The Colt Model 1917 was the first of many successful Browning-designed machine-guns, and many of these are in use to this day. Chambered for the American 0.3-in (7.62-mm) cartridge, the Model 1917 was used by the US Army in France.*

known as the short recoil system, in which the recoil force produced on firing the cartridge pushes back the barrel and breech block toward the rear of the gun; after the barrel and bolt have travelled back together for a short distance, the two components part company and the barrel movement is halted; a swinging lever known as an accelerator then throws the bolt to the rear, and as it travels a series of cams move the belt feed mechanism to insert another round; a return spring compressed by the bolt's rearward movement then checks, halts and finally pushes forward the bolt toward the barrel, and the whole assembly is then returned for the cycle to start again. This basic mechanism was retained for all future Browning machine-gun designs, from the air-cooled 0.3-in (7.62-mm) weapons to the large 0.5-in (12.7-mm) M2 weapons.

***Completely unprepared for a major conflict, the US Army was compelled to rely on the UK and France for much of the equipment for its Expeditionary Force. One honourable exception was the Browning M1917 machine-gun, a fine weapon destined to enjoy a long career.***

### Pistol grip

Apart from its wholly different internal mechanism, one component that differentiated the M1917 from the Vickers machine-gun was the firing grip: the Vickers machine-gun used two spade grips with the trigger mechanism (pushed forward to fire) between them, while the M1917 used a pistol grip and a conventional trigger that was pulled to fire the weapon. Close inspection between the two types will reveal many other differences, but the pistol grip is easily noticed.

### Problem-free

The M1917 was rushed into production at several manufacturing centres and was churned out in such numbers that by the time World War I ended in November 1918 no fewer than 68,000 of the weapon had been manufactured.

Not all of these reached the troops in France, but after 1918 the M1917 became one of the standard American sustained-fire machine-guns, and remained in service until well after the end of World War II. After 1918 some slight alterations were introduced as the lessons of the US Army's combat experience were digested and implemented, but these changes were slight. More drastic changes came after 1918 when the water cooling jacket was removed altogether to produce the lightened M1919 machine-gun.

### Important service

In service, the M1917 proved to be relatively trouble-free, and despite the rush with which it was placed in production and service, it appears that few problems were recorded. The weapons that arrived in France were extensively used, for the M1917 was among the few wholly American weapons issued to American troops: up until then all they had from home were their Springfield rifles and a few other sundry equipment items.

**SPECIFICATION**

**M1917**
**Calibre:** 0.3-in (7.62-mm)
**Length overall:** 981 mm (38.64 in)
**Length of barrel:** 607 mm (23.9 in)
**Weights:** gun less water 14.79 kg (32.6 lb); tripod 24.1 kg (53.15 lb)
**Muzzle velocity:** 853 m (2,800 ft) per second
**Rate of fire, cyclic:** 450-600 rpm
**Feed:** 250-round belt

# Browning Automatic Rifle Light machine-gun

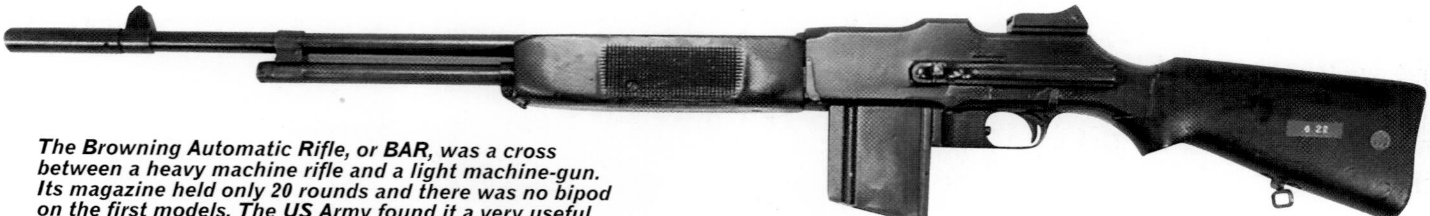


***The Browning Automatic Rifle, or BAR, was a cross between a heavy machine rifle and a light machine-gun. Its magazine held only 20 rounds and there was no bipod on the first models. The US Army found it a very useful weapon and therefore used it in large numbers.***

In 1917 Browning demonstrated two new automatic weapon designs to the Congress in Washington: one was the heavy machine-gun that was to become the M1917, and the other a weapon that is still regarded by many as a hybrid and which became known to all as the **BAR**, or **Browning Automatic Rifle**. The BAR was in an odd category, for to many the weapon was a light machine-gun but to the US Army it was an automatic rifle, in some ways an early assault rifle. It was a light and portable weapon that could fire single-shot or automatic, and could be carried and used by one man.

By early 1918 the BAR was in production at several centres, but as Colt held the Browning patents at that time it produced the drawings and gauges that the other centres were to use. It was September 1918 before the **BAR M1918** entered combat, but then it made a tremendous impact on US soldiers, who soon grew to value the weapon highly – so highly in fact that they were still using the BAR during the Korean War of the 1950s. Exactly why the Americans went so overboard regarding the BAR was, and still is, rather difficult to determine. The first BARs, as used in World War I, were simply hand-held weapons. There was no bipod or any form of support for use when the weapon was fired on automatic in the prone position, and as the box magazine held only 20 rounds the length of bursts was strictly limited. As a light machine-gun the BAR was really too light, and as an automatic rifle it was too large and heavy.

### Instant hit

But the American soldiers took to the BAR very well, no doubt as a relief from the appalling Chauchat. Apart from the Springfield rifles, the BAR was one of the first 'all-American' weapons to reach them, and no doubt they wanted to demonstrate the quality of American small arms.

The BAR was certainly a weapon of impressive looks. It was excellently made, was provided with well-finished wooden furniture, and was capable of taking hard knocks. The mechanism was gas-operated and so arranged that at the instant of firing the mechanism was locked in place by the bolt engaging in a notch in the top of the receiver. This notch was the source of the 'hump' on top of the gun just in front of the rear sights. For maintenance and repairs the BAR could be rapidly and easily stripped down to its 70 component parts and reassembled just as easily.

In the field the US Army devised some combat drills for the BAR. One that did not last long was a drill in which infantry fired one shot every time the left foot touched the ground. In fact most of the tactical drills involving the BAR were formulated after 1918, when the lessons of the few months of combat that the US Army had to endure were analysed.

The BAR itself was changed by the addition of a bipod and shoulder strap (**BAR M1918A1**), and as such was more of a section support weapon that could deliver automatic fire in support of riflemen. The World War II variant was the **BAR M1919A2** with a butt monopod and, instead of a selective-fire capability, automatic fire at either of two selectable rates.

**SPECIFICATION**

**Browning Automatic Rifle**
**Calibre:** 0.3-in (7.62-mm)
**Length overall:** 1194 mm (47 in)
**Length of barrel:** 610 mm (24 in)
**Weight:** 7.26 kg (16 lb)
**Muzzle velocity:** 853 m (2,800 ft) per second
**Rate of fire, cyclic:** 550 rpm
**Feed:** 20-round straight box

# Lehky Kulomet ZB vz 26 and vz 30
## Light machine-guns

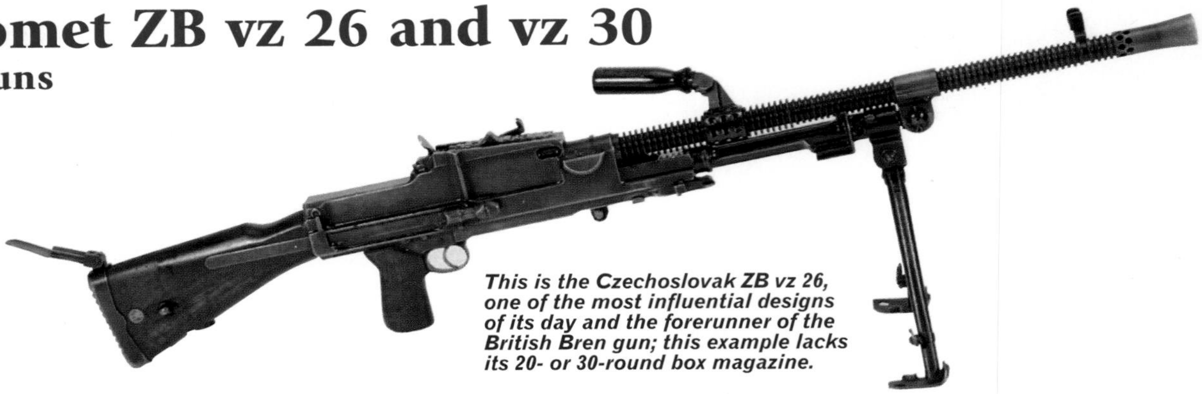

***This is the Czechoslovak ZB vz 26, one of the most influential designs of its day and the forerunner of the British Bren gun; this example lacks its 20- or 30-round box magazine.***

When Czechoslovakia was established as a state after 1919 it contained within its borders a wide range of skills and talents, and among them was small arms expertise. In the early 1920s a company was established at Brno under the name of Ceskoslovenska Zbrojovka for the design and production of all types of small arms. An early product was a machine-gun known as the **Lehky Kulomet ZB vz 24** using a box magazine feed, but it remained a prototype only for an even better design was on the stocks. Using some details from the vz 24 the new design was designated the **Lehky Kulomet ZB vz 26**.

This light machine-gun was an immediate success and has remained one of the most inspirational of all such weapons ever since. The vz 26 was a gas-operated weapon with, under its barrel, a long gas piston operated by propellant gas tapped from the barrel via an adjustable gas vent about half-way down the finned barrel. Gas operating on the piston pushed it to the rear and a simple arrangement of a hinged breech block on a ramp formed the locking and firing basis. Ammunition was fed downward from a simple inclined box magazine, and the overall design emphasised the virtues of ease in stripping, maintaining and using the weapon. Barrel cooling was assisted by the use of prominent fins all along the barrel, but a simple and rapid barrel change method was also incorporated.

The vz 26 was adopted by the Czechoslovak army and soon became a great export success, being used by a whole string of nations that included China, Yugoslavia and Spain. The vz 26 was followed in production by a slightly improved model, the **Lehky Kulomet ZB vz 30**, but to the layman the two models were identical, the vz 30 differing only in the way it was manufactured and in some of the internal details. Like the vz 26, the vz 30 was also an export success, being sold to such countries as Persia and Romania. Many nations set up their own licensed production lines, and by 1939 the two were among the world's most numerous light machine-gun types.

### German use

When Germany started to seize most of Europe, starting with Czechoslovakia, the vz 26 and vz 30 became German weapons as the **MG 26(t)** and **MG 30(t)** respectively, and even remained in production at Brno for a while to satisfy the demands of the German forces. They were used all over the world and were even issued as standard German civil and military police machine-guns.

Of all the nations involved in World War II, none took to the type more avidly than China where production facilities were established. Perhaps the most lasting influence the vz 26 and vz 30 had was on other designs. The Japanese copied them, and so did the Spanish who produced a machine-gun known as the **FAO**. The vz 26 was also the starting point for the British Bren, and the Yugoslavs produced their own variants.

**SPECIFICATION**

**ZB vz 26**
**Calibre:** 7.92-mm (0.312-in)
**Length overall:** 1161 mm (45.7 in)
**Length of barrel:** 672 mm (26.46 in)
**Weight:** 9.65 kg (21.3 lb)
**Muzzle velocity:** 762 m (2,500 ft) per second
**Rate of fire, cyclic:** 500 rpm
**Feed:** 20- or 30-round inclined box

**ZB vz 30**
**Calibre:** 7.92-mm (0.312-in)
**Length overall:** 1161 mm (45.7 in)
**Length of barrel:** 672 mm (26.46 in)
**Weight:** 10.04 kg (22.13 lb)
**Muzzle velocity:** 762 m (2,500 ft) per second
**Rate of fire, cyclic:** 500 rpm
**Feed:** 30-round inclined box

# Fusil Mitrailleur mle 1924/29 and Mitrailleuse mle 1931
## Machine-guns

***The Chatellerault modèle 1924/29 was the standard French light machine-gun of 1940; it had a calibre of 7.5-mm (0.295-in) and used two triggers, one for automatic fire and the other for single shots.***

France's effort after World War I to develop an effective light machine-gun led to a weapon whose action was based on that of the BAR but altered to suit the new French 7.5-mm (0.295-in) cartridge. The first model was the **Fusil Mitrailleur modèle 1924** (Automatic Rifle M1924). The design was modern and used an overhead 25- or 26-round box magazine. Separate triggers provided single-shot or automatic fire.

### Teething problems

Neither the gun nor the cartridge was fully developed before introduction to service, resulting in barrel explosions. The solution was found in reducing the power of the cartridge and beefing up some of the weapon's parts to create the **Fusil Mitrailleur modèle 1924/29**. A special variant of the mle 1924/29 was produced, initially for use in the Maginot Line defences but then also for tanks and other AFVs, as the **Mitrailleuse modèle 1931**. The mle 1931 had a peculiarly shaped butt and a prominent side-mounted 150-round drum magazine. The internal arrangements were the same as those of the mle 1924/29, even if the overall length and barrel length were increased. In static defences the increased weight was no handicap and the mle 1931 was produced in large numbers.

### German service

France's defeat in June 1940 yielded large numbers of mle 1924/29 and mle 1931 weapons that the Germans used as the **leichte MG 116(f)** and **Kpfw MG 331(f)** respectively. Only a relatively few remained in French hands in the Middle East and North Africa. After 1945 the mle 1924/29 was returned to production and remained in service for many years.

The German booty of 1940 meant that many mle 1924/29s and mle 1931 machine-guns were later incorporated into the defences of the Atlantic Wall, and the mle 1931 was especially favoured by the Germans as an anti-aircraft weapon. But for all this widespread use the mle 1924/29 and mle 1931 were never entirely trouble-free, and their cartridge was generally underpowered and lacking in range: maximum useful range was only 500 to 550 m (550 to 600 yards) instead of the 600 m (655 yards) or more of many contemporary designs.

**SPECIFICATION**

**Fusil Mitrailleur mle 1924/29**
**Calibre:** 7.5-mm (0.295-in)
**Length overall:** 1007 mm (39.6 in)
**Length of barrel:** 500 mm (19.69 in)
**Weight:** 8.93 kg (19.7 lb)
**Muzzle velocity:** 820 m (2,690 ft) per second
**Rate of fire, cyclic:** 450-600 rpm
**Feed:** 25-round box

**Mitrailleuse mle 1931**
**Calibre:** 7.5-mm (0.295-in)
**Length overall:** 1030 mm (40.55 in)
**Length of barrel:** 600 mm (23.6 in)
**Weight:** 11.8 kg (26.0 lb)
**Muzzle velocity:** 850 m (2,790 ft) per second
**Rate of fire, cyclic:** 750 rpm
**Feed:** 150-round drum

# Breda Machine-guns

***A 6.5-mm (0.256-in) Breda modello 30 light machine-gun, one of the least successful machine-guns ever designed. Despite a litany of faults, the gun served the Italians throughout World War II.***

During World War I the standard Italian machine-gun was the water-cooled Fiat modello 1914, and after the war this was modernised as the air-cooled Mitriaglice Fiat modello 1914/35. It was heavy, even in its new air-cooled form, and the design of a new light machine-gun was initiated. This was produced by Breda, which used the experience gained by the production of earlier models in 1924, 1928 and 1929 to produce the **Fucile Mitriagliatori Breda modello 30** that became the Italians' standard light machine-gun.

## Many design failings

The modello 30 was one of those machine-gun designs that could at best be deemed unsatisfactory. In appearance it looked to be all odd shapes and projections, and this was no doubt a hindrance to anyone who had to carry it as these projections snagged on clothing and other equipment. But this was not all, for the designers introduced a novel feed system using 20-round chargers which were rather flimsy and gave frequent trouble. These chargers were fed into a folding magazine that had a delicate hinge, and if this magazine or the fitting was damaged the gun could not be used.

To compound this problem, the extraction of the used cartridge cases was the weakest part of the whole gas-operated mechanism, and to make the gun work an internal oil pump was used to lubricate the spent cases and so aid extraction. While this system worked in theory, the added oil soon picked up dust and other debris to clog the mechanism, and in North Africa sand was an ever-present threat. As if this were not enough, the barrel-change method, although operable, was rendered awkward by the fact that there was no barrel handle (and thus no carrying handle), so the operator had to use gloves. With no other type in production the modello 30 had to be tolerated, and there was even a later **modello 38** version in 7.35-mm (0.29-in) calibre.

The other two Breda machine-guns were better than the modello 30. One was the **Mitrigliera Breda RM modello 31**, produced for mounting on the light tanks operated by the Italian army. This had a 12.7-mm (0.5-in) calibre and used a large curved vertical box magazine that must have restricted the weapon's use in AFV interiors.

## Heavy machine-gun

As a heavy machine-gun the company produced the **Mitragliace Breda modello 37**. In overall terms this was a satisfactory weapon, but was tactically hampered by its unusual feed arrangement: a flat 20-round feed tray which worked its way through the receiver to accept the spent cartridge cases. Exactly why this complex and quite unnecessary system was adopted is now impossible to ascertain, for the spent cases had to be removed from the tray before it could be reloaded with fresh rounds. The oil-pump extraction method was retained, thereby rendering the modello 37 prone to the same debris clogging as the lighter modello 30. Thus the modello 37 was no more than adequate, even though the type became the Italian army's standard heavy machine-gun.

A version of the modello 37 for tank mountings was produced as the **Mitriaglice Breda modello 38**.

**SPECIFICATION**

| modello 30 | modello 37 |
|---|---|
| **Calibre:** 6.5-mm (0.256-in) | **Calibre:** 8-mm (0.315-in) |
| **Length overall:** 1232 mm (48.5 in) | **Length overall:** 1270 mm (50 in) |
| **Length of barrel:** 520 mm (20.47 in) | **Length of barrel:** 740 mm (29.13 in) |
| **Weight:** 10.32 kg (22.75 lb) | **Weights:** gun 19.4 kg (42.8 lb) and tripod 18.7 kg (41.2 lb) |
| **Muzzle velocity:** 629 m (2,065 ft) per second | **Muzzle velocity:** 790 m (2,590 ft) per second |
| **Rate of fire, cyclic:** 450-500 rpm | **Rate of fire, cyclic:** 450-500 rpm |
| **Feed:** 20-round charger | **Feed:** 20-round tray |

# Type 11 & Type 96 Light machine-guns

***The Japanese 6.5-mm (0.256-in) Type 96 light machine-gun was one of the few machine-guns ever equipped with a bayonet, and was a combination of Czechoslovak and French designs.***

The heavy machine-guns the Japanese used between 1941 and 1945 were both derivatives of the French Hotchkiss machine-gun. When it came to lighter machine-guns, the Japanese designed their own, the first of which was based on the same operating principles as the Hotchkiss but with the usual local variations.

The first of these was the 6.5-mm (0.256-in) **Light Machine-Gun Type 11** that entered service in 1922 and remained in service until 1945. Its Hotchkiss origins were readily apparent in the heavily ribbed barrel and less obviously in the internal mechanisms. The design was credited to General Kijiro Nambu and it was as the 'Nambu' that the type was known to the Allies.

It was in its ammunition feed system that the Type 11 was unique, for it used a hopper system employed by no other machine-gun. The idea was that a small hopper on the left of the receiver could be kept filled with the rounds fired by the rest of the Japanese infantry squad. The rounds could be fed into the hopper still in their five-round clips, thus rendering special magazines or ammunition belts unnecessary. But in practice this advantage was negated by the fact that the internal mechanism was so delicate and complex that firing the standard rifle round caused problems. Thus a special low-powered round had to be used, and matters were exacerbated by having to use a cartridge lubrication system that attracted the usual dust and other action-clogging debris.

## Automatic fire only

The Type 11 was capable only of automatic fire, and when the weapon was fired the ammunition hopper tended to make the whole system unbalanced and awkward to fire. A special version, the **Tank Machine-Gun Type 91**, was produced for use in tanks, with a 50-round hopper.

The bad points of the Type 11 became very apparent after early combat experience in China during the 1930s, and in 1936 there appeared a new **Light Machine-Gun Type 96**. While the Type 96 was a definite improvement on the Type 11, it did not replace the earlier model in service as Japanese industry could never produce enough weapons of any type to meet demand.

The Type 96 used a mix of features from Hotchkiss and Czechoslovak ZB vz 26 weapons. One of the latter was the overhead box magazine that replaced the hopper of the Type 11, but internally the cartridge-oiling system had to be retained along with the attendant clogging. But the Type 96 did have a quick-change barrel system and there was a choice of drum or telescopic rear sights. The telescopic sights soon became the exception, but a handy magazine-filling device was retained. One accessory that was unique to the Type 96 among all other machine-gun designs was that it had a muzzle attachment to take a bayonet.

**SPECIFICATION**

| Light Machine-Gun Type 11 | Light Machine-Gun Type 96 |
|---|---|
| **Calibre:** 6.5-mm (0.256-in) | **Calibre:** 6.5-mm (0.256-in) |
| **Length overall:** 1105 mm (43.5 in) | **Length overall:** 1054 mm (41.5 in) |
| **Length of barrel:** 483 mm (19.0 in) | **Length of barrel:** 552 mm (21.75 in) |
| **Weight:** 10.2 kg (22.5 lb) | **Weight:** 9.07 kg (20 lb) |
| **Muzzle velocity:** 700 m (2,295 ft) per second | **Muzzle velocity:** 730 m (2,395 ft) per second |
| **Rate of fire, cyclic:** 500 rpm | **Rate of fire, cyclic:** 550 rpm |
| **Feed:** 30-round hopper | **Feed:** 30-round box |

# Browning Automatic Rifle

***The Browning Automatic Rifle M1918A2. This last production variant of the BAR light machine-gun and/or automatic assault rifle used a 20-round box magazine and lacked the rapid-change barrel of other more modern light machine-guns.***

The **Browning Automatic Rifle**, or **BAR** as it is usually known, is one of those odd weapons that falls into no precise category. It may be regarded as a rather light machine-gun or as a rather heavy assault rifle, but in practice it was generally used as a light machine-gun.

As its name implies, the BAR was a product of John M. Browning's inventive mind, and Browning produced the first prototypes in 1917. When demonstrated they were immediately adopted for US Army service and were thus taken to France for active use during 1918. But the numbers involved at that time were not large, and the few used were employed as heavy rifles. This was not surprising as the first variant was the **BAR M1918** that had no bipod and could be fired only from the hip or shoulder. A bipod was not introduced until 1937 with the **BAR M1918A1**, and the BAR **M1918A2** final production version had a revised bipod and the facility for a monopod stock rest to be added for added stability. It was the M1918A1 and M1918A2 that were to become the main American operational models, and they were issued to bolster squad fire power rather than as a squad support weapon.

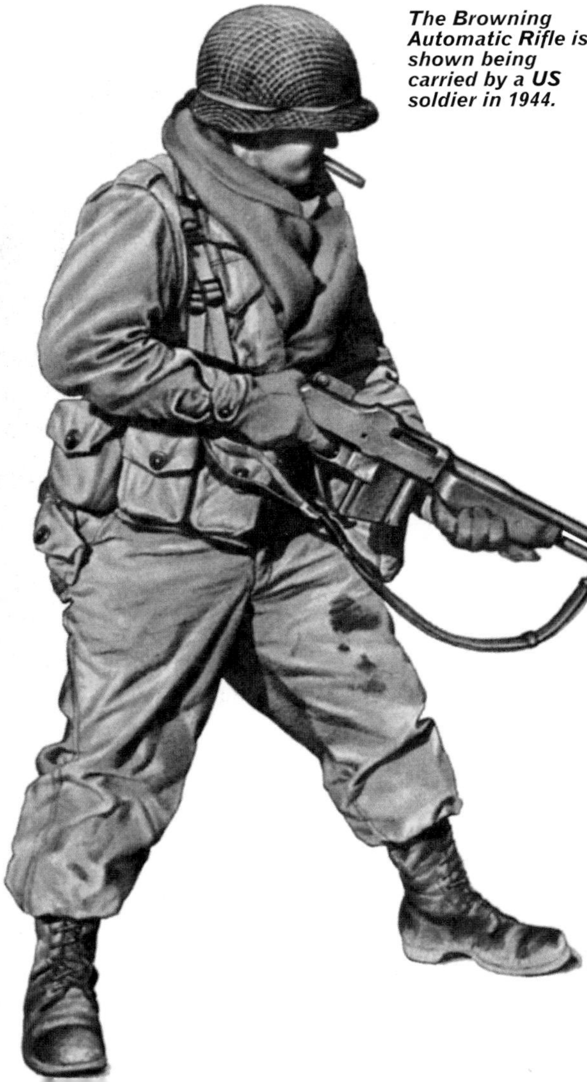

***The Browning Automatic Rifle is shown being carried by a US soldier in 1944.***

***Combining assault rifle and light machine-gun capabilities, the Browning Automatic Rifle was popular with its users in two world wars. Its weakest point was a magazine holding only 20 rounds.***

The original M1918 did have a role to play in World War II, for the type was delivered to the UK in 1940 to provide additional fire-power for the British Home Guard, and some found their way into other second-line use. The later models were produced in considerable numbers and, once in service in large numbers, they became a weapon upon which soldiers came to rely.

## Not enough rounds

This is not to say that the BAR did not have faults, for the box magazine had a capacity of only 20 rounds, which was far too limited for most infantry operations. Created as something of an interim weapon, the BAR had few tactical adherents in the theoretical field, but soldiers swore by the BAR and always wanted more.

The BAR was used again in Korea in the early 1950s and was not replaced in US Army service until 1957.

## Belgian manufacture

One little-known facet of BAR production is the pre-1939 output of a Belgian **modèle 30** variant by Fabrique Nationale. From this source there emerged a string of BAR models in various calibres for many armies. Poland set up an assembly line for the BAR in 7.92-mm (0.312-in) calibre rather than the 7.65 mm (0.3 in) typical of Belgian production.

Many Polish BARs ended in Soviet hands after 1939, and even the German army used BARs captured from a variety of sources. The Poles thought very highly of the BAR and even mounted the weapon on a specially produced, very complex and heavy tripod; there was also a special anti-aircraft version.

### SPECIFICATION

**BAR M1918A2**
**Calibre:** 0.3-in (7.62-mm)
**Length overall:** 1214 mm (47.8 in)
**Length of barrel:** 610 mm (24.0 in)
**Weight:** 8.8 kg (19.4 lb)
**Muzzle velocity:** 808 m (2,650 ft) per second
**Rate of fire, cyclic:** 500-600 rpm (fast rate) or 300-450 rpm (slow rate)
**Feed:** 20-round straight box

***The M1918A2 variant of the BAR was introduced shortly before World War II, and brought in a number of changes. The most readily seen of these was the mounting of the bipod on the cylindrical flash hider.***

# Browning M1919 Machine-gun

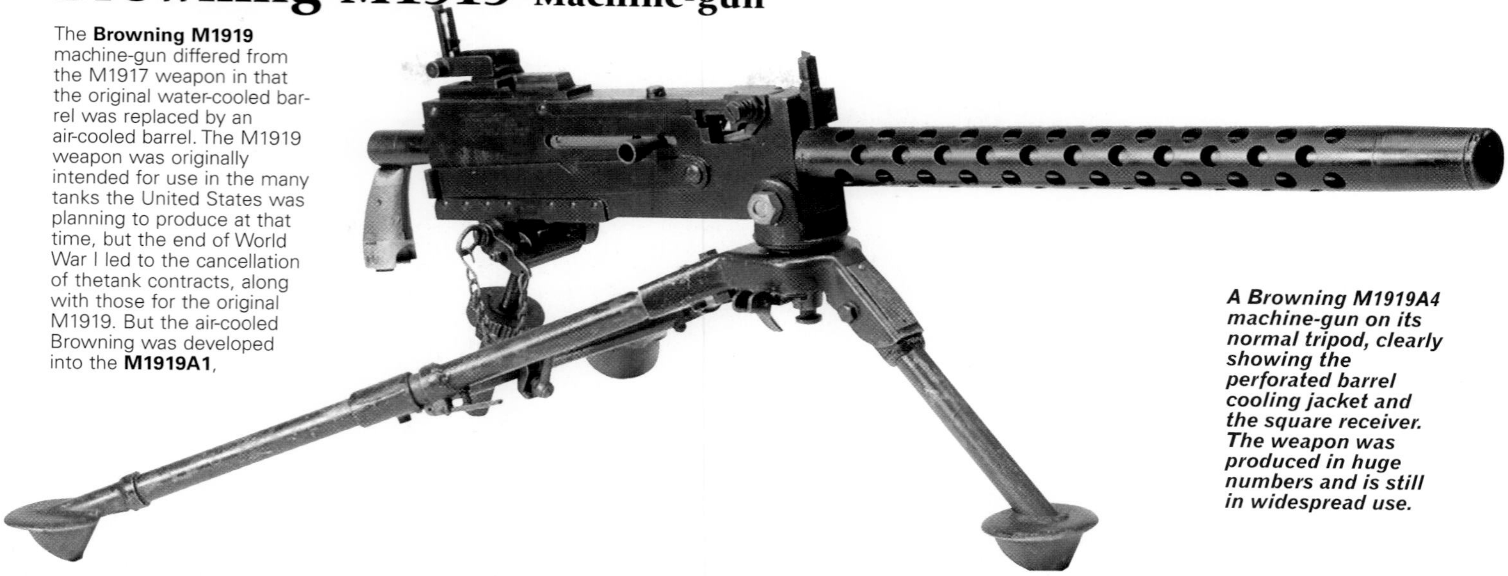

*A Browning M1919A4 machine-gun on its normal tripod, clearly showing the perforated barrel cooling jacket and the square receiver. The weapon was produced in huge numbers and is still in widespread use.*

The **Browning M1919** machine-gun differed from the M1917 weapon in that the original water-cooled barrel was replaced by an air-cooled barrel. The M1919 weapon was originally intended for use in the many tanks the United States was planning to produce at that time, but the end of World War I led to the cancellation of thetank contracts, along with those for the original M1919. But the air-cooled Browning was developed into the **M1919A1**, **M1919A2** (for use by the US Cavalry) and then **M1919A3**. The production totals for these early models were never very high, but with the **M1919A4** the totals soared. By 1945 the production total stood at 438,971, and more have been produced after that.

The M1919A4 was produced mainly for infantry use, and proved to be a first-class heavy machine-gun capable of pouring out masses of fire and absorbing all manner of abuse and punishment. As a partner for this infantry version, a special model for use on tanks was produced as the **M1919A5**. There was also a US Army Air Corps model, the **M2**, for use in both fixed and trainable installations, and the US Navy had its own range based on the M1919A4 and known as the **AN-M2**.

Among all these types, and in such a long production run, there were numerous minor and major modifications and production alterations, but the basic M1919 design was retained throughout. The M1919 used a fabric or metal-link belt feed. The normal mount was a tripod, and of these there were many designs ranging from normal infantry tripods to large and complex anti-aircraft mountings. There were ring- and gallows-type mountings for use on all sorts of trucks from jeeps to fuel tankers, and there were numerous special mountings for all manner of small craft.

## Light machine-gun

Perhaps the strangest of the M1919 variants was the **M1919A6**. This was produced as a form of light machine-gun to bolster infantry squad power, which until the introduction of the M1919A6 had to depend on the firepower of the BAR and the rifle. The M1919A6 was a 1943 innovation: it was basically the M1919A4 fitted with an awkward-looking shoulder stock, a bipod, a carrying handle and a lighter barrel. The result was a light machine-gun that was rather heavy but at least had the advantage that it could be produced quickly on existing production lines. Disadvantages were the general awkwardness of the weapon and the need to wear a mitten to change the barrel after it had become hot. Despite these factors, the M1919A6 was churned out in large numbers (43,479 by the time production ended), and troops had to put up with it as it was better in its role than the BAR.

If there was one overall asset that was enjoyed by all the versions of the M1919 series of machine-guns it was reliability, for the types would carry on working even in conditions in which other designs (other than perhaps the Vickers) would have given up. They all used the same recoil method of operation: muzzle gases push back the entire barrel and breech mechanism until a bolt accelerator continues the rearward movement to a point at which springs return the whole mechanism to restart the process.

The M1919 series (including the unlovely M1919A6) is still in widespread use, the M1919A6 is now being used by only a few South American states.

*A Jeep of the Long Range Desert Group armed with Vickers-Berthier G.O. machine-guns and also with a Browning M1919A4 mounted at the front; this gun has every appearance of being adapted from an aircraft mounting.*

*Despite the fact that it was an air- rather than water-cooled weapon, the Browning M1919A4 was a capable machine-gun for the sustained-fire role. Ammunition was delivered in boxed fabric or metal-link belts.*

**SPECIFICATION**

**Browning M1919A4**
**Calibre:** 0.3-in (7.62-mm)
**Length overall:** 1041 mm (41 in)
**Length of barrel:** 610 mm (24 in)
**Weight:** 14.06 kg (31 lb)
**Muzzle velocity:** 854 m (2,800 ft) per second
**Rate of fire, cyclic:** 400-500 rpm
**Feed:** 250-round fabric or metal-link belt

**Browning M1919A6**
**Calibre:** 0.3-in (7.62-mm)
**Length overall:** 1346 mm (53 in)
**Length of barrel:** 610 mm (24 in)
**Weight:** 14.74 kg (32.5 lb)
**Muzzle velocity:** 854 m (2,800 ft) per second
**Rate of fire, cyclic:** 400-500 rpm
**Feed:** 250-round fabric or metal-link belt

# Browning 0.5-in (12.7-mm) Heavy machine-gun

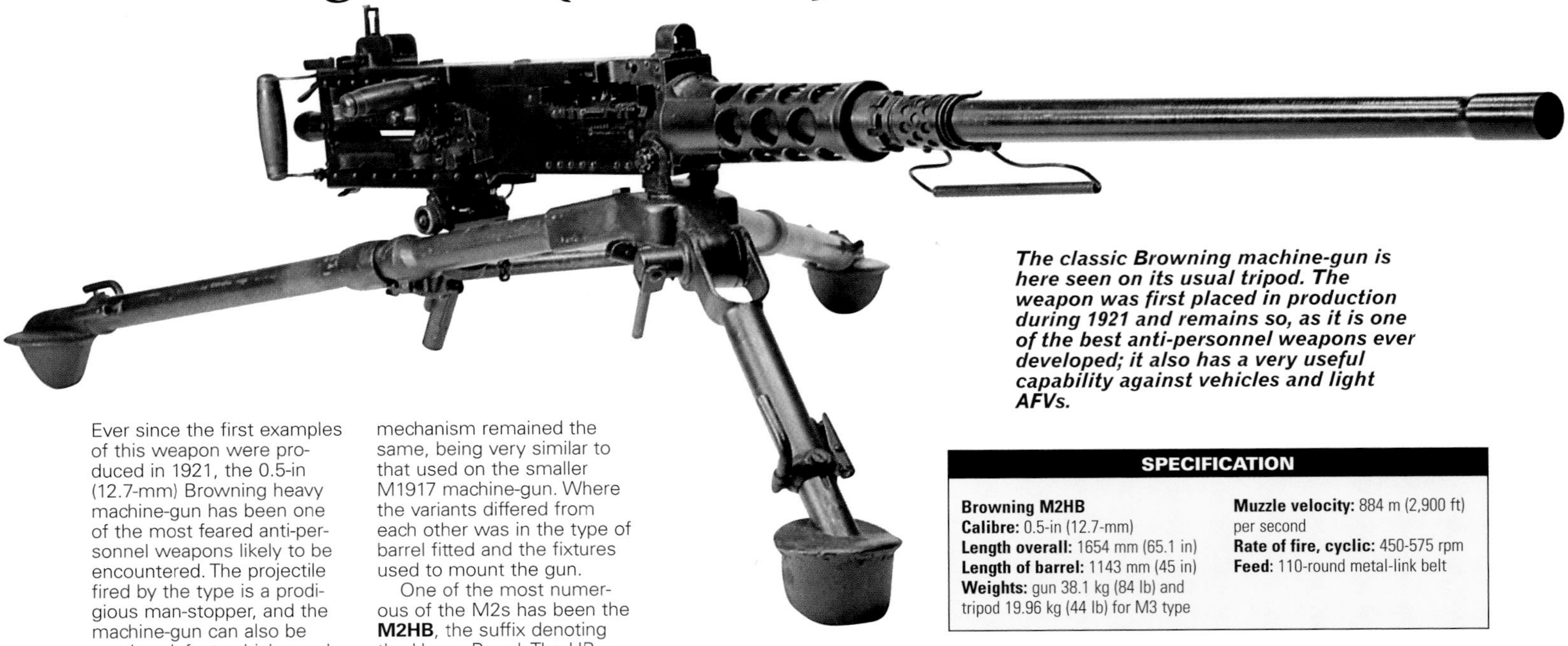

***The classic Browning machine-gun is here seen on its usual tripod. The weapon was first placed in production during 1921 and remains so, as it is one of the best anti-personnel weapons ever developed; it also has a very useful capability against vehicles and light AFVs.***

Ever since the first examples of this weapon were produced in 1921, the 0.5-in (12.7-mm) Browning heavy machine-gun has been one of the most feared anti-personnel weapons likely to be encountered. The projectile fired by the type is a prodigious man-stopper, and the machine-gun can also be used to defeat vehicles and light armour, especially when firing armour-piercing rounds. The round is really the heart of the gun and early attempts by Browning to produce a heavy machine-gun all foundered on the lack of a suitable cartridge.

## German round

It was not until the examination of a captured German round, the 13-mm (0.51-in) type fired by the Mauser T-Gewehr anti-tank rifle, that the solution was found, and thereafter all was well. The basic cartridge has remained essentially unchanged, although there have been numerous alternative propellants and projectile types.

From the original **Browning M1921** heavy machine-gun evolved a whole string of variants based on what was to become known as the **M2**. On all these variants the gun mechanism remained the same, being very similar to that used on the smaller M1917 machine-gun. Where the variants differed from each other was in the type of barrel fitted and the fixtures used to mount the gun.

One of the most numerous of the M2s has been the **M2HB**, the suffix denoting the Heavy Barrel. The HB version can be used in all manner of installations, and in the past has been employed as an infantry gun, as an anti-aircraft gun and also as a fixed and trainable aircraft gun. For infantry use the M2HB is usually mounted on a heavy tripod, but it can also be used mounted on vehicle pintles, ring mountings and pivots. Other M2s have included versions with water-cooled barrels, usually employed as anti-aircraft weapons, especially on US Navy vessels on which in World War II they were often fixed in multiple mountings for use against low-flying attack aircraft. Single water-cooled mountings were often used to provide anti-aircraft defence for shore installations.

## Barrel lengths

The main change between ground and air versions is that the aircraft model has a barrel 914 mm (36 in) long whereas the ground version had a barrel 1143 mm (45 in) long. Apart from the barrel and some mounting fixtures, any part of the M1921 and M2 machine-guns are interchangeable.

More 0.5-in Browning machine-guns have been produced in the USA than any other design. The figure runs into millions, and during the late 1970s two US companies found it worth putting the type back into production. The same was true of the Belgian FN concern.

There are many companies throughout the world who find it profitable to provide spares and other such backing for the M2, and ammunition producers frequently introduce new types of cartridge. Many dealers find it profitable just to sell or purchase such weapons alone. The M2 will be around for decades to come, and there is no sign of any replacement entering the lists. It is true to say that the M2 must rank as one of the most successful machine-gun designs ever produced.

**SPECIFICATION**

**Browning M2HB**
**Calibre:** 0.5-in (12.7-mm)
**Length overall:** 1654 mm (65.1 in)
**Length of barrel:** 1143 mm (45 in)
**Weights:** gun 38.1 kg (84 lb) and tripod 19.96 kg (44 lb) for M3 type
**Muzzle velocity:** 884 m (2,900 ft) per second
**Rate of fire, cyclic:** 450-575 rpm
**Feed:** 110-round metal-link belt

***A Browning M2 heavy machine-gun team of the US army in action: the tripod mount is low to the ground, and no doubt there is a plentiful supply of ammunition to hand.***

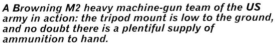

***This anti-aircraft mounting, known as the M45 Maxson Mount, carried four Browning M2HB machine-guns.***

# Bren Light machine-gun

The **Bren Gun** was evolved from the Czechoslovak ZB vz 26 light machine-gun, but the development path was one that involved as much British as Czechoslovak expertise. During the 1920s the British army sought far and wide for a new light machine-gun to replace the generally unsatisfactory Lewis Gun, trying all manner of designs of which most were found wanting in some way or other. In 1930 there began a series of trials involving several designs, among them the vz 26 in the form of a slightly revised model, the vz 27. The vz 27 emerged as a clear winner from these trials. It was made only in 7.92-mm (0.312-in) calibre, though, and the British army wanted to retain the 0.303-in (7.7-mm) cartridge with its outdated cordite propellant and its awkward rimmed case.

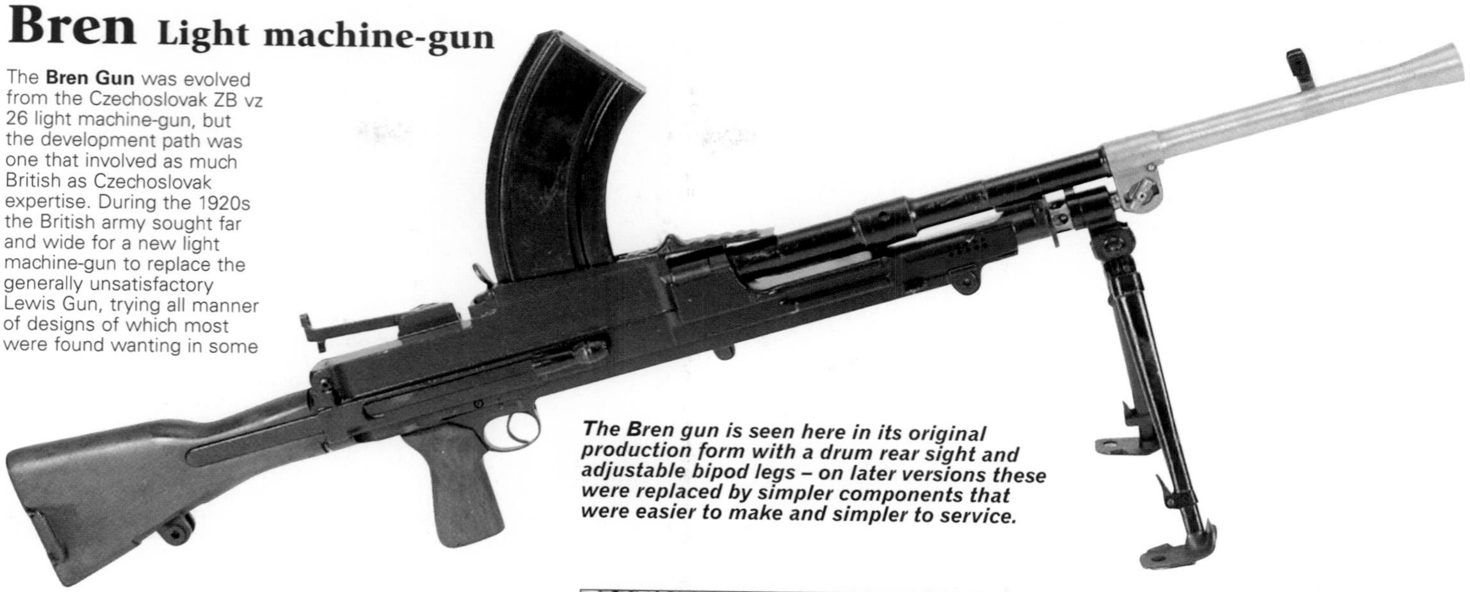

*The Bren gun is seen here in its original production form with a drum rear sight and adjustable bipod legs – on later versions these were replaced by simpler components that were easier to make and simpler to service.*

Thus started a series of development models that involved the vz 27, the later vz 30 and eventually an interim model, the vz 32. Then came the vz 33, and it was from this that the Royal Small Arms Factory at Enfield Lock evolved the prototype of what became the Bren Gun (Bren from the 'Br' of Brno, the place of origin, and the 'en' of Enfield Lock). Tooling up at Enfield Lock resulted in the completion in 1937 of the first production **Bren Gun Mk 1**, and thereafter the type remained in production at Enfield and elsewhere until well after 1945. By 1940 well over 30,000 Bren Guns had been produced and the type was firmly established in service, but the result of Dunkirk gave the Germans a useful stock of Bren Guns, for service with the revised designation **leichte MG 138(e)**, and ammunition, and also led to a great demand for new Bren Guns to re-equip the British army.

## Simplified design

The original design was thus much modified to speed production, and new lines were established. The original gas-operated mechanism of the ZB design was retained, as were the the breech locking system and general appearance, but out went the rather complicated drum sights and extras such as the under-butt handle in the **Bren Gun Mk 2**. The bipod became much simpler but the curved box magazine of the 0.303-in Bren was carried over. In time more simplifications were made (**Bren Gun Mk 3** with a shorter barrel and **Bren Gun Mk 4** with a modified butt assembly), and there was even a reversion to the 7.92-mm calibre when Bren Guns were manufactured in Canada for China.

*A combined American and Australian infantry attack in close New Guinea terrain benefits from the fire support of a bipod-mounted Bren light machine-gun.*

## Classic of its type

The Bren Gun was a superb light machine-gun. It was robust, reliable, easy to handle and to maintain, and it was not too heavy for its role. It was also very accurate. In time a whole range of mountings and accessories was introduced, including some rather complex anti-aircraft mountings that included the Motley and the Gallows mountings. A 200-round drum was developed but little used, and various vehicle mountings were designed and introduced. The Bren Gun outlived all these accessories, for after 1945 the type remained in service and the wartime 'extras' were phased out as being irrelevant to the increasingly 'hi-tech' modern battlefield, and also costly to maintain.

The Bren Gun on its basic bipod did linger on, however, and is still in limited service with some armies as the Bren Gun L4 series. It has revisions to fire the NATO standard 7.62-mm (0.3-in) cartridge through a barrel chrome-plated to reduce wear; its barrels are changed during prolonged fire using the simple barrel-change device.

*Against a backdrop of palms and a Stuart light tank, Australians attack a Japanese strongpoint in New Guinea. The men in the foreground have Bren light machine-guns.*

**SPECIFICATION**

**Bren Light Machine-Gun Mk 1**
**Calibre:** 0.303-in (7.7-mm)
**Length overall:** 1156 mm (45.5 in)
**Length of barrel:** 635 mm (25 in)
**Weight:** 10.03 kg (22.12 lb)
**Muzzle velocity:** 744 m (2,440 ft) per second
**Rate of fire, cyclic:** 500 rpm
**Feed:** 20-round curved box magazine

# Vickers Machine-guns

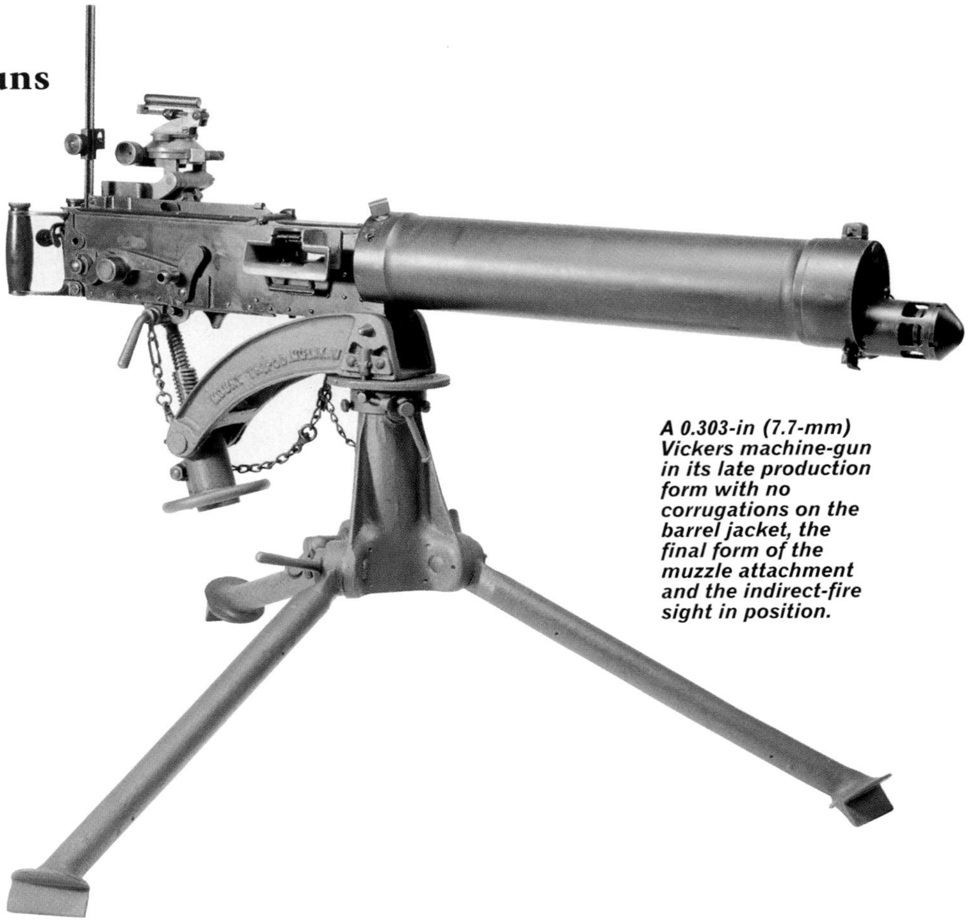

**A 0.303-in (7.7-mm) Vickers machine-gun in its late production form with no corrugations on the barrel jacket, the final form of the muzzle attachment and the indirect-fire sight in position.**

The series of Vickers machine-guns had its origins in the Maxim gun of the late 19th century, and was little changed from the original other than that the Maxim locking toggle design was inverted in the Vickers product. The **Vickers Machine-Gun Mk 1** had done magnificently in World War I, out-performing nearly all of its contemporaries in many respects. After 1918, therefore, the Vickers remained the standard heavy machine-gun of both the British army and many of the Commonwealth forces. Many were exported all over the world but much of these were ex-stock weapons as production was kept at a very low ebb at Vickers' main production plant at Crayford in Kent.

However, some innovations were introduced before 1939; the introduction of the tank in all its various forms had led to the design of Vickers machine-guns to arm the new fighting machines, and by 1939 Vickers had in production two types of special tank machine-gun.

## Two calibres

These were produced in two calibres: the **Vickers Machine-Gun Mks 4B, 6, 6*** and **7** were of 0.303-in (7.7-mm) calibre and the **Vickers Machine-Gun Mks 4** and **5** of 0.5-in (12.7-mm) calibre to fire a special cartridge. Both were produced for all types of tank initially, but the introduction of the Besa air-cooled machine-guns for use in most heavier tanks meant that the majority of the Vickers tank machine-guns ended either in light tanks, or infantry tank types such as the Matilda 1 and 2. The 0.5-in machine-guns were also produced in a variety of forms for the Royal Navy as the **Vickers Machine-Gun Mk 3** for installation on several types of mounting for the anti-aircraft defence of ships and shore installations. The ship installations included quadruple mountings, but the cartridge produced for this weapon was underpowered and therefore not a success. Nevertheless, in the absence of any alternative, the weapon was produced in considerable numbers, only later being replaced by 20-mm cannon and other such weapons.

Thus 1939 found the Vickers machine-gun still in large-scale service. By 1940 stockpiled older weapons were being used in a host of roles including emergency anti-aircraft mountings to bolster home defences, and large-scale manufacture was soon under way once more. Demand was so heavy, most of the British army's machine-gun stocks having been before or during the Dunkirk episode, that production shortcuts were introduced. The most obvious of these was the replacement of the corrugated water jacket round the barrel by a simpler smooth jacket. Later a new muzzle booster design was introduced and by 1943 the new Mk 8Z boat-tailed bullet was in widespread use to provide a useful effective range of 4115 m (4,500 yards), enabling the Vickers machine-gun to be used for the indirect fire role once a mortar sight had been adapted for the role.

After World War II the Vickers served on (and still does) with armies such as those of India and Pakistan. The British army ceased to use the type in 1968 but the Royal Marines continued to use theirs until well into the 1970s.

***Above:** The machine-gun seen here is not the usual 0.303-in (7.7-mm) version but a heavier 0.5-in (12.7-mm) version which was originally produced for use as light tank armament.*

***Right:** Men of the Cheshire Regiment using their Vickers machine-guns on a range, circa 1940; note the water cans to condense steam from the barrel jacket back into cooling water.*

### SPECIFICATION

**Vickers Machine-Gun Mk 1**
**Calibre:** 0.303-in (7.7-mm)
**Length overall:** 1156 mm (45.5 in)
**Length of barrel:** 721 mm (28.4 in)
**Weight: gun** 18.1 kg (40 lb) with water, and tripod 22 kg (48.5 lb)
**Muzzle velocity:** 744 m (2,440 ft) per second
**Rate of fire, cyclic:** 450-500 rpm
**Feed:** 250-round fabric belt

# Vickers-Berthier Light machine-guns

The Vickers-Berthier Mk 3B produced for the Indian Army, showing the overall clean lines and general resemblance to the Bren Gun. The 30-round box magazine is not fitted.

The Vickers-Berthier series of light machine-guns was evolved from a French design of just before World War I. Despite some promising features, the design was not adopted in numbers by any nation, but in 1925 the British Vickers company purchased rights to the type, mainly to give its Crayford factory a new model to replace the Vickers machine-gun. After a series of British army trials the type was adopted by the Indian Army as its standard light machine-gun, and eventually a production line for this **Vickers-Berthier Light Machine-Gun Mk 3** was established at Ishapore in India.

## Bren similarities

In general appearance and design the Vickers-Berthier light machine-gun was similar to the Bren Gun, but internally and in detail there were many differences. Thus at times observers thought that the Vickers-Berthier weapon was a Bren Gun.

Apart from the large Indian Army contract the only other sales were to a few Baltic and South American states, and today the Vickers-Berthier is one of the least known of all World War II machine guns. This is not because there was anything wrong with the type, which was a sound and reliable design, but because it had poor 'press' coverage and numerically was well outnumbered by the Bren Gun. But even today it remains in reserve use in India.

There was one Vickers-Berthier gun derivative that did, however, obtain a much better showing. This was a much modified version of the basic design with a large drum magazine mounted above the receiver, and a spade grip at the rear where the butt would normally have been fitted. The weapon was a special design for installation on a Scarff ring mounting on open-cockpit aircraft, in which it would be used by the observer/gunner.

## Aircraft use

Large numbers of this design were produced for the Royal Air Force, by which it was known as the Vickers G.O (G.O. for gas operated) or **Vickers K** gun, but almost as soon as the type had been introduced to service the era of the open cockpit came to a sudden close with the introduction of higher-speed aircraft. The G.O. proved difficult to use in the close confines of aircraft turrets and impossible to use in wing installations, so almost immediately it was placed in store; some were used by the Fleet Air arm on aircraft such as the Fairey Swordfish and thus remained in use until 1945, but their numbers were relatively few.

In 1940 many G.O. guns were taken out of store for extensive use in the airfield defence and related roles. In North Africa the G.O. was widely used by the irregular forces that sprang up for behind-the-lines operations, such as 'Popski's Private Army', on heavily armed jeeps and trucks. The weapon proved ideal in the role and gave a good indication of how the original Vickers-Berthier machine-guns would have performed given a greater opportunity. The G.O. guns were used right until the end of the war in Italy and a few other theatres, and then passed right out of use.

This sepoy, carrying a Vickers-Berthier Mk 3, is dressed in standard issue khaki drill, with two large pouches for spare magazines. The Indian Army was the major user of the Vickers-Berthier gun.

### SPECIFICATION

| Vickers-Berthier Light Machine-Gun Mk 3 | Vickers G.O. Gun |
|---|---|
| **Calibre:** 0.303-in (7.7-mm) | **Calibre:** 0.303-in (7.7-mm) |
| **Length overall:** 1156 mm (45.5 in) | **Length overall:** 1016 mm (40 in) |
| **Length of barrel:** 600 mm (23.6 in) | **Length of barrel:** 529 mm (20.83 in) |
| **Weight:** 11.1 kg (24.4 lb) | **Weight:** 9.5 kg (21 lb) |
| **Muzzle velocity:** 745 m (2,450 ft) per second | **Muzzle velocity:** 745 m (2,450 ft) per second |
| **Rate of fire, cyclic:** 450-600 rpm | **Rate of fire, cyclic:** 1,000 rpm |
| **Feed:** 30-round box magazine | **Feed:** 96-round drum magazine |

A patrol of the newly formed SAS in North Africa in 1943. The patrol's jeeps are liberally armed with Vickers-Berthier G.O. guns carrying 96-round drum magazines.

# Maschinengewehr MG 34 General-purpose machine-gun

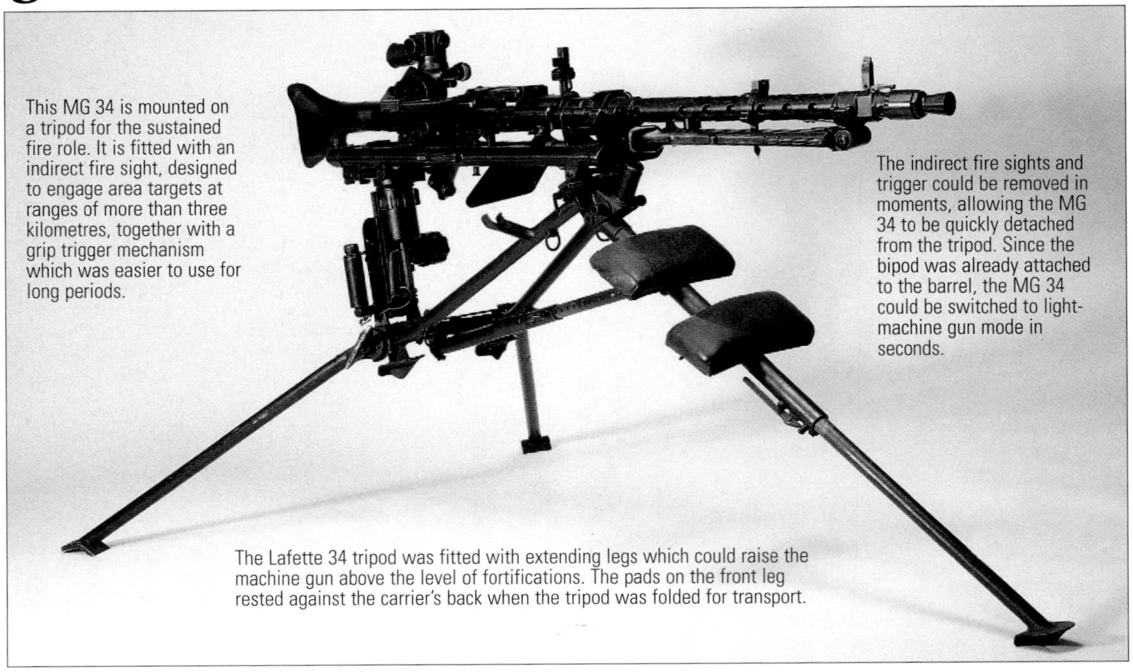

This MG 34 is mounted on a tripod for the sustained fire role. It is fitted with an indirect fire sight, designed to engage area targets at ranges of more than three kilometres, together with a grip trigger mechanism which was easier to use for long periods.

The indirect fire sights and trigger could be removed in moments, allowing the MG 34 to be quickly detached from the tripod. Since the bipod was already attached to the barrel, the MG 34 could be switched to light-machine gun mode in seconds.

The Lafette 34 tripod was fitted with extending legs which could raise the machine gun above the level of fortifications. The pads on the front leg rested against the carrier's back when the tripod was folded for transport.

The terms of the Versailles Treaty of 1919 specifically prohibited the development of any form of sustained-fire weapon by Germany. However, this provision was circumvented by the Rheinmetall-Borsig arms concern during the early 1920s by the simple expedient of setting up a 'shadow' company under its control over the border at Solothurn in Switzerland.

Research carried out into air-cooled machine-gun designs led to a weapon that evolved into the Solothurn Modell 1930, an advanced design that introduced many of the features that were incorporated in later weapons. A few production orders were received, but it was felt by the Germans that something better was required and thus the Modell 1929 had only a short production run before being used as the starting point for an aircraft machine- gun, the Rheinmetall MG 15. This long remained in production for the Luftwaffe.

## First GPMG

From the Rheinmetall designs came what remains viewed as one of the finest machine-guns ever made, the **Maschinengewehr 34** or MG 34. Mauser designers at the Obendorff plant used the Modell 1929 and the MG 15 as starting points for what was to be a new breed of weapon, the general-purpose machine gun (GPMG). Fired from a bipod, it could be carried and used by an infantry squad. Mounted on a heavier tripod it could be equally effective in providing long periods of sustained fire.

## Selective fire

The mechanism was of the all-in-line type, with a quick-change barrel for use in sustained fire. The ammunition could be fed either from a saddle-drum magazine holding 75 rounds inherited from the MG 15, or a belt feed. To add to all this technical innovation, the MG 34 had a high rate of fire and could thus be effective against low-flying aircraft.

The MG 34 was also one of the first selective-fire weapons. The trigger mechanism was hinged in the centre: pressure on the top half of the trigger gave the firer single shots, while pressure on the lower half provided fully automatic fire.

The MG 34 was an immediate success, and went straight into production for the German armed forces and police. Demand for the MG 34 remained high through to 1945, and consistently outstripped supply. The supply situation was not aided by the number of mounts and gadgets that were introduced.

These varied from heavy tripods and twin mountings to expensive and complex fortress and tank mountings. There was even a periscopic sight to enable the weapon to be fired from trenches. These accessories consumed a great deal of production potential to the detriment of gun production proper, but production of the MG 34 was in any case not aided by the fact that the design was really too good for military use.

The MG 34 took too long to manufacture, and involved too many complex and expensive machining processes. The result was a weapon without peer, but actually using it was rather like using a Rolls-Royce as a taxi – it did the job superbly, but at much too high a cost.

Variants of the basic machine gun included the **MG 34m** with a heavier barrel jacket for use in AFVs, and the shorter **MG 34s** and **MG 34/41** intended for use in the AA role and capable of automatic fire only. The overall length and barrel length of the latter two were about 1170 mm (46 in) and 560 mm (22 in) respectively.

***Right: The MG 34 was the first 'light' machine gun to use belt fed ammunition, giving it much greater firepower than its contemporaries which almost exclusively used magazines.***

***Below: Mounted on a tripod, the MG 34 was a steady and effective weapon, but its relatively light weight and high rate of fire meant that on a bipod it was less steady and could not achieve the accuracy of which it was capable.***

**SPECIFICATION**

**MG 34**
**Calibre:** 7.92 mm (0. 31 in)
**Length:** 1219 mm (48 in)
**Length of barrel:** 627 mm (24⅝ in)
**Weight:** 11.5 kg (25 lb 6 oz) with bipod
**Muzzle velocity:** 755 m (2,475 ft) per second
**Rate of fire, cyclic:** 800-900 rounds per minute
**Feed:** 250 round belt (comprising five linked 50-round belt lengths), or 75-round saddle drum
**Effective range:** 700 m (2,296 ft) direct fire, 3500 m (11,483 ft) indirect fire

# Maschinengewehr MG 42 General-purpose machine-gun

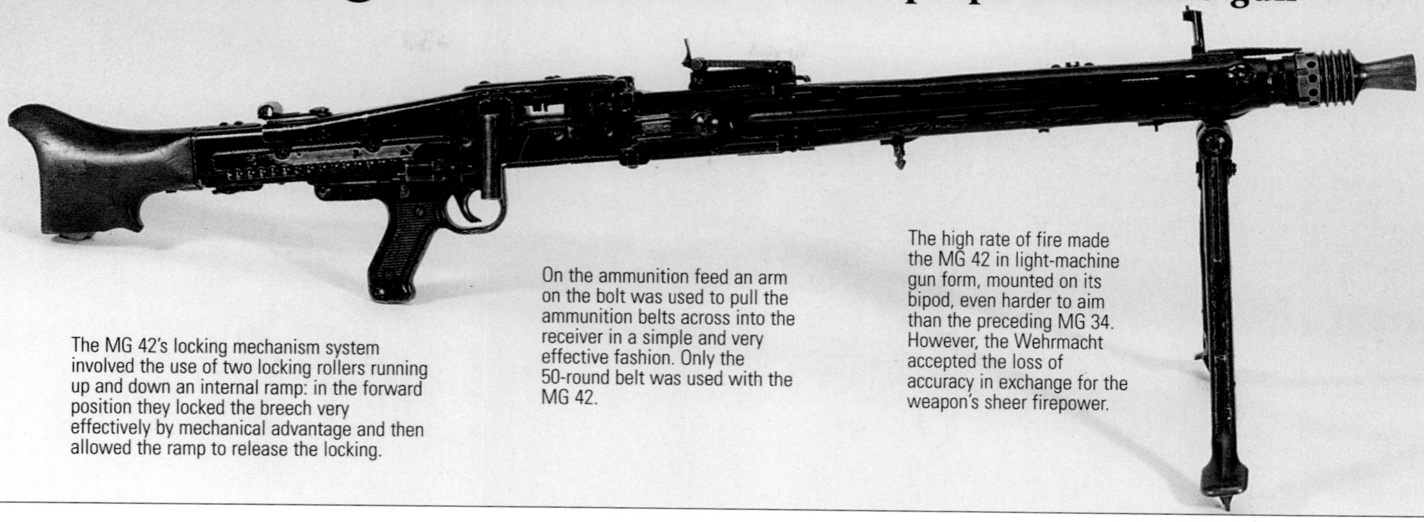

The MG 42's locking mechanism system involved the use of two locking rollers running up and down an internal ramp: in the forward position they locked the breech very effectively by mechanical advantage and then allowed the ramp to release the locking.

On the ammunition feed an arm on the bolt was used to pull the ammunition belts across into the receiver in a simple and very effective fashion. Only the 50-round belt was used with the MG 42.

The high rate of fire made the MG 42 in light-machine gun form, mounted on its bipod, even harder to aim than the preceding MG 34. However, the Wehrmacht accepted the loss of accuracy in exchange for the weapon's sheer firepower.

***German mountain troops with an MG 42. The Allies came to fear the distinctive 'ripping linoleum' sound produced by the sheer number of rounds the machine-gun could put out.***

The MG 34 was an excellent weapon but was really too good for its task in terms of cost and production requirements. Despite the setting up of a full production facility and constant demand, by 1940 the Mauser designers were examining simpler options. The manufacturers of the 9-mm MP 40 sub-machine gun had showed what could be done to introduce production simplicity and reduce cost. Following this example the Mauser designers decided to adopt new production methods using as few expensive machining processes as possible allied with new operating mechanisms.

## Hybrid design

The new mechanisms came from a number of sources. Experience with the MG 34 had indicated how the feed could be revised. Polish designs from arms factories over-run in 1939 promised a new and radical breech locking system, and other ideas came from Czechoslovakia. From this wealth of innovation came a new design, the **MG 39/41**, and out of a series of trials carried out with this design emerged the **Maschinengewehr 42** or **MG 42**, one of the most effective and influential fireams in history.

The MG 42 introduced mass production techniques to the machine-gun on a large scale. Earlier designs had used some simple sheet metal stampings and production short-cuts, but the harsh environment that the machine-gun has to endure meant that few had any success.

Unlike earlier guns made on the cheap, the MG 42 was an immediate success. Sheet metal stampings were extensively used for the receiver and for the barrel housing, which incorporated an ingenious barrel-change system. The ability to change barrels easily and quickly was vital, for the MG 42 had a prodigious rate of fire of up to 1400 rounds per minute, which was twice as fast as any Allied weapon.

## Rate of fire

This was a result of the new locking mechanism, which the designers had borrowed from several sources and was both simple and reliable.

These design details merged to form a very effective general-purpose machine-gun, which could be attached to a wide range of mounts and accessories.

The MG 42's operational debut came in 1942, appearing simultaneously in both the USSR and North Africa. Thereafter it was used on every front. In general, issue was made to front-line troops only, for though intended to supplant the MG 34, in fact the MG 42 only supplemented it.

Not content with producing one of the finest machine-gun designs ever produced, the Mauser design team tried to go one better and came up with the MG 45 with an even higher rate of fire. The end of the war put paid to that design for the time being, but the MG 42 and its descendants will continue to serve armies all over the world into the 21st century.

***Right: The MG 42 was the primary weapon of the German infantry squad. All members carried a part of the load on the move. The gunner carried the gun itself, a second man carried the tripod, and everyone in the squad carried spare links of ammunition.***

### SPECIFICATION

**MG 42**
**Calibre:** 7.92 mm (0.303 in)
**Length:** 1220 mm (48 in)
**Length of barrel:** 533 mm (21 in)
**Weight:** 11.5 kg (25 lb 6 oz) with bipod
**Muzzle velocity:** 755 m (2,475 ft) per second
**Rate of fire:** up to 1,550 rounds per minute cyclic
**Feed:** 50-round belt
**Effective range:** 3000 m (9,842 ft) indirect, 600 m (1,968 ft) direct fire

# DShK1938, SG43 & others
## Heavy machine-guns

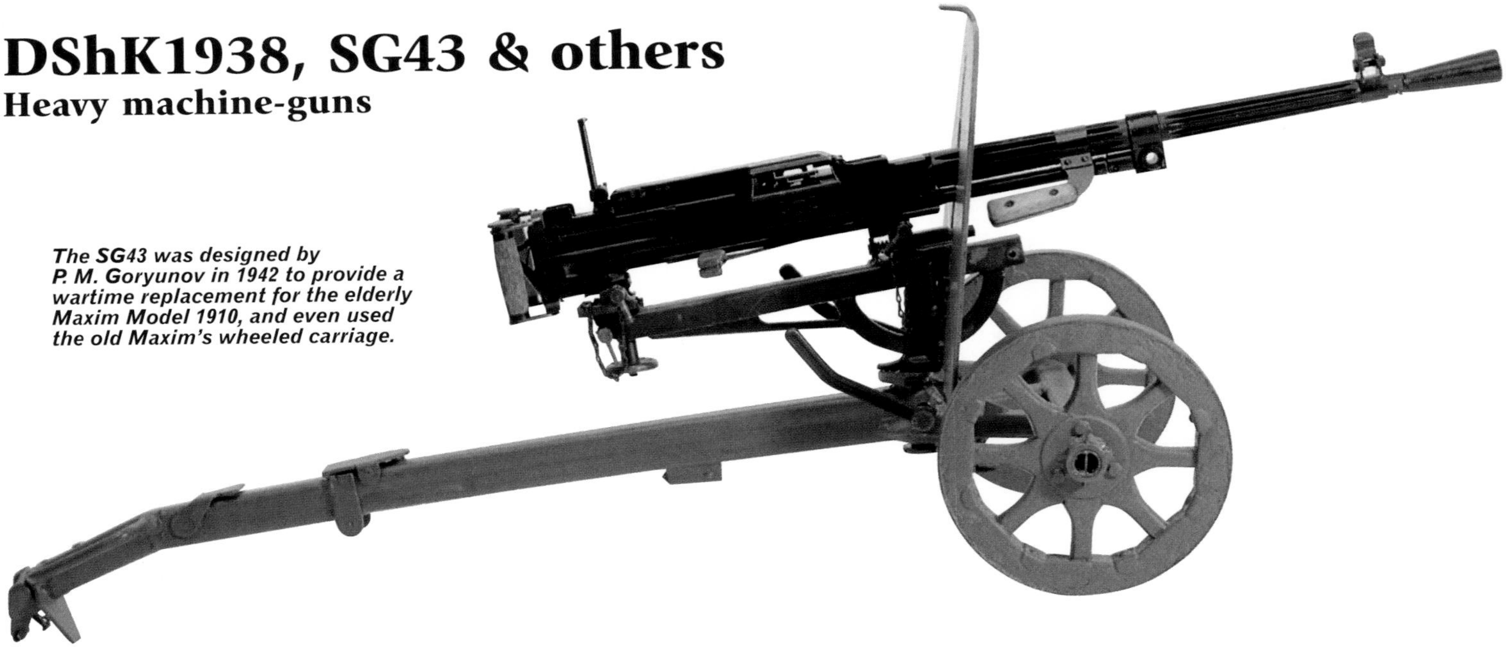

***The SG43 was designed by P. M. Goryunov in 1942 to provide a wartime replacement for the elderly Maxim Model 1910, and even used the old Maxim's wheeled carriage.***

If there has ever been a single factor differentiating machine-guns of Russian and Soviet design from those created in other nations it has been the simple factor of weight. For many years Russian and Soviet machine-guns were built to such a standard of robustness that weight alone was used as a means of incorporating strength, the ultimate example being the old M1910 Maxim guns that almost resembled small artillery pieces with their wheeled and shielded carriages. Eventually this avoidable trait was recognised by the Red Army at the time that mobility began to make its importance felt within the context of long-term planning. By the mid-1930s, when there appeared the requirement for a new heavy machine-gun, emphasis was finally placed more on strength as a factor that could be created by design rather than as a by-product of mass.

The new heavy machine-gun was intended to be in the same class as the 0.5-in (12.7-mm) Browning designed in the USA, but the Soviet equivalent turned out to be slightly lighter than its American counterpart. It used a 12.7-mm (0.5-in) cartridge and was intended for a variety of roles. To its long-lasting credit, the new **DShK1938** (in full the *Krasnoi Pulyemet Degtyereva-Shpagina obrazets 1938g*) has proved to be almost as successful as the Browning weapon, for it long remained in production, albeit in a modified form after World War II as the **DShK1938/46**, and is still in widespread service.

### Massive carriage

If the DShK1938 was lighter as a gun than the Browning, the same could not be said of its mount, for as an infantry gun the DShK1938 retained the old wheeled carriage of the M1910, although a special anti-aircraft tripod was also introduced and is still in use. The type became a virtual fixture on most Soviet tanks from the IS-2 heavy tanks onward, and Czechoslovakia produced a quadruple mounting with DShK1938s for anti-aircraft use. There was even a special version for use on armoured trains.

| SPECIFICATIONS | |
|---|---|
| **DShK1938** | **SG43** |
| **Calibre:** 12.7-mm (0.5-in) | **Calibre:** 7.62-mm (0.3-in) |
| **Length overall:** 1602 mm (63.1 in) | **Length overall:** 1120 mm (44.1 in) |
| **Length of barrel:** 1002 mm (39.45 in) | **Length of barrel:** 719 mm (28.3 in) |
| **Weight:** 33.3 kg (73.5 lb) | **Weight:** 13.8 kg (30.4 lb) |
| **Muzzle velocity:** 843 m (2,765 ft) per second | **Muzzle velocity:** 863 m (2,830 ft) per second |
| **Rate of fire, cyclic:** 550-600 rpm | **Rate of fire, cyclic:** 500-640 rpm |
| **Feed:** 50-round metal-link belt | **Feed:** 50-round metal-link belt |

The smaller **SG43** was introduced during 1943 to replace earlier 7.62-mm (0.3-in) machine-guns, including the venerable M1910. During the initial phases of the German invasion of the USSR the Soviet forces lost huge amounts of *materiel*, including machine-guns, and if their new production facilities were to replace these losses they might as well be modern designs. Thus the *Stankovii Pulyemet Goryunova obrazets 1943g* came into being. It was a gas-operated and air-cooled design that combined several operating principles (including the well-established Browning principles), but the overall design was original and soon proved to be sound. The SG43 was issued in very large numbers and even today the basic weapon is still in widespread use in a modified and upgraded **SGM** form.

Both the SG43 and the larger DShK1938 have the same basic operational simplicity. Working parts have been kept to a minimum and very little routine maintenance, apart from simple cleaning, is required. Both designs can operate under extremes of temperature and they are most forgiving of dirt and dust in their works. In other words both weapons are exactly suited to the environment for which they were designed.

***Similar in performance to the 0.5-in (12.7-mm) Browning M2, the DShK1938/46 is still in large-scale service.***

# DP/DPM/DT/DTM
## Light machine-guns

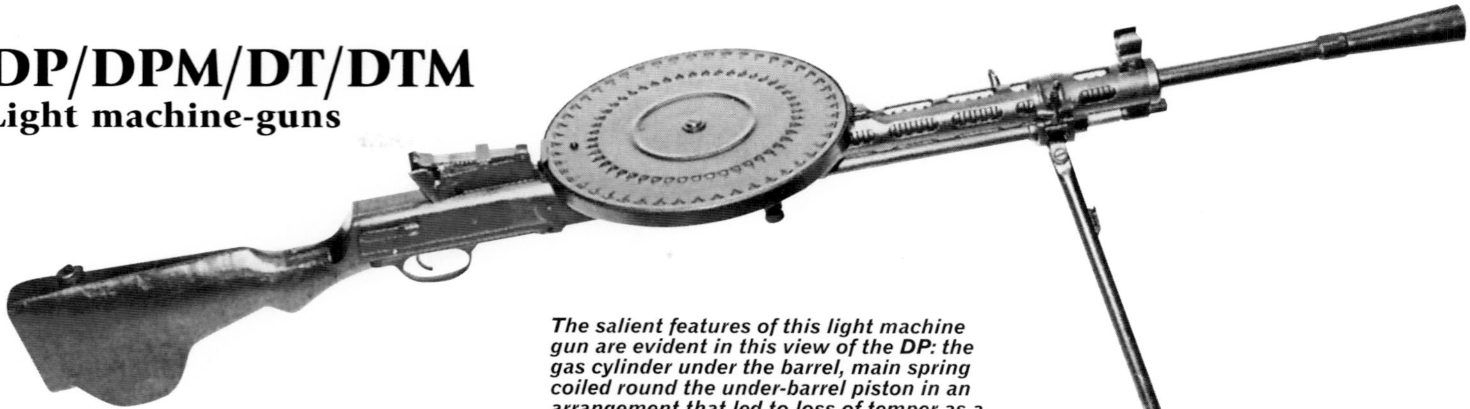

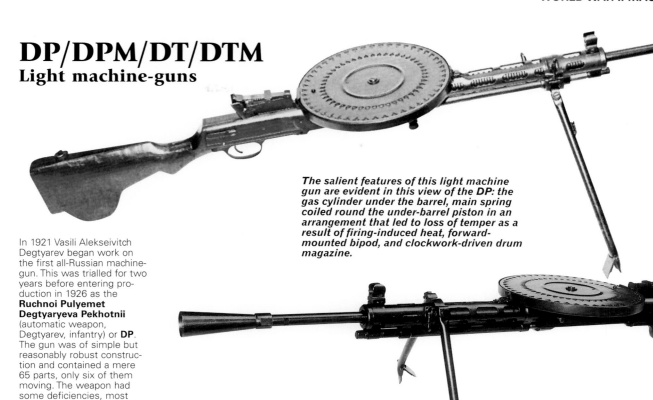

***The salient features of this light machine gun are evident in this view of the DP: the gas cylinder under the barrel, main spring coiled round the under-barrel piston in an arrangement that led to loss of temper as a result of firing-induced heat, forward-mounted bipod, and clockwork-driven drum magazine.***

In 1921 Vasili Alekseivitch Degtyarev began work on the first all-Russian machine-gun. This was trialled for two years before entering production in 1926 as the **Ruchnoi Pulyemet Degtyaryeva Pekhotnii** (automatic weapon, Degtyarev, infantry) or **DP**. The gun was of simple but reasonably robust construction and contained a mere 65 parts, only six of them moving. The weapon had some deficiencies, most especially excessive friction in the action, susceptibility to the ingress of dirt, and overheating because barrel removal was slow and tedious (and useless as there was no spare barrel). The first guns had finned barrels to help dissipate the heat, but the problem was never fully overcome: thus the rate of fire had to be limited to the capacity of the barrel to disperse heat. The gun was used in the Spanish Civil War of 1936-39, and as a result improvements were made.

The gun is gas-operated, and the bolt-locking arrangement is relatively unusual. On each side of the bolt is a hinged lug lying in its own recess. When the bolt face is firm against the base of the round in the chamber the bolt halts, but the piston continues briefly, taking with it a slider to which the firing pin is attached. During this final movement the firing pin cams the locking lugs into recesses in the receiver's side walls, thus locking the breech mechanism at the instant of firing.

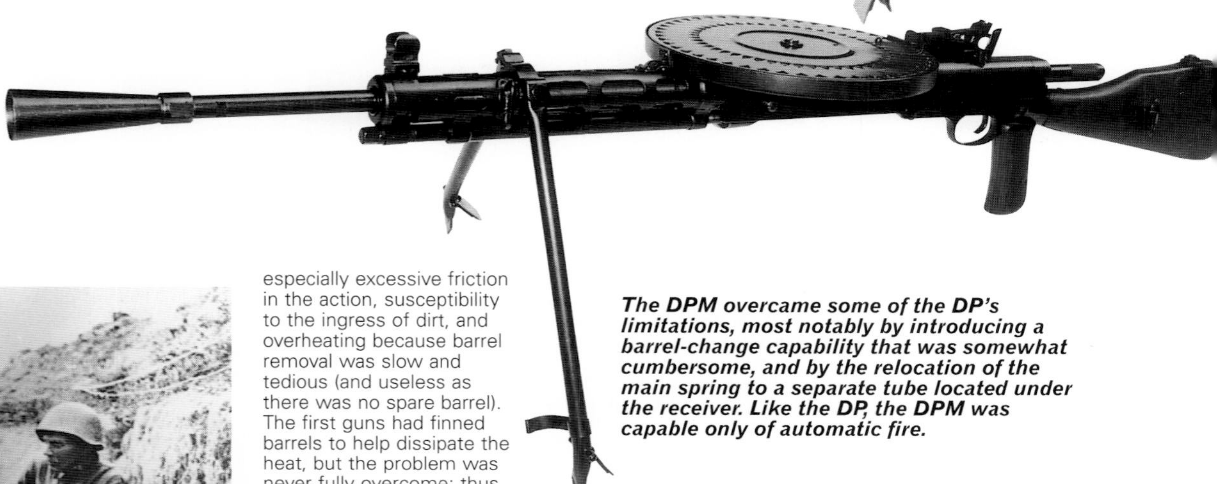

***The DPM overcame some of the DP's limitations, most notably by introducing a barrel-change capability that was somewhat cumbersome, and by the relocation of the main spring to a separate tube located under the receiver. Like the DP, the DPM was capable only of automatic fire.***

***Like all successful tactical weapons of Soviet design and manufacture, the DP was notable for its ability to remain wholly functional under the most adverse terrain and climatic conditions.***

***The DP was both cheap and easy to manufacture using indifferent equipment and semi-skilled labour, and despite its operational limitations was a weapon with which the Soviets were justifiably satisfied.***

### Drum magazine

The feed arrangement is reasonably good: rimmed cartridges usually cause problems in light automatic weapons, but are generally worse in those using box magazines. The large flat single-deck drum of the Degtyarev, driven by a clockwork mechanism rather than by the action of the gun, at least eliminates the problem of double feed. The magazine was originally 49 rounds, generally reduced in practice to 47 rounds to reduce the chance of jams.

In 1944 there appeared the **DPM** with a barrel that could be removed somewhat laboriously with the aid of a special spanner, and the main spring moved to a tube under the barrel to eliminate the heat-induced weakening to which it had previously been prone.

The versions of the DP and DPM for use in tanks were the **DT** and **DTM**. Though technically obsolete, the DP and DPM are still found in some parts of the world.

**SPECIFICATIONS**

| Degtyarev DP | Degtyarev DTM |
|---|---|
| **Calibre:** 7.62-mm (0.3-in) | **Calibre:** 7.62-mm (0.3-in) |
| **Length overall:** 1265 mm (49.8 in) | **Length overall:** 1181 mm (46.5 in) |
| **Length of barrel:** 605 mm (23.8 in) | **Length of barrel:** 597 mm (23.5 in) |
| **Weight:** 11.9 kg (26.13 lb) | **Weight:** 12.9 kg (28.4 lb) |
| **Muzzle velocity:** 845 m (2,772 ft) per second | **Muzzle velocity:** 840 m (2,756 ft) per second |
| **Rate of fire, cyclic:** 520-580 rounds per minute | **Rate of fire, cyclic:** 600 rounds per minute |
| **Feed:** 47-round drum magazine | **Feed:** 60-round drum magazine |

# FN MAG Medium machine-gun

***The Belgian FN MAG is one of the most widely used of the post-World War II general-purpose machine-guns. Well made from what are usually solid metal billets machined to specification, the MAG is a very sturdy but heavy weapon that is still in world-wide production.***

World War II established the general-purpose machine-gun (GPMG) as an essential weapon offering the provision for being fired from a light bipod in the assault role and from a heavy tripod in the defensive or sustained-fire roles. After 1945 many designers tried to produce their own version of the GPMG concept, and one of the best was produced in Belgium during the early 1950s. The company concerned was Fabrique Nationale (FN) based at Herstal, and its design became known as the **FN Mitrailleuse d'Appui Général** or **MAG**. It was not long before the MAG was adopted by many nations, and today it is one of the most widely used of all modern machine-guns.

The MAG fires the standard NATO 7.62-mm (0.3-in) cartridge and is based on a conventional gas-operated mechanism in which gases, tapped off from the barrel, are used to drive the breech block and other components to the rear once a round has been fired. Where the FN MAG scores over many comparable designs is that the tapping-off point under the barrel incorporates a regulator device that allows the firer to control the amount of gas used and thus vary the fire rate to suit the ammunition and other variables. For the sustained-fire role the barrel can be changed easily and quickly.

## High-grade weapon

In construction the MAG is very sturdy. Some use is made of steel pressings riveted together, but many components are machined from solid metal, making the weapon somewhat heavy for easy transport. But this structural strength enables the weapon to absorb all manner of rough use, and it can be used for long periods without maintenance other than changing the barrels when they get too hot. The ammunition is belt-fed, which can be awkward when the weapon has to be carried with lengths of ammunition belt left hanging from the feed and snagging on just about everything.

When used as an LMG the MAG uses a butt and simple bipod, but as a sustained-fire weapon (with the butt usually removed) is placed on a heavy tripod, usually with some form of buffering to absorb part of the recoil. However, the MAG can be adapted to a number of other mountings, and is often used as a co-axial weapon on armoured vehicles or as a vehicle defence weapon in a ball mounting, and as an anti-aircraft weapon on a tripod or vehicle-hatch mounting. It is also used on many light naval vessels.

| SPECIFICATION | |
|---|---|
| **FN MAG** | |
| **Calibre:** 7.62-mm (0.3-in) | tripod 10.5 kg (23.15 lb); barrel 3 kg (6.6 lb) |
| **Length overall:** 1260 mm (49.6 in) | **Muzzle velocity:** 840 m (2,756 ft) per second |
| **Length of barrel:** 545 mm (21.46 in) | **Rate of fire, cyclic:** 600-1000 rpm |
| **Weights:** gun 10.1 kg (22.27 lb); | **Feed:** 50-round metal-link belt |

## British model

The MAG has been widely produced under licence. One of the better-known nations is the UK, where the MAG is known as the **L7A2**. The British introduced some modifications and have produced the weapon for export, and there is no sign of it being replaced in the foreseeable future as far as the British armed forces are concerned. Other nations that produce the MAG for their own use include Israel, South Africa, Singapore and Argentina, and there are others. Even longer is the list of MAG users: a brief summary includes Sweden, Ireland, Greece, Canada, New Zealand, the Netherlands and so on. There is little chance of the MAG falling out of fashion.

***Left: During the Falkland Islands campaign of 1982 the L7A1 was hastily pressed into use on improvised anti-aircraft mountings to provide some measure of defence against Argentine air attacks on the shipping in San Carlos harbour.***

***Right: The FN MAG is licence-produced in Israel by Israel Military Industries and is used by all branches of the Israeli armed forces.***

***The FN MAG is fitted turrets of the German tanks in service with the Dutch army. Pictured here in September 1984 on Exercise 'Lionheart', the MAG has been fitted with a blank-firing adaptor.***

# FN Minimi Light machine-gun

***The FN Minimi has been adopted by the US Army for the Squad Automatic Weapon (SAW) role as the M249. It entered service first with the airborne divisions of what was at the time the Rapid Deployment Joint Task Force.***

With the switch from the heavy 7.62-mm (0.3-in) cartridge toward the lighter 5.56-mm (0.219-in) round for use by the standard rifles of most of the NATO nations and many others, there emerged the need for a light machine-gun in the smaller calibre. FN accordingly designed a new weapon that eventually became known as the **FN Minimi** and was first shown in 1974.

The Minimi is intended for use only as a squad support weapon as there is no way that the 5.56-mm cartridge can be used effectively for the heavy support or sustained-fire role as its round is ineffective at ranges over 400 m (437 yards). Thus heavier-calibre weapons such as the FN MAG are retained for this longer-range role.

## Mix of old and new

The Minimi uses some design features from the earlier FN MAG, including the quick-change barrel and the gas regulator, but a new rotary locking device is used for the breech block, which is guided inside the receiver by two guide rails to ensure a smooth transport. These changes have made the Minimi a remarkably reliable weapon, and further reliability was introduced in the ammunition feed. This is one of the Minimi's major contributions to modern light machine-gun design as it does away with the long and awkward flapping ammunition belts typical of many other designs. The Minimi uses a simple box (fitted under the gun body) to carry the neatly folded belt. When the weapon is fired from a bipod, the box is so arranged that it will not interfere with normal use, and on the move the box is out of the way of the carrier. But the Minimi goes one step further: if required, the belt feed can be replaced by a magazine feed.

FN shrewdly decided that the American M16 rifle would quickly become the standard weapon in its class, and thus made provision for the Minimi to use the M16's 30-round magazine. This can clip into the receiver just under the belt feed guides after the belt has been removed.

***The ammunition belt for the Minimi is tucked neatly into a box under the weapon's body in a fashion that offers no encumbrance to the firer in tactical operations, even when firing in the prone position.***

## Into US service

The association with the M16 has benefited FN, for the Minimi has been adopted as the squad fire-support weapon of the US Army, to whom the Minimi is known as the **M249 Squad Automatic Weapon**. This fires the new standard NATO SS109 cartridge rather than the earlier M193 cartridge. The SS109 has a longer and heavier bullet than the earlier cartridge and uses a different rifling in the barrel, but is otherwise similar to the US cartridge.

Two possible variants of the Minimi are a 'para' version with a shorter barrel and a sliding butt, and a butt-less model for AFV mountings. The Minimi itself has many ingenious detail points: the trigger guard may be removed to allow operation by a man wearing winter or NBC warfare gloves, the front handguard contains a cleaning kit, the ammunition feed box has a simple indicator to show how many rounds are left, and so on.

### SPECIFICATION

**FN Minimi**
**Calibre:** 5.56-mm (0.219-in)
**Length overall:** 1050 mm (41.3 in)
**Length of barrel:** 465 mm (18.3 in)
**Weights:** with bipod 6.5 kg (14.33 lb); with 200 rounds 9.7 kg (21.38 lb)
**Muzzle velocity:** (SS109) 915 m (3,002 ft) per second
**Rate of fire, cyclic:** 750-1000 rpm
**Type of feed:** 100- or 200-round belt or 30-round box magazine

***Below: The Minimi is light, and also comfortable to carry and use. The handle above the weapon doubles for carrying the weapon and also changing the barrel.***

***Bottom: The Minimi is fitted as standard with a folding bipod, all that is necessary to stabilize the weapon for support fire at short and medium ranges.***

***Below: Modern weapons have to be tolerant of effective and reliable use in any and every part of the world under the most adverse of conditions.***

# Chinese machine-guns

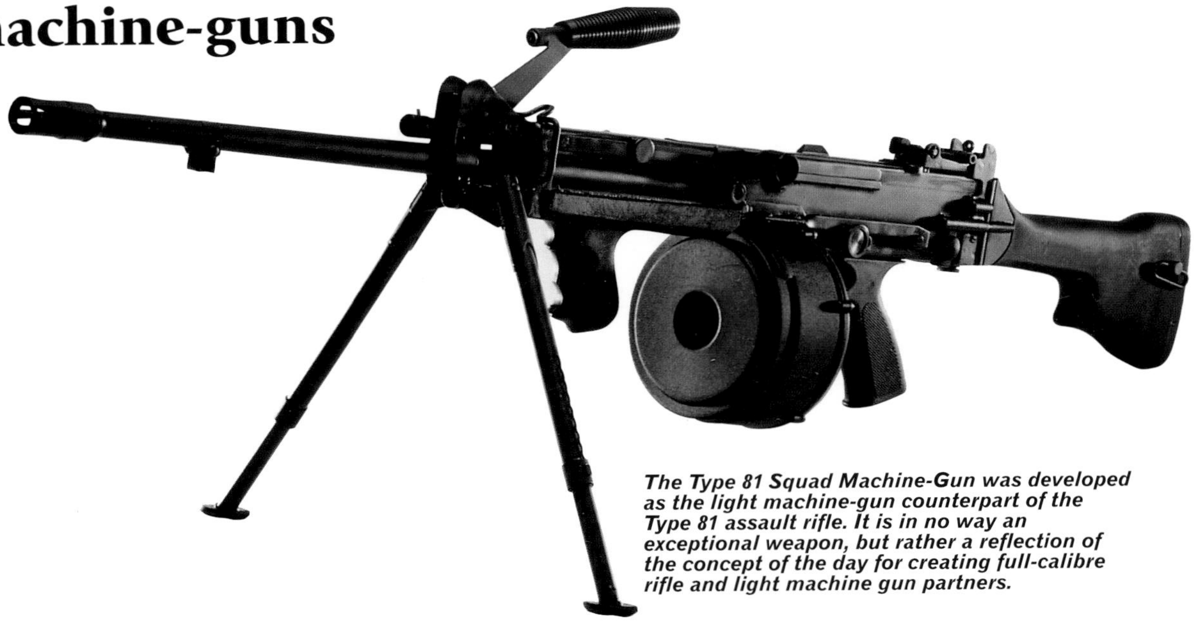

*The Type 81 Squad Machine-Gun was developed as the light machine-gun counterpart of the Type 81 assault rifle. It is in no way an exceptional weapon, but rather a reflection of the concept of the day for creating full-calibre rifle and light machine gun partners.*

For many years after the end of the Chinese Civil War in 1949, the army of the victorious communists used old weapons bought by the defeated nationalist regime and newer designs of Soviet origin but manufactured in China.

The first machine-gun of Chinese design was the gas-operated **Type 67**, a 7.62-mm (0.3-in) light machine-gun that drew its inspiration from a number of weapons, including the Soviet DPM, RPD and SGM for its trigger mechanism, gas regulator and barrel-change arrangement, as well as features of the feed mechanism and the bolt and piston from the MG 08 and vz 26 respectively. The Type 67 was standardised in 1967 to replace the Type 53 and Type 57 in the battalion-level heavy machine-gun role on a tripod mounting, and the Type 58 in the company-level medium machine-gun role on its folding bipod mounting. The Type 67 weighs 24 kg (52.9 lb), and its other data includes an overall length of 1650 mm (64.96 in), barrel length of 605 mm (23.82 in), cyclic rate of fire of 700 rounds per minute and feed from a metal-link belt carrying 250 7.62-mm x 54 cartridges fired with a velocity of 840 m (2,756 ft) per second.

## Improved models

Development of the basic weapon, standardised in 1978 and 1982 respectively, are the **Type 67-1** and **Type 67-2** with their overall length reduced to 1345 mm (52.95 in). The Type 67-1 weighs 25 kg (55.1 lb) and is a modestly improved version of the Type 67, while the Type 67-2 was introduced to replace both the Type 67 and Type 67-1. The Type 67-2 makes use of composite materials to reduce weight and uses a 25-round segmented feed arrangement.

In the mid-1980s the Chinese introduced another 7.62-mm machine-gun, the **Type 80** that had been standardised in 1980 as the Chinese version of the Soviet PKMS. The Type 80 is lighter than the Type 67 models, and possesses better performance.

## Light machine-Gun

The **Type 81 Squad Machine-gun** was the light machine-gun counterpart of the 7.62-mm Type 81 assault rifle, and can fire from its own 75-round drum magazine or the rifle's 30-round box magazine. The machine-gun has an inbuilt bipod, loaded weight of 5.15 kg (11.35 lb) and cyclic rate of 700 rpm.

China's new standard calibre is 8.5-mm (0.335-in), and the machine-gun designed to fire the Type 87 cartridge in this calibre is the **QJY-88**. This is intended as successor to the older 12.7-mm (0.5-in) and 7.62-mm machine-guns in Chinese service. The QJY-88 is a gas-operated and air-cooled weapon that can be mounted on a tripod or its inbuilt folding bipod, and weighs 11.8 kg (26 lb).

The **Type 95 Squad Machine-Gun** counterpart of the new Type 95 light-weight assault rifle. This is a bullpup design with a folding bipod and feed from a 75-round drum magazine.

**SPECIFICATION**

**Type 67-2**
**Calibre:** 7.62-mm (0.3-in)
**Length overall:** 1345 mm (52.95 in)
**Length of barrel:** 606 mm (23.86 in)
**Weights:** gun 15.5 kg (34.17 kg); tripod 5 kg (11 lb)
**Muzzle velocity:** 840 m (2,756 ft) per second
**Rate of fire, cyclic:** 650 rpm
**Feed:** 25-round belt segments

# Lehky Kulomet vz 59 Machine-gun

*The Czechoslovak 7.62-mm (0.3-in) vz 59 is a development of the earlier vz 52/57, but much easier to produce. Created with an eye to the international export market, the vz 59 was adopted by the Czechoslovak armed forces, but others crop up in various corners of the world.*

Czechoslovak machine-gun designers can trace their progeny back to the range of highly successful machine-guns started with the vz (*vzor*, or model) 26 in 1926 and which led to the famous Bren gun. As successor to these designs the Czechoslovaks produced a new model during the early 1950s as the Lehky Kulomet vz 52, essentially the old design updated to use an ammunition belt-feed system. This was not the success of the earlier weapons, and is now rarely encountered other than in the hands of 'freedom fighters' and the like, and was therefore superseded by the **Lehky Kulomet vz 59**.

This is much simpler than the vz 52 but follows the same general lines in appearance and operation. In fact many of the operating principles of the vz 52 were carried over to the new weapon, these including the gas-operated mechanism. The ammunition feed system was also a carry-over from the vz 52, in which it was regarded by many as being the only successful feature. In this feed system the belt is carried into the receiver by guides where a cam system takes over and pushes the cartridge forward through the belt link into the weapon. This system was copied on the Soviet PK series, but on the vz 59 the belts are fed from metal boxes. Another change in the vz 59 was the adoption of the more powerful Soviet 7.62-mm (0.3-in) x 54 cartridge in place of the shorter cartridge of the same notional calibre that was used in the vz 52 series.

For the light machine-gun role with a light barrel and designation **vz 59L**, one of these boxes can be hung from the right-hand side of the gun in a rather unbalanced fashion. The weapon can be operated in the light machine-gun role on bipod and tripod mountings.

## Heavy barrel

For the sustained-fire role the vz 59 is fitted with a heavy barrel. In this form the weapon is known merely as

**SPECIFICATION**

**Lehky Kulomet vz 59**
**Calibre:** 7.62-mm (0.3-in)
**Length overall:** light barrel 1116 mm (43.94 in); heavy barrel 1215 mm (47.84 in)
**Barrel length:** light 593 mm (23.35 in); heavy 693 mm (27.28 in)
**Weights:** with bipod and light barrel 8.67 kg (19.1 lb); with tripod and heavy barrel 19.24 kg (42.42 lb)
**Muzzle velocity:** with light barrel 810 m (2,657 ft) per second; heavy barrel 830 m (2,723 ft) per second
**Rate of fire, cyclic:** 700-800 rpm
**Feed:** 50- or 250-round metal-link belt

the vz 59, but fitted with a solenoid for installation in AFVs in a co-axial or similar mount it is the **vz 59T**. This did not exhaust the variations of the vz 59 series for, with an eye to sales outside Czechoslovakia, there is a version that fires standard NATO 7.62-mm (0.3-in) ammunition and is known as the **vz 59N** or, later, as the **Universalny Kulomet vz 68**, which is still in production by Zbrojovka Vsetin.

### Telescopic sight

One rather unusual feature of the vz 59 is the x4 telescopic sight, which can be used with the bipod and the tripod. This sight may be illuminated internally for use at night and is also used for anti-aircraft fire, for which role the vz 59 is placed on top of a tubular extension to the normal tripod.

In the past Czechoslovak weapons have appeared wherever there was a market for small arms, and are still popular with many purchasers. Czechoslovak weapons have therefore been encountered in the Middle East, and especially in Lebanon during the 1970s and 1980s; some vz 52s were certainly seen in that troubled region.

***The vz 59 is a useful machine-gun that can be operated in the light role with a short, light barrel and a boxed belt, or in the sustained-fire role with a long, heavy barrel and belted ammunition. The weapon is cocked by movement of the pistol grip.***

# MAS AAT 52 Machine-gun

***The French AAT 52 uses a delayed blowback mechanism with a fluted chamber to ease extraction. A 7.62-mm (0.3-in) version – known as the AAT F1 – may also be encountered, but neither model is now in production. Bipod and tripod versions are in use, as are vehicle-mounted models.***

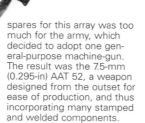

The machine-gun now known as the **MAS AAT 52** was developed as a direct result of the Indo-China campaigns of the early 1950s. At that time the French army was equipped with a wide array of American, British and ex-German weapons, and the furnishing of support and spares for this array was too much for the army, which decided to adopt one general-purpose machine-gun. The result was the 7.5-mm (0.295-in) AAT 52, a weapon designed from the outset for ease of production, and thus incorporating many stamped and welded components.

### Delayed blowback

The AAT 52 is unusual among modem machine-guns in relying on a form of delayed-blowback operation, in which the force of the cartridge firing is employed to drive back the breech block to the starting position, and also to power the feed mechanism. This system works very well with pistol cartridges in sub-machine guns, but the use of rifle cartridges in machine-guns demands something more positive if safety is to be assured. On the AAT 52 a two-part block is used: a lever device is so arranged that it holds the forward part of the block in position while the rear half starts to move to the rear; only when the lever has moved a predetermined distance does it allow the forward part of the block to move back. In order to make the spent cartridge easier to extract the chamber has grooves that allow gas to enter between the chamber wall and the fired cartridge to prevent 'sticking', and a cartridge fired in an AAT 52 can always be recognised by the fluted grooves around the case neck.

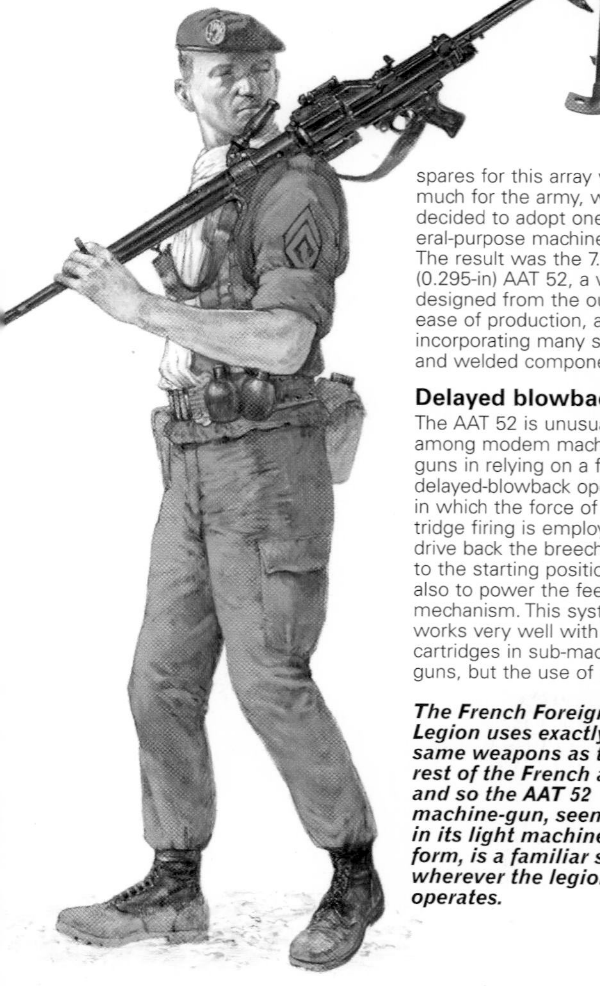

***The French Foreign Legion uses exactly the same weapons as the rest of the French army and so the AAT 52 machine-gun, seen here in its light machine-gun form, is a familiar sight wherever the legion operates.***

### Bipod and tripod

The AAT 52 can be fired from a bipod or a tripod, but when a tripod is used for the sustained fire role a heavy barrel is fitted to the weapon. When used in the light machine-gun role the AAT 52 is a rather clumsy weapon to carry, especially if a 50-round ammunition box is carried on the left-hand side. For this reason the box is often left off and the ammunition belt allowed to hang free. An unusual feature of the AA 52 is that for the light machine-gun role a monopod is fitted under the butt. This can be awkward, as can be the barrel-change feature: the barrel can be removed readily enough, but the bipod is permanently attached to the barrel and in the light machine-gun role this can make barrel-changing very difficult, especially as the AAT 52 barrels have no plating to reduce its temperature.

The AAT 52 was originally intended to fire a 7.5-mm cartridge first developed for use by the mle 1929 light machine-gun. This cartridge is powerful enough, but the switch to the NATO 7.62-mm (0.3-in) cartridge left the French army using a non-standard cartridge, and export prospects for the AAT 52 were thus reduced. The basic design was therefore adapted to fire the NATO cartridge in a version known as the **AAT F1**. Some of these were issued to French army units, but exports did not materialise.

Overall the AA 52 is an adequate machine-gun, but it has many features that are at best undesirable and; in the eyes of some, inherently unsafe. The weapon is no longer in production but is still in service.

#### SPECIFICATION

**MAS AAT 52**
**Calibre:** 7.5-mm (0.295-in)
**Length overall:** with butt extended (light barrel) 1145 mm (45.08 in) or (heavy barrel) 1245 mm (49.02 in)
**Length of barrel:** light 500 mm (19.69 in); heavy 600 mm (23.62 in)
**Weights:** with bipod and light barrel 9.97 kg (21.98 lb); with bipod and heavy barrel 11.37 kg (25.07 lb); tripod 10.6 kg (23.37 lb)
**Muzzle velocity:** 840 m (2,756 ft) per second
**Rate of fire, cyclic:** 700 rpm
**Feed:** 50-round metal-link belt

# Heckler & Koch
## Machine-guns

The West German small arms designer and manufacturer Heckler & Koch, based at Oberndorf-Neckar and now owned by BAE Systems of the UK, is among the most prolific of all modern small arms design organisations, and in addition to its successful range of assault rifles and sub-machine guns, also produces a wide variety of air-cooled machine-guns.

It may be an over-simplification to describe them thus, but Heckler & Koch machine-guns are basically modified versions of the company's G3 and associated assault rifles. They all use the same delay-roller mechanism on their two-part breech blocks, and some of the light machine-guns could be described as little more than assault rifles with heavier barrels and a bipod mounting.

To confuse the issue, Heckler & Koch produces virtually every one of its models in both belt- and magazine-fed versions, and some are produced in 7.62-mm (0.3-in) or 5.56-mm (0.219-in) calibres, with the added variation in the latter for the new SS109 cartridge or the older American M193 cartridge. A feature of several of the magazine-fed weapons is that the standard type of 20- or 30-round box magazine can be replaced by an 80-round double-drum plastic magazine.

### Basic model

One of the 'base' models in the range is the 7.62-mm **HK-21A1**, a development of the original **HK-21** which entered production in 1970 but is no longer in production. The HK-21A1 uses only the belt-feed system, and can be operated as a light machine-gun on a bipod or in the medium machine-gun (otherwise sustained-fire) role when installed on a tripod mounting. For the sustained-fire role, a barrel-change capability is built into the weapon so that an overheating barrel can quickly be replaced.

The HK-21A1 is now made under licence only in Greece and Portugal. Even in this version of the Heckler & Koch range the outline of the G3 rifle is apparent, and this is carried over to the current version of the HK-21, the **HK-21E**, which has a longer sight radius and a three-round burst selection feature. The barrel is longer, and changes have been made to the ammunition feed. There is also a 5.56-mm counterpart to this variant, the **HK-23E**.

All the variants mentioned above are belt-fed weapons. There is also a magazine-fed version for every one of them: the **HK-11A1** is the magazine counterpart of the HK 21A1, while the **HK-11E** and **HK-13E** are the magazine-fed counterparts of the HK-21E and HK-23E. The weapons of the **HK-13** series entered production in 1972, and were designed to complement the HK-33 series of assault rifles in 5.56-mm calibre. Like the assault rifle, they found their initial market largely in South-East Asia where the small size, light weight and modest recoil forces of weapons associated with the 5.56-mm round first received universal approval during the first part of the 1970s.

### Great flexibility

All this may sound rather confusing, but the basic factor that emerges from this diversity of calibres, ammunition feed systems and mountings is the ability of Heckler & Koch to produce a machine-gun suited to virtually any and every tactical requirement. The belt-fed versions may be regarded as general-purpose machine-guns, although the 5.56-mm versions may really be too light for the sustained-fire role, and the magazine-fed versions may be seen as true light machine-guns. The weapons of this important series offer a surprising amount of interchangeability of spare parts, and the magazines are usually the same as those used on their equivalent assault rifles, facilitating the use of the automatic as a squad support weapon.

Heckler & Koch's latest light machine-gun offering is the **MG 36** in 5.56-mm calibre. This is a state-of-the-art weapon with an overall length of 998 mm (39.3 in), barrel length of 480 mm (18.9 in) and weight of 3.57 kg (7.87 lb) with a bipod mount but without a magazine. The MG 36 reflects modern assault rifle design in its compact design, extensive use of composite materials, carrying handle with an inbuilt sight arrangement and feed from a 30-round box magazine or alternatively a dual-drum 'Beta-C' magazine carrying 100 rounds.

| SPECIFICATION | |
|---|---|
| **HK-21A1**<br>**Calibre:** 7.62-mm (0.3-in)<br>**Length overall:** 1030 mm (40.55 in)<br>**Length of barrel:** 450 mm (17.72 in) | **Weight:** 8.3 kg (18.3 lb) with bipod<br>**Muzzle velocity:** 800 m (2,625 ft) per second<br>**Rate of fire, cyclic:** 900 rounds per minute<br>**Feed:** 100-round metal-link belt |

***The Heckler & Koch HK-11 is the box magazine feed variant of the HK-21 and is a 7.62-mm (0.3-in) weapon.***

***The Heckler & Koch HK-13 is produced in several versions. This model accommodates a 40-round box magazine.***

***The Heckler & Koch HK-13E has a three-round burst capability as well as full automatic fire.***

***The Heckler & Koch HK-21 is no longer produced in Germany, but is still in use with nations such as Portugal.***

***The HK-21A1 is a development of the earlier HK-21. It uses a belt feed only, and the belt can be contained in a box slung under the receiver.***

# MG3 Machine-gun

***The West German MG3 is the modern version of the MG 42 of World War II fame, and is currently rated as one of the best machine-guns of its type used by NATO. It has a high rate of fire and an easy and rapid barrel-change capability, and can be fired from the bipod shown or from a heavy tripod for the sustained fire-support role.***

One of the outstanding machine-gun designs of World War II was the MG 42. This German air-cooled weapon introduced the advantages of mass production to an area of weapon design that had for long clung to traditional methods of construction using large numbers of time-consuming and expensive machining operations to create high-quality components from solid metal. With the MG 42, the new era of construction through the use of steel pressings and welded components was allied to an excellent design that attracted widespread respect and attention.

## Old for new

When the Federal Republic of Germany became a member of NATO and was once more allowed a measure of weapon production for the equipment of the new armed forces, the MG 42 was one of the first designs to be resurrected.

The original MG 42 had been designed to fire Germany's standard 7.92-mm (0.312-in) ammunition of the period up to the end of World War II. But with the adoption of the standard NATO small arms ammunition in 7.62-mm (0.3-in) calibre, the original design was reworked to accommodate the new type of ammunition. At first stockpiled MG 42 machine-guns were simply modified to this calibre with the designation **MG2**, but in parallel with this activity a production programme was launched by Rheinmetall for the manufacture of new weapons in the 7.62-mm calibre. There were several variants of this production version, all having the designation **MG1**, although there were some minor changes to suit ammunition feed and so on.

## Current model

The current production version is the **MG3**, which is still manufactured in Germany by Rheinmetall.

In appearance, the wartime MG 42 and the MG3 are identical apart from some minor details, few of which can be detected by the untrained eye, and there are more changes between the MG1 and MG3. Overall, however, the modern MG3 retains all the attributes of the original, and many of the mountings used with the MG3 are just adaptations or simple modifications of the World War II originals. Thus the MG3 can be used on a tripod that is virtually identical to the original, and the twin mounting for anti-aircraft use could still accommodate the MG 42 without trouble. There are now available many mountings for the MG3.

As noted above, the original MG 42 was designed for ease of mass production, and this same feature makes the MG3 very suitable for manufacture in some of the world's less industrialized nations. The MG3 has proved to be relatively easy for such facilities and it is now or has been licence-produced in nations such as Chile, Pakistan, Spain and Turkey; some of these nations, it should be noted, fabricate versions of the MG1 rather than the MG3 proper. Yugoslavia also produces a version of this weapon, but the Yugoslav model is a direct copy of the MG 42, still in 7.92-mm calibre and designated **SARAC M1953**.

## Widespread service

Within NATO the MG3, or one or other of its variants, is used by the German and Italian armed forces, and also by the forces of nations such as Denmark and Norway. Portugal makes the MG3 for use by the Portuguese armed forces, and has also offered the type for export. Thus from many sources the old MG 42 design soldiers on, for the basic design of the MG3 is still as sound as it ever was, and any attempt to improve or modify the original appears to many to be a pointless exercise.

| SPECIFICATION | |
|---|---|
| **MG3** | (23.15 lb); bipod 0.55 kg (1.213 lb) |
| **Calibre:** 7.62-mm (0.3-in) | **Muzzle velocity:** 820 m (2,690 ft) per second |
| **Length overall:** 1225 mm (48.23 in) with butt | **Rate of fire, cyclic:** 700-1,300 rounds per minute |
| **Length of barrel:** 531 mm (20.91 in) | **Feed:** 50-round metal-link belt |
| **Weight:** basic gun 10.5 kg | |

***The overall tactical flexibility of the German MG3 machine-gun is enhanced by the weapon's long pedigree of reliability and the availability of several types of mounting.***

***The MG3, seen here on its bipod mount, is operated by a two-man crew comprising the gunner and his loader, who feeds the metallic-link belts of ammunition from man-portable boxes.***

# PK Machine-gun

*The Soviet 7.62-mm (0.3-in) PK machine-gun is seen here in its PKM light machine-gun form. It is a simple and sturdy weapon with few moving parts, and has been widely used by Warsaw Pact and other armed forces around the world.*

One very noticeable feature in Soviet small-arms design is the strange mixture of innovation and conservatism that seems typical of every generation of weapons. Despite the impact made by the then-novel 7.62-mm (0.3-in) x 39 cartridge used in the AK-47 assault rifle family, Soviet machine-guns continued to use the more powerful 7.62-mm x 54R cartridge with a rimmed base. This rim was originally used for extraction from the Mosin-Nagant rifle series, and the cartridge was also adopted for the **PK** general-purpose machine-guns.

There are several members of the PK family. The PK is the basic gun with a heavy barrel marked by flutes along its exterior. This was first seen in 1946, and after that the **IKM** arrived on the scene as an improved version of the PK with features to lighten it and simplify its construction. The **PKS** is a PK mounted on a tripod for use in the anti-aircraft as well as ground fire roles. The **PKT** is for use in AFVs, while the **PKM** is the PK with a bipod. When the PKM is mounted on a tripod it becomes the **PKMS**. The **PKB** has the usual butt and trigger mechanism replaced by spade grips and a 'butterfly' trigger arrangement.

The PK appears to be all things to all men, and as far as the Red Army is concerned it was a true multi-role type that was used in roles ranging from infantry squad support to AFV use in special mountings.

The PK machine-guns operate on the same principle, based on the Kalashnikov rotary-bolt system. The interior of the PK is populated by surprisingly few parts: the bolt/breech block, a piston, a few springs, the ammunition feed's few more parts, and that is about it. Thus the PK has few parts to break or jam. When used in the light machine-gun role, the weapon generally has its ammunition in a metal box slung under the gun. For tripod operation variable-length belts are used. In the sustained-fire role the barrel has to be changed at regular intervals even though it is chromium-plated to reduce wear and promote heat dissipation.

The latest development of the PKM is the **Pecheneg**, which has an 80% commonality of parts but introduces a new, fixed barrel with a forced-draught cooling system allowing the gun to fire about 1,000 rounds per hour or 600 rounds in 40/50-round bursts.

The PK weapons must rank among the most numerous of all modern machine-guns, being used not only by the Soviet and Warsaw Pact armies and their successors, but also by a large number of export customers including the Chinese, who use the type in the form of their **Type 80** copy made in China.

***When mounted on a tripod for the sustained-fire role, the PKM becomes the PKMS, the bipod legs being folded back under the barrel.***

**SPECIFICATION**

**PK**
**Calibre:** 7.62-mm (0.3-in)
**Length overall:** 1160 mm (45.7 in)
**Length of barrel:** 658 mm (25.9 in)
**Weights:** gun empty 9 kg (19.84 lb); tripod 7.5 kg (16.53 lb); 100-round belt 2.44 kg (5.38 lb)
**Muzzle velocity:** 825 m (2,707 ft) per second
**Rate of fire, cyclic:** 690-720 rpm
**Feed:** 100-, 200- and 250-round metal-link belts

# RPK Machine-gun

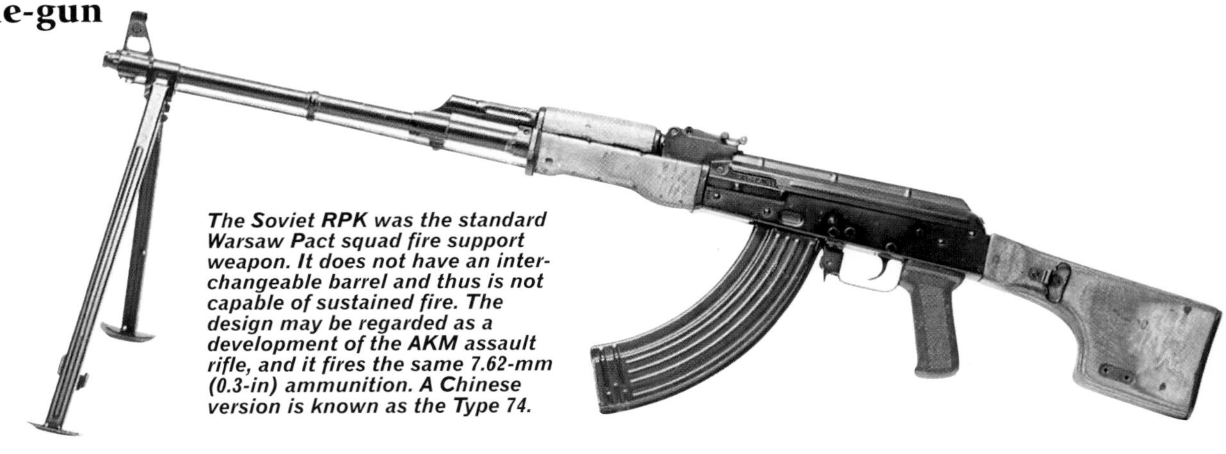

***The Soviet RPK was the standard Warsaw Pact squad fire support weapon. It does not have an interchangeable barrel and thus is not capable of sustained fire. The design may be regarded as a development of the AKM assault rifle, and it fires the same 7.62-mm (0.3-in) ammunition. A Chinese version is known as the Type 74.***

Though the PK series was developed for the general-purpose machine-gun role, the 7.62-mm (0.3-in) **RPK** was created for the light machine-gun or squad support task. The RPK was first noted in 1966 and may be regarded as an enlarged version of the AKM assault rifle. It has a longer and heavier barrel and a light bipod, but is otherwise the same weapon as the AKM.

This commonality of weapons makes a great deal of sense. The AKM fires the same 7.62-mm x 39 ammunition as the assault rifle, but the commonality goes further as some spare parts can be interchanged, and any soldier who can use the AKM can pick up and fire the RPK with equal facility. In the absence of its special 75-round drum magazine, the RPK can be fitted with an AKM box magazine. However, the RPK has no bayonet-mounting lug.

## Fixed barrel

Given that the weapon was intended as a light machine-gun, it is surprising that the RPK does not have provision for changing the barrel when it gets hot. In order to ensure the barrel does not overheat, recruits are trained to limit burst-firing to about 80 shots per minute. For most tactical purposes this is more than adequate, but there must be times when this fire rate has its disadvantages. Apart from the 75-round drum already mentioned, there are curved box magazines holding 30 or 40 rounds. Some RPKs have been seen with infra-red night sights, and a copy produced by the Chinese is the

**Type 74**.

In the early 1970s the Red Army changed its standard rifle cartridge to the 5.45-mm (0.215-in) x 18 type, and to fire this cartridge the AK-47 was developed into the AK-74. It was clear that a new version of the RPK would follow, and this materialised as the **RPK-74**. Apart from scaling down some parts to suit the smaller calibre, the RPK-74 is identical to the RPK.

## Popular weapon

The RPK was a popular weapon with the Soviet and many Warsaw Pact nations to which it was delivered. The type appears to have been produced in East Germany, and as far as can be determined the RPK is still in production in what are now the countries of the CIS. The weapon was delivered to a number of countries sympathetic to the Soviet way of thinking, and needless to say the RPK has also found its way into the hands of many 'freedom fighters'. The RPK was seen in action during the Lebanese civil war of the 1970s and 1980s, and the type also saw considerable action in Angola both against the Portuguese and then in the following civil war. Despite its rate-of-fire limitations, the RPK will no doubt be around for many years to come, and the Russian army and its allies of the CIS still retain huge numbers of the type despite the introduction of the RPK-74.

**SPECIFICATION**

**RPK**
**Calibre:** 7.62-mm (0.3-in)
**Length overall:** 1035 mm (40.75 in)
**Length of barrel:** 591 mm (23.3 in)
**Weights:** gun 5 kg (11.02 lb); 75-round drum 2.1 kg (4.63 lb)
**Muzzle velocity:** 732 m (2,402 ft) per second
**Rate of fire, cyclic:** 660 rpm
**Feed:** 75-round drum, or 30- and 40-round box magazines

# Russian heavy machine-guns

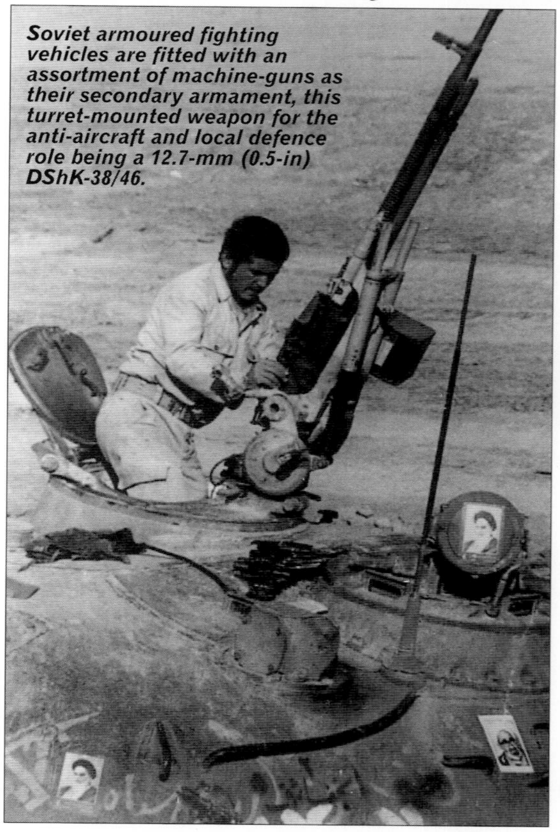

***Soviet armoured fighting vehicles are fitted with an assortment of machine-guns as their secondary armament, this turret-mounted weapon for the anti-aircraft and local defence role being a 12.7-mm (0.5-in) DShK-38/46.***

***Fitted with a shoulder yoke and telescopic sight, and mounted on the 6T7 tripod, the NSV heavy machine-gun offers devastating firepower against personnel and vehicles in the surface-to-surface role.***

***Below: On a towed four-wheel carriage, the ZPU-4 offers considerable firepower in the light anti-aircraft role, but lacks power operation and anything but a simple on-carriage sighting system.***

The world's most powerful machine-gun in large-scale service is the **KPV** (**Krasnoy Pulemet Vladimorova**), a weapon designed in the USSR from 1944 to use the Soviet 14.5-mm (0.57-in) x 115 cartridge, whose API and HEIT bullets have twice as much energy as a 12.7-mm (0.5-in) projectile.

The KPV entered service in the later 1940s, and is generally associated with wheeled mountings towed by light vehicles. The standard mountings are the ZPU-1, -2 and -4 carrying one, two or four such weapons, which have also been used on a number of AFVs. Weighing 49.1 kg (108.25 lb), increasing to 161.5 kg (356 lb) in its ZPU-1 form, the KPV is air-cooled with a chromed barrel, and operated on the short-recoil system with gas assistance. The bolt is of the rotary type, and the weapon is fed from the left- or right-hand sides by a 40-round belt for a cyclic rate of 600 rounds per minute and a muzzle velocity of 3,281 ft (1000 m) per second. The KPV is sighted to 2000 m (2,185 yards) and is 2006 mm (78.98 in) long with a 1346-mm (53-in) changeable barrel.

## One calibre down

Next down the calibre ladder is 12.7-mm, in which the DShK is complemented by the **NSV**, so named for the design team of Nikitin, Volkhov and Sokolov. This is an air-cooled and belt-fed weapon firing a projectile capable of penetrating 16 mm (0.63 in) of armour at 500 m (545 yards). The weapon is gas operated and locked by a tilting block arrangement, and has a recoil buffer inside the receiver to smooth the action. The standard NSV, issued with an SPP x3 to x6 telescopic sight, is complemented by the **NSVT**, which is the AFV variant.

Both NSV weapons are to be replaced early in the 21st century by the 25.5-kg (56.22-lb) **Kord** in the same calibre. This has a different locking system and is a gas-operated weapon, but again has a chromed barrel and is claimed to offer far greater accuracy than the NSV, especially with optional telescopic or night sights. There are no dimensional data for the Kord, which weighs 41.5 kg (91.5 lb) on its tripod with a full 50-round belt, but the weapon's other data include a muzzle velocity of 820-860 m (2,690-2,822 ft) per second, and a cyclic rate of 650-750 rounds per minute.

**SPECIFICATION**

**NSV**
**Calibre:** 12.7-mm (0.5-in)
**Length overall:** 1560 mm (61.42 in)
**Length of barrel:** not available
**Weights:** gun 25 kg (55.1 lb); complete weapon with tripod mounting and 50 rounds of ammunition 41 kg (90.4 kg)
**Muzzle velocity:** 845 m (2,772 ft) per second
**Rate of fire, cyclic:** 700-800 rounds per minute
**Feed:** 50-round metal-link belt

# IMI Negev
## Machine-gun

*In its standard form, the Negev light machine-gun is fitted with a bipod and fed with ammunition by means of a disintegrating metal-link belt.*

The **IMI Negev** machine-gun, one of the standard light automatic weapons of the Israel Defence Forces, seems very similar to a Belgian weapon of the same class, the FN Minimi. This similarity extends further than just the appearance of the two weapons, however, for the Belgian and Israeli machine-guns have about the same performance and share a high degree of accuracy, reliability and light overall weight.

### Replacement weapon

Just as the Minimi has partially replaced the FN MAG in many armies, Israel plans that the Negev should supplant its MAG 58 weapons not only in the troop-carried role but also in armoured fighting vehicle and helicopter installations.The Negev will also replace the Minimi, which was supplied in small numbers but proved unpopular, and also captured Soviet weapons such as the PK and RPD machine-guns. The final trials of the Negev were completed in 1996, and large-scale manufacture of the new machine-gun began in the following year.

The Negev is a gas-operated weapon of modern concept and construction, and is produced in two variants as the Negev standard light machine-gun and the shorter and lighter **Negev Commando** with an overall length of 890 mm (35.04 in) with the butt extended and 680 mm (26.77 in) with the butt folded, barrel length of 330 mm (12.99 in) and weight of 6.95 kg (15.32 lb).

The Negev Commando also lacks the rail adapter used in the standard model to carry an ITL AIM1/D laser pointer, and is generally fitted with a forward assault handle rather than the standard weapon's bipod. A feature of both variants is a soft ammunition drum carrying 150 rounds; the Negev can also use rifle magazines.

**SPECIFICATION**

**IMI Negev**
**Calibre:** 5.56-mm (0.219-in)
**Length overall:** 1020 mm (40.16 in) with the buttstock extended and 780 mm (30.71 in) with the buttstock folded
**Length of barrel:** 460 mm (18.11 in)
**Weight:** 7.6 kg (16.75 lb) with bipod but without ammunition
**Muzzle velocity:** not available
**Rate of fire, cyclic**: selectable between 700-850 or 850-1,000 rounds per minute
**Feed:** 150-round metal-link belt, or M16 or Galil assault rifle magazines

# CIS Ultimax 100 Machine-gun

The relatively small nation of Singapore has in recent years become a major member of the international defence matériel market. Starting from virtually nothing, Singapore has rapidly built up a defence manufacturing industry and among recent products has been a light machine-gun called the **CIS Ultimax 100** or **3U-100**.

The Ultimax 100 can trace its origins back to 1978. To provide a framework in which to work, the newly-formed Chartered Industries of Singapore (now ST Kinetics) had obtained a licence to produce the 5.56-mm (0.219-in) AR-18 and M16A1 rifles. CIS then decided to build in some ideas of its own, and the result was the Ultimax 100. After some early development problems, the Ultimax 100 is now one of the best weapons in its class.

### Ammunition

The Ultimax 100 fires the 5.56-mm M193 cartridge, but could be converted to fire the new SS109. It is a light machine-gun that is really light, for the company was understandably keen to produce a weapon suited to the relatively light physiques of Asian personnel.

The result is that the Ultimax 100 handles very like an assault rifle. CIS has taken great pains to reduce recoil forces to a minimum, and has even introduced a feature it calls 'constant recoil'. With this feature the breech block does not use the back-plate of the receiver as a buffer, as is normal in many similar designs, but instead a system of springs that absorb the forces to the extent that the weapon can be handled with ease and smoothness. The Ultimax 100 can be fired from the shoulder with no problems at all.

*The Ultimax 100 Mk 3 light machine-gun is a small weapon that is ideally suited to many Southeast Asian armed forces. It is light and easy to handle, and after its development difficulties is now a reliable and efficient weapon that is in full-scale production in Singapore.*

The likeness to an assault rifle is carried over to the ammunition feed. The Ultimax 100 uses a 100-round drum magazine under the body that can be changed with the same facility as a conventional box magazine. The drum magazines can be carried in a special webbing carrier. For firing on the move a forward grip is provided, and to make the weapon even handier the butt may be removed. For more accurate firing a bipod is a fixture and the barrel change is rapid and easy. If required normal M16A1 20- or 30-round box magazines can be used in place of the drum.

Already accessories for the Ultimax 100 abound. Perhaps the most unusual of them is a silencer which is used in conjunction with a special barrel. More orthodox items include a special twin mounting in which two weapons are secured on their sides with the drum magazines pointing outward. One very unusual extra is a bayonet, a feature which few similar weapons possess. Rifle grenades can be fired from the muzzle without preparation.

To date the Ultimax 100 is available in two versions: the **Ultimax 100 Mk 2** with a fixed barrel and the **Ultimax 100 Mk 3** with a quick-change barrel. More versions are certain, for the Ultimax 100 has a most promising future. It is already in service with the Singapore armed forces and many more nations are showing a great interest in the weapon. It is certainly one of the handiest and most attractive of light machine-guns.

**SPECIFICATION**

**Ultimax 100**
**Calibre:** 5.56-mm (0.219-in)
**Length overall:** 1030 mm (40.55 in)
**Length of barrel:** 508 mm (20 in)
**Weight loaded:** 6.5 kg (14.33 lb) with 100-round drum
**Muzzle velocity:** 990 m (3,248 ft) per second
**Rate of fire, cyclic:** 400-600 rpm
**Type of feed:** 100-round drum, or 20- or 30-round curved box

# Santa Barbara (CETME) Ameli Machine-gun

Although it possesses striking visual similarity to the MG 42 of World War II and its MG3 modern-day development, the **CETME Ameli** machine-gun is in fact an entirely new weapon. It uses the same type of roller-delayed blowback action (with a semi-rigid bolt) as the Heckler & Koch assault rifles and machine-guns, and also the Model L assault rifle created by CETME, which is now controlled by the Empresa Nacional Santa Barbara de Industrias Militares, itself owned by General Dynamics of the USA. The relationship between the Ameli and Model L is sufficiently close that there is a modicum of interchangeability between the two weapons' parts.

***The Ameli is an effective machine-gun that can be operated in the light and sustained-fire roles. On the left-hand side of the weapon's body is the disposable plastic box carrying the weapon's ammunition belt.***

## Quick-change barrel

The Ameli fires from an open bolt, and has a quick-change barrel to enhance its utility for the sustained-fire role in which barrel overheating would otherwise be a major problem. The tactical versatility of the weapon is also magnified by its provision with a bipod for use when the weapon is used in the light machine-gun role, but in the sustained-fire role the weapon is generally mounted on a tripod. The Ameli fires NATO standard 5.56-mm (0.219-in) ammunition carried in belts in disposable plastic boxes holding 100 or 200 rounds, and provision is made for two rates of fire: the use of a heavy bolt results in a rate of fire of between 850 and 900 rounds per minute, while the installation of the light bolt leads to an increase in the rate of fire to some 1,200 rounds per minute.

Without doubt one of the best light/sustained-fire machine-guns of the 5.56-mm calibre currently on offer, the Ameli is clearly an effective battlefield weapon. However, it has run into a considerable measure of political antipathy as it is a type favoured by terrorist and guerrilla forces. The reason for this is the fact that the Ameli can be broken down into comparatively small sections that can then be carried in a suitcase-like container. This offers the possibility of the weapon being moved around civilian areas without being seen. For this reason, the Ameli has been banned in several countries.

The Ameli incorporates a number of features to ensure that the weapon can be assembled in only the correct fashion.

**SPECIFICATION**

**Ameli**
**Calibre:** 5.56-mm (0.219-in)
**Length overall:** 900 mm (35.43 in)
**Length of barre:** 400 mm (15.75 in)
**Weight empty:** 5.3 kg (11.68 lb)
**Muzzle velocity:** not available
**Rate of fire, cyclic:** see text
**Feed:** 100- or 200-round belt

# SIG 710-3 Machine-gun

The Swiss 7.62-mm (0.3-in) **SIG 710-3** machine-gun is a weapon that on paper appears to be one of the finest of its class. The overall design, construction and reliability of the SIG design are such that it would appear to be a world leader. In fact nothing of the kind has occurred, for this most promising of machine-gun designs has now been taken out of production and can be found in service only with nations such as Bolivia, Brunei and Chile.

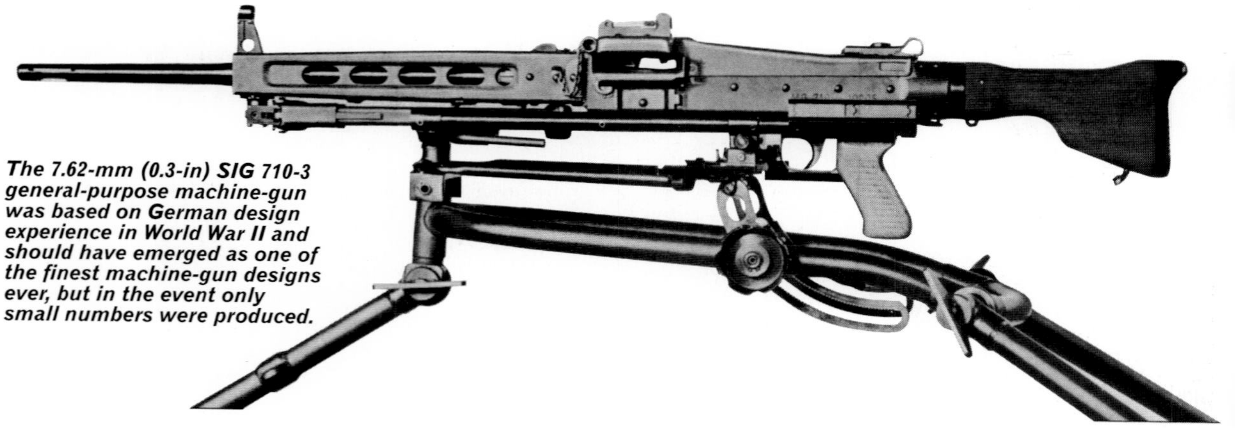

***The 7.62-mm (0.3-in) SIG 710-3 general-purpose machine-gun was based on German design experience in World War II and should have emerged as one of the finest machine-gun designs ever, but in the event only small numbers were produced.***

## Superlative weapon

The reason for this strange state of affairs can perhaps be seen in the fact that when the Swiss produce any weapon design they do so in a manner that can only attract superlatives. The Swiss produce weapons with a magnificent degree of care and attention to finish, but while people may be willing to pay heavily for similarly engineered Swiss watches, they are not willing to pay on the same scale for machine-guns, especially when such weapons can be produced on simple machine tools and metal stamping jigs.

The SIG 710-3 is the third in a series of machine-guns, the first of which were produced soon after World War II. In simple terms the first SIG 710s were machine-gun versions of the Swiss Sturmgewehr Modell 57 (assault rifle model 1957), and the machine-gun employs the same delayed roller and block locking system as the CETME and Heckler & Koch rifles. On the SIG 710 the system is a form of delayed blowback with the chamber fluted to prevent spent cases 'sticking'. The first SIG 710s were virtually hand-made weapons that attracted much attention but few orders, so an increasing number of production expedients was incorporated to the point where the SIG 710-3 makes use of some stampings.

The Swiss were very influenced by the MG 42, and in the years after the war produced several designs based on features of the model. The SIG 710-3 trigger mechanism is the same as that of the MG 42, and so is the ammunition feed, which is so efficient that it accommodates both American and German belt linkings without trouble. The locking system is identical to that employed on the Sturmgewehr 45, which failed to reach service with the German army before the surrender of May 1945.

However, the SIG 710-3 does have many original Swiss features, not the least of which is the type of rapid barrel change. Many extras were developed for these machine-guns, including a buffered tripod for sustained fire. Special features such as dial sights and telescopic sights were also produced, and in the end the SIG 710-3 could be regarded as one of the most advanced machine-guns available anywhere. However, it was all for nothing as far as SIG was concerned – high development and production costs (combined with the strict rules of the Swiss government regarding arms sales) led to an early exit from production.

**SPECIFICATION**

**SIG 710-3**
**Calibre:** 7.62-mm (0.3-in)
**Length overall:** 1143 mm (45 in)
**Length of barrel:** 559 mm (22 in)
**Weights:** gun 9.25 kg (20.39 lb); heavy barrel 2.5 kg (5.51 lb); light barrel 2.04 kg (4.5 lb)
**Muzzle velocity:** 790 m (2,592 ft) per second
**Rate of fire, cyclic:** 800-950 rounds per minute
**Feed:** belt

# L4 Bren Machine-gun

***The latest version of the venerable Bren gun of World War II vintage is the L4A4 firing the NATO 7.62-mm (0.3-in) round. It has a new barrel, breech block and vertical 30-round box magazine, and has now been retired from British service.***

When considering modern machine-guns, it seems something of a surprise that a weapon as old as the **Bren Gun** should be included, especially as the origins of this classic weapon can be traced back to a time as early as the first part of the 1930s. But the original Bren machine-guns were chambered for the 0.303-in (7.7-mm) rimmed cartridge that was the standard rifle and machine-gun round of the British army at that time. Moreover, when the decision was made in the 1950s to convert to the new standard NATO 7.62-mm (0.3-in) cartridge, the British armed forces still had large stockpiles of the Bren machine-gun to hand. In these circumstances, therefore, it made very good financial sense to convert these elderly but still effective weapons to use the new-calibre ammunition, and such a programme was soon put into effect at the Royal Small Arms Factory at Enfield Lock in Middlesex.

## Simple evolution

The conversion to the new calibre entailed a complete overhaul, but the task was made easier by the fact that during World War II a Canadian company produced numbers of Bren machine-guns in 7.92-mm (0.312-in) calibre for China. As this round was rimless, it was found that the breech blocks intended for the 'China contract' were equally suitable for the new 7.62-mm cartridge, and these were used in place of the original breech blocks. A new barrel was produced with a chromium-plated interior: this not only diminished wear on the barrel, but also reduced the need for the frequent barrel changes required on World War II versions. Thus the new gun was issued with only the one barrel.

The last version of the Bren machine-gun used by the British army before its switch to the L7 British version of the Belgian FN MAG general-purpose machine-gun was the **L4A4**. This was produced as a conversion of Bren Mk III weapons, and was not used as a front-line infantry weapon, but instead issued to the many other arms of the service which had need of a machine-gun. Thus the L4A4 was used by the Royal Artillery for the anti-aircraft and ground-defence of its batteries, by the Royal Signals for the defence of its installations in the field, by units assigned for home defence, and so on. The L4A4 was also used by the Royal Air Force.

***Although the Bren Gun had seen extensive and sometimes effective use as a light anti-aircraft weapon in World War II, no manner of later updating could retain this utility in the face of faster attack aircraft and their helicopter brethren.***

A version known as the **L4A5**, produced by conversion of Bren Mk II weapons, was used by the Royal Navy, and this was issued with two steel barrels rather than one barrel with a chromium-plated bore.

## Lesser variants

There was also a version known as the **L4A3** that was never encountered in any substantial numbers as it was a conversion of the old Bren Mk II gun. Other seldom-seen variants were the **L4A1** (originally **X10E1**) for development of the L4 series and produced as conversions from Bren Mk III standard with a pair of steel barrels; the **L4A2** (otherwise **X10E2**) development model produced as conversions from Bren Mk III standard with two steel barrels and a bipod; and the **L4A6** conversion from L4A1 standard with one chromium-plated barrel. The **L4A7** was developed to the drawings stage to meet the requirements of the Indian army, which needed a more modern weapon produced by conversions from Bren Mk I standard with a chromium-plated barrel.

***Even after its relegation from first-line service, the L4 series went on to enjoy a lengthy second-line career in the hands of gunners and other specialist troops unlikely to become directly embroiled in battlefield fighting.***

In all these L4 versions the gas-operated mechanism of the original 0.303-in Bren machine-gun remained unchanged. So few were the modifications involved in the change of calibre that the only points of note were that the 7.62-mm versions used a nearly vertical straight magazine in place of the curved magazine of the 0.303-in weapons, and a muzzle without the pronounced cone shape of the weapons comprising the original series.

For the anti-aircraft role the L4A4 was provided with some fairly sophisticated sighting arrangements. The L4A4 was not mounted on a tripod, as had been the old Bren machine-guns, but instead was designed for installation on the roof hatches of self-propelled guns and howitzers as well as on other armoured fighting vehicles.

So the Bren gun soldiered on in its new form, and there seems to be no sign of its passing completely from use in the foreseeable future. Several commonwealth nations still use the Bren, some in its original 0.303-in form, so although the original design may be old, the weapon is still regarded as an effective one and in its L4A4 form the weapon is as good as many far more modern designs.

| SPECIFICATION | |
|---|---|
| **L4A4** | **Muzzle velocity:** 823 m (2,700 ft) per second |
| **Calibre:** 7.62-mm (0.3-in) | **Rate of fire, cyclic:** 500 rounds per minute |
| **Length overall:** 1133 mm (44.6 in) | **Feed:** 30-round straight box |
| **Length of barrel:** 536 mm (21.1 in) | |
| **Weight empty:** 9.53 kg (21 lb) | |

# L86 Machine-gun

For many years the standard squad light machine-gun for the British army has been a version of the FN MAG fitted with a bipod and known as the L7A2. While this is a fine weapon, it is rather a cumbersome load for the infantryman and fires a cartridge that is now generally considered too powerful for the squad support role. With the imminent arrival of the Enfield Weapon System (or Small Arms 80, otherwise SA80 and L85), the L7A2 became due for replacement in the squad support role by a new weapon known in its development phase as the **XL73E2 Light Support Weapon** or **LSW**. It was decided that the L7A2 would be retained for the sustained-fire function for some years to come.

***Seen here in front of the GPMG is the 4.85-mm (0.19-in) original development version of the Light Support Weapon, produced to complement the proposed 4.85-mm rifle. When NATO adopted the Belgian 5.56-mm (0.219-in) round, the 4.85-mm designs were changed despite their superior capabilities.***

Entering service as the **L86A1**, the LSW is half of the Enfield Weapon System with the L85A1 standard assault rifle. The two weapons have many things in common and can be easily recognised as coming from the same stable, but the LSW has a heavier barrel and a light bipod mounted well forward under the barrel. There is also a rear grip under what might be regarded as the butt to provide the firer with a better hold for sustained firing.

The term butt is rather misleading as the LSW is based on a 'bullpup' layout in which the trigger group is placed forward of the magazine. This arrangement makes the LSW more compact than a conventional weapon. Much of the LSW is steel, but the fore grip and pistol grip for the trigger are tough nylonite. The LSW uses the same magazine as the IW, namely a standard M16A1 30-round box.

## Calibre change

The LSW has undergone several changes of calibre since it was first mooted. Originally it was calibred for the British experimental 4.85-mm (0.19-in) cartridge, but this was overruled in favour of the American 5.56-mm (0.219-in) M193 cartridge, which in turn was superseded yet again in favour of the NATO standard 5.56-mm SS109. The first production versions were chambered for the SS109 round, and also had an optical sight known as the Sight Unit Small Arms Trilux, or SUSAT, mounted on a bracket over the receiver. It is possible to change this sight for a night sight.

***The L86A1 Light Support Weapon shares many components with the 5.56-mm L85 rifle; obvious differences are the heavier barrel, the bipod and the rear grip. The LSW uses the same magazine as the Individual Weapon.***

## Planned accessories

Various accessories were planned for the LSW once it had entered service as the L86A1 after the start of production in 1985. A training adapter firing low-powered ammunition was created as one of these options, and another was a blank-firing attachment. A multi-purpose tool is in use for stripping and first-line repairs, and it is possible to fit a sling for carrying. The muzzle attachment is so arranged that it is feasible for rifle grenades to be fired from the muzzle, although it is not envisaged that the LSW will be used extensively for this purpose.

The LSW underwent a protracted development period, some of the period being elongated by the change of NATO standard calibre and other considerations. By the time it reached the hands of the troops, the LSW should have been an excellent weapon with no bugs left to iron out, but in fact the weapon suffered from the same type of problems as encountered by the L85A1 rifle.

**SPECIFICATION**

| | |
|---|---|
| **L86A1** | **Muzzle velocity:** 970 m (3,182 ft) per second |
| **Calibre:** 5.56-mm (0.219-in) | **Rate of fire, cyclic:** 700-850 rounds per minute |
| **Length overall:** 900 mm (35.43 in) | **Feed:** 30-round curved box |
| **Length of barrel:** 646 mm (25.43 in) | |
| **Weight loaded:** 6.88 kg (15.17 lb) | |

***With the L1A1 rifle replaced by the 5.56-mm (0.219-in) L85, the British Army adopted a squad support weapon of the same calibre to replace the L7 general-purpose machine-gun, which has been retained for the sustained-fire role.***

# Browning M2HB
## Heavy machine-gun

The oldest machine-gun design still in production and large-scale service, the **Browning M2** was designed by John Browning as an aircraft gun, but entered service as the **Model 1921** ground weapon. It was upgraded to M2 standard in 1932 and then reached its definitive form as the **M2HB** for the sustained-fire role with a heavy barrel offering increases in the practical rate of fire and number of rounds that could be fired between barrel changes. The changing of a barrel entailed the time-consuming head space and timing adjustments. This drawback was accepted with relatively good grace for a long period by operators delighted by the performance and reliability of the M2HB, but in more recent years the weapon's current US manufacturer, Ramo Defense, has introduced a QCB (Quick Change Barrel) kit applicable to all M2 variants to create the **M2HB-QCB** or **M2HQB**.

Another limitation to the tactical employment of the M2 has for long been its comparatively high weight, and Ramo Defence therefore introduced the **M2 Lightweight Machine-Gun**. This is still based on the recoil-based operating system of the M2 and retains a 75% commonality of parts with that weapon, but is 11 kg (24.25 lb) lighter at a mere 27 kg (59.5 lb). The opportunity was also taken to upgrade the weapon with an adjustable buffer to allow the weapon's rate of fire to be adjusted between 550 and 750 rounds per minute, a quick-change lightweight barrel with a Stellite-lined chromed bore with a flash suppressor, the Max Safe charging system, and a trigger safety switch.

***Despite the age of its basic design, the M2 remains the classic heavy machine-gun of the Western world, and offers excellent capabilities against personnel and lighter materiel up to AFVs and helicopters.***

***The M2HB mounted on a vehicle provides a high level of offensive and defensive capability in mobile operations. In this instance, sand bags are piled round the weapon to create a 'pit' offering good protection against machine-gun fire.***

### Ammunition range

The M2 machine-gun has remained in production and service for a long time not only as a result of its reliability and long-range accuracy, but also for the excellence of the ammunition designed for it. The standard range includes the M2 AP, FN 169 APEI, M8 API, M20 API-T, M2 and M33 Ball, M1 and M23 Incendiary, and M10, M17 and M21 Tracer. Each of these has a complete cartridge length of 138.4 mm (5.45 in) and weight of 120 g (4.23 oz), and fires a projectile of between 39.7 and 46.8 g (1.4 and 1.65 oz) at a muzzle velocity of between 850 and 920 m (2,789 and 3,018 ft) per second out to a maximum effective range of some 3000 m (3,280 yards).

Additional capability is offered by more modern ammunition types, of which perhaps the best is that offered by the Norwegian company Nammo, which took over Raufoss, the originator of the range. The object of the new ammunition range was to exploit the capabilities offered by the machine-gun on its new 'soft mount' that improves accuracy to a marked extent at the penalty of an additional 18 kg (40 lb) of mount weight, and it is claimed that the ammunition provided capabilities no markedly inferior to those of 20-mm cannon ammunition.

***Seen here on the turret mounting of an experimental AFV, the lightweight version of the M2 offers all the capabilities of the original weapon as well as less weight and greater flexibility of operation in firing rate.***

### Matched rounds

All three rounds have the same dimensions and weight, and fire projectiles massing between 43 and 47 g (1.52 and 1.66 oz) at a muzzle velocity of 915 m (3,002 ft) per second. The MP NM140 will penetrate 11 m (0.43 in) of armour at 45 degrees at 1000 m (1,095 yards) and generally breaks into some 20 effective fragments after striking 2 mm (0.08 in) of Dural. The MP-T NM160 is the slightly less accurate tracer variant. The AP-S NM173 round has the accuracy of the MP NM140 round and can pierce 11 mm of armour at 30 degrees at a range of 1500 m (1,640 yards).

**SPECIFICATION**

**Browning M2HB**
**Calibre:** 0.5-in (12.7-mm)
**Length overall:** 1650 mm (65 in)
**Length of barrel:** 1143 mm (45 in)
**Weights:** gun 38 kg (83.8 lb); M3 tripod 20 kg (44 lb)
**Muzzle velocity:** 930 m (3,051 ft) per second
**Rate of fire, cyclic:** 450-600 rpm
**Feed:** 100-round metal-link belt

# M60 Medium machine-gun

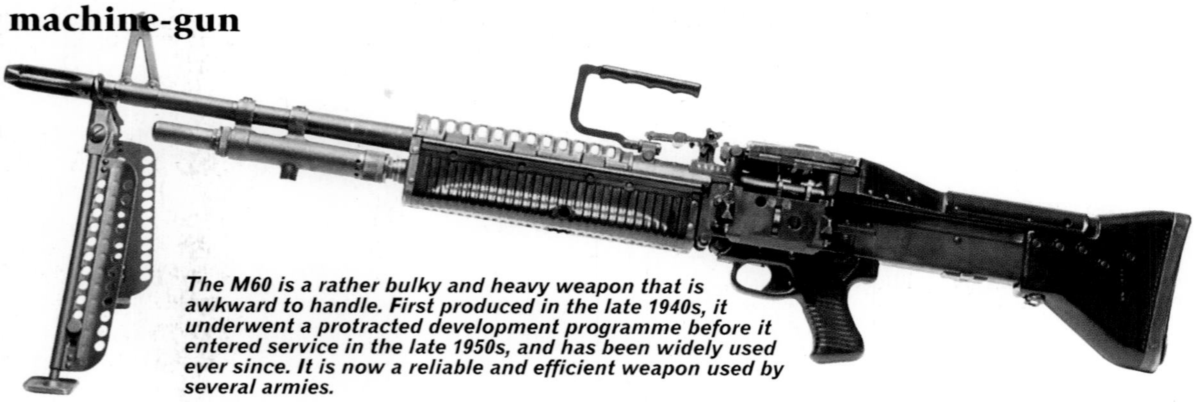

*The M60 is a rather bulky and heavy weapon that is awkward to handle. First produced in the late 1940s, it underwent a protracted development programme before it entered service in the late 1950s, and has been widely used ever since. It is now a reliable and efficient weapon used by several armies.*

The **M60** is an American general-purpose machine-gun that can trace its origins back to the latter period of World War II, when it was known as the **T44**. The design was greatly influenced by the superb German machine-guns of the day: the ammunition feed is a direct lift from the MG 42, and the piston and bolt assembly was copied from the revolutionary 7.92-mm (0.312-in) Fallschirmjägergewehr 42 (FG 42). The T44 and its production version, the M60, made extensive use of steel stampings and plastics, and the first examples were issued for service with the US Army in the late 1950s.

These first examples were not successful. They handled badly and some of the detail design was so poor that changing a barrel, for example, involved taking half the weapon apart. The early difficulties were gradually eliminated, and the M60 is now as efficient a weapon as any, but many serving soldiers still profess not to like the weapon for its generally awkward handling properties. But the M60 is the US Army's first general-purpose machine-gun, and it now serves in many roles.

## Several roles

In its basic form as a squad support weapon, the M60 is fitted with a stamped steel bipod mounted just behind the muzzle. In this role it is carried by a small handle which is rather flimsy for the loads placed on it; moreover the point of balance of the handle is entirely wrong. Many soldiers prefer to use a sling, and the weapon is often fired on the move while being steadied by the sling. For the light machine-gun role the M60 is a bit hefty, but it is being replaced in US Army service by the 5.56-mm (0.219-in) M249 Minimi. For heavier use the M60 can be mounted on a tripod or on a vehicle pedestal mount.

## Special-role guns

Some special versions of the M60 have also been produced. The **M60C** is a remotely fired version for external mounting on helicopters. The **M60D** is a pintle-mounted buttless version for mounting in helicopter gunships and some vehicles. The **M60E2** is a much-altered variant for use as a co-axial gun on armoured vehicles.

Throughout much of its production life the M60 has been manufactured by the Saco Defense Systems Division of the Maremount Corporation, which was always aware of the shortcomings of the M60's design, especially in the light machine-gun role.

The company therefore developed what it calls the **Maremount Lightweight Machine-Gun**, which is essentially the M60 much modified to reduce weight and improve handling. The bipod has been moved back under the receiver and a foregrip has been added. The gas-operated mechanism has been simplified, and there is now provision for a winter trigger. The result is a much lighter and handier weapon than the original, although it can now be used only for the light machine-gun role. The revised weapon was evaluated by several armies.

The M60 is now in service with several armies other than the US Army. Taiwan not only uses the M60 but produces it as well. South Korea is another Asian operator, while farther south the Australian army also has the M60 in service.

*Above: Once located on its bipod or tripod, the M60 is an excellent and reliable machine-gun whose primary limitation is the laborious process of changing the barrel. This dictates that the air-cooled M60 should not be used to fire long bursts without adequate cooling periods.*

*Left: Being a full-calibre weapon firing the NATO standard 7.62-mm (0.3-in) cartridge, the M60 is well suited to the long-range fire-support role. In this capacity the weapon is mounted on a sturdy tripod to provide a stable firing base, the light bipod legs attached near the muzzle being folded back alongside the gas cylinder.*

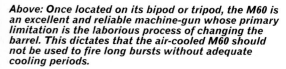

### SPECIFICATION

**M60**
**Calibre:** 7.62-mm (0.3-in)
**Length overall:** 1105 mm (43.5 in)
**Length of barrel:** 559 mm (22 in)
**Weights:** gun 10.51 kg (23.17 lb); barrel 3.74 kg (8.245 lb)
**Muzzle velocity:** 855 m (2,805 ft) per second
**Rate of fire, cyclic:** 550 rpm
**Feed:** 50-round metal link belt

# Support weapons

**The infantry battalion's support company has the unit's heavier weapons. These range from simple yet devastating short-range weapons such as mortars and anti-tank launchers of several types to longer-range weapons such as anti-aircraft and anti-tank missiles. Many weapons can be used in more than one role.**

A modern infantry battalion is divided into three, sometimes four, rifle companies and a support company. Depending on the individual army, the latter includes mortars, anti-tank weapons, sustained-fire machine-guns, anti-aircraft weapons and sometimes other specialist weapons such as automatic grenade launchers or 'bunker-buster' rocket launchers.

The threat of German invasion had been present for so long by 1914 that Belgium, France and Russia had built fortresses to guard their borders. The German response was to engineer units equipped with mortars that ranged from the man-portable to the famous 420-mm (16.54-in) 'Big Bertha' howitzers. In the event it was not the fortresses that checked Germany's advances, but trench lines. By November 1914 these stretched from Switzerland to the North Sea, and the Germans had the advantage of plentiful supplies of mortars, ammunition and crews.

The German Minenwerfer mortars were feared and hated by Allied soldiers. The mortars could drop projectiles right into a trench and, being positioned within a few hundred metres, could be aimed with great accuracy. The Allies then developed mortars of their own, which became steadily lighter and more portable during the war. Mortars formed a key part of the armoury of the German assault troop units that spearheaded their great offensive in March 1918.

*The mortar can be used for nocturnal support missions (as here in Canadian hands during World War II's Italian campaign) when under the supervision of an adequate fire-control system.*

*Men of a British support company in action with the 81-mm (3.2-in) L16 mortar, one of the best such weapons now in service anywhere in the world.*

## German mortar lead

Mortars improved considerably between the wars but the Germans retained their lead over the British and French. German infantry battalions had a fearsome collection of mortars at their disposal, ranging from light, hand-held 50-mm (1.98-in) weapons to excellent 81.4-mm (3.2-in) weapons that gave them a firepower much greater than that of their opponents in 1940. Indeed, German infantry regiments included an integral battery of six 150-mm (5.91-in) howitzers. In combination with their far superior machine-guns, this gave them so much more organic firepower than an equivalent British force that they were more capable of independent operations. The Red Army invested heavily in mortars too: its signature weapon was the 120-mm (4.72-in) heavy mortar which so impressed the Germans that they used captured weapons and also placed the type in production. Many were deployed in Normandy in 1944 and inflicted massive losses on the Allied infantry.

The mortar has remained the mainstay of the infantry since 1945, especially in campaigns over terrain that does not favour artillery, such as Vietnam. The French and, later, the US armies both emphasised the use of mortars against the Viet Minh/ Viet Cong and the North Vietnamese (the latter made plentiful use of Soviet-supplied mortars).

*Carrying his 0.3-in (7.62-mm) M1 carbine personal weapon slung on his back, an American infantryman of World War II prepares to fire his bazooka, possibly at a German infantry strongpoint.*

## Anti-tank weapons

Infantry anti-tank weapons became evident within a year of the tank's first appearance, and have been part of the support companies ever since. They can often serve a dual purpose: in the Falklands the British used MILAN anti-tank guided weapons to knock out Argentine bunkers, and during the Dieppe operation of 1942 a British commando used a Boys anti-tank rifle as a long-range sniper weapon to kill Germans manning an

## BUNKER BUSTING

Prepared defences of the permanent type built of concrete or of the field type extemporised from timber and earth to improve a natural defensive position, can often check if not halt the movement of mobile forces, and can sometimes channel the attacking forces into killing zones pre-registered by artillery or heavily mined. Thus all armies need a useful measure of 'bunker-busting' capability. In World War II this was provided at first by artillery and tank fire, preferably at direct-fire range, and the efforts of combat engineers with weapons such as the Bangalore torpedo and satchel charge. These were later complemented by flamethrowers, anti-tank rocket launchers and specialised combat engineer vehicles carrying a heavy explosive charge that was deposited on the target before the armoured vehicle backed off and detonated the charge. These tactics are still effective, but were complemented initially by recoilless rifles and then by anti-tank missiles carrying hollow-charge penetrative warheads.

***The flamethrower saw a surge in popularity during World War II among soldiers faced with the complex and dangerous task of clearing an enemy's prepared defences, often centred on concrete bunkers.***

observation post. The Red Army retained the anti-tank rifle right through World War II despite the weapon's inability to penetrate the armour of most German tanks. Massed volleys from these weapons could cut the tracks of even heavy armoured vehicles, and were useful against infantry strongpoints.

In World War II both sides developed recoilless rifles as anti-tank weapons. Initially created as lightweight tank killers for airborne forces, they became standard anti-tank weapons after the war for tasks that included bunker-busting and, in the Falklands campaign, the crippling of an Argentine warship. The Viet Minh/Viet Cong relied on Chinese-supplied 82-mm (3.23-in) and 107-mm (4.22-in) recoilless rifles from the 1950s to 1975, often beginning their attacks with a volley from these weapons. The US forces countered with 90- and 106-mm (3.54- and 4.17-in) recoilless rifles, often firing a 'beehive' anti-personnel round.

### Dual-role AA weapons

The development of the machine-gun and its use in the sustained-fire role is treated elsewhere, but anti-aircraft weapons have often played a dual role in the same way as anti-tank weapons. By 1939 the better armies were equipping their infantry regiments with anti-aircraft artillery (AAA) of up to 40-mm (1.575-in) calibre. As the threat from the German air force diminished, Allied infantry units began to employ their AAA in the ground role. Bofors 40-mm guns, mounted on trucks, were used to shoot-in ground assaults.

***German troops in action with a 37-mm anti-aircraft gun. Designed to loft their shells as quickly as possible to the height of aircraft, such guns had a high muzzle velocity and thus were useful in the anti-vehicle role.***

Since the 1960s support companies have included shoulder-fired anti-aircraft missiles. Early weapons like the US Redeye and Soviet SA-7 were short-ranged, unreliable and capable only of pursuit-course attacks. The US Stinger, with an all-aspect attack capability, has since proved more effective against helicopters and low-flying attack aircraft.

Several ground weapons have made useful extempore anti-aircraft weapons. The enterprising Afghan mujahideen guerrillas used RPG-7 anti-tank rockets against Soviet helicopters, firing volleys from mountainsides above helicopters.

Support weapons boosted the firepower of an infantry battalion to a fantastic degree in the 20th century. They enable the battalion to defend itself against armoured vehicles and aircraft as well as to fight its way forward, using its integral artillery (mortars and grenade launchers), machine-guns and ultimately 'bunker busters' (anti-tank weapons or dedicated rocket launchers) to attack strongpoints. The downside of this firepower is that someone has to carry all this kit and, in the absence of motor transport, that means the infantry. Thus military technology has made great strides since Roman times, but the average load of the foot soldier remains much as it was then, 2,000 years ago.

***Although optimised for the heavyweight anti-tank role, weapons such as the Euromissile HOT missile system also offer a potent capability against strongpoints and bunkers at long tactic ranges.***

# Panzerfaust

The excellence of Soviet tanks came as a nasty shock to the German army in 1941. German anti-tank guns could only knock out a Soviet tank at point-blank range. The race began in order to develop an infantry anti-tank system. Bigger guns were quickly produced, but they were bulky, needing large crews and a vehicle to tow them. The Germans first encountered the T-34 near Grodno in June 1941, and found it to be vastly superior to their own PzKpfw IV. At that time, German infantry relied on anti-tank rifles and small calibre guns (used in the attack, as opposed to British tactics which only used anti-tank guns in the defence); but they found to their horror that the only weapon effective against the T-34 was the 88-mm (3.46-in) flak gun. During late 1941 a Soviet KV-1 tank held up an entire German division for 48 hours, dug in by a bridge, until an 88-mm gun was called in to destroy it. Even then it took seven rounds, of which only two actually penetrated! In the absence of an 88-mm gun, the standard defence against the T-34 entailed some brave but foolhardy soldier rushing up to the tank and dropping a fused Teller mine under the tracks or turret overhang.

## German response

The ultimate German response to the T-34 was the **Panzerfaust** (tank fist). A small bomb fired from a disposable launcher it went some way to redress the balance against the T-34. It was not just used against the T-34: after D-Day, entire Volkssturm units were armed with nothing else; and their capabilities are attested by the fact that on 29 March 1945 a small party of Volkssturm held up a squadron from the 1st Royal Tank Regiment for the best part of a day.

## Monroe effect

The Panzerfaust project was initiated by Dr Langweiter of Hugo Schneider AG. What Langweiter required was a delivery system for a new type of bomb or projectile that he felt would be effective against well-armoured tanks. This bomb used the Monroe effect: the high explosive warhead was produced with a cone-shaped hollow interior, copper-lined and open end facing forward, so that when the head was detonated at the optimum distance away from armour plate, the explosive force went forward. At the same time, a thin, focused jet of molten metal and superheated gas was directed at the armour plate at some 6000 m (19,685 ft) per second. In the case of a tank, this jet melted a hole in the armour allowing the ingress of hot gas and vaporised metal. This caused the tank's ammunition to explode, generally making life untenable for the crew. The problem was how to deliver the bomb. Artillery shells were too fast and too powerful to achieve this optimum distance: they either bounced off the tank or exploded too close to the armour, and although the difference could often be measured in millimetres – this was usually enough to make the warhead ineffective. Langweiter's solution was the disposable rocket launcher. This was manufactured by Volkswagen Werker at Fallersleben, and by 1943, over 200,000 missiles per month were being produced.

Desperate to halt the Allies, the Nazis set up the Volkssturm. Men previously considered unsuitable for front-line combat were armed with Panzerfausts and, with the minimum of training, were thrown into the battle.

The original weapon was called the **Faustpatrone**, and was designed to be fired at arm's length and at right angles to the body. After it was found that this made aiming slightly difficult unless the operator was very close to the T-34, the first **Panzerfaust (Gretchen)** was developed.

Its official classification was the **Panzerfaust 30 (klein).** It was a 76.2-cm (30-in) long tube, firing a 1.5-kg (3.3-lb) bomb at 30 m (98 ft) per second and possessing a maximum effective range of 30 m (98 ft); the bomb's diameter was 100 mm (3.94 in), and the explosive charge could penetrate 140-mm (5.5-in) of armour sloped at 30°.

Propulsion was by a charge in the tube base, and a rocket-charge through later versions. The Panzerfaust 30 (klein) was superseded by the **Panzerfaust 30**, **60** and **100** (the numbers indicating the range in metres) which fired a 3-kg bomb (6.6-lb) at 30, 45 and 62 m (98, 148 and 203 ft) per second respectively. Each one could penetrate up to 200 mm (7.87 in) of armour, at a 30° slope.

*The first type of Panzerfaust to enter widespread service was the Panzerfaust 30. The number referred to the 30 m-range (98 ft 4¾ in). Final versions boasted an increased range of 100 m (328 ft).*

*Above: The more complex sight indicates that this is a Panzerfaust 60. The fired bomb weighed 3 kg (6.6 lb) and the warhead could penetrate 200 mm (7.87 in) of armour.*

**SPECIFICATION**

**Panzerfaust 30 (klein)**
**Range:** 30 m (98 ft 4¾ in)
**Weights:** total 1.475 kg (3¼ lb); projectile 0.68 kg (1½ lb)
**Projectile diameter:** 10 cm (4 in)
**Muzzle velocity:** 30 m (98 ft) per second
**Armour penetration:** 140 mm (6 in)

**SPECIFICATION**

**Panzerfaust 60**
**Range:** 60 m (197 ft)
**Weights:** total 6.8 kg (15 lb); projectile 3 kg (6.6 lb)
**Projectile diameter:** 150 mm (6 in)
**Muzzle velocity:** 45 m (148 ft) per second
**Armour penetration:** 200 mm (8 in)

# Panzerfaust

The Panzerfaust was the scourge of Red Army and Allied tanks alike. It proved to be an important weapon in the dying days of World War II in the European theatre. Hitler Youth and Volkssturm troops used them to great effect during the Battle of Berlin. As can be seen from the illustration, one of their great assets was their simplicity in operation.

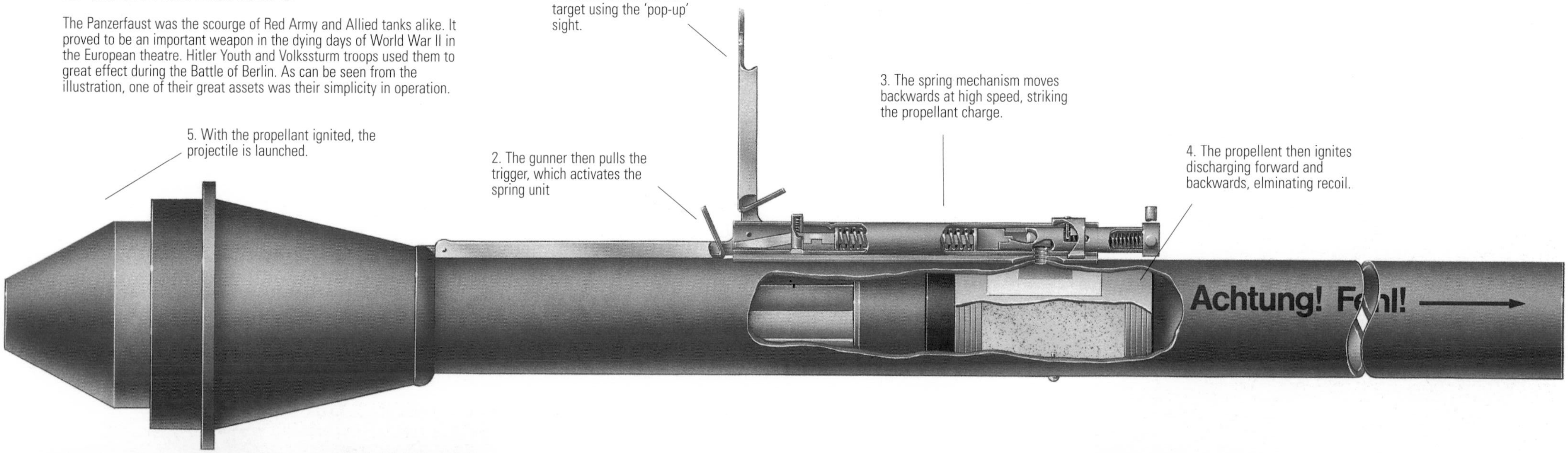

1. Gunner identifies the target using the 'pop-up' sight.
2. The gunner then pulls the trigger, which activates the spring unit
3. The spring mechanism moves backwards at high speed, striking the propellant charge.
4. The propellent then ignites discharging forward and backwards, elminating recoil.
5. With the propellant ignited, the projectile is launched.
Achtung! Fehl!

**_Left: By mid-1944 the Panzerfaust was widely issued to all front-line combat troops. This unfortunate German solider was killed at Sept Vents, Normandy, on 30 July 1944, a Panzerfaust 30 (klein) at his side._**

**_Below: Raising the simple leaf sights armed the trigger mechanism of the Panzerfaust 30, and the firer used the sight and a mark on the bomb to aim the weapon. After being fired the bomb was stabilised by folding fins._**

**_The Panzerfaust suited the German defensive tactics of 1943–45 exactly. Allied tank crews feared the weapon. It was available in huge numbers, and if aimed properly from the correct distance, every German could have at least one Allied tank to his credit._**

# Panzerschreck Anti-tank rocket launcher

In the first months of 1943 German troops trying to stem the Allied advance into Tunisia captured numbers of American 2.36-in (60-mm) M1 bazooka anti-tank rocket launchers. These were quickly returned to Germany for examination and evaluation by German technicians, who rapidly appreciated that the simple, and therefore cheap, construction of the rocket launcher could be used to good advantage by the Germans themselves. Thus it was not long before the German equivalent to the bazooka first appeared.

The German rocket-launcher fired a rocket very similar to that used on the Püppchen but modified for electrical firing. This first German launcher was known as the **8.8-cm Raketenpanzerbüchse 43** (generally abbreviated to **8.8-cm RPzB 43**), and was little more than a simple tube open at both ends: the rocket was loaded into the rear of the tube, and was then launched out of the front. The firer rested the 'pip' on his shoulder and, after the rocket had been loaded, operated a lever to power a small electrical generator before pulling the trigger, which allowed the power so produced to be passed via wires to the rocket motor for firing. The weapon was completed by a simple sighting system.

The RPzB 43 was an immediate success. Firing a larger rocket than the bazooka, it had better armour-penetration capability as the ability of a hollow-charge warhead to project its focused stream of hot gas and vapourised metal through the target armour is directly related to the warhead's diameter. But the rocket itself was limited in range to about 150 m (165 yards). The weapon had another disadvantage in that the motor was still burning as the rocket left the muzzle, which meant that the firer had to wear protective clothing and a gas mask to avoid being burnt. The rocket exhaust was dangerous for a distance up to 4 m (13.1 ft) to the rear of the tube on firing, and this exhaust could also kick up clouds of dust and debris: both of these had the unfortunate consequences of betraying the firer's position for rapid retaliation. As a result the RPzB 43 was generally unpopular with users despite the demonstrated capability of the warhead.

## Improved models

Further development of the basic concept produced the **RPzB 54**, which had a shield to protect the firer and thereby removed the need for the firer to wear protective clothing. The improved **RPzB 54/1** also fired a more developed rocket that required a shorter launching tube but nevertheless offered the slightly increased range of 180 m (195 yards). The RPzB 54 and RPzB 54/1 replaced the earlier RPzB 43 in production, whereupon surviving examples of the early models were passed to second-line and reserve units.

Weapons of these types soon became very widely distributed and used in the German army, to the extent that they were encountered on every front in large numbers. The later rockets could penetrate up to 160 mm (6.3 in) of tank armour, but they were essentially close-range weapons that required careful handling in action; moreover, special care had to be taken regarding the dangerous effects of the back blast on firing. The usual crew for these weapons was two men, one aiming and the other loading the rockets and connecting the ignition wires to the launcher contacts. Tank targets often had to be stalked for the crews to get within effective range, but if a hit was registered the target tank was usually dead. The only counter to the RPzB series was extra protection such as sandbags, track links or stand-off armour, along with special infantry squads that were specially introduced to move with the tanks and provide them with a measure of protection.

The RPzB series had several nicknames including **Ofenrohr** (oven chimney) and also **Panzerschreck** (tank terror).

***Above: The RPzB 54 was an improved RPzB 43, itself inspired by the American bazooka weapon but firing a larger-calibre rocket with a more potent warhead.***

***Above: The RPzB 54 introduced a small shield, complete with an aiming window, to prevent the firer's face from being burned by the back blast of the rocket as it emerged from the front of the launcher.***

***Left: The RPzB 54 is seen in text-book form with the two-man crew well clear of the line of the back blast and the loader inserting the rocket into the rear of the launcher before making the electrical connections.***

### SPECIFICATIONS

**RPzB 43**
**Calibre:** 88-mm (3.46-in)
**Length:** 1638 mm (64.5 in)
**Launcher weight:** 9.2 kg (20.3 lb)
**Rocket:** RPGr 4322 grenade weight 3.27 kg (7.21 lb); grenade warhead 0.65 kg (1.43 lb)
**Range:** maximum 150 m (165 yards)
**Armour penetration:** 210 mm (8.25 in)

**RPzB 54**
**Calibre:** 88-mm (3.46-in)
**Length:** RPzB 54 1638 mm (64.5 in) and RPzB 54/1 1333 mm (52.5 in)
**Launcher weight:** RPzB 54 with shield 11 kg (24.25 lb) and RPzB 54/1 with shield 9.45 kg (21 lb)
**Rocket:** RPGr 4992 grenade weight 3.25 kg (7.165 lb); grenade warhead weight not available
**Range:** maximum 200 m (220 yards)
**Armour penetration:** 160 mm (6.3 in)

# Goliath Demolition vehicle

*A German combat engineer prepares to launch his SdKfz 302 Goliath demolition vehicle against a target. In its electrically powered form the Goliath was too costly.*

In 1940 a small demolition carrier developed by the French company Kegresse was sunk in the Seine river but salved by the Germans. After examination of this little machine, the Germans contracted in November 1940 with Borgward for the development of a small remotely controlled vehicle of the fully tracked type able to carry a charge of at least 50 kg (110 lb). This **leichte Ladungsträger Goliath**, which was blown up in its entirety on reaching its target, was schemed as a means of destroying bunkers, strong points and even tanks from a safe distance under the remote control of combat engineers.

The **SdKfz 302** prototype had four large wheels on each side and was powered by two electric motors drawing power from a pair of batteries. The production version reflected a modified standard in its use of small roadwheels attached to leaf-springs, and this left space inside the track outline on each side for a sponson carrying a battery, thus freeing internal volume for a larger explosive charge, now amounting to 60 kg (132 lb). On each side the idler was of the solid disc type, and there were three track-return rollers.

## First production

This initial production variant was the **SdKfz 302 E-Motor** that was otherwise known as the Gerät 67. Between April 1942 and January 1944 the Borgward and Zündapp companies manufactured some 2,650 weapons of this type, which was made of 5-mm (0.2-in) steel and delivered to the front on a two-wheel trailer. On the vehicle's rear was a drum carrying the command wire: this was of the three-strand type with two used for control of the vehicle and the third for detonation of the demolition charge.

The first SdKfz 302 vehicles were allocated to Panzerpionierkompanien (Goliath) 811 to 815 within the Heerespionierbataillon (mot) zbV 600 (Taifun). Another operator was the Pioniersturmbrigade 627. Only a few examples of the SdKfz 302 were used in action for the two reasons that the HE charge was tactically too small, and the vehicle's unit cost considerably too high.

## Too expensive

In January 1944, therefore, the SdKfz 302 was taken out of production as the programme to create a cheaper but more capable variant with an internal combustion engine was speeded. In March 1945, on the eve of Germany's defeat, there were still 2,527 unused SdKfz 302 vehicles.

It was as early as November 1942 that the first demands had been made for a longer-ranged and more powerfully armed demolition vehicle. The Zundapp and Zachertz companies developed this successor as the **SdKfz 303 V-Motor**. The Zundapp variant was the **SdKfz 303a** (otherwise the **Gerat 671**), while the Zachertz model was the **SdKfz 303b** (otherwise the **Gerat 672**). The SdKfz 303a was built to the extent of 4,604 vehicles between April 1943 and September 1944, and carried a 75-kg (165-lb) charge. The vehicle was made of 10-mm (0.4-in) metal plate, and had a spoked rather than solid idler as well as only two track-return rollers on each side. Other differences included a raised air inlet cowl on top of the hull and road wheels carried by swing arms and coil springs.

## Little operational use

Production of the SdKfz 303b amounted to 325 vehicles completed from November 1944. This version carried a 100-kg (220-lb) charge, was slightly larger and, despite its greater weight, moderately faster. The lateral sponsons now carried two batteries, the control unit and the air filters. The charge was located in the front of the hull, the engine in the centre and the 6-litre (1.3-Imp gal) fuel tank and 650 m (710 yards) of wire on a drum at the rear.

Production of the SdKfz 303 required some 542 kg (1,195 lb) of iron and 10 kg (22 lb) of steel, and the cost of the SdKfz 303 was 1,000 Reichsmarks to the SdKfz 302's price of 3,000 Reichsmarks. Even so, the SdKfz 303 was not very successful and therefore little used in action. Thus 3,797 of the little vehicles still remained unused during January 1945.

*The Goliath was interesting in concept but tactically of little significance as it was short-ranged and carried only a comparatively light explosive charge as its payload.*

### SPECIFICATIONS

| SdKfz 302 | SdKfz 303a |
|---|---|
| **Weight:** 370 kg (816 lb) | **Weight:** 370 kg (816 lb) |
| **Dimensions:** length 1.5 m (4 ft 11 in); width 0.85 m (2 ft 9.5 in); height 0.56 m (1 ft 10 in) | **Dimensions:** length 1.62 m (5 ft 3.75 in); width 0.84 m (2 ft 9 in); height 0.6 m (1 ft 11.67 in) |
| **Powerplant:** two Bosch MM/RQL 2500/24 RL2 electric motors each delivering 2.5 kW (3.35 hp) | **Powerplant:** one Zundapp SZ7 two-cylinder two-stroke petrol engine delivering 9.3 kW (12.5 bhp) |
| **Performance:** maximum speed 10 km/h (6.2 mph); maximum range 1500 m (1,640 yards) on roads and 800 m (875 yards) across country; trench crossing 0.6 m (1 ft 11.5 in) | **Performance:** maximum speed 10 km/h (6.2 mph); maximum range 12 km (7.46 miles) on roads and 6-8 km (3.7-5 miles) across country; trench crossing not available |
| **Payload:** 60 kg (132 lb) of HE | **Payload:** 70 kg (165 lb) of HE |

# Panzerwurfmine (L)
## Anti-tank grenade

The **Panzerwurfmine (L)** was developed to provide special German tank-killer squads with a potent one-man stand-off weapon. It was a specialised form of anti-tank grenade with a hollow-charge warhead to defeat the target tank's armour, and to ensure that the warhead was facing the target armour when it struck the tank, the grenade was fitted with a finned tail for stabilisation and guidance.

The Panzerwurfmine was thrown at its target in a special manner. Behind the grenade warhead was a steel body attached to a wooden handle. The user gripped this handle and held it behind his back with the warhead pointing vertically upward. When ready, the user swung his arm forward and released the handle. As soon as the grenade was in flight, four canvas fins unfolded from the handle, and the drogue effect of these fins maintained the warhead in its correct forward position for maximum effect as it struck. In practice the Panzerwurfmine was not an easy weapon to use effectively. For a start the maximum possible range was limited by the strength and ability of the thrower, and was usually no more than 30 m (32.8 yards) and frequently less. Accuracy could only be ensured by practice with an inert training version.

Despite these disadvantages, some German anti-tank personnel favoured the Panzerwurfmine. Compared with other German close-in anti-tank weapons, the Panzerwurfmine was relatively small, light and handy. It was also potent, for the warhead was made up of RDX and TNT in equal measures and weighed 0.52 kg (1.146 lb). Combined with the hollow-charge principle, this usually ensured penetration of even the thickest armour. It also had the advantage of not requiring the user actually to approach the tank to place the grenade on the target. Further safety was provided by the fact that the warhead was not fully fused until the grenade was in flight.

Despite its success, the Panzerwurfmine was not copied closely by any of the Allies. Captured examples were used when they fell into Allied hands, especially by the Red Army, but the Americans often misused them for at first they thought that the weapon should be thrown as an oversized dart. After 1945 the principle was used by various Warsaw Pact nations, and in the 1970s Egypt in effect copied the Panzerwurfmine as part of the output of their new indigenous arms industry. The Egyptians discovered that this type of anti-tank weapon was exactly suited to their infantry anti-tank tactics, and their version was reported to be quite capable of 'killing' the modern tanks.

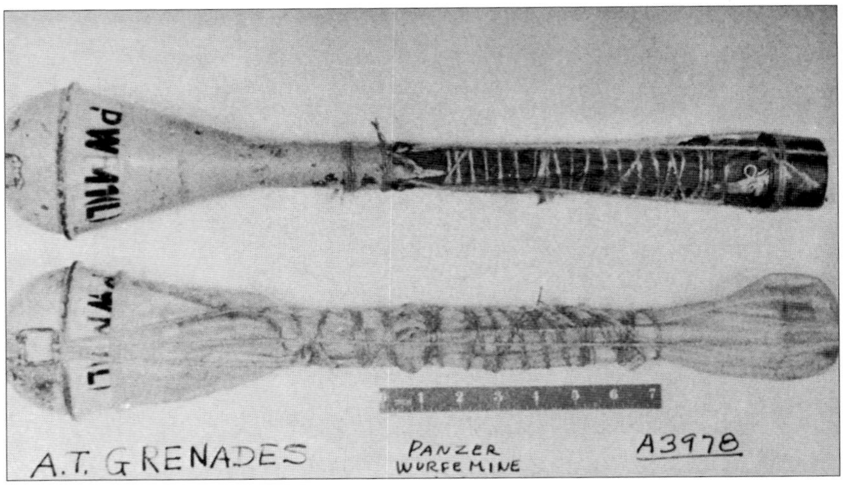


***Two examples of the German Panzerwurfmine (L) are shown as they would have been issued, with their stabiliser tails wrapped in cord around the throwing handle. These grenades were not a general issue as they required some skill for use in an effective manner, and they were therefore issued mainly to specialist close-in tank killer squads.***

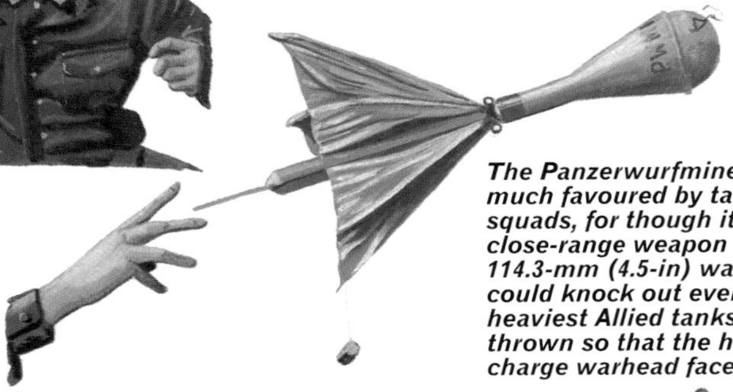

***The Panzerwurfmine (L) was much favoured by tank killer squads, for though it was a close-range weapon it had a 114.3-mm (4.5-in) warhead that could knock out even the heaviest Allied tanks. It was thrown so that the hollow-charge warhead faced forward.***

| SPECIFICATION | |
|---|---|
| **Panzerwurfmine (L)** | |
| **Body diameter:** 114.3 mm (4.5 in) | |
| **Lengths:** overall 533 mm (21 in); body 228.6 mm (9 in); fins 279.4 mm (11 in) | |
| **Weights:** overall 1.35 kg (2.98 lb); warhead 0.52 kg (1.146 lb) | |

# Püppchen
## Rocket launcher

Once the Germans learned that the artillery projectile was not the most efficient way to deliver a hollow-charge warhead to an armoured target (it moved too fast for the hollow-charge to have full effect), they moved to the rocket as a delivery system. The result was a small 8.8-cm (3.46-in) rocket carrying a hollow-charge warhead able to penetrate the armour of any Allied tank.

The German designers appear to have had little experience of what a rocket-launcher should be, and in the end developed what was in effect a small artillery piece to 'fire' the rocket. This device was known as the **Püppchen** (dolly), or more formally as the **8.8-cm Raketenwerfer 43**, and it had all the appearances of a small gun. There was a shield, and the launcher was moved on wheels. Once in position the wheels could be removed to lower the silhouette of the weapon, which then rested on rockers. The

***A British soldier demonstrates a Püppchen captured in Tunisia in 1943, clearly showing its low silhouette. This rocket launcher had no recoil mechanism and used a simple breech, but compared with the RP 43 series it was much more complex and expensive to produce. The wheels could be removed to lower the silhouette.***

***The 8.8-cm (3.46-in) Raketenwerfer 43 or 'Püppchen' was a form of anti-tank rocket launcher that was superseded, almost as soon as it entered service in 1943, by the RP 43 series, firing a very similar rocket. The RP 43 could be produced far more cheaply and quickly than the Püppchen, seen here while being examined by American soldiers.***

rocket was even loaded using a conventional breech mechanism. Where the Püppchen differed from artillery pieces was that there was no recoil mechanism. The recoil forces produced by firing the rocket were absorbed by the mass of the carriage alone, and the aimer could point the launcher tube by using a twin-handled grip and looking along the barrel.

The Püppchen was introduced into service in 1943, and in use had a maximum range of about 700 m (765 yards), though for anti-tank use the maximum effective range was about 230 m (250 yards) as the sighting system was rather rudimentary and the time of flight of the rocket could be measured in seconds. It was possible to fire up to 10 rockets per minute. Other design features of the Püppchen were that it could be broken down into seven loads for pack transport, and that skis could be used for movement over snow. There were even instructions printed on the inside of the shield for untrained personnel to use it on a battlefield.

### Phased out

The Püppchen did not remain in production for long. Almost as soon at the first items had been issued, American bazookas were captured in Tunisia and examined by German technical personnel, who realised that the simple pipe was all that was needed to launch their 8.8-cm rocket without the complexity of the Püppchen. Production was then switched to the simple RPzB series. But those Püppchen equipments that had been made and issued were not wasted. They were retained in use until the war ended, especially in Italy where a sizeable number were captured by the Allies and subjected to close investigation..

It seems that there were plans to mount modified Püppchen launchers on light armoured vehicles, but none of these came to anything.

**SPECIFICATION**

**Püppchen**
**Calibre:** 88-mm (3.46-in)
**Lengths:** overall 2.87 m (9 ft 5 in); barrel 1.60 m (5 ft 3 in)
**Weights:** travelling 146 kg (322 lb); in action 100 kg (220 lb); rocket 2.66 kg (5.86 lb)
**Elevation:** -18 to +15 degrees
**Traverse:** 60 degrees
**Ranges:** maximum 700 m (766 yards); practical 230 m (252 yards)

# Raketenpanzerbüchse Rocket launcher

In 1943 examples of the US 60-mm (2.36-in) M1 bazooka were captured in Tunisia and soon examined by German technicians, who quickly appreciated the advantages of its simple and cheap construction. Before long the first German equivalent appeared. This German launcher fired a rocket very similar to that used on the Püppchen but modified for electrical firing. This first German launcher was known as the **8.8-cm Raketenpanzerbüchse 43** (**RPzB 43**) and was little more than a simple tube, open at both ends, from which the rocket could be launched. The firer rested the 'pip' on his shoulder and operated a lever to power a small electrical generator. Releasing a trigger allowed the power so produced to be passed via wires to the rocket motor for firing. The weapon was completed by a simple sight system.

***The German RP 43 was inspired by the American bazooka, but used a larger 8.8-cm (3.46-in) rocket. Sometimes known as Panzerschreck, this weapon had a range of 150 m (165 yards) and could knock out all Allied tanks.***

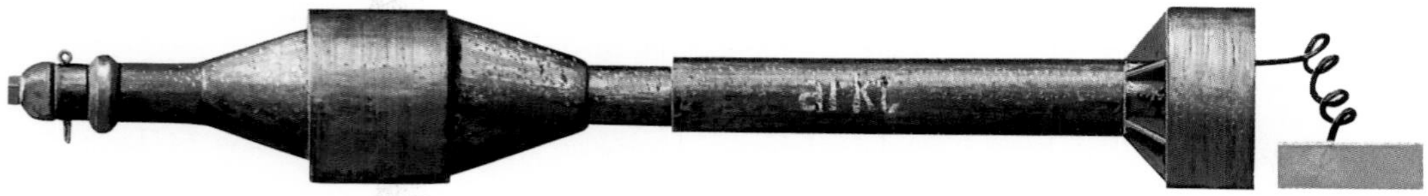

### Instant success

The RPzB 43 was an immediate success. Firing a large-calibre rocket, it had a better anti-armour capability than the bazooka, but the rocket was limited in range to about 150 m (165 yards). Another disadvantage was that the rocket motor was still burning as it left the muzzle, so the user had to wear protective clothing and a gas mask to avoid being burnt. The rocket exhaust was dangerous for a distance up to 4 m (13.1 ft) to the rear of the tube on firing, and this exhaust could also kick up clouds of dust and debris to betray the firing position. This did little to endear the RPzB 43 to its users.

Further development produced the **RPzB 54**, which had a shield to protect the firer and so remove the need for protective clothing, and the later **RPzB 54/1** fired a more advanced rocket needing a shorter launching tube but offering the increased range of 180 m (197 yards). The RPzB 54 and RPzB 54/1 replaced the RPzB 43 in production, and the early models were passed to second- line and reserve units.

***British troops examine an RPzB 54 captured in Normandy, July 1944. The shield can be seen, as can the main lever for the electrical generator used for firing: this looks like a large trigger under the tube. The RPzB 54/1 was essentially similar but used a shorter launching tube.***

### Major service

These weapons soon became very widely distributed and used. The later rockets could penetrate up to 160 mm (6.3 in) of armour, but they were close-range weapons that meant crews often had to 'stalk' a target. The usual crew was two men, one aiming and firing, and the other loading the rockets and connecting the ignition wires to the launcher contacts. The RPzB series had several nicknames, including **Ofenrohr** (oven chimney) and **Panzerschreck** (tank terror).

**SPECIFICATION**

**RPzB 43**
**Calibre:** 88-mm (3.46-in)
**Weights:** launcher 9.2 kg (20.3 lb); rocket 3.27 kg (7.21 lb); warhead 0.65 kg (1.43 lb)
**Length:** 1.638 m (5 ft 4½ in)
**Range:** maximum 150 m (164 yards)

**RPzB 54**
**Calibre:** 88 mm (3.46 in)
**Weights:** launcher 11 kg (24.25 lb); rocket 3.25 kg (7.165 lb)
**Length:** 1.638 m (5 ft 4½ in)
**Range:** maximum 150 m (164 yards)
**Rate of fire:** 4-5 rpm

# Anti-tank rifles

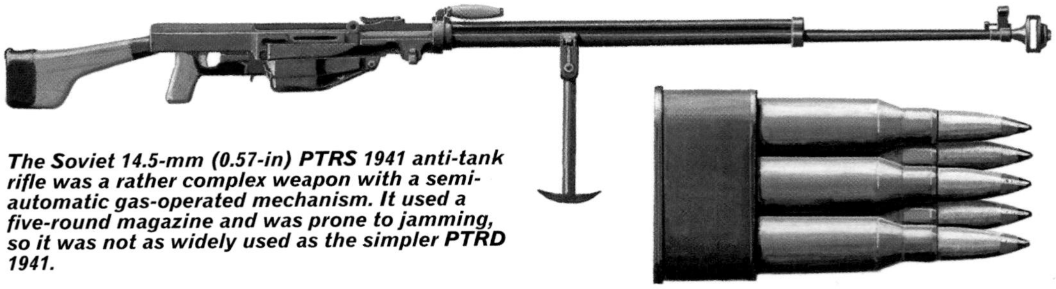

The Soviet 14.5-mm (0.57-in) PTRS 1941 anti-tank rifle was a rather complex weapon with a semi-automatic gas-operated mechanism. It used a five-round magazine and was prone to jamming, so it was not as widely used as the simpler PTRD 1941.

The Soviet PTRD 1941 fired the same steel-cored ammunition as the more complex PTRS 1941. It fired single shots only, but used a semi-automatic breech. It was widely used by the Red Army and partisans, and even the Germans used captured examples to arm garrison units. It was used for many years after 1945.

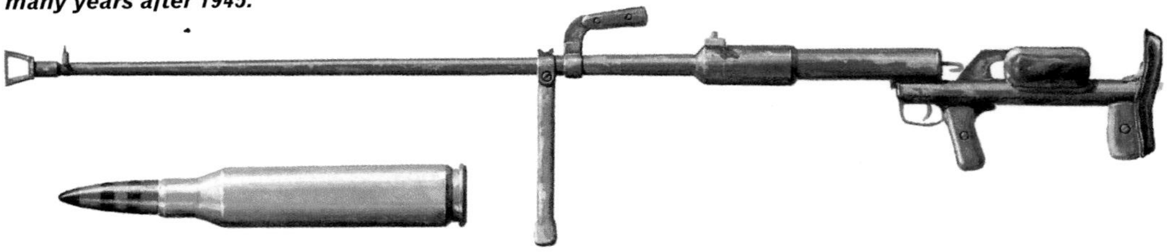

The Red Army used two anti-tank rifles during World War II, both of them very distinctive as they were long weapons firing the same 14.5-mm (0.57-in) round. The Soviets had neglected the anti-tank rifle when other nations were just adopting the type, and introduced it only at the time that others were discarding it. It must be said, though, that the Soviet rifles were more viable weapons than most in use at the time.

The more numerous of the Soviet rifles was the **PTRD 1941** (or **PTRD-41**) from the Degtyarov bureau and introduced in mid-1941 just in time for the German invasion. A very long weapon that was nearly all barrel, the PTRD-41 had a semi-automatic breech and its steel- or tungsten-cored projectile could penetrate up to 25 mm (0.98 in) of armour at 500 m (545 yards). A large muzzle brake and a bipod were fitted.

The second weapon was the **PTRS 1941** (or **PTRS-41**) from the Simonov bureau. Compared with the PTRD-41 it was a heavier and more complex weapon but had identical performance. The main change in the PTRS-41 was the use of a gas-operated mechanism and the addition of a five-round magazine, which combined to make the PTRS-41 a more trouble-prone weapon than the simpler and lighter PTRD-41. Further complexity was added by a feature that allowed the barrel to be removed for ease in carrying.

Despite the fact that these two anti-tank rifles reached the Red Army at a time when its anti-armour capability was being reduced by a rapid increase in German tank armour thicknesses, they remained in service until well after 1945. The Red Army found the PTRD-41 and PTRS-41 to be very useful all-round weapons: they were useful against soft-skin targets such as trucks, in house-to-house fighting they were unhandy but very powerful weapons and, when the opportunity arose, the Red Army even used these rifles against low-flying aircraft. Some light armoured cars carried the rifles as their main armament, and Lend-Lease vehicles such as Universal Carriers often mounted one.

The Red Army was not the only World War II operator of these anti-tank rifles, for the Germans pressed into their own use captured weapons: in German service up to 1943 the PTRD-41 was the **14.5-mm Panzerabwehrbüchse 783(r)** and the PTRS-41 was the **14.5-mm Pab 784(r)**.

The German army used two main types of anti-tank rifle but attempted to develop many more models. The first in-service weapon was the **7.92-mm Panzerbüchse 38**, a 0.312-in rifle from Rheinmetall-Borsig. It was a complex and expensive weapon whose breech fea-

This Soviet 14.5-mm (0.57-in) PTRD 1941 anti-tank rifle has had a round loaded into the breech with the loader's left hand, a subsequent tap on the firer's helmet then indicating that the rifle is ready to fire.

tured a small sliding breech block and an automatic ejector for the spent case. About 1,600 of the weapons were bought by the German army, but the type was not accepted as for full service although those that had been delivered were retained in service and were used during the early years of the war. Fired from a necked-down 13-mm (0.51-in) cartridge, the bullet could pierce 30 mm (118 in) of armour at 100 m (110 yards) at an impact angle of 60°.

The standard German anti-tank rifle was the **7.92-mm Panzerbüchse 39**. Created by the Gustloff-Werke of Suhl, this was a much simpler weapon than the Pzb 38 but with the same armour-penetration capability. Even though it still had a sliding breech block, this was operated by pulling down the pistol grip. Like the earlier rifle it was a single-shot weapon and the stock could be folded to make carriage more handy. Extra ammunition could be carried on the weapon in small boxes on the sides of the breech.

The two anti-tank rifles fired the same ammunition, which originally used a hard steel core. In 1939 Polish Marosczek anti-tank rifles were captured, and examination revealed that its bullets had a tungsten core that gave much better armour penetration. The Germans seized upon this principle as a means of extending the operational viability of their own anti-tank rifles, which would otherwise have been made obsolete by increases in tank armour thicknesses.

The Germans developed a surprising number of follow-on designs in an effort to replace the Pzb 39, and though several manufacturers produced a series of prototypes, all of them in 7.92-mm calibre, none of these got past the prototype stage. There was even a programme to develop an anti-tank machine-gun, the MG 141, but again this did not proceed far.

One other anti-tank rifle used by the Germans was a Swiss product known as the **7.92-mm M SS 41**. This was produced by the Waffenfabrik Solothurn to a German specification, but not many appear to have been made or delivered (some were used in North Africa). Solothurn also made a weapon more accurately described as an anti-tank cannon. This **2-cm Pab 785(s)** was a bulky weapon towed on a two-wheeled mounting, and again only a few were procured by the Germans. Others went to Italy, where the type was known as the **Fucile anti-carro**. It was an automatic weapon that used five- or 10-round magazines, and was sometimes known as the **s18-1100**; some were used by the Netherlands in 1939-40 as the **Geweer tp 181110**.

*The Panzerbüchse 39 is shown in the travelling position (below) and with the bipod lowered and stock extended ready for action (above). German anti-tank rifles were rendered obsolete by the increasing thickness of tank armour.*

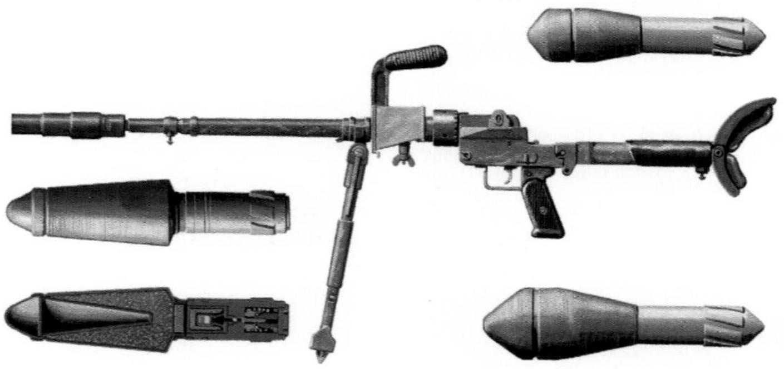

*The German Granatbüchse 39 was a converted Pzb 39 anti-tank rifle fitted with a 'Schiessbecker' grenade-launcher cup on the muzzle. The grenades fired by this weapon included small hollow-charge anti-tank grenades (see cross-section) that were effective only against the very lightest armour at ranges up to 125 m (135 yards).*

*A German soldier is seen in North Africa with a 7.92-mm (0.312-in) Panzerbüchse 39. This was a single-shot rifle firing a projectile (even when tungsten-cored) with only limited armour-piercing capability, denying the weapon the facility to tackle anything but the lightest tanks after 1940.*

# Improvised anti-tank weapons

Easy to make and use, the **Molotov cocktail** appears to have had its operational debut during the Spanish Civil War of 1936-39, when it was first used against Nationalist tanks by the Republican forces.

The basic weapon is simply a glass bottle containing petrol (or some other flammable substance) with an oil-soaked rag or something similar around the neck. This rag is ignited immediately before the weapon is thrown at a target, the breaking of the bottle as it hits its target allowing the contents to be ignited. It is very simple, easily understood and easily used, but the snag was that it was not very efficient. It was also discovered that petrol alone was not a very efficient anti-armour weapon as it simply runs off the sides of a tank even as it is burning. In order to make the flame-producing mixture 'stick', the petrol had to be mixed with a thickening agent such as diesel or oil or in some cases various forms of latex.

## Phosphorus grenade

An offshoot of the petrol bomb was the phosphorus grenade. Used by several nations, this was designed as a smoke grenade, but the white phosphorus, which started to burn as soon as it was exposed to the air, also made it a very useful anti-personnel and anti-armour weapon. There were several of these types of grenade but typical was the British **Grenade, Self-Igniting, Phosphorus, No. 76**. This was a glass milk bottle filled with a mix of phosphorus, water and benzine, and was intended primarily for the anti-tank role. It could be thrown at its target or launched from the Northover Projector, and contained a piece of smoked rubber that gradually dissolved in the mixture to make it 'stick' better to its target. Each No. 76 grenade weighed about 0.535 kg (1.18 lb).

## Boys anti-tank rifle

The **Rifle, Anti-tank, 0.55-in, Boys, Mk 1** was originally known as the **Stanchion Gun**, and was designed as the standard infantry anti-tank weapon of the British army. The first of the type entered service during the late 1930s and by 1942 the weapon was obsolete.

The Boys anti-tank rifle had a calibre of 13.97 mm and fired a powerful cartridge whose projectile could pierce 21 mm (0.827 in) at 300 m (330 yards). The cartridge produced an equally powerful recoil, and to reduce this recoil somewhat the long slender barrel was fitted with a muzzle brake. Ammunition was fed into the bolt-action firing mechanism from a five-round overhead box magazine. The Boys was long and heavy, so it was often mounted as the main weapon on board Bren Gun or Universal Carriers, or as the main armament of light armoured cars.

The first production Boys anti-tank rifles used a forward-mounted monopod combined with a handgrip under the butt plate, After Dunkirk various modifications were made to speed production, and among the measures taken was replacement of the forward monopod by a Bren Gun bipod and of the circular muzzle brake attachment by a new Solothurn muzzle brake with holes drilled along the sides; this latter was easier to produce than the original. In this form the Boys saw out its short service life, as by late 1940 it was regarded as being of only limited use as an anti-armour weapon. It was found to be a very effective anti-personnel weapon during the North African campaigns of 1941-42: here it was fired at rocks over or near a concealed enemy, the resultant rock splinters acting as anti-personnel fragments. The Boys also found its way into US Marine Corps hands during the Philippines campaign of early 1942, when some were used very sparingly against dug-in Japanese infantry positions. Captured Boys rifles also saw limited service with the Germans for a short while after Dunkirk as the **13.9-mm Panzerabwehrbüchse 782(e)**.

In 1940 there were plans to produce a Boys Mk 2 as a shortened and lightened version for airborne forces, but it did not get very far before the project was terminated.

## Northover Projector

In the aftermath of Dunkirk the British army was left with virtually no anti-tank weapons. With invasion imminent there was a need for an easily produced weapon that could be used to equip the army and also the newly formed Local Defence Volunteers, later to become

***The Molotov cocktail was an international weapon, and shown here from the left are examples from the Soviet Union, (the second an 'official' Red Army version), Britain (using a milk bottle), Japan and Finland. All use the same basic form, with petrol-soaked rags acting as fuses for ignition.***

***British troops train with Molotov cocktails in 1940. The British Army referred to these weapons as 'bottle bombs' and even established production lines for them, often using milk bottles filled with petrol and phosphorus.***

***Left: A French officer about to receive the hefty recoil of the Boys anti-tank rifle. The French army used a number of these rifles in 1940 provided by the British in exchange for a number of 25-mm (0.98-in) Hotchkiss anti-tank cannons. This example is the original Mk 1 with the monopod supporting leg.***

***An armourer services a Boys Anti-Tank Rifle Mk 1, easily recognisable by its monopod and circular muzzle brake. These rifles were little used after 1941 as they could penetrate only the lightest armour, yet they were awkward to carry and when fired had a recoil that was best described as fearful.***

**SPECIFICATION**

**Northover Projector**
**Calibre:** 63.5-mm (2.5-in)
**Weights:** projector 27.2 kg (60 lb); mounting 33.6 kg (74 lb)
**Range:** effective 90 m (100 yards); maximum 275 m (300 yards)

**Boys Anti-Tank Rifle Mk 1**
**Calibre:** 13.97-mm (0.55-in)
**Length overall:** 1625 mm (64 in)
**Length of barrel:** 914 mm (36 in)
**Weight:** 16.33 kg (36 lb)
**Muzzle velocity:** 991 m (3,250 ft) per second
**Armour penetration:** 21 mm (0.827 in) at 300 m (330 yards)

*The Northover Projector was a weapon developed in 1940 to equip the Home Guard. It was supposed to be used as an anti-tank weapon to fire the No. 76 bottle grenade filled with phosphorus. There was no recoil mechanism as the frame carriage was supposed to absorb the recoil, and the propelling charge was black powder.*

the Home Guard. One of the weapons that was rushed into production was the Northover mortar, also known as the bottle mortar but later designated the **Northover Projector**. This was was little more than a steel pipe with a rudimentary breech at one end. The ammunition consisted of orthodox hand and rifle grenades that were propelled from the muzzle by a small black-powder charge. Later the No. 76 phosphorus grenade was fired, and it was this that gave rise to the name bottle mortar. There was no appreciable recoil, the sights were basic but accurate enough up to about 90 m (100 yards), and the maximum range was about 275 m (300 yards).

For some time after 1940 the Northover Projector was a standard Home Guard weapon, and it was also issued to many army units for a while. In practice the Northover was only as good as the projectiles it fired, and as these were orthodox hand or rifle grenades their efficiency against most tanks was doubtful. The use of the white phosphorus grenade would no doubt have been more successful, but this was not a popular weapon with the projector crews for the simple reason that the glass bottle often broke inside the barrel on firing. The usual crew was two men, with possibly another in charge of the weapon and for designating targets. Many Home Guard units introduced their own local modifications to enable the Northover to be moved around more easily.

To make the normal four-legged carriage easier to handle, a lightened **Northover Projector Mk 2** was introduced during 1941, but only relatively few of these carriages were produced.

# Anti-tank grenades

The British army used three types of anti-armour hand grenade. The first was the **Grenade, Hand, Anti-tank, No. 73**, known as the 'Thermos' bomb from its shape and size. It was a pure blast weapon which often had little effect on armour, so it was mainly used for demolition work. More common during the early war years was the infamous **Grenade, Hand, Anti-tank, No. 74 (ST)**, the 'sticky bomb' which was coated in a gooey adhesive to make it stick to the side of a tank after landing: the sticky surface was normally contained within two shell halves which were removed just before throwing. The No. 74 was a most unpopular weapon as the sticky substance tended to make it stick to anything, even before throwing, and the type was used as little as possible.

The best of the British anti-tank grenades was the **Grenade, Hand, Anti-tank, No. 75**, otherwise known as the **Hawkins Grenade**. It was intended to be either thrown or laid as a mine to blow off a tank's tracks. It used a crush igniter fuse and about half of its weight of 1.02 kg (2.25 lb) was made up of the bursting charge. The type was often used in clusters for better effect, and the Germans captured so many of them before Dunkirk that they were later used as part of the minefields defending the Atlantic Wall with the designation **Panzerabwehrmine 429/1 (e)**.

The **Grenade, Rifle, Anti-tank, No. 68** was a rifle grenade fired from a muzzle cup fitted to the No. 1 Mk III rifle. It was withdrawn after 1941 as it was not much use against anything other than very light armour. It weighed 0.79 kg (1.75 lb) and could also be fired from the Northover Projector.

## American grenades

The American equivalent of the No. 68 was the **Antitank Rifle Grenade M9A1**, a much more successful grenade that could be fired from an M7 launcher fitted to the M1 Garand rifle or an M8 launcher fitted to an M1 carbine. The M9A1 weighed 0.59 kg (1.31 lb) and had an 0. 113-kg (0.25-lb) warhead behind a thin steel metal nose fitted with an impact fuse. Its capability against tanks was somewhat limited, but it was retained in service for some time as it was a very useful weapon against targets such as pillboxes. A ring tail was used for inflight stabilisation.

## Soviet grenades

As with the anti-tank rifle, the Soviets tended to neglect the anti-tank grenade and had to rush something into service in rather a hurry in 1940. Their first attempt was the **RPG 1940**, which resembled a short stick grenade and relied mainly on blast for its effect; it was not a great success and was gradually replaced. The contemporary **VPGS 1940** was a rifle grenade which featured a long rod that fitted into the rifle barrel before firing. It too was no great success. The best of the wartime Soviet anti-tank grenades was the **RPG 1943** of 1943. This was a hand-thrown grenade which in some ways imitated the German Panzerwurfmine, but had a tail unit that trailed on two canvas strips to keep the warhead with its hollow charge pointed towards the target. The RPG 1943 weighed 1.247 kg (2.75 lb), and was thus quite a weight to throw, but it had a heavy explosive content and could be very effective. The RPG 1943 was capable enough to be retained in service for some time after 1945.

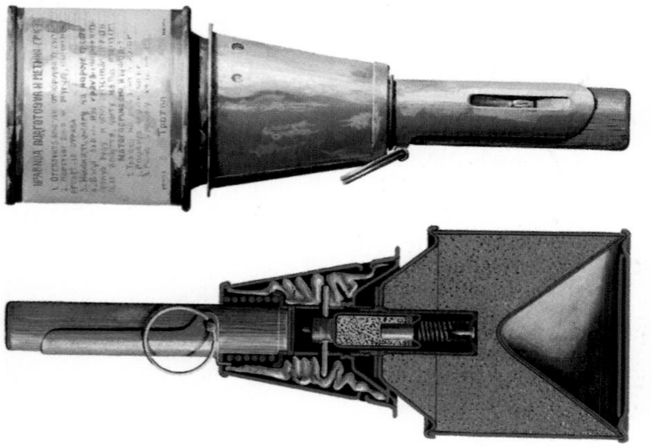

***The RPG 1943 was the Soviet equivalent of the German Panzerwurfmine, but in flight was reliant on a fabric strip stabiliser tail to keep the hollow charge warhead pointing toward the target tank. The tail was ejected from the throwing handle after the grenade had been thrown and after the arming pin had been removed.***

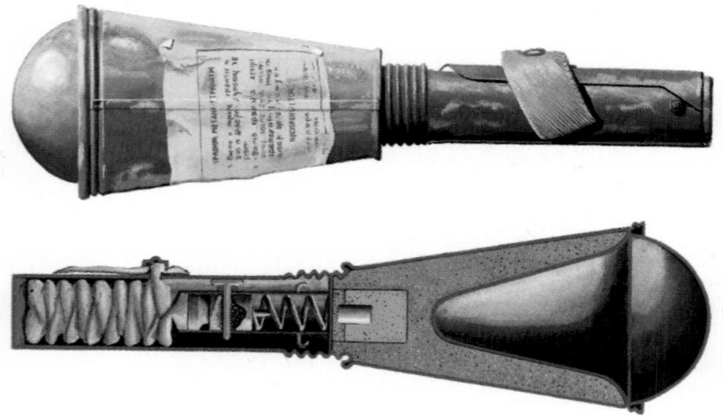

***The Soviet RPG-6 was a late-war version of the RPG 1943. It used a revised warhead shape and four fabric tails to stabilise the warhead in flight. The revised warhead also had a very useful fragmentation effect, so it could also be used as an anti-personnel weapon. It was used for many years after 1945.***

***The American Antitank Rifle Grenade M9A1 could be fired from a muzzle attachment fitted to the M1 Garand rifle to a range of about 100 m (110 yards). Its hollow-charge warhead could penetrate up to 102 mm (4 in) of armour. It could also be fired from the M1 carbine using the M8 launcher.***

# PIAT

The **Projector, Infantry, Anti-Tank Mk 1** (**PIAT**) was a British anti-tank weapon that somehow bypassed the usual stringent weapon selection procedures used by the War Office as it was a product of the unusual department known colloquially as 'Winston Churchill's Toy Shop'. It was designed to exploit the armour-piercing effect of the hollow-charge warhead, and fired a useful grenade that could penetrate almost any contemporary tank's protection. Thus it came into the same general category as the American bazooka and German Panzerfaust.

However, the PIAT relied upon coiled-spring rather than chemical energy to deliver its grenade, for the weapon worked on the spigot mortar principle. In this launching method, the PIAT grenade was projected from an open trough and supported for the initial part of its travel by a central spigot. Pulling the trigger released a powerful main spring and this spring enabled the spigot to strike the grenade's propelling charge to fire it from the trough. The propelling charge also recocked the main spring ready for another grenade to be loaded.

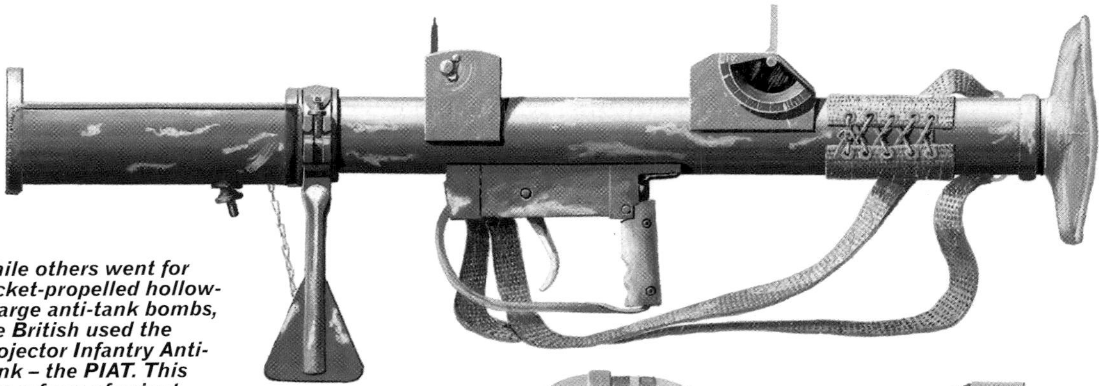

***While others went for rocket-propelled hollow-charge anti-tank bombs, the British used the Projector Infantry Anti-Tank – the PIAT. This was a form of spigot mortar using a powerful central spring to fire its projectile from a front-mounted 'trough'. It was not a popular weapon, but it could kill tanks.***

## Multi-role weapon

The PIAT was intended primarily as an anti-tank weapon, but it could also fire HE and smoke grenades, which made it much more versatile than many of its contemporaries. It was a very useful weapon in house-to-house and urban combat, for the forward monopod could be extended to provide a fair degree of elevation for use in confined spaces.

The PIAT replaced the Boys anti-tank rifle as the infantry's standard anti-tank weapon, and it was issued widely throughout the British and some Commonwealth armies. However, it cannot be said to have been very popular for it was bulky and needed a two-man team to handle it. The main point of unpopularity was the powerful mainspring. This generally required the efforts of two men to cock it. If a grenade failed to fire the weapon was all but useless, for recocking the PIAT when the enemy was nearby was a very risky business. The use of the PIAT spread outside the ranks of the infantry, for it was often the main armament of light armoured vehicles such as light armoured cars. There was also some limited use of the weapon on carriers, which mounted up to 14 PIATs on a multiple mounting as a mobile mortar battery.

The PIAT remained in service with the British army for some years after World War II. Although it was an effective tank-killer, it used a principle that was not adopted by any other designers. However, it did have the advantage that it could be produced in quantity and at a relatively low cost at a time when anti-tank weapons of any type were in great demand.

***The PIAT was the British army's standard squad anti-tank weapon after 1941, and was carried and used by most combat arms and services. It was a rather hefty load to carry, but it could knock out most enemy tanks at close ranges and could also fire HE and smoke bombs.***

**SPECIFICATION**

**PIAT**
**Length:** overall 990 mm (3 ft 0 in)
**Weights:** launcher 14.51 kg (32 lb); grenade 1.36 kg (3 lb)
**Muzzle velocity:** 76-137 m (250-450 ft) per second
**Ranges:** combat 100 m (110 yards); maximum 340 m (370 yards)

***Here the crew members of a knocked out British tank are covering their position armed with a PIAT until a recovery vehicle can arrive to retrieve the damaged vehicle. The men are from the 13/18th Hussars, and the location is near Mount Pincon, northern France, July 1944. Note the No. 4 rifle near the PIAT.***

# Bazooka

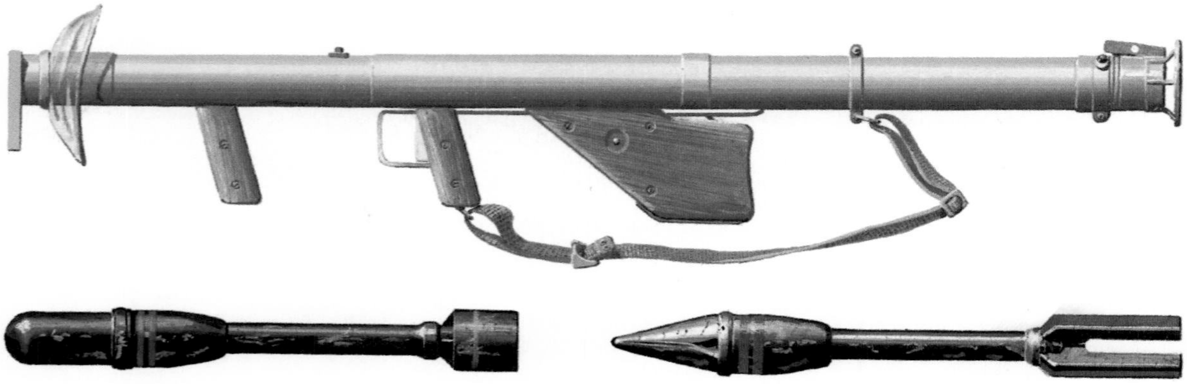

The American **Bazooka** was one of the more original weapons of World War II and was founded on basic rocket research that had been conducted at the Aberdeen Proving Ground, Maryland, since 1933. The active service development of the weapon began in earnest early in 1942, and led to the creation of a weapon whose first examples were introduced straight into combat in North Africa during November 1942 within the context of the Allies' Operation 'Torch' landings in north-west Africa. However, it was the following year before any found their way into action against Axis armour.

The full designation of the first model was **2.36-in Rocket Launcher, M1**. The 60-mm rocket fired from the tube launcher was the **M6A3**, and the practice rocket was known as the **M7A3**.

The bazooka was a very simple weapon, being nothing more than a steel tube that was open at each end and along which the rocket-propelled weapon was launched. A shoulder rest or wooden stock was provided, together with two grips, to facilitate the aiming of the tube; the rear grip included the trigger group. Once loaded, the rocket was fired electrically. In low temperatures, however, not all the propellant was consumed before the rocket left the launcher, allowing unburnt powder to be blasted into the firer's face. To prevent this it was possible to fit a small circular wire mesh screen just behind the muzzle. In practice the bazooka could be used at point targets up to 274 m (300 yards) distant, but for most purposes the range was confined to about 90 m (100 yards) as the rocket was not notably accurate in its flight.

***The American 2.36-in (60-mm) Rocket Launcher M1 was the first of the bazookas and was used by the Germans as the original for their RP series. The M1 used a one-piece barrel that could not fold and early versions (shown here) used a wire mesh shield around the muzzle to protect against rocket blast.***

| SPECIFICATION | |
|---|---|
| **M1A1** | (650 yards) |
| **Calibre:** 60-mm (2.36-in) | **Muzzle velocity:** 82.3 m (270 ft) per second |
| **Length:** 1384 mm (4 ft 6.5 in) | **Armour penetration:** 119.4 mm (4.7 in) at 0° |
| **Weights:** launcher 6.01 kg (13.25 lb); rocket 1.54 kg (3.4 lb) | |
| **Range:** maximum 594 m | |

## Improved models

Soon after the M1 bazooka entered service it was replaced by the essentially similar **M1A1**. It was a popular weapon that could knock out any enemy tank and was normally served by a two-man team, one aiming and the other loading the rockets and connecting their electrical firing circuits. The versatility of the weapons soon meant that the bazooka found a great number of battlefield tasks other than its designed anti-tank role: this was the result of the use of a hollow-charge warhead in the rocket, and this was very good at knocking out pillboxes of all kinds, and could even blast holes through barbed-wire obstacles; the bazooka could be used against area targets such as vehicle parks at ranges up to 595 m (650 yards), and at times the weapon was also used to clear combat lanes through minefields. There are even records of the bazooka being used against artillery pieces at close ranges.

***Left: The rocket fired from the American bazookas was fin-stabilised and weighed 1.53 kg (3.4 lb). It had a maximum range of 640 m (700 yards), but was accurate only to ranges much shorter than that.***

## Tank killer

But it was in the war against the tank that the bazooka made its main mark, and so successful was the bazooka in this task that the Germans seized upon the concept as the design basis of their own Raketenpanzerbüchse series after examples of the M1 had been captured in Tunisia early in 1943. Although the German counterparts were much larger in calibre, the Americans stuck to their 60-mm (2.36-in) calibre until after 1945.

By then they had introduced a new model, the **M9**, that differed from the M1 in being breakable into two halves for ease of carrying. Smoke and incendiary rockets were developed and used before 1945, although much of their use was confined to the Pacific theatre. As the war ended the all-aluminium **M18** launcher was being introduced to service.

***The original M1 bazooka is shown on the left and the M9 on the right. The M9 could be broken down into two halves, which greatly assisted carriage and stowage inside vehicles. By the time the war ended, a version of the M9 was being produced in aluminium for lightness; this was the M18.***

# German flamethrowers

The first time the German army used flamethrowers was in 1914, when early weapons of this type were used against the French during the fighting in the Argonne region, but their first large-scale use was once again against the French, this time during the 1916 Verdun campaign. These early flamethrowers were large items of equipment requiring up to three men to handle them, but development led to a much lighter version that weighed 'only' 35.8 kg (79 lb).

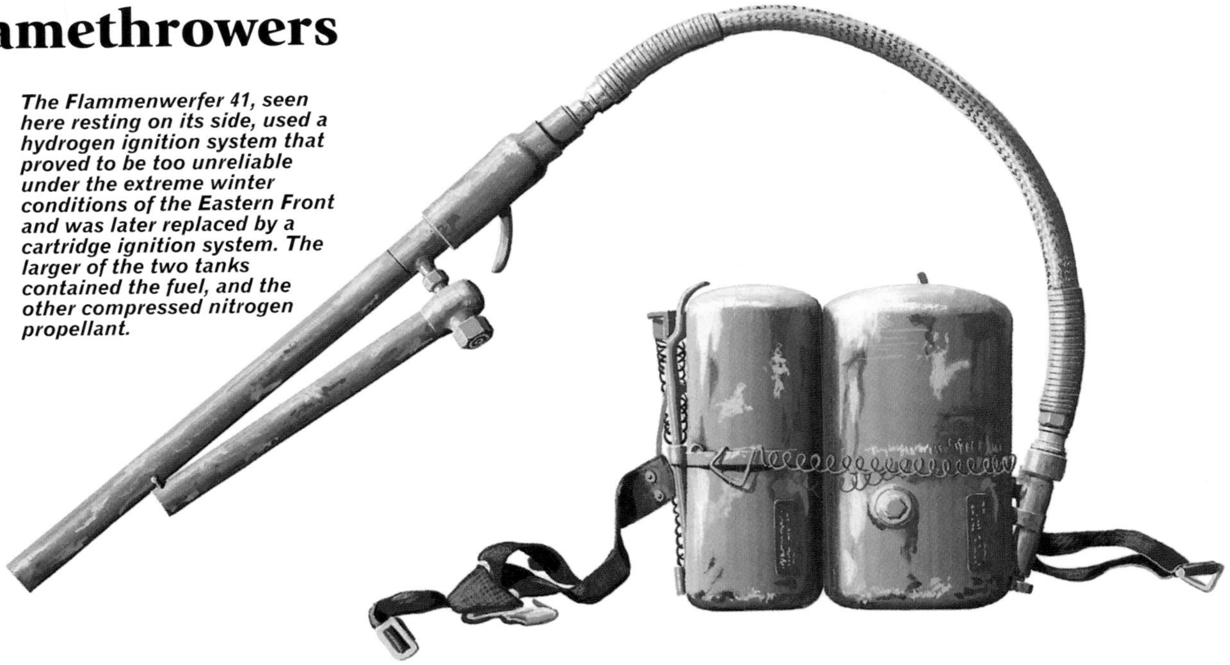

***The Flammenwerfer 41, seen here resting on its side, used a hydrogen ignition system that proved to be too unreliable under the extreme winter conditions of the Eastern Front and was later replaced by a cartridge ignition system. The larger of the two tanks contained the fuel, and the other compressed nitrogen propellant.***

## Nazi expansion

Based on the flamethrower introduced to German service in 1918, this was the **Flammenwerfer 35**, which was issued to units of the new and much expanded German army during the 1930s. In design terms the Flammenwerfer 35 owed much to the World War I equipment, and remained in production into 1941.

## Steady evolution

From this year the Flammenwerfer 35 was gradually supplemented by later models. The first of these was the **Flammenwerfer klein verbessert 40**, a much lighter 'lifebuoy' model that carried less inflammable fuel. Relatively few of these equipments were produced as the type was soon replaced in manufacture and service by the improved **Flammenwerfer 41**. This reverted to the arrangement of the Flammenwerfer 35, with side-by-side fuel and compressed-gas propellant tanks, and was the standard German flamethrower of the rest of World War II. One important modification was introduced after the grim winter of 1941-42, when the intense cold prevented the normal flame ignition system from working. This system was replaced by a cartridge ignition device that was much more reliable at other temperatures as well. When full this version, the **Flammenwerfer mit Strahlrohrpatrone 41**, which was otherwise identical to the standard 1941 model, weighed 18.14 kg (40 lb) and the range at best was 32 m (35 yards).

***A Flammenwerfer 35 is seen in action against a concrete emplacement in Poland after the 1939 campaign. The Flammenwerfer 35 had a range of 25.6 to 30 m (28 to 33 yards) and carried enough fuel for 10 seconds of use, but it weighed 35.8 kg (79 lb) and so was often carried into action by two men.***

***The fearsome blast of a man-pack flamethrower is seen during a night attack at Stalingrad. Flamethrower operators had to be well protected by friendly infantry as they were both vulnerable and conspicuous.***

## Single-shot weapon

These multiple-burst weapons were complemented by an odd model for airborne and assault unit troops. This was a single-shot model known as the **Einstoss Flammenwerfer tragbar** which delivered a 0.5-second burst of fire to a range of about 27 m (30 yards). Not many were produced.

It should not be thought that the above were the only German flamethrower equipments for the Germans proved themselves extremely prolific, as indeed they did with virtually all their weapon types, in the creation of derived and separate models of greater or lesser practical-

***A German assault pioneer team is seen with one member of the team carrying the weight and bulk of a Flammenwerfer 35. This equipment was an awkward load for a single man, especially in an assault situation, but the equipment remained in production until 1941.***

ity. In addition to the Flammenwerfer 35 back-pack equipment mentioned above, for instance, there was also a two-man version known as the **mittlerer Flammenwerfer**, whose main fuel tank was carried on a small trolley: the fuel capacity of this equipment was thus increased to 30 litres (6.6 Imp gal) from the Flammenwerfer 41's figure of 7 litres (1.54 Imp gal). As if this was not enough, there was also a much larger model carried on a trailer towed behind a light vehicle: this carried enough fuel to produce flame for 24 seconds. Finally, for use in static situations there was a device known as the **Abwehrflammenwerfer 42**, a single-shot device to be buried into the ground with only the flame projector nozzle above ground and pointing towards a target area. This was set off by remote control as an enemy approached.

Needless to say, the Germans also made as much use as possible of captured equipments of any and all types.

**SPECIFICATION**

**Flammenwerfer 35**
**Weight:** 35.8 kg (79 lb)
**Fuel capacity:** 11.8 litres (2.6 Imp gal)
**Range:** 25.6 to 30 m (28 to 33 yards)
**Duration of fire:** 10 seconds

# German flamethrower tanks

In World War II the Germans were not particularly energetic in the use of flamethrower tanks, even though they were fielding a light flamethrower tank at a time when no other nation was doing so. This was in 1941 when, following a period of trials, PzKpfw I light tanks were converted to **Flammpanzer I** standard with a Flammenpanzer 40 flame projector in place of one of the turret machine-guns. The first 'production' conversions were used in action by the Deutsches Afrika Korps in North Africa.

***This is a Flammpanzer III with a flame projector in place of the usual gun. These vehicles used later PkKpfw III tank chassis: a machine-gun was mounted co-axially and the fuel was carried internally in two tanks, enough for 70 to 80 two- to three-second bursts. The normal crew was three men.***

## Two flame guns

This expedient was soon followed by another, this time the **Flammpanzer II** which was a conversion of the otherwise little used PzKpfw II Ausf D or E. On this model two flame projectors were used, one on each side of the front hull. Each projector had a range of about 36.5 m (40 yards). Not many of these conversions were effected, and most of the vehicles were operated on the Eastern Front.

The most numerous Flammpanzer conversions were those based on the PzKpfw III Ausf H or M. At least 100 tanks were converted with a flame gun in place of the main gun, and there was capacity for 1000 litres (220 Imp gal) of fuel. These **Flammpanzer III** vehicles were very effective, but do not appear to have been much used in combat, largely as a result of their lack of any means of self-defence against the attentions of Allied tanks: on the occasions they were used in action, they had to be escorted and protected by 'gun' tanks.

Apart from the odd trials model, no PzKpfw IV tank was converted to the Flammpanzer role. Apparently there were plans to convert various marks of Panther and Tiger II to the flame role, but none appear to have seen fruition.

## Small but capable

Instead the little **Flammpanzer 38(t)** was placed in production during 1944 as the standard flame tank. This small vehicle was well suited to the role as the flamethrower version used the low and easily concealed hull of the Hetzer tank destroyer based on the obsolete PzKpfw 38(t) tank. Once again the flame gun took the place of the main gun, and some of the internal space was devoted to fuel capacity for the flame projector.

## Half-track flamethrower

A few captured tanks were used by the Germans for the flame role. One example was the large Char B, one of the French tanks captured by the Germans in 1940, but the numbers were probably only about 10.

For much of the war the German army relied on the **SdKfz 251/16 mittlerer Flammpanzerwagen** half-track. First used during 1942, this carried two fuel tanks, each containing 700 litres (154 Imp gal) of fuel, enough for 80 two-second bursts of flame. Each fuel tank supplied its own projector, one on each side of the open vehicle rear, and some had a third but smaller projector at the front although on most vehicles this position was occupied by a machine-gun. The usual range of these projectors was about 35 m (38 yards).

***One of the forward-mounted flame projectors carried by the Flammpanzer II, a type which was used mainly on the Eastern Front although not many were actually produced. This projector is firing a rod of unlit fuel that will be ignited later as its lies on the ground.***

**SPECIFICATION**

**bFlammpanzer III**
**Crew:** 3
**Weight:** 21.13 tonnes
**Dimensions:** length 6.55 m (21 ft 5¾ in); width 2.97 m (9 ft 9 in); height 2.50 m (8 ft 2½ in)
**Powerplant:** one Maybach HL 120 engine developing 224 kW (300 hp)

# Lanciafiamme
## Modello 35 & 40

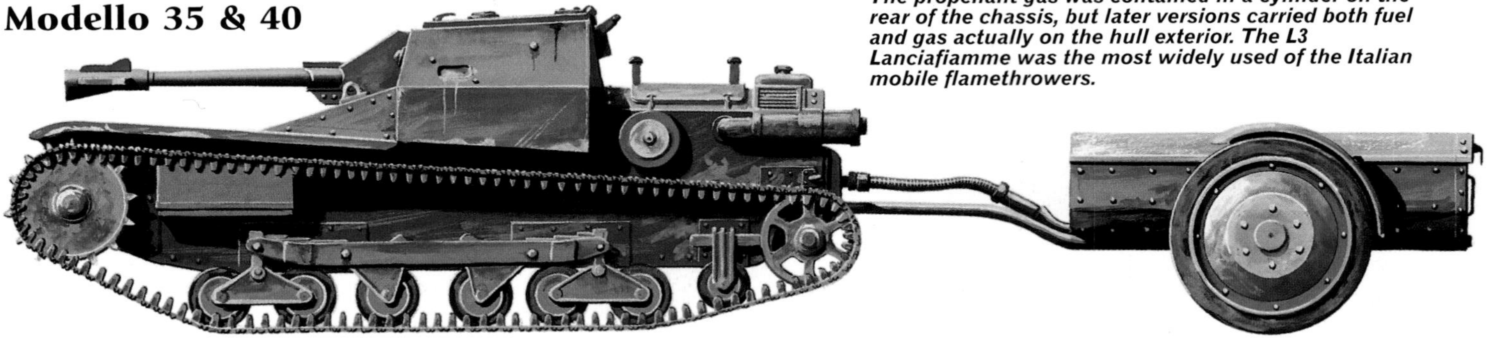

***The Italian L3 Lanciafiamme carried its fuel in a trailer connected to the flame gun by a flexible hose. The propellant gas was contained in a cylinder on the rear of the chassis, but later versions carried both fuel and gas actually on the hull exterior. The L3 Lanciafiamme was the most widely used of the Italian mobile flamethrowers.***

As its designation implies, the Italian **Lanciafiamme modello 35** entered service in 1935, just in time to make its operational debut during the Italian invasion of Abyssinia, in which it proved a major success. In design terms, there was nothing really remarkable about the modello 35. It was a relatively portable twin-cylinder backpack equipment that used a rather cumbersome flame projector. This projector was fitted at the end with a large collar housing the flame ignition system. For various reasons this ignition system was not considered sufficiently reliable, so it was modified to produce the **Lanciafiamme modello 40**. In general appearance and use the modello 40 was otherwise identical to the modello 35.

These flamethrowers were used by special troops known as Guastori, or assault pioneers, who had to wear thick protective clothing with their faces covered by normal service gas respirators. When so clothed their operational mobility and vision was restricted, so they were usually guarded by teams of supporting infantry. On the move their flamethrower equipments were usually carried on special brackets fitted to trucks or, if the formation was not mechanised, mules with special harnesses. The fuel for the flamethrowers was carried in specially marked containers.

### Africa and Russia

Both flamethrower types were used in some numbers by Italian troops operating in North Africa and on the Eastern Front. In both theatres the modello 35 and 40 worked well enough, but it was increasingly noticed that the equipments lacked range by comparison with contemporary equivalents, and especially the later German designs.

The success of the flamethrower in Abyssinia moved the Italian army authorities to fit a special version of a lanciafiamme, much larger than the man-pack version, to the L3 tankette. As space within the low hull of this **L3-35Lf** vehicle was very limited, the fuel was carried externally in a lightly armoured trailer, with a corrugated pipe passing the fuel from the trailer to the projector. There was also a version that dispensed with the trailer and carried a much smaller flat fuel tank over the top of the vehicle's rear. Although much was made of these two flamethrowing tankettes, they appear to have been little used.

***The flame projector of the L3 Lanciafiamme was mounted in place of the machine-gun carried on the L3 tankettes. These Italian flamethrower tanks were of very limited tactical value as they were very lightly armoured and had a crew of only two.***

| SPECIFICATION | |
|---|---|
| **Lanciafiamme modello 35** | (2.6 Imp gal) |
| **Weight:** 27 kg (59.5 lb) | **Range:** about 25 m (27 yards) |
| **Fuel capacity:** 11.8 litres | **Duration of fire:** 20 seconds |

# Portable flamethrower
## Types 93 & 100

***The Japanese Model 93 and Model 100 portable flamethrowers were almost identical – this is the Model 93 – and differed only in the shape of the flame gun and other minor changes. Two tanks held the fuel and the other was the nitrogen pressure tank, providing a flame jet duration of 10 to 12 seconds.***

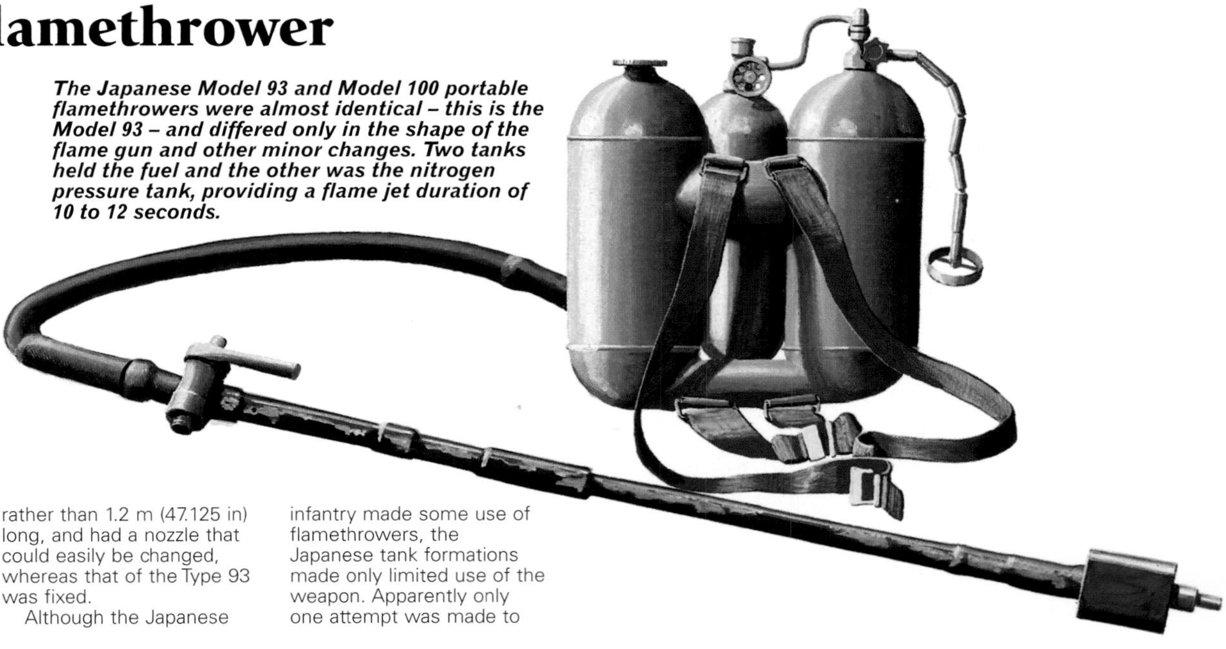

The first Japanese flamethrower of World War II was the **Portable Flamethrower Type 93**. This was first issued during 1933 and was an orthodox design that made much use of German experience in World War I. It used three cylinders on a rather awkward back-pack arrangement, two of the cylinders containing the fuel and the central (and smaller) cylinder containing the compressed gas propellant. From 1939 a small petrol-driven air compressor was issued with each equipment.

It was never satisfactory, and in 1940 was replaced by the outwardly similar **Portable Flamethrower Type 100**. The new flame gun was 0.9 m (35.5 in) rather than 1.2 m (47.125 in) long, and had a nozzle that could easily be changed, whereas that of the Type 93 was fixed.

Although the Japanese infantry made some use of flamethrowers, the Japanese tank formations made only limited use of the weapon. Apparently only one attempt was made to

***If war-time propaganda photographs are to be believed, the Japanese army and marines made extensive use of flamethrowers during World War II. This impression came from a series of 'official' photographs, which were taken during Japan's long war against China, where weapons such as flamethrowers had a psychological effect that far outweighed their real utility as combat weapons.***

produce a flamethrower tank, which was used by a small unit encountered on the Philippines island of Luzon in 1944. These turretless tanks were fitted with obstacle clearing equipment on the front hull, and mounted a single flamethrower forward. Both internal and external fuel tanks were carried. The tank used as the basis appears to have been the Medium Tank Type 98, and the only other armament was a single machine-gun.

| SPECIFICATION | |
|---|---|
| **Portable Flamethrower Type 100** | **Range:** about 23 to 27 m (25 to 30 yards) |
| **Weight:** 25 kg (55 lb) | **Duration of fire:** 10 to 12 seconds |
| **Fuel capacity:** 14.77 litres (3.25 Imp gal) | |

# Soviet flamethrowers

In 1941 the USSR was using the **ROKS-2** portable flamethrower. In design terms there was nothing remarkable about this weapon other than the attention paid to making it look like an ordinary infantry weapon: the fuel tank was shaped like a soldier's back-pack, and the flame projector looked like a rifle. The only prominent flamethrower features were the small gas pressure bottle under the 'pack', the hose leading to the projector, and the rather prominent igniter at the muzzle.

In an effort to meet rising production requirements after Germany's June 1941 invasion, there appeared the simpler **ROKS-3** based on two cylinders on a frame carried on the back. The flame projector still resembled a rifle, but it was much simpler to make.

After they had discovered how to make thicker fuel for improved flame effects and range, they used this in the ROKS-2 and ROKS-3 for a maximum range of 45 m (49 yards). The Soviets also made static flame-throwers to be buried in the ground with only the projector nozzle pointing towards the target area. This type's designation is not known, but the Germans copied it to produce their own Abwehrflammenwerfer 42.

## Flamethrower tank

The Soviets also developed flamethrower tanks, starting with the T-26. This was not a success and from 1941 was replaced by the **ATO-41** flamethrower: installed next to the main gun of the KV heavy tank this created the **KV-8**, and in place of the bow machine-gun of the T-34/76 produced the **OT-34**. These early weapons had only 100 litres (22 Imp gal) of fuel, and were replaced by the **ATO-42** with more fuel. A few of these equipments were installed in the KV-1S heavy tank to produce the **KV-8S**, but most of the ATO-42s were installed in place of the bow machine-gun of the T-34/85 which then became the **TO-34**. The ATO-42 could fire four or five flame bursts in 10 seconds, and the maximum range with thickened fuel was 120 m (130 yards).

## 'Carcass' projector

The weapon known as the **Ampulenyot 1941 System Kartukov** was not a flamethrower but rather a launcher for incendiary projectiles. It was a very simple 'pipe gun' weapon: a length of steel pipe closed at one end and with a minimum of fire-control equipment and carried on a pillar-mounted yoke for the defence of fixed installations. The 'carcass' type of muzzle-loaded projectile was fired probably by a black powder charge. The projectile burst into flames as it struck the target and spread flames or burning material in the general target area. It would appear that by 1942 the Kartukov guns had been scrapped.

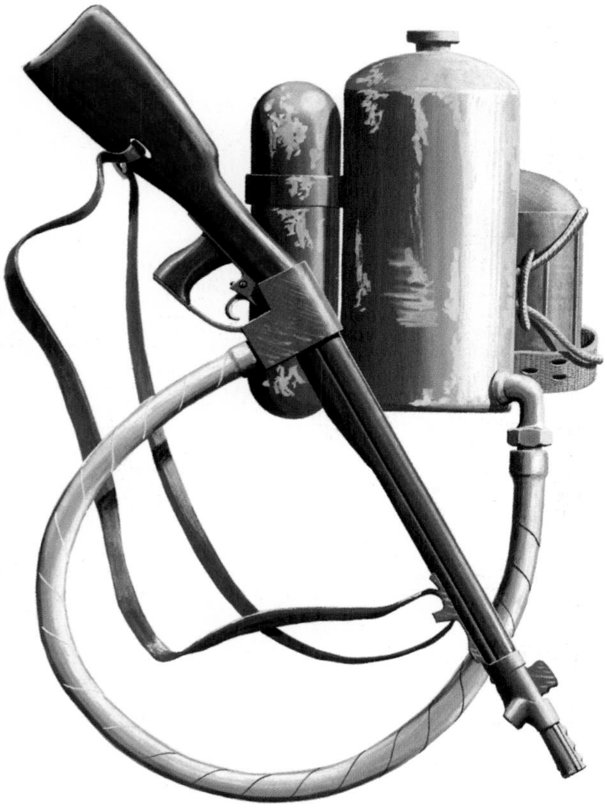

***The ROKS-2 flamethrower was carried as a back-pack with the cylinder tanks vertical. The flame gun was designed to resemble a rifle to conceal its function, as flamethrower operators usually attracted a great deal of enemy attention and fire. The large tank contained enough fuel for about eight seconds of use.***

| SPECIFICATION | |
|---|---|
| **ROKS-2** | **Range:** 36.5 to 45 m (40 to 49 yards) |
| **Weight:** 22.7 kg (50 lb) | **Duration of fire:** 6 to 8 seconds |
| **Fuel capacity:** 9 litres (2 Imp gal) | |

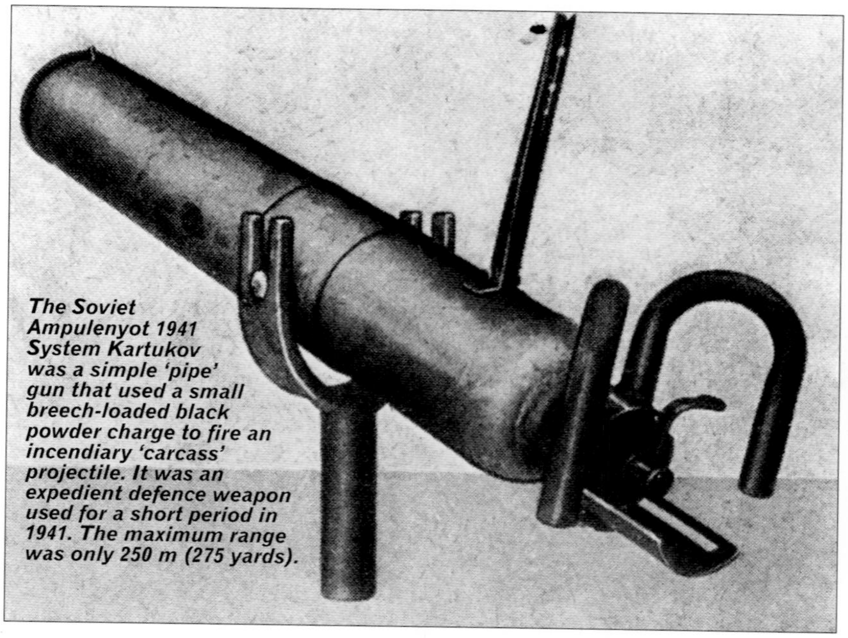

***The Soviet Ampulenyot 1941 System Kartukov was a simple 'pipe' gun that used a small breech-loaded black powder charge to fire an incendiary 'carcass' projectile. It was an expedient defence weapon used for a short period in 1941. The maximum range was only 250 m (275 yards).***

| SPECIFICATION | |
|---|---|
| **Ampulenyot 1941 System Kartukov** | **Traverse:** 360° |
| **Calibre:** 127 mm (5 in) | **Muzzle velocity:** 50 m (164 ft) per second |
| **Length overall:** 1020 mm (40.16 in) | **Maximum range:** 250 m (275 yards) |
| **Weight:** 26 kg (57 3 lb) | **Projectile weight:** 15 or 18 kg (3.3 or 3.97 lb) |
| **Elevation:** 0° to +12° | |

# Lifebuoy Flamethrower

Development of what was to become officially known as the **Flame-Thrower, Portable, No. 2 Mk I** began during 1941. This British flamethrower appears to have been influenced by the German Flammenwerfer 40, but the basic design of any portable flamethrower is fixed by physical constraints. This results from the fact that for a vessel that has to contain gas at high pressure, a sphere is the best possible shape. On a flamethrower the fuel tank has to contain as much fuel as possible within as small a volume as can be managed. These design criteria virtually dictate the shape of the equipment, i.e. a central sphere containing pressurised gas in the centre of a doughnut-shaped fuel tank. This produces the classic shape which gave the British equipment its **Lifebuoy** nickname, a name that stuck.

## Over-hasty production

The first pilot model was ready by mid-1942 and production orders followed before troop and other trials had been completed. This was unfortunate, for after only a short time in service the Lifebuoy began to demonstrate a number of serious defects, many of them caused by hurried manufacture of the tanks' complex shapes. Ignition proved to be somewhat unreliable, and the position of the fuel valve under the tanks proved to be awkward. As a result the production run of the Mk I weapon was short, the equipment then being used only for training from mid-1943.

## Improved model

It was not until the following year that there appeared the improved **Flame-Thrower, Portable, No. 2 Mk II**. It was this version that the British army used until the end of World War II and for many years after it. In appearance there was little to differentiate the Mk I from the Mk II. This was ready for service by June 1944, and was used during and after the Normandy landings, and in the Far East. The British army was never really enthusiastic about the portable flamethrower, however, and decided that not many would be required: manufacture of the Mk II ended as early as July 1944, after 7,500 had been made. Even the Mk II proved to be generally unreliable as it depended on a small battery to ignite the flame, and in the wet or after even a short period of use the battery often failed. In an effort to reduce weight, there was developed the smaller **Ack-Pack** device, which weighed 21.8 kg (48 lb) for possible use in the Far East. In the event the Ack-Pack was developed so slowly that it was not produced until after the war's end.

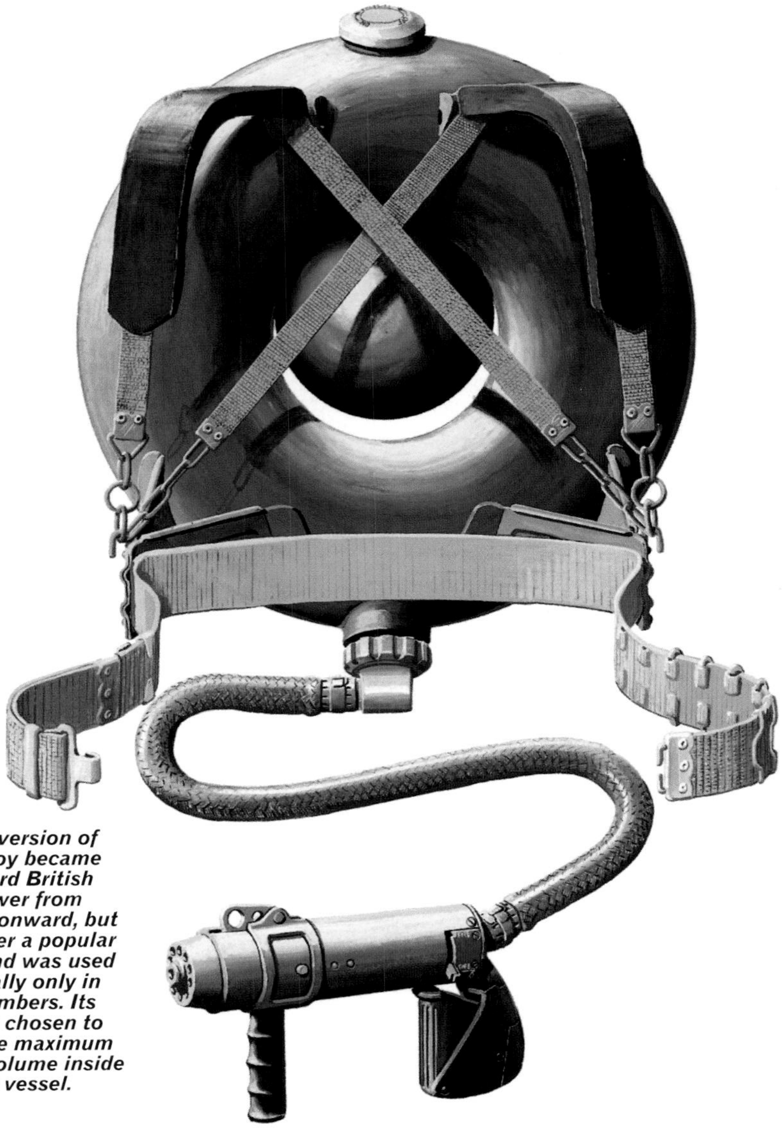

*The Mk II version of the Lifebuoy became the standard British flamethrower from early 1944 onward, but it was never a popular weapon and was used operationally only in limited numbers. Its shape was chosen to provide the maximum possible volume inside a pressure vessel.*

*The Mk I version of the Flame Thrower, Portable, No. 2 was usually known as the Lifebuoy from its shape. It was not a great success and saw only limited operational use before being replaced in late 1944 by the Mk II.*

| SPECIFICATION | |
|---|---|
| **Lifebuoy** | **Range:** 27.4 to 36.5 m (30 to 40 yards) |
| **Weight:** 29 kg (64 lb) | **Duration of fire:** 10 seconds |
| **Fuel capacity:** 18.2 litres (4 Imp gal) | |

*The operator of a Lifebuoy flamethrower brings up the rear of a file of British infantrymen moving up toward the front line somewhere in Northwest Europe.*

# Wasp & Harvey Flamethrowers

***The Wasp Mk IIC was the Canadian version of the British Wasp, and carried its fuel in a single tank at the rear; the British Wasp Mk II had two internal tanks. The Wasp was a conversion of the Universal Carrier for the flame role and was first tested in 1943.***

The first British use of flamethrowers for mobile warfare was in 1940, when the newly established Petroleum Warfare Department developed a flame projector known as the **Ronson**. This had a relatively short range and was mounted on a Universal Carrier with the fuel and compressed gas tanks over the rear of the vehicle. For various reasons the British army decided not to proceed with the Ronson, requesting more range, but the Canadians persevered with the design and later in the war it was adopted by the US Army as the **Satan**.

By 1942 the PWD had developed the Ronson to the stage where ranges of 73 to 91.5 m (80 to 100 yards) were being reached, and this improved device was put into production as the **Wasp Mk I**. In September 1942 an order for 1,000 was placed and by November the following year all had been delivered, The Wasp Mk I used a large projector gun that was routed over the top of the Carrier and connected to two fuel tanks inside the Carrier hull. However, the Mk I was deemed unsuitable for service as by then a **Wasp Mk II** had appeared with a much smaller and handier flame projector mounted at the front in place of the machine-gun otherwise carried. This new flame projector was a great advance over the previous design and gave a much better flame performance although without any improvement in range; the same type of projector was also used with the Churchill Crocodile. It was also easier to aim and safer to use.

The Wasp Mk II first went into action during the Normandy fighting of July 1944, and was used mainly in support of infantry operations, whereas the Crocodile was used in conjunction with armoured formations. They were dreadfully effective weapons, and greatly feared by the unfortunate Germans who had to bear their effects.

## Canadian Wasp

It was not long before the Wasp Mk II was joined by yet another Wasp variant, this time the **Wasp Mk IIC**, the suffix denoting Canada as the Canadians had developed their own Wasp version. They decided that to devote a Universal Carrier just to the flamethrower role was wasteful of vehicles, and therefore redesigned the Wasp so that the Carrier could also function as a normal vehicle if required: the fuel tankage was moved outside the rear of the vehicle and revised as a single 341-litre (75-Imp gal) tank in place of two smaller tanks. This gave room inside the open hull for a third crew member, who could carry a light machine-gun. This gave the Wasp Mk IIC much more tactical flexibility, and it gradually came to be the preferred type. In June 1944 all Wasp production was switched to the Mk IIC standard, and field conversions were also made, using the existing Mk II 272.2-litre (60-Imp gal) tanks. Operational experience demonstrated the need for more frontal armour, and many Wasp Mk IICs were fitted with plastic armour over the front hull plates.

***The Wasp Mk II differed from the earlier Mk I in having a much smaller flame projector mounted in the front hull. British Wasps had a crew of two while the Canadian version had three, one of whom usually operated a machine-gun or light mortar.***

## Smoking Wasp

Some Wasps were fitted with smoke-producing equipment, and a few had wading screens for possible use in amphibious operations. The Canadians demonstrated their interest in flamethrower tanks by fitting Wasp equipments to old Ram tanks to produce the **Badger**. These conversions were carried out in the UK for the Canadian 1st Army. Early Badgers did not have turrets, though later versions did, the turretless versions being based on Ram Kangaroo personnel carriers. They were used by the Canadians from February 1945 onwards.

Early in 1945 three Wasps and a quantity of their thickened fuel were sent to the USSR. What the Soviets made of them is not known.

## Enter 'Harvey'

It is also worth noting in any account of British flamethrower developments an expedient dating from the summer of 1940, when a German invasion was feared. This was officially known as the **Flame-Thrower, Transportable, No. 1 Mk I**, but to the troops it was simply the **'Harvey'**. This was not schemed as a man-portable weapon, the 'Transportable' indicating that it could be moved about on a carriage with two agricultural wheels. The main fuel tank was easily manufactured and the compressed air was contained in a commercial compressed air cylinder.

The flame projector was connected to the fuel tank by a 9.14-m (30-ft) hose, and the projector itself was a simple device on a monopod. The idea was that the Harvey would be taken to a selected site and set up with its tanks under cover and its projector near the target area.

The first Harveys were issued to regular troops defending the UK, but it was not long before the Home Guard got them as well. They were cumbersome things and were not greatly liked, but they worked after a fashion. Some of them even found their way to the Middle East where they were used only for smoke production.

***This was the flame jet produced by a Harvey flamethrower, a static defensive device produced in 1940 mainly for use of the Home Guard. Although meant to be used in a static role, it could be moved on a simple two-wheeled carriage, but it was a cheap and crude weapon.***

**SPECIFICATION**

| | |
|---|---|
| **Harvey** | **Range:** about 46 to 55 m (50 to 60 yards) |
| **Weight:** not known | **Duration of fire:** 12 seconds |
| **Fuel capacity:** 127.3 litres (28 Imp gal) | |

# Flame-Thrower M1 & M2

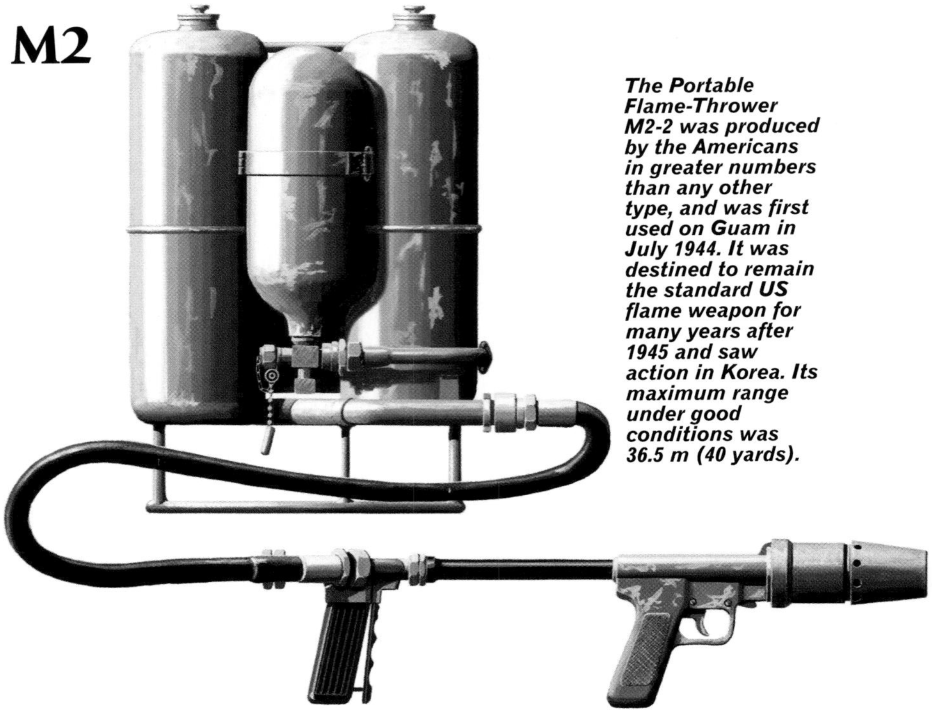

***The Portable Flame-Thrower M2-2 was produced by the Americans in greater numbers than any other type, and was first used on Guam in July 1944. It was destined to remain the standard US flame weapon for many years after 1945 and saw action in Korea. Its maximum range under good conditions was 36.5 m (40 yards).***

When the US army requested a man-portable flamethrower in July 1940, the Chemical Warfare Service had no knowledge base upon which to work. From the **Portable Flame-Thrower E1** development model the service evolved the **E1R1** for troop trials, some of which were carried out under combat conditions in Papua. The E1R1 was easily broken and its controls were difficult to reach, but a more rugged version was accepted for service as the **M1**. This was much like the E1R1 in that it had two tanks, one for fuel and the other for compressed hydrogen.

The M1 went into production in March 1942, and the weapon was in action during the Guadalcanal operations of June 1942. It proved to be something of a disappointment: the ignition circuit used electrical power supplied by batteries that often failed under service conditions, and the tanks were liable to pin-hole corrosion spots that allowed pressure to escape.

***The American M1 Flame-Thrower was a development of the earlier E1R1 which, although technically an experimental model, was used in action in 1943. The M1 was used for the first time during the Guadalcanal campaign, and used the original 'thin' fuel.***

## Improved but flawed

By June 1943 the new **M1A1**, of which 14,000 were made, was in service. This was the M1 modified for use of fuels thickened by the additives and giving better flame effects and a range of up to 46 m (50 yards) compared with the 27.5-m (30-yard) maximum of the M1. Unfortunately the troublesome ignition system was not improved in any way.

By mid-1943 the Chemical Warfare Service had a much better idea of what kind of portable flamethrower the troops required. Based on the **E3** experimental design, the **M2-2** featured several improvements. The M2-2 used the new thickened fuel but was a much more rugged weapon carried on a back-pack frame (very similar to that used to carry ammunition) and with a cartridge ignition system using a revolver-type mechanism that allowed up to six flame jet shots before new cartridges had to be inserted.

The M2-2 was first used in action on Guam in July 1944 and by the time the war ended almost 25,000 had been produced. The M2-2 was also used by other nations.

## Continued progress

Although the M2-2 was an improvement over the M1 and M1A1, the US Army still considered that it was not what was really wanted, and development continued to find a better and lighter weapon. Some work was carried out to evolve a single-shot flamethrower that could be discarded after use. A model that used a combustible powder to produce pressure to eject 9 litres (2 Imp gal) of thickened petrol-based fuel from a cylinder was under development as the war ended, but the project was then terminated. It would have had a range of 27.5 m (30 yards).

| SPECIFICATIONS | |
|---|---|
| **M1A1** | **M2-2** |
| **Weight:** 31.8 kg (70 lb) | **Weight:** 28.1 to 32.7 kg (62 to 72 lb) |
| **Fuel capacity:** 18.2 litres (4 Imp gal) | **Fuel capacity:** 18.2 litres (4 Imp gal) |
| **Range:** 41 to 45.5 m (45 to 50 yards) | **Range:** 22.9 to 36. 5 m (25 to 40 yards) |
| **Duration of fire:** 8 to 10 seconds | **Duration of fire:** 8 to 9 seconds |

***In addition to their noise, flamethrowers had a powerful visual effect on morale, and the mere sight of their flame jets was often enough to make even the strongest men quail. This is an American M2-2 in action on Ie Shima in June 1945.***

# American flamethrower tanks

***The Sherman Crocodile was a British development to use the Sherman in the flamethrowing role, but only four were produced as US Army interest in the project waned almost as soon as it started. The flame gun was mounted to the right of the hull gunner's escape hatch.***

The first American tank flamethrower was produced in 1940, and this combination of the Flame Projector E2 and M2 medium tank was demonstrated to US Army tank officers in mid-1940. They were not impressed and the project lapsed. It was not long before opinions changed, but by that time the Chemical Warfare Service designers had to start once again from the beginning and before long had a pump-operated Flame Projector E3 mounted in the turret of an M3 medium tank. The pump system tended to break up the fuel structure and so reduce flame performance and range, but when the pump was replaced by a compressed gas system the problems disappeared.

Another programme to produce a service weapon rapidly was initiated under the V (Quickie) designation. The British/Canadian Ronson flame system was obtained from Canada, but initial trials had to be conducted with the system mounted on the rear of a truck as no tanks were available. The 'Q' project continued until an installation to be fitted to the turret of the M5A1 light tank was developed, but the tanks were not allocated and the programme suffered inordinate delay. It was early 1945 before any of the 'Q' systems, by then known as the **M5-4**, were ready for service, and four were used in the Philippines.

## Local initiative

While all this development work was conducted in the continental USA, troops in Hawaii were busy producing actual weapons. Using the Ronson flame projector as their basis, they mounted flame systems in place of the old turret guns on obsolete M3A1 light tanks which were renamed **Satan**. The Satan used compressed carbon dioxide as the propellant, and could fire thickened fuel to a range of 73 m (80 yards); each vehicle carried 773 litres (170 Imp gal) of fuel. The initial 'production run' was for 24 Satans, which entered service in June 1944 on Saipan.

## Extemporised model

The success of the Satan led commanders to request a similar installation in the M4 medium tank. Old 75-mm (2.95-in) tank gun barrels were used to mount the Ronson flame projectors and this new tank version, known officially as the **POA-CWS 75 HI**, was used in action during the Ryukyus operation. The type was later used on Okinawa, in a special application to flame out defending Japanese from deep caves.

Both of these flame-producing systems mounted the flame projector in place of the main armament, a feature not greatly liked by the 'tankies', who wanted to retain a potent defensive armament. Attempts had already been made to mount a flame projector alongside the main gun on some M4 flame tanks and in the latter stages some M4 tanks mounting 75-mm guns or 105-mm (4.13-in) howitzers also carried co-axial flamethrowers, but lack of spare parts prevented many conversions being made.

Other earlier attempts to mount portable flamethrowers that could fire through ports at the front of light tanks had been made but without much success. In October 1943 therefore the Chemical Warfare Service was asked to produce a flamethrower that could be mounted in place of the bow machine-gun on M3, M4 and M5 tanks, so that if required the machine-gun could be reinstalled. Consequently 1,784 M3-4-3 flamethrowers were produced for installation in M4 tanks, and 300 E5R2-M3 flamethrowers were produced for use in M3 and M5 light tanks. Many of these were used in Europe and in the Pacific theatre.

Many tank commanders did not like the idea of losing their bow machine-guns, so an alternative installation that could be mounted next to the commander's periscope on the turret top was developed. One of these, the M3-4-E6R3, was placed into production but was too late for war use.

Once again the troops stationed in Hawaii did not wait for weapons to arrive from the continental USA, and set about producing their own auxiliary flamethrowers. This time the M1A1 portable flamethrower was used as the basis for a projector that could be mounted in place of the bow machine-gun of the M4 tank. Some 176 of these conversions were made, and were on hand for the Okinawa and Iwo jima campaigns, but they were not much used as the troops preferred the 'local' conversions with turret-mounted flamethrower equipments on otherwise standard M4 medium tanks.

Mention must also be made of the installation of the 'Q' project M5-4 flamethrower in the LVT4 amphibious carrier. Six of these were used on Peleliu, but the carrier proved to be rather unsatisfactory for flame operations. Although they were used very effectively, the LVT4 was really too lightly armoured for the assault task.

**SPECIFICATION**

**POA-CWS 75 HI**
**Crew:** 5
**Weight:** 31.55 tones
**Dimensions:** length (overall) 20 ft 7 in (6.27 m); width 2.67 m (8 ft 9 in); height 3.38 m (11 ft 1 in)
**Armament:** one Mk I flamethrower in the barrel of the 75-mm (2.95-in) gun, two 0.3-in (7.62-mm) Browning machine-guns (one co-axial and one hull), and one 0.5-in (12.7-mm) Browning AA machine-gun
**Armour:** 38 to 51 mm (1.5 to 2 in)
**Powerplant:** one Ford GAA liquid-cooled V-8 petrol engine developing 373 kW (500 hp)
**Performance:** speed 42 km/h (26 mph)

***The Satan flamethrower was used on US Marine Corps M3A1 light tanks in place of the main turret gun. This example is in use on Saipan during July 1944, and the Satan was so successful that many more old M3A1 light tanks were converted for the flame warfare role.***

# Mortars in action

**The main advantage of the mortar is its ability to bring down fire on targets at night and through smoke, mist or fog – as long as targets have previously been registered and recorded. Mortars are classic indirect-fire weapons at short ranges.**

*Light and therefore man-portable – even if only for modest distances – the medium mortar is the ideal infantry support weapon as it can be brought into action quickly and rain bombs down on to the target.*

The medium mortar is an extremely effective weapon, and much more flexible than conventional artillery. It can engage widely separated targets at differing ranges with a minimum of delay. The pattern formed on the ground by the best weapons, known as the beaten zone, is relatively small with shells fired at the same angle of elevation and with the same propellant charge.

Small corrections can be made by moving the barrel – a screw-thread system allows for a few degrees of traverse without having to move the baseplate or supporting bipod.

## Plunging fire

The high trajectory of their shells makes mortars particularly good at taking out targets in the lee of a hill or in a built-up area that is difficult to reach with conventional artillery. Mortars can also fire blind from behind high cover such as hillsides, cliffs and buildings.

Another crucial advantage is the relatively low weight of the medium infantry mortar. It can be moved into and out of action quickly, and is man-portable. It is particularly suitable in helicopter assault operations, and is highly mobile on the ground, whether transported by light 4x4 vehicles and fired from the ground, or transported in an APC and fired from within it.

There are, of course, some disadvantages. The relatively low muzzle velocity and the high elevation of the barrel mean that the round is in the air for a long time, and gusts of wind can reduce accuracy. The range of infantry mortars can be seriously decreased by damp or rain in the barrel. And because there is no inbuilt recoil system, as in a conventional artillery piece, it is essential that mortar crews find firm ground that can take the shock of firing. Mortars will function in the most appaling conditions, but accuracy will be affected. Finally, mortars are vulnerable. When they fire, the round can be detected by sound and radar locating devices, and the grid reference of the mortar line can be computed. So, if possible, mortars should be fired from dead ground where they can not be engaged by field artillery.

## British experience

The British army is fairly typical in the way it uses its 81-mm (3.2-in) mortars. The mortar platoon is divided into a platoon HQ and four sections, and each section has two mortar detachments. Orders to the mortars are provided by the platoon's control post operator (CPO).

Each detachment consists of four men, who are numbered. No. 1 commands the detachment and is responsible for laying the mortar on to the correct bearing and elevation. No. 2 places the rounds down the mortar barrel on the correct charge and fuse setting. No. 3 prepares the correct quantity of rounds and passes them to No. 2. The fourth man is the driver.

In addition, there are two mortar fire controllers (MFCs), who move and operate with the company or squadron they are supporting. The MFCs observe the target and control the fire of the mortars on to the target over the radio.

*Right: The fact that mortar fire can be brought down just in front of friendly troops places great emphasis in mortar operations on ensuring the exact locations of friendly and enemy forces.*

*Below: The location of a mortar can be worked out by backtracking the trajectory of its bombs with sound and radar systems, and the mortar itself is also highly visible when firing at night.*

*Left: The three primary numbers of a mortar team prepare their L16 weapon for action. No. 1 lays the weapon in azimuth and elevation, No. 2 prepares to load the bomb and No. 3 readies more bombs.*

*Below: The main elements of a mortar are simple and light, and include the baseplate, barrel, bipod, sights and laying gear, and cleaning and maintenance equipment.*

The mortar platoon can go into action either as a platoon (eight mortars), a half platoon (four mortars) or as four individual sections of two mortars each. If the sections are deployed separately, their fire can engage up to four separate targets simultaneously (one per section) or alternatively be co-ordinated to fire on to the same target from four separate mortar lines, or directions of fire. The advantage of four separate mortar lines is that they are more difficult for the enemy to detect than one large one. It is also easier to select four relatively small section mortar lines rather than one large one.

Once the mortar line has been selected, it is necessary to lay, or point, the mortars. For the fire orders sent by the MFC to make any sense, the mortars must have a common starting or reference point to which both the MFC and the CPO can refer. This is a bit like synchronising watches. To do this, the mortars align the cross hairs on their sights with an aiming post planted in the ground in front of them. Next, the mortars have to fire in parallel. If they are not, the pattern of rounds on the ground will be unpredictable and ineffective. By using the sights and following simple geometric principles, each mortar can be aligned precisely.

The MFCs send fire orders giving the bearing of the target and its distance from them. The CPO then converts these figures into a direction and range from the mortar line to the target. The actual orders to the mortars will be in the form of an elevation and a bearing, which have the effect of moving the mortar barrel up or down and left or right.

### Corrected fire

Providing the information given by the MFC is accurate and the computations of the CPO are correct, then the rounds should arrive on target. This seldom happens first time, and corrections usually have to be made before fire for effect is ordered.

The 81-mm mortar can be used effectively in defence, attack or withdrawal. It is the battalion commander's own 'private artillery'. It can provide support where he wants it more quickly than any other form of fire support. And he knows it is always there to support him – whereas the artillery may have priority targets.

## MORTAR AMMUNITION

The primary round for most infantry mortars is the HE fragmentation round. This is lethal up to 40 m (45 yards) from the impact point, and can cause casualties up to 190 m (210 yards) farther out. Mortars are also effective for production of a smokescreen with the white phosphorus (WP) round, while the parachute illuminating round provides white light over a large area at night.

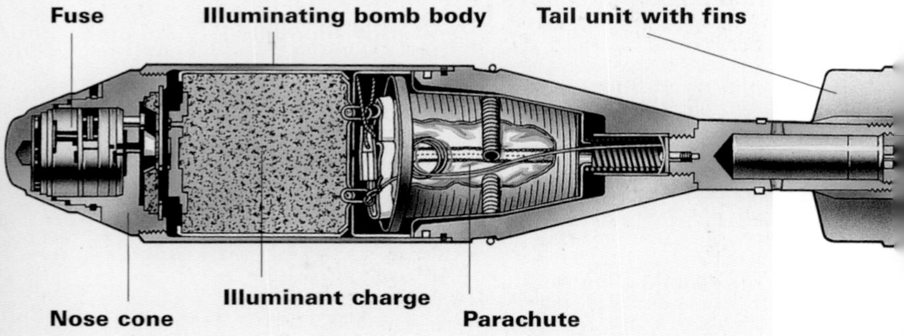


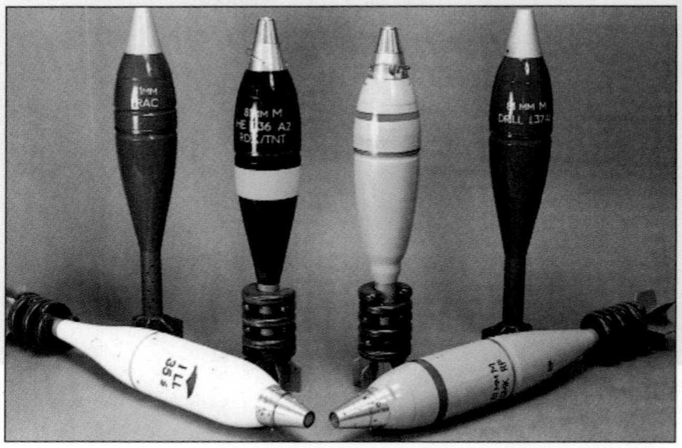

*Mortar bombs are colour-coded and also have marking stripes as well as a stencilled designation to help ensure that there is no confusion as to exactly which type of bomb is about to be readied and fired.*

# Mortier Brandt de 81 mm modèle 27/31

Even though the Stokes Mortar of World War I established the overall design shape and form of the modern mortar, it was still a very rudimentary weapon. The Stokes Mortar was little more than a pipe supported on a simple frame and sitting on a base plate to take the recoil forces. The French Brandt company changed all that in the years after World War I by a careful redesign and drastic improvement in the type of bomb fired. At first sight the modifications inspired by Brandt were difficult to detect, for there remained the overall form of the Stokes design, but improvements were there nonetheless. The weapon's overall handiness was one of the first of these improvements, and was apparent on a new Brandt model, introduced as the **Mortier Brandt de 81 mm modèle 27** in 1927 and updated in 1931 as the **modèle 27/31** to take advantage of ammunition improvements.

Setting up the original Stokes Mortar often took time, but the redesign of the Brandt bipod was such that it could be set up on any piece of ground: the levelling of the sights was easily carried out by the bipod leg design, on which only one leg needed to be adjusted. The sights were clamped to a position close to the muzzle, one that was convenient for the layer to peer through without having to stand over the weapon, and slight changes of traverse were easily made using a screw mechanism on the sight bracket. But the main changes came with the ammunition. The early grenades of the Stokes Mortar were replaced by well-shaped bombs that not only carried more explosive payload but also offered a much greater range. In fact Brandt produced a wide range of mortar bombs for its mle 26/31, but they fell into three main brackets. First there was one with an HE payload, and this was used as the standard bomb. Then there was a bomb that was twice the weight of the standard, but which had a shorter range. The third type of bomb used was smoke. Within these three categories came numerous marks and sub-marks: various coloured smokes were available, for instance.

### Influential design

The mle 27/31 greatly influenced mortar designs from the moment it was announced. Within a few years the mle 27/31 was being either produced under licence or simply plagiarised all over Europe and elsewhere. The mortar's calibre, 81.4 mm (3.2 in), became the virtual standard European calibre for infantry mortars, and nearly every infantry mortar in use during World War II had some feature or other derived from the mle 27/81, and many were indeed direct copies. This influence was wide enough to encompass the standard mortars of Germany, the USA, the Netherlands, China and even the USSR. All of these nations made their own alterations and innovations, but the resultant weapons were all basically the mle 27/31 at heart.

The Brandt influence survives today, although the weapons of the current generation of 81-mm mortars outrange the mle 27/61 by a factor of nearly six. But the mle 27/31 was more than good enough to be used in its many forms throughout World War II and for years after it.

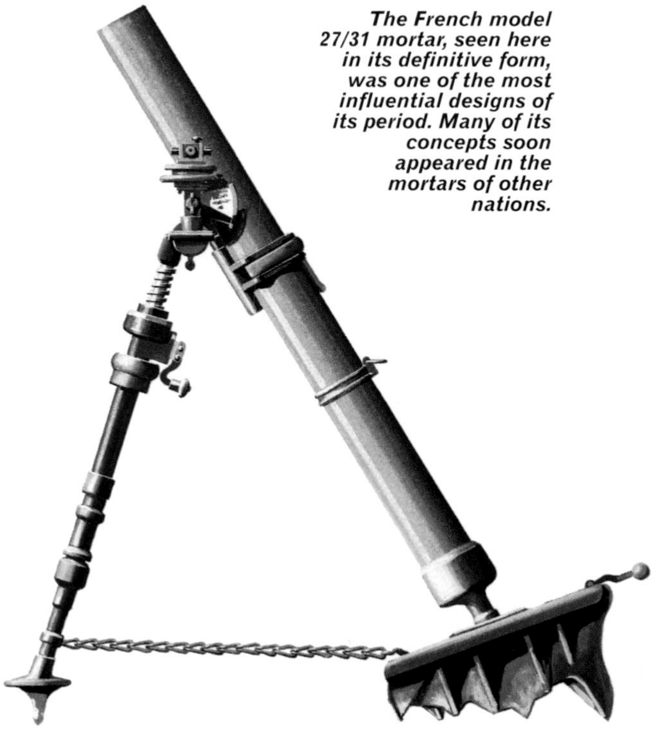

***The French model 27/31 mortar, seen here in its definitive form, was one of the most influential designs of its period. Many of its concepts soon appeared in the mortars of other nations.***

**SPECIFICATION**

**Mortier Brandt de 81 mm modèle 27/31**
**Calibre:** 81.4-mm (3.2-in)
**Lengths:** barrel 1.2675 m (49.9 in); bore 1.167 m (45.94 in)
**Weights**: in action 59.7 kg (131.6 lb); barrel 20.7 kg (45.6 lb); bipod 18.5 kg (40.8 lb); base plate 20.5 kg (45.2 lb)
**Elevation:** +45 to +80 degrees
**Traverse:** 8 to 12 degrees variable with elevation
**Maximum range:** standard bomb 1900 m (2,078 yards); heavy bomb 1000 m (1,094 yards)
**Bomb weight:** standard 3.25 kg (7.165 lb); heavy 6.9 kg (15.21 lb)

# 45/5 modello 35 'Brixia'

To the little **45/5 modello 35 'Brixia'** must go the prize for being the World War II mortar that offered a level of over-design and over-engineering unexcelled in any other weapon. Quite why the designers of the modello 35 went to such lengths, introducing wholly needless complexities, in a light support mortar with a very limited performance and a relatively ineffective projectile is now difficult to fathom. Nevertheless the result was issued to the Italian armed forces.

In this weapon's designation, 45/5 indicates the calibre of 45 mm (1.77 in) and the length of the barrel in calibres, i.e. 5 x 45 mm, although actually it was marginally longer. So small a calibre could fire only a very light bomb that turned the scales at a mere 0.465 kg (1.025 lb), with a correspondingly small explosive payload. The barrel was breech-loaded: operating a lever opened the breech and closing it also fed a charge from a magazine holding 10 cartridges. A trigger was used to fire the bomb, and to vary the range a gas port was opened or closed to vent some of the propellant gases. There were also complex elevation and traverse controls.

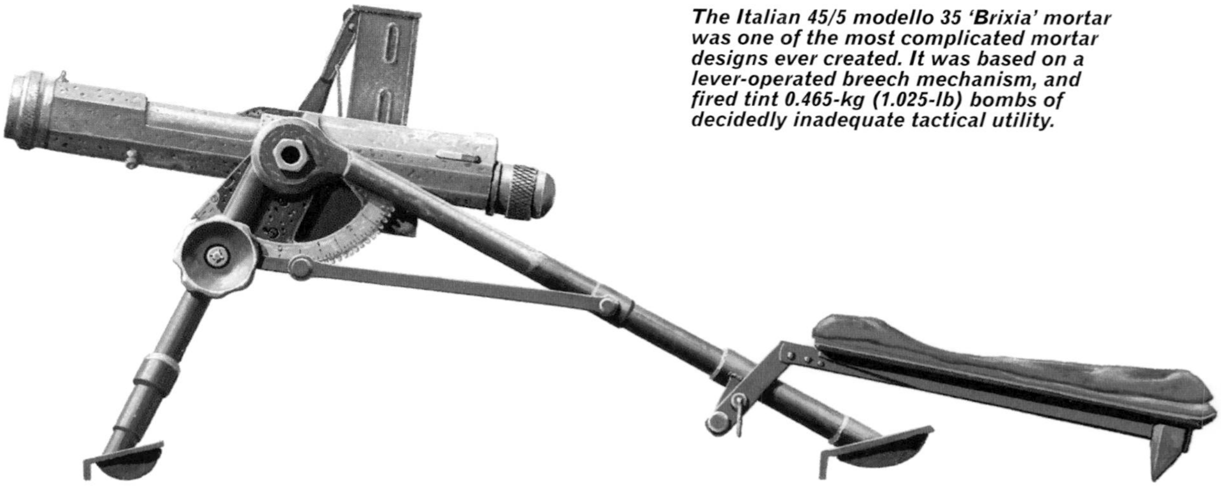

***The Italian 45/5 modello 35 'Brixia' mortar was one of the most complicated mortar designs ever created. It was based on a lever-operated breech mechanism, and fired tint 0.465-kg (1.025-lb) bombs of decidedly inadequate tactical utility.***

### Man-portable

The barrel of the modello 35 was located in a folding frame arrangement that rested against a carrier's back using a cushion pad to ease the load against the body. In use this frame was unfolded in such a way that the firer could then sit astride the weapon if required. In action the modello 35 could manage a fire rate of up to about 10 rounds per minute, and in trained hands the weapon was quite accurate. But even when they landed right on target, the little bombs were relatively ineffective, mainly as a result of the small payload that often resulted in erratic and ineffective fragmentation.

The modello 35 was widely used by the Italian armed forces, mainly at platoon level. All Italian soldiers were trained in its use, some of them while still in one or other of the Italian youth movements, which were issued with an equally complex but even less effective version of the modello 35, this time in 35-mm (1.38-in) calibre. These weapons were meant only for training, usually firing inert bombs.

**SPECIFICATION**

**45/5 modello 35 'Brixia'**
**Calibre:** 45-mm (1.77-in)
**Lengths:** barrel 0.26 m (10.2 in); bore 0.241 m (9.49 in)
**Weight:** in action 15.5 kg (34.17 lb)
**Elevation:** +10 to +90 degrees
**Traverse:** 20 degrees
**Maximum range:** 536 m (586 yards)
**Bomb weight:** 0.465 kg (1.025 lb)

The Italians were not the only users of the modello 35. During the North African campaigns the Afrika Korps also used them, often for logistical reasons when serving alongside Italian formations. There was even a German instruction manual for this very purpose, the German designation of the weapon being **4.5-cm Granatwerfer 176(i)**.

It is probable that Italian soldiers found to their cost the limitations of the modello 35 and retained it in service for the only reason that there was little chance of Italian industry being able to produce anything better in the then-foreseeable future. Having expended so much time and effort into getting the modello 35 into the hands of the troops, the limited ability of the Italian defence industries would have required too much time to design, develop and produce yet another weapon. So the Italian soldiers simply had to make do with what they were given; no doubt many of them thought it was not much.

# 50-mm light mortars

There were two main types of 50-mm (1.97-in) mortar in service with the Imperial Japanese army in World War II. Both of them were grenade launchers rather than real mortars, for they used projectiles that were little more than finned hand grenades. The weapons were mainly used at squad level for purely local support.

The first version to enter service was the **Grenade Discharger Type 10**, which entered service in 1921. This was a simple weapon of the smooth-bore type, and fired its grenade by means of a trigger mechanism. An adjustable gas vent was provided to give variations in range. The Type 10 originally fired HE grenades, but with the introduction of the later model it was used more and more to fire pyrotechnic grenades for target illumination and similar purposes. The main drawback of the Type 10 was its limited range, which was only some 160 m (175 yards), a fact that gave rise to development of the second weapon in this class, the **Type 89** discharger.

## Universal service

By 1941 the Type 89 had all but replaced the Type 10 in service, and differed from the earlier weapon in several respects, one being that the barrel was rifled instead of smooth-bored. The other main change was the elimination of the previous gas vent system in favour of a firing pin that could be moved up and down the barrel: the higher the firing pin was up the barrel the shorter the resultant range. The Type 89 mortar fired a new series of grenades to an effective range of 650 m (710 yards), which was a substantial increase over that possible with the Type 10. Grenades developed for the Type 89 included the usual HE, smoke, signalling and flares. Development of this weapon reached the point where a special version for use by airborne troops was produced. Normally both the Type 10 and Type 89 could be dismantled for carrying in a special leather case.

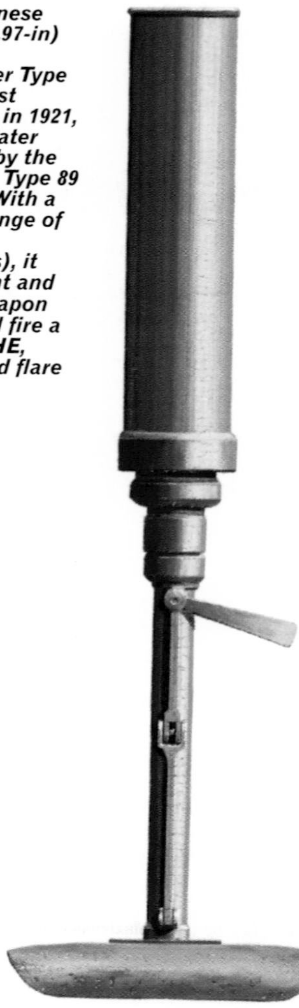

*The Japanese 50-mm (1.97-in) Grenade Discharger Type 10 was first produced in 1921, and was later replaced by the improved Type 89 weapon. With a limited range of 160 m (175 yards), it was a light and handy weapon that could fire a range of HE, smoke and flare grenades.*

*How not to do it: for some reasons the Americans decided quite wrongly that the small spade baseplate enabled the weapon to be fired from the thigh or knee (hence 'knee mortar').*

**SPECIFICATION**

**Grenade Discharger Type 89**
**Calibre:** 50-mm (1.97-in)
**Lengths:** overall 0.61 m (24 in); barrel 0. 254 m (10 in)
**Weight:** 4.65 kg (10.25 lb)
**Maximum range:** 650 m (711 yards)
**Grenade weight:** 0.79 kg (1.74 lb)

## 'Knee' mortar

The main version encountered by the Allies was the Type 89. Somehow the word spread among the Allies that these little mortars were 'knee' mortars and the name stuck. Exactly how many fractured thighs this completely misleading nickname caused among untrained users is now impossible to determine, but attempting to fire either of these mortars with the baseplate resting against a leg would result in immediate injury. The recoil of these little weapons was considerable and the baseplate had to be held against the ground or something really substantial. Aiming was rudimentary, for there were no sights other than a line marked on the barrel, but in a short time almost any soldier could learn to use the weapon fairly effectively. The mortar was readily man-portable and handy in action, but the grenade was somewhat on the light side for real effectiveness. What mattered, though, was that any soldier could carry one slung over a shoulder while still carrying a normal load, and the resultant increase in squad firepower was appreciable, especially when using the longer-range Type 89.

# Soviet light mortars

The Red Army used great numbers of mortars throughout World War II. In general they were sound weapons usually much heavier than their counterparts elsewhere, and also very robust.

During the 1930s Soviet arms designers developed several light infantry mortars. The smallest of these was an odd little 37-mm (1.45-in) weapon that could be configured as a mortar with its barrel supported by a monopod, or as an entrenching tool with the baseplate attached to the rear of the barrel to create a spade blade and handle. The Germans accorded the type the reporting designation **3.7 cm Spatengranatwerfer 161(r)**.

The primary capable for light mortars was standardised as 50 mm (1.97 in). The main series began with the **50-PM 38**, captured examples of which were used by the Germans with the designation **5-cm Granatwerfer 205/1(r)**. This was a conventional design with range varied by gas vents at the base of the barrel, which was held in its bipod at either of two fixed angles. This model was difficult to produce and replaced by the **50-PM 39** (**5-cm Granatwerfer 205/2(r)** to the Germans) without the gas vent feature but with standard bipod elevation methods. While effective, this model was still thought too difficult to produce and it was therefore replaced by the **50-PM 40** (**5-cm Granatwerfer 205/3(r)** to the Germans).

## Mass production

This was designed for genuinely mass production, and the bipod legs and baseplate were simple pressed steel components. The 50-PM 40 proved reliable and useful, even though the range was somewhat limited. There was one further model in this calibre, the **50-PM 41** (**5-cm Granatwerfer 200(r)** to the Germans) on which the bipod was replaced by a barrel yoke attached to a large baseplate. A gas venting system was also used, but not many were made as production was concentrated on the 50-PM 40.

While the 50-mm mortars were used at company or squad level, battalion mortars had an 82-mm (3.228-in) calibre. There were three models in this family, the **82-PM 36** which was a direct copy of the Brandt mle 27/31 and known to the Germans as the **8.2-cm Granatwerfer 274/1(r)**, the revised **82-PM 37** with recoil springs to reduce firing loads on the bipod and designated **8.2-cm Granatwerfer 274/2(r)** by the Germans, and the much simplified **82-PM 41** making extensive use of stampings to ease production, and known as the **8.2-cm Granatwerfer 274/3(r)** to the Germans. Wheels could be added to the ends of the short bipod for hand-towing, and this was taken further on the **82-PM 43** with an even simpler bipod to ease towing.

## Mountain mortar

There remains one further 'light' mortar worthy of mention. This was the 107-mm (4.21-in) **107-PBHM 38**, a specialised mountain mortar that was known to the Germans as the **10.7-cm Gebirgsgranatwerfer 328(r)**. This was an enlarged version of the 82-PM 37, and was used with a light limber for horse traction. Alternatively the mortar could be broken down into loads for pack transport. Firing could be by the normal 'drop' method or by means of a trigger. This mountain version saw extensive use during and after World War II.

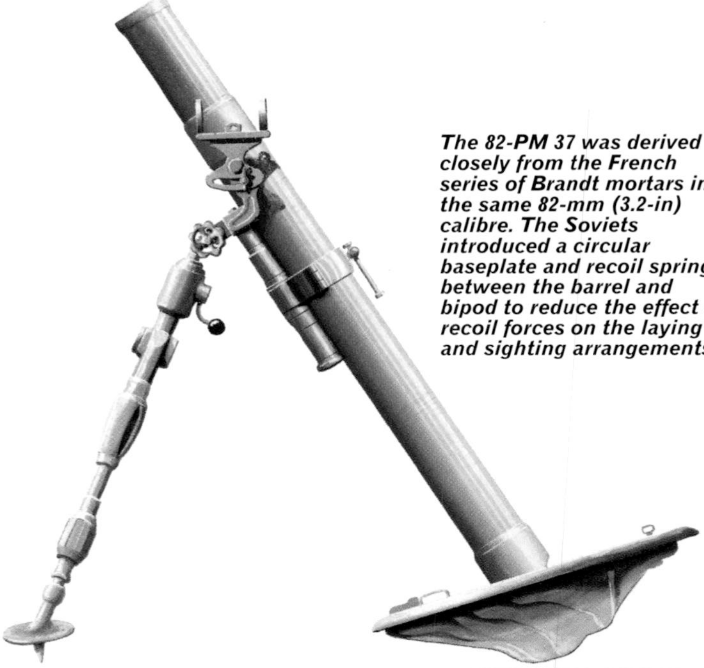

***The 82-PM 37 was derived closely from the French series of Brandt mortars in the same 82-mm (3.2-in) calibre. The Soviets introduced a circular baseplate and recoil springs between the barrel and bipod to reduce the effect of recoil forces on the laying and sighting arrangements.***

***The Soviet army found that the mortar, such as this 50-mm weapon, was suited to urban warfare as its high trajectory allowed bombs to be lobbed over buildings.***

***Left: Used in very large numbers by first-line units, the 82-mm mortars allowed infantry to lay down a barrage of anti-personnel fire before they moved forward.***

***Below: A major advantage of the mortar over tube artillery is its ability to land bombs over a range that can be brought down to a very small figure if needed.***

### SPECIFICATIONS

**50-PM 40**
**Calibre:** 50-mm (1.97-in)
**Lengths:** barrel 630 mm (24.8 in); bore 533 mm (20.98 in)
**Weight:** in action 9.3 kg (20.5 lb)
**Elevation:** 45° or 75° fixed
**Traverse:** 9° or 16°
**Maximum range:** 800 m (875 yards)
**Bomb weight:** 0.85 kg (1.874 lb)

**82-PM 41**
**Calibre:** 82-mm (3.228-in)
**Lengths:** barrel 1320 mm (51.97 in); bore 1225 mm (48.23 in)
**Weight:** in action 45 kg (99.2 lb)
**Elevation:** +45° to +85°
**Traverse:** 5° to 10° variable
**Maximum range:** 3100 m (3,390 yards)
**Bomb weight:** 3.4 kg (7.5 lb)

**107-PBHM 38**
**Calibre:** 107-mm (4.21-in)
**Lengths:** barrel 1570 mm (61.8 in); bore 1400 m (55.12 in)
**Weight:** in action 170.7 kg (376 lb)
**Elevation:** +45° to +80°
**Traverse:** 6°
**Maximum range:** 6315 m (6,905 yards)
**Bomb weight:** 8 kg (17.64 lb)

# 120-HM 38 mortar

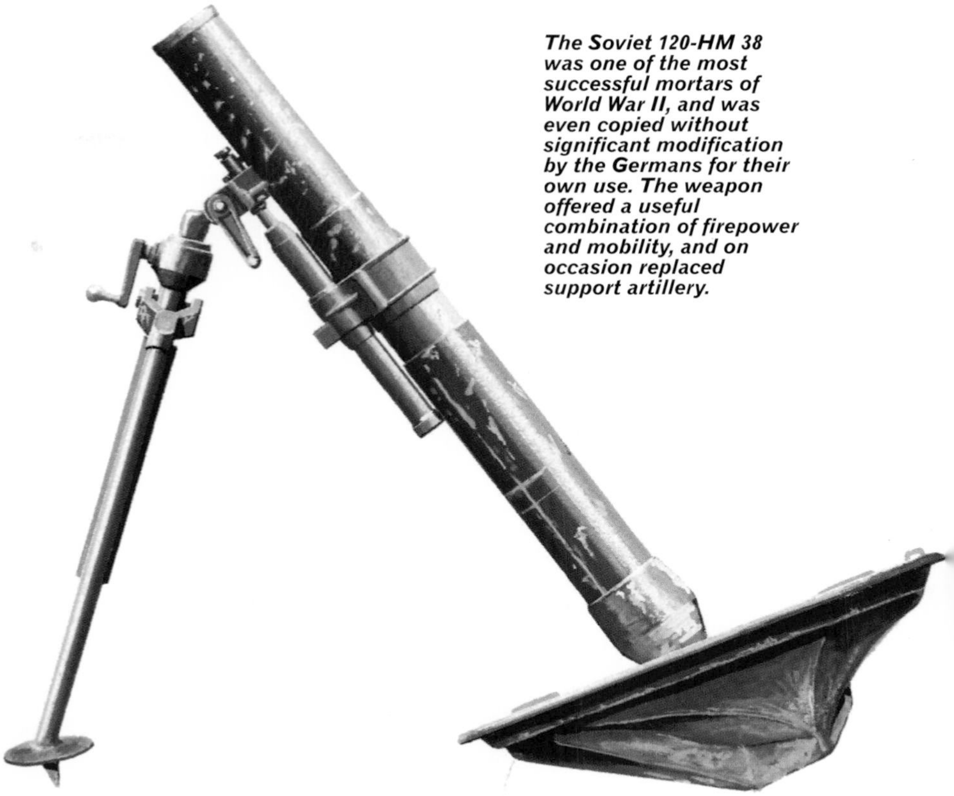

*The Soviet 120-HM 38 was one of the most successful mortars of World War II, and was even copied without significant modification by the Germans for their own use. The weapon offered a useful combination of firepower and mobility, and on occasion replaced support artillery.*

The Soviet 120-mm (4.72-in) **120-HM 38** is one of the great success stories in the history of mortars, for it was introduced to service during 1938 and it is still in relatively widespread service today. The primary reason for the weapon's longevity is the excellent combination of bomb weight, mobility and range it offers. When introduced, the weapon was regarded as a regimental mortar for the production of fire support in place of conventional tube artillery, and as World War II continued and production allowed the fielding of more weapons, it was issued down to battalion level.

In design terms there was nothing really remarkable about the 120-HM 38. One feature that proved to be very useful was the large circular baseplate, for this allowed rapid changes in traverse as there was none of the usual need to dig out the baseplate and align it to the new direction of fire, as would have been the case with the more conventional rectangular baseplate. The weapon was towed with the baseplate still attached and the weapon lying on a wheeled frame. A lunette was fitted into the muzzle as the towing ring, and this was attached to the same limber as used for the smaller 107-PBHM 38 mortar. This limber usually incorporated an ammunition box holding 20 rounds, and the combination was towed by either a light vehicle or a team of horses.

## High mobility

Getting the 120-HM 38 in to and out of action was therefore relatively rapid and easy, so after fire had been opened it was usually a simple matter to move off again before the Germans could begin retaliatory fire.

*Left: The 120-HM 38 is seen here in travelling order – the eye of the lunettte in the muzzle attachment is connected to the towing vehicle or draft animal.*

*Below: Part of a Red Army mortar battery equipped with the 120-HM 38, seen here in action during September 1942 in the foothills of the Caucasian range.*

As the Germans moved across the USSR in 1941 and 1942 they were much impressed by the firepower and mobility combination offered by the 120-HM 38 mortar. As the recipients of the weapon's efficiency and overall capabilities on many occasions, they had good reason to note the power of the bomb's warhead, and therefore decided to adopt the design for their own manufacture and use. In the short term the Germans had recourse to the expedient of using as many captured examples as they could lay their hands on, under the designation **12-cm Granatwerfer 378(r)**. The Germans then went one stage further and copied the design exactly for production in Germany. This was known to them as the **12-cm Granatwerfer 42** and was widely issued, even taking the place of short-barrel support guns in some infantry formations. Thus what was essentially the same weapon was used by both sides during the fighting on the Eastern Front.

## Effective bomb

The usual bomb fired by the 120-HM 38 on both sides was the HE round, but smoke and chemical rounds were produced (although the latter were never used). The rate of fire could be as high as 10 rounds per minute, so a battery of four of these mortars could lay down considerable amounts of fire in a very short period. Over a period of action the baseplates did have a tendency to 'bed in', making relaying necessary, but this was partially eliminated by introduction of the improved **120-HM 43**, which differed from its predecessor in its use of a spring-loaded shock absorber mechanism on the barrel/bipod mounting. It is this version, which was otherwise unchanged from the original, that is most likely to be encountered today. Over the years some changes have been made to the ammunition, which now has a longer range than the wartime equivalent, and another change is that many modern versions are now carried on various types of self-propelled carriage.

The Soviets also developed and used a scaled-up 160-mm (6.3-in) version of the 120-HM 38 under the designation **160-HM 43**. This was breech-loaded and trigger-fired, and was allocated to divisional artillery units as it could fire a 41.14-kg (90.17-lb) HE bomb from a minimum range of 750 m (820 yards) out to a maximum of 5150 m (5,630 yards) at the rate of three bombs per minute.

### SPECIFICATION

**120-HM 38**
**Calibre:** 120-mm (4.72-in)
**Lengths:** barrel 1862 mm (73.3 in); bore 1536 mm (60.47 in)
**Weight:** in action 280.1 kg (617 lb)
**Elevation:** +45° to +80°
**Traverse:** 6°
**Maximum range:** 6000 m (6,560 yards)
**Bomb weight:** HE 16 kg (35.3 lb)

# German infantry support weapons

German weapon designers between the world wars were presented with virtually a clean slate on which to work. Thus when a requirement was released for a light infantry mortar for issue at squad level, Rheinmetall-Borsig's design team opted not to follow the usual barrel/ baseplate/bipod form but instead to create a design in which the barrel was permanently secured to the baseplate and the bipod was virtually eliminated in favour of a monopod device fixed to the baseplate. The result was a complex little 50-mm (1.97-in) weapon known as the **5-cm leichte Granatwerfer 36** or **leGrW 36** (light grenade-launcher model 1936) and first issued during 1936.

The leGrW 36 was a good example of the Germans' general love of gadgetry in their weapons, and ranged from the traverse controls built onto the baseplate to a very complicated but wholly superfluous telescopic sight. This latter was very much the designers' attempt to make the weapon as perfect as possible and ensure accuracy. But the ranges at which the little leGrW 36 was used were such that a simple line painted on the barrel was all that was needed, and the sight was dropped during 1938.

The weapon could be carried by one man using a handle at the base of the barrel. For all it was small, at 14 kg (30.8 lb) the leGrW 36 was rather heavy. Thus one man had to carry the mortar and another the ammunition (only HE bombs were fired) in a steel box. In action the baseplate was placed on the ground and all barrel adjustments were made using coarse and fine control knobs. A trigger-actuated firing mechanism was used.

While the designers were rather proud of the leGrW 36, troops in the field were less enthusiastic. They felt that the leGrW 36, quite apart from its weight problem, was too complicated and the bomb not worth all the trouble involved. The bomb weighed only 0.9 kg (1.98 lb) and the maximum range was a mere 520 m (570 yards).

## Expensive to make

Added to this, as far as higher authorities were concerned, was the fact that the weapon took too much time and money to manufacture in relation to its capabilities. Such a situation could not endure once war had started, of course, and by 1941 the leGrW 36 had been removed from production. Existing weapons were gradually withdrawn from front-line service in favour of something better, and passed on to second-line and garrison units: many were allocated to units manning the Atlantic Wall as part of the beach defences. Some were passed on to the Italian army.

In overall terms, therefore, the leGrW 36 was not one of the German weapon designers' best efforts. They allowed a small weapon to become far too complex and costly to justify the result, and the German army was astute enough to realise the fact and so progressed to the use of more effective weapons.

***The schwere Granatwerfer 34 was a mortar much respected by the Allied forces who came in for its attentions. The weapon was accurate and capable of a rapid rate of fire, but its overall success was attributable more to the training of its crews than any superiority of the weapon itself.***

**SPECIFICATION**

| | |
|---|---|
| **leGrW 36** | **Elevation:** + 42° to + 90° |
| **Calibre:** 50-mm (1.969-in) | **Traverse:** 34° |
| **Lengths:** barrel 0.465 m (18.3 in); bore 0.35 m (13.78 in) | **Maximum range:** 520 m (570 yards) |
| **Weight:** in action 14 kg (30.8 lb) | **Bomb weight:** 0.9 kg (1.98 lb) |

***The 5-cm leGrW was the German army's standard light mortar in the first part of World War II, but it fired too small a bomb and was overly complex in its features. As a result it was phased out of first-line service from 1941.***

## Up the calibre ladder

The German army's **8-cm schwere Granatwerfer 34** or **8-cm sGrW 34** (heavy grenade-launcher model 1934) gained an enviable reputation among Allied front-line soldiers for its accuracy and rate of fire. The weapon was encountered wherever the German army fought, for the sGrW 34 was one of the Germans' standard weapons from 1939 right through to the last days of World War II in May 1945. The mortar was designed and made by Rheinmetall-Borsig once again, but truth to tell was little more than a German version of the Brandt mle 27/31 in the same 81.4-mm (3.2-in) calibre.

Despite its reputation as a high-quality weapon, there was nothing remarkable in the design of the sGrW 34. So much of the respect it gained as a weapon should instead have gone to the thorough training and efficiency of the men who used it: throughout the war the German mortar crews seemed always to have an edge over their rivals. They became experts at getting their sGrW 34s in and out of action rapidly, and by careful use of plotting boards and other fire-control aids were able to obtain maximum accuracy from their fire.

The sGrW 34 was straightforward in design and very well made. It was consequently very robust and could be broken down into three loads for man-pack portability; more men were needed to carry the ammunition. There was also a special version for mounting in the rear of SdKfz 250/7 half-track vehicles.

Several centres were involved in production of the weapon, and more with the manufacture of the associated ammunition, for the types of bombs that could be fired from the sGrW 34 were numerous. There were the usual HE and smoke

***Left: The shape of the 8-cm sGrW 34 mortar's bomb can be clearly seen here as it is held ready for loading into the weapon's muzzle. The bomb weighed 3.5 kg (7.72 lb) and had a ring of multiple fins round its tail for stability in flight. The layer is making fine azimuth adjustments using the simple sight mounted on the bipod.***

***Below: An 8-cm sGrW 34 crew in action. The pear-shaped bomb is being introduced into the muzzle, from which it will fall down the barrel on to a fixed firing pin to initiate the propellant charge and propel the bomb out to a maximum range of 2400 m (2,625 yards).***

**SPECIFICATION**

**sGrW 34**
**Calibre:** 81.4-mm (3.2-in)
**Lengths:** barrel 1.143 m (45 in); bore 1.033 m (40.67 in)
**Weight:** in action 56.7 kg (125 lb)
**Elevation:** +40° to +90°
**Traverse:** 9° to 15° variable with elevation
**Maximum range:** 2400 m (2,625 yards)
**Bomb weight:** 3.5 kg (7.72 lb)

***Right: This is a propaganda photograph of the 8-cm sGrW 34 in action, clearly revealing the elevation, traverse and levelling controls fitted on the bipod that braced the weapon's forward portion. The crew member on the right is holding the bipod to help stabilise the weapon as it is fired.***

bombs, but innovations included illuminating and target-marking bombs to aid ground-attack aircraft, and there was even a special 'bouncing bomb' known as the 8-cm Wurfgranate 39 that was driven back up into the air after it had struck the ground. This was achieved by the use of a tiny rocket motor, and at a predetermined height the bomb exploded to scatter its fragments over a much wider area than would be the case with a conventional ground-detonated bomb. Again, this was a typically German weapon innovation that was really too expensive and unreliable for general use, and the numbers produced were never large. One extra bonus for the sGrW 34 was that it could fire a wide range of captured ammunition, although usually with some loss in range performance.

For airborne use a special shortened version of the sGrW 34 was developed in 1940 as the **kurzer Granatwerfer 42**, known as the **Stummelwerfer** in general use. This was issued in quantity from about 1942 onward, but saw little service with airborne forces and instead became a replacement for the little 5-cm leGrW 36. It fired the same bombs as the sGrW 34 but to a maximum range reduced by more than half.

## Infantry gun

One of the many tactical lessons learned by the German army in World War I was the desirability of providing each infantry battalion with a measure of organic artillery support. This led to the allocation of lightweight infantry guns to each battalion. During the 1920s one of the first priorities of the then severely restricted German weapons industry was the development of a new light infantry gun, or *leichte Infantriegeschütz*. A 75-mm (2.95-in) design was produced by Rheinmetall-Borsig as early as 1927 and was issued for service in 1932 as the **7.5-cm leIG 18**, or **7.5-cm leichte Infantriegeschütz 18**.

The first examples had wooden spoked wheels, but later versions for service with motorised formations had metal disc wheels with rubber tyres. The leIG 18 had an unusual loading mechanism: operation of a lever opened not the breech but instead moved the entire barrel section upwards in a square slipper to expose the loading chamber. This system was yet another example of German design innovation simply for its own sake, and the mechanism offered no real advantage over conventional systems. The rest of the gun was orthodox, and in action it was sturdy and reliable. The range was limited as a result of the short barrel.

## Two variants

There were two variants of the leIG 18. One was developed for mountain warfare units and known as the **leichte Gebirgs Infantriegeschütz 18** or **leGebIG 18** (light mountain infantry gun model 18). This was developed from 1935 as an leIG 18 that could be broken down into 10 loads for pack transport on mules or light vehicles. To save weight the ordinary box trail was replaced by tubular steel trail legs, and the shield became optional. The leGebIG 18 was heavier than the original but the pack load feature made it much more suitable for its intended role. It was meant as an interim weapon, but remained in service up to 1945.

There was also an airborne forces' version of the leIG 18, the **leIG 18F**, the F indicating *Fallschirmjäger* (paratrooper). This could be broken down into four loads for paradropping in special containers. This version had small metal wheels, no shield and tubular trail legs. Only six were produced before the task was taken over by the recoilless gun.

***The crew of a 7.5-cm leIG 18 is captured by the camera in training during 1940. Note the relatively small size of the round being handed to the loader, and the way in which one crew member is kneeling on the end of the trail to stabilise it.***

**SPECIFICATION**

**leIG 18**
**Calibre:** 75-mm (2.95-in)
**Lengths:** gun overall 0.9 m (35.43 in); barrel 0.884 m (34.8 in)
**Weight:** in action 400 kg (882 lb)
**Elevation:** 10° to +73°
**Traverse:** 12°
**Muzzle velocity:** 210 m (689 ft) per second
**Maximum range:** 3550 m (3,882 yards)
**Projectile weight:** HE 5.45 or 6 kg (12 or 13.2 lb); hollow charge 3 kg (6.6 lb)

# British mortars

The first British 2-in (50.8-mm) mortar made its appearance in 1918 toward the end of World War I, but this did not remain in service for long, being rendered obsolete in 1919. This was followed with a light mortar interregnum, for it was not until the 1930s that the notion of reintroducing a light mortar for use at platoon or squad level was put forward. There was no 'history' of the development of such small mortars in the UK at that time, so it was decided to run a selection competition between the offerings from various armaments manufacturers. The first result of this procurement process was a flood of models from a number of concerns, and after a series of trials one of these was selected for production and service.

## Winning design

The winner was a design from the Spanish manufacturer ECIA. In its original form this weapon was thought needy of improvement, and the further work was carried out in the UK, leading to full production during 1938. The first production version was the **Ordnance, ML 2-inch Mortar Mk II** (ML for muzzle loading), but this was only the first of a long string of marks and sub-marks. In basic terms there were two types of 2-inch mortar. One was the pure infantry version, which was a simple barrel with a small baseplate and a trigger mechanism to fire the bomb after it had been loaded. The second was meant for use on Bren Gun or Universal Carrier light tracked vehicles and had a much larger baseplate and a more complicated aiming system. If required, the carrier version could be dismounted for ground use, and a handle was supplied for this purpose. However, between these two types there were at the least 14 different variants, with differences in barrel length, sighting arrangements and production variations. There were even special versions for use by the Indian Army and by airborne divisions.

## Bomb types

To go with this array of weapon variants there was an equally daunting range of ammunition types. The usual bomb fired by the 2-inch mortar was HE, but smoke and flare types were also fired, the latter being particularly useful for target illumination at night. Having a trigger firing mechanism, the weapon could be used at angles close to the horizontal, a factor that was especially useful in house-to-house combat. The bombs were normally carried in tubes, each holding three, and arranged in handy packs of three tubes. The normal 2-inch Mortar team consisted of two men, one carrying the mortar and the other carrying the ammunition.

## 3-inch mortar

The first 3-in (76.2-mm) mortar used by the British army was the original Stokes Mortar that saw its initial service during March 1917. This version remained in use for many years after World War I, and as funds for weapon development were sparse in the financially straitened times between the two world wars the Stokes Mortar remained in service virtually unchanged for some years. However, a measure of development work was carried out on the basic design to the point at which it was decided during the early 1930s that the Ordnance, ML Mortar, 3-inch would remain in first-line service as the standard infantry support weapon: this resulted from the 1932 decision that the mortar would replace the 3.7-in (94-mm) howitzer as the British army's standard infantry support weapon. The weapon standardised for this task was not the original Ordnance, ML Mortar, 3-inch Mk I but rather the **Ordnance, ML Mortar 3-inch Mk II**, which was thus the weapon in service with the British when World War II broke out in September 1939. This modernised Mk II weapon had numerous changes from the original Mk I mortar of World War I, especially in the ammunition, which introduced many of the innovatory features of the mortar bombs created by the French Brandt armaments company.

## Greater range needed

It was not long after the start of the war that it began to become apparent that although the Mk II was a sturdy and reliable weapon, it lacked the range of many of its contemporaries. The early versions had a range of only some 1465 m (1,600 yards), which compared badly with the 2400 m (2,625 yards) of its German equivalent, the 8-cm sGrW 34. A long series of experiments and trials using new

*Above: Soldiers of the 1st Battalion, the Hampshire Regiment, in action in Sicily with a 2-in mortar. The gunner is operating the trigger while his partner watches for the bomb's fall.*

*Left: A 2-in mortar team of the Royal Scots Fusiliers in action in Normandy, late June 1944. The mortar's small size made it a handy and portable weapon.*

*Below: Demonstration of loading the 2-in mortar with the larger Carrier baseplate.*

**SPECIFICATION**

| | |
|---|---|
| **2-inch Mortar Mk II***** | **Weight:** 4.1 kg (9 lb) |
| **Calibre:** 2-in (50.8-mm) | **Maximum range:** 455 m (500 yards) |
| **Lengths**: barrel 665 mm (26.2 in); bore 506.5 mm (19.94 in) | **Bomb weight:** HE 1.02 kg (2.25 lb) |

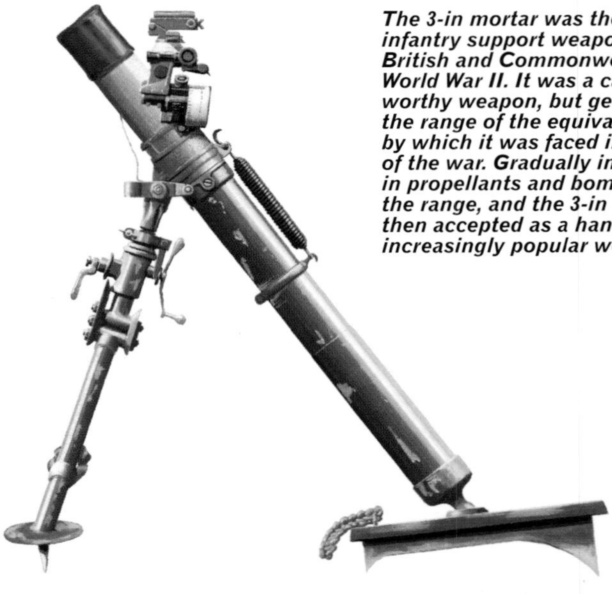

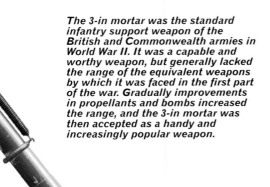

*The 3-in mortar was the standard infantry support weapon of the British and Commonwealth armies in World War II. It was a capable and worthy weapon, but generally lacked the range of the equivalent weapons by which it was faced in the first part of the war. Gradually improvements in propellants and bombs increased the range, and the 3-in mortar was then accepted as a handy and increasingly popular weapon.*

***Men of the Black Watch in action with a 3-in mortar in Normandy during June 1944, the weapon emplaced in a purpose-dug pit with camouflage netting to hand.***

***A 3-in mortar attacks German positions across the Maas river in the bitter January of 1945. Judging by the pile of ready-use bombs, the team had a long mission.***

propellants then succeeded in increasing this range to 2515 m (2,750 yards), which overcame many of the original drawbacks, but it took some time to get the new propellants into the hands of British front-line troops, so at times many captured German and Italian mortars were used by British troops, especially in the course of the North African campaigns.

Apart from the ammunition changes, other alterations were made to the basic design. Later developments, starting with the **Ordnance, ML Mortar, 3-inch Mk IV**, were equipped with a new and heavier baseplate design as well as improved sighting arrangements, and there was even a specially lightened version (the **Ordnance, Mortar, 3-inch Mk V**) developed for use in the Far East, but only 5,000 of these were made and, for obvious reasons, some were issued to the British airborne divisions.

## Transport options

The usual method of getting the weapon into action was pack carriage in three loads by men, but the British army's mechanised battalions carried their weapons on specially equipped Universal Carriers. On these the mortar was carried on the back of the vehicle ready to be assembled for normal ground use; the mortar was not fired from the carrier itself, which also had stowage for the mortar's ammunition. When the mortar was para-dropped, the barrel and the bipod were dropped in one container, a second container carried the baseplate, and a third container held the ammunition.

## Short minimum range

The ammunition for the family was largely confined to HE and smoke, although other payloads such as illuminants were developed. By juggling with the propelling charge increments and barrel elevation angles it was possible to drop a bomb as close as 115 m (125 yards) away, a useful feature in close-quarter combat.

Somehow the 3-in mortar never achieved the respect that was given to its opponents, but this should not be allowed to disguise the fact that once the weapon's original range shortcomings had been rectified, the 3-in mortar proved to be a sound enough weapon that remained in service with the British army until the 1960s, and indeed is used by some of the smaller ex-Commonwealth armies.

## 4.2-in mortar

By 1941 it had been noted by British army staff planners that there had appeared a pressing need for a mortar that could fire projectiles producing large amounts of tactical smoke for screening and other purposes: in this appreciation the planners had no doubt been impressed by reports from front-line formations of the capabilities of the 10-cm Nebelwerfer mortars used by German Nebeltruppen (smoke troops).

Accordingly a new design of 4.2-in (106.7-mm) heavy mortar was developed. But almost as soon as the first examples were ready for issue to Royal Engineer smoke production units, the requirement was changed to convert the new weapon into a heavy mortar firing conventional HE bombs for issue to Royal Artillery batteries. Thus the new mortar became the **Ordnance, SB 4.2-inch Mortar** (SB standing for smooth-bore).

The 4.2-in mortar was produced at a time when the British defence industry was fully stretched and production facilities of all kinds were in short supply. This was particularly noticeable in the production of the bombs to be fired by the new weapon. The designers wanted the bombs to have forged bodies to reduce weight and also produce a better ballistic shape. At that time the required forging facilities were not available, though, so the bomb bodies had to be cast. This resulted in a maximum range of only 3020 m (3,300 yards) as opposed to the required 4025 m (4,400 yards).

## No option

These bombs had to be used, for they were all that could be made at the time pending the introduction of a new design with a streamlined body. Again, these had to be manufactured using cast iron but they did manage a range of 3660 m (4,000 yards). By that time HE bombs were the main projectile used, but the original smoke function had not been entirely forgotten and some smoke bombs were also produced.

## Hefty equipment

The 4.2-in mortar was fairly hefty to move around, so the usual method of getting it into action was to tow it using a Jeep or other light vehicle. The baseplate and the barrel/bipod were so arranged that they could be lifted without undue difficulty onto a small wheeled mounting. Once on site they could be lowered from the mounting and the barrel and bipod quickly assembled. When carried on a Universal Carrier things were even simpler. The baseplate was simply dropped off the back, the barrel was inserted and the bipod shoved into place, and firing could start almost at once. Getting out of action was just as rapid. This led to the 4.2-in mortar being viewed with some suspicion by the troops who relied upon its firepower support. While they valued its supporting fire they knew that as soon as a 4.2-in mortar battery was brought into action nearby it would be off again before the incoming counter-battery fire from the enemy arrived. By that time the 4.2-in mortar battery would be some distance away, leaving the units close to their former position to receive the fire meant for the battery.

The 4.2-in mortar was widely used by the Royal Artillery, many field regiments having alternative gun or 4.2-in mortar complements. The 4.2-in mortar was used wherever British troops served from late 1942 onwards, and the weapon was still in use during the Korean War, in which it was used to tackle targets situated on reverse slopes behind hills or in valleys.

**SPECIFICATION**

**Mortar, 3-inch Mk II**
**Calibre:** 3-in (76.2-mm)
**Length overall:** 1295 mm (51 in)
**Length of barrel:** 1190 mm (46.8 in)
**Weight:** in action 57.2 kg (126 lb)
**Elevation:** +45° to +80°
**Traverse:** 11°
**Maximum range:** 2515 m (2,750 yards)
**Bomb weight:** HE 4.54 kg (10 lb)

***A 4.2-in mortar fires on German positions in the foot hills of Mt Etna during the Sicilian campaign of 1943, the crew protecting their ears against muzzle blast.***

**SPECIFICATION**

**4.2-inch Mortar**
**Calibre:** 4.2-in (106.7-mm)
**Lengths:** barrel 1730 mm (68.1 in); bore 1565 mm (61.6 in)
**Weight:** in action 599 kg (1,320 lb)
**Elevation:** +45° to +80°
**Traverse:** 10°
**Maximum range:** 3750 m (4,100 yards)
**Bomb weight:** 9.07 kg (20 lb)

# US mortars

The mortar teams of the US army have always referred to their charges as 'cannon' and during World War II they had a lot of these cannons to hand. The smallest of these was not an American by origin, but rather a French weapon as this **60-mm Mortar M2** was a direct licence-produced copy of a Brandt design. It was in 1938 that the US Army bought eight examples of the French mortar for evaluation as **60-mm Mortar M1** weapons in the USA, where the type's capabilities were immediately realised and the weapon ordered into American production. The 60-mm Mortar M2 soon became the standard US Army mortar for use down to company level, and for it American industry produced a wide range of ammunition types, including the standard M49A2 HE bomb but also one odd projectile, the M83 bomb that was meant to illuminate low-flying aircraft at night so that light anti-aircraft weapons could deal with them.

Although the 60-mm mortar M2 was a capable weapon that offered the US army a new level of battlefield support down to unit level, the planners of the US army soon become conscious of the fact that American know-how could be used to effect major improvements on this pioneering mortar, largely with a view to reducing weight and enhancing mobility.

## Poor performance

From the M2 the Americans therefore developed their **60-mm Mortar M19**, which can be regarded as the US equivalent of the British 2-in Mortar, which it closely resembled. By comparison with the 60-mm Mortar M2, the main changes were the elimination of the bipod supporting the front of the barrel and the replacement of the large square baseplate, with rounded-off corners, by a smaller rectangular baseplate, again with rounded-off corners, that was curved downward to earth side of its longitudinal centreline so that the edges bedded themselves into the each as the weapon was fired.

Not many M19s were produced, for it was appreciated soon after the type entered service that it lacked both range and accuracy, and most of these went to airborne formations as these had great need for lightweight support weapons for their paratroop and gliderborne forces. The M19 fired the same range of bombs as the M2, but with only one charge rather than the M2's propellant arrangement of up to five charges. The data for the 60-mm mortar M2 included a calibre of 60.5-mm (2.38-in), overall length of 0.726 m (28.6 in), weight in action of 9 kg (19.8 lb), unlimited elevation and traverse angles as the weapon was installed on a

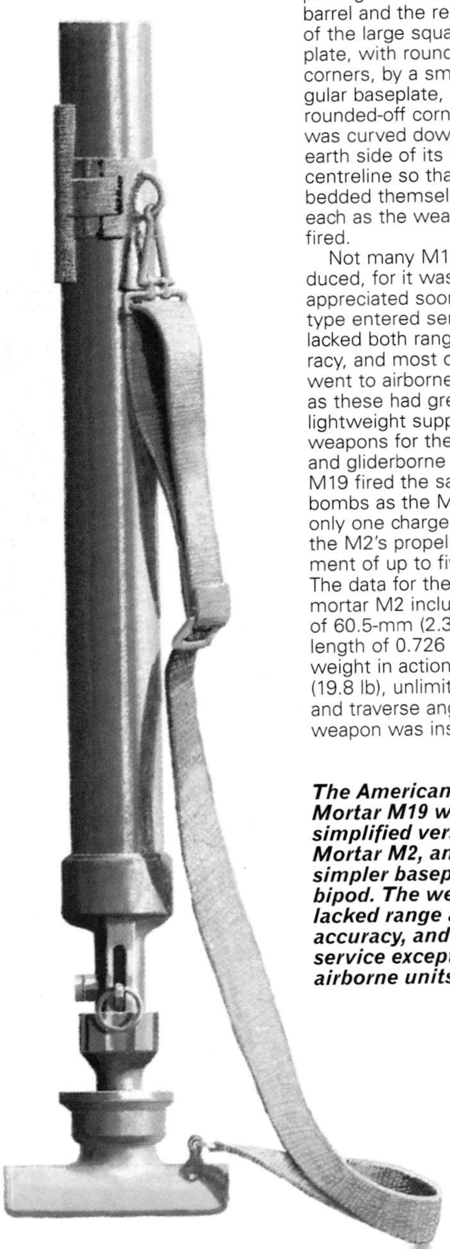

***The American 60-mm Mortar M19 was a much simplified version of the Mortar M2, and used a simpler baseplate but no bipod. The weapon lacked range and accuracy, and saw little service except with airborne units.***

***A 4.2-in Chemical Mortar is seen in action on Arundel Island during the Solomons campaign. Note the stack of bombs for this mortar, and how the shape of these projectiles resembles that of the conventional artillery shell.***

***This 81-mm Mortar M1 is seen in action in the type of terrain in which the mortar came into its own. Firing at a high angle of elevation, the mortar could lob its bombs over obstacles such as trees to deliver plunging fire into the enemy's lines.***

***The light weight of the 60-mm Mortar M2 made it an ideal weapon for front-line support right down to small unit level. The bomb left the tube with a velocity of 158 m (518 ft) per second.***

**SPECIFICATION**

**60-mm Mortar M2**
**Calibre:** 60-mm (2.38-in)
**Length:** barrel 0.726 m (28.6 in)
**Weight:** in action 19.05 kg (42 lb)
**Elevation:** +40 to +85 degrees
**Traverse:** 14 degrees
**Maximum range:** 1815 m (1,985 yards)
**Bomb weight:** 1.36 kg (3 lb)

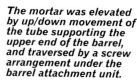

***The mortar was elevated by up/down movement of the tube supporting the upper end of the barrel, and traversed by a screw arrangement under the barrel attachment unit.***

universal joint, and range between minimum and maximum figures of 68 and 750 m (75 and 815 yards) with an HE bomb weighing 1.36 kg (3 lb) fired with a muzzle velocity of 89 m (292 ft) per second. The practical range was 320 m (350 yards).

## Heavier firepower

The standard battalion mortar of the US Army was another Brandt licence-built product, yet one more variation of the mle 27/31 design. The Americans produced their version as the **81-mm Mortar M1**, and with some slight alterations to suit local production methods this was manufactured throughout World War II and in every theatre where Americans forces fought. This M1 weapon was provided with a number of bomb types, including at least two HE and one smoke bombs, and its range bracket was made very flexible at the tactical level by the use of a six-charge propellant arrangement.

One odd American piece of equipment used with this weapon was a small hand cart onto which the mortar and its ammunition could be loaded. Just two men were required to tow this handy little carrier, known as the Hand Cart M6A1. Other carriers included mules, for which a special harness set was devised, but perhaps the most universally used was the M21 half-track carrier from which the M1 mortar could be fired without the need to dismount the weapon.

## Little modification

Throughout its service life the M1 remained virtually unchanged. A special T1 barrel extension tube was devised to increase range but this was little used, and a shortened version, known as the **T27 'Universal'** and of which much was expected, was not accepted for service on a large scale.

Perhaps the best known of all World War II American mortars was the **4.2-in Chemical Mortar**, the main reason for its fame probably being that it remained in service with the US Army until comparatively recent times. As with its British counterpart, this was devised to be a mortar firing smoke projectiles (hence the Chemical Mortar designation), but it was not long before it was realised that HE bombs would be very effective as well. It was a large and cumbersome weapon with a massive and heavy baseplate that was later replaced by much lighter designs, and the barrel was rifled to fire bombs that closely resembled conventional artillery projectiles. The rifling made the 4.2-in Chemical Mortar very accurate, and the projectiles were much heavier than their smooth-bore equivalents. In action they were often used as infantry support weapons, but many were issued to smoke screen units. The one major drawback to the 4.2-in Chemical Mortar was its weight and bulk. It was not an easy weapon to deploy and to overcome this various self-propelled carriages were devised for it.

## Special-role mortars

The Americans also made very limited use of the **105-mm Mortar T13** in 4.13-in calibre, and the **155-mm Mortar T25** in 6.1-in calibre. The T13 was introduced in 1944 and was intended for the immediate support of forces that had just made an amphibious landing, pending the arrival of heavier weapons. This substantial weapon weighed only 86.4 kg (190.3 lb) and fired a 15.9-kg (35-lb) bomb to a maximum range of 3660 m (4,000 yards). However, the availability of the 4.2-in Chemical Mortar firing a wide range of ammunition types effectively made the T13 superfluous to requirement, and the few weapons completed and issued were withdrawn from service almost immediately after World War II's end.

The basically contemporary T25 was designed for heavier support of amphibious forces, and was used in small numbers in the South-West Pacific theatre, largely for evaluation purposes. The T25 weighed 259.2 kg (571 lb) and fired a 28.83-kg (63.5-lb) bomb to a maximum range of 2285 m (2,500 yards).

***This is a piece of equipment typical of those used by mortar crews, here that of an 81-mm Mortar MM1 operating in mountain terrain. Such a weapon needed ammunition supply personnel in addition to its two-man crew if a high rate of fire was to be maintained.***

***Weapons such as the 81-mm Mortar M1 were invaluable in the war of the infantryman as they could respond virtually instantly with great accuracy right down to very short battlefield ranges.***

### SPECIFICATION

**81-mm Mortar M1**
**Calibre:** 81.4-mm (3.2-in)
**Length:** barrel 1.257 m (49.5 in)
**Weight:** in action 61.7 kg (136 lb)
**Elevation:** +40 to +85 degrees
**Traverse:** 14 degrees
**Maximum range:** 3008 m (3,290 yards)
**Bomb weight:** 3.12 kg (6.87 lb)

### SPECIFICATION

**4.2-in Chemical Mortar**
**Calibre:** 106.7-mm (4.2-in)
**Length:** barrel 1.019 m (40.1 in)
**Weight:** in action 149.7 kg (330 lb)
**Elevation:** +45 to +59 degrees
**Traverse:** 7 degrees
**Maximum range:** 4023 m (4,400 yards)
**Bomb weight:** 14.5 kg (32 lb)

# Light mortars

***This is the US Army's M224 Lightweight Company Mortar in its simplest form with the auxiliary baseplate and no bipod. The M224's most useful capabilities derive from its use of ammunition with an advanced fuse system.***

The light mortar is generally regarded as a weapon with a calibre up to a maximum of 60-mm (2.26-in) and a weight (when broken down into main assemblies) light enough to permit a high level of man-portability.

The Austrian company Südsteirische Metallindustrie has made a considerable impact though its ability to design, develop and manufacture weapons of remarkable performance using the resources of its associated metal producing facilities. Mortars are in fact just one of SMI's weapons activities, and the company produces some very advanced types within this category.

### Three subvariants

The smallest of these weapons in calibre terms is the 60-mm (2.36-in) **M6** range encompassing three weapons, namely the **M6/214 Standard**, the **M6/314 Long Range** and the **M6/530 Light**. Of these three the M6/214 is the most orthodox in concept, while the M6/314 is much longer in the barrel. The M6/530 Light, also known as the **M6/350 Commando**, uses a lightweight barrel with no bipod and only a small baseplate as it is intended for one-man use and may be fitted with a trigger mechanism. All three mortars can fire virtually any 60-mm mortar bomb, but SMI produces its own bomb, the HE-80 weighing 1.6 kg (3.527 lb) and capable of ranging out to a very respectable 4200 m (4,595 yards) when fired from the M6/314 Long Range.

### Advanced weapon

The British **51-mm Mortar** was developed as successor to the 2-in (51-mm) mortar designed before World War II. Work on the new weapon started in the early 1970s mainly by the RARDE (Royal Armament Research and Development Establishment) at Fort Halstead in Kent. For much of its early development life the new mortar had a monopod supporting leg, but this was eventually discarded as being unnecessary.

The 51-mm is used by the British army at platoon level. In its production form the weapon outwardly resembles one of the many commando-type mortars in use elsewhere, but it is more complex. It consists mainly of a barrel and baseplate, but the design detail is quite involved. The mortar uses a lanyard-operated trigger mechanism, and aiming is assisted by a complex sight with an inbuilt Trilux illuminating source for use at night. The mortar was designed for really close-range operations at ranges as close as 50 m (55 yards), and this is achieved by the use of a short-range insert (SRI) normally carried inside the barrel fitted to the muzzle cap. In use the SRI is inserted in the base of the barrel to serve as a firing pin extension while at the same time allowing propellant gases to expand around the SRI to produce lower barrel pressures and thus decrease muzzle velocity and range.

The normal minimum range is 150 m (165 yards), while the maximum is 800 m (875 yards). The mortar can be carried by one man using a webbing sling, and in action a webbing gaiter around the barrel is gripped to aim and steady the barrel. Ammunition is carried in a canvas satchel and a webbing satchel, and a webbing wallet is used to carry cleaning rods and a few ancillary equipment items.

The ammunition range includes HE, illuminating and smoke bombs. The HE bomb contains a wall liner of pre-notched wire for anti-personnel use. One detail design point is that the

***A British infantryman prepares to load a bomb into the muzzle of his 2-in mortar. Issued at squad level, the weapon fires smoke and illuminating bombs as well as the more overtly offensive HE bomb.***

***On exercise in South Korea, a US army infantryman shoulders the weight of the tripod for the M29 mortar, an 81-mm (3.2-in) weapon that the service decided was too heavy for modern battlefield requirements. This led to the M224 mortar in 60-mm (2.36-in) calibre.***

**SPECIFICATIONS**

**M6/314**
**Calibre:** 60-mm (2.36-in)
**Length:** 1.082 m (42.6 in)
**Weights:** mortar 18.3 kg (40.34 lb); bomb 1.6 kg (3.527 lb)
**Maximum range:** 4200 m (4,595 yards)

**51-mm Mortar**
**Calibre:** 5-mm (2-in)
**Length:** 0.75 m (29.53 in)
**Weights:** mortar 6.28 kg (13.84 lb); HE bomb 0.92 kg (2.03 lb); illuminating bomb 0.8 kg (1.76 lb); smoke bomb 0.9 kg (1.98 lb)
**Maximum range:** 800 m (875 yards)

**Lyran**
**Calibre:** 71-mm (2.795-in)
**Weights:** barrel pack 9 kg (19.84 lb); ammunition pack 8 kg (17.64 lb)
**Maximum range:** 800 m (875 yards)

***This Swedish soldier is seen with a complete Lyran system: in his right hand the barrel and two bombs, and in his left hand four bombs, all in two plastic containers. The Lyran system is used only for nocturnal target illumination.***

bombs cannot be double-loaded in the heat of action: if they are the second bomb protrudes from the muzzle. The HE bomb is stated to be capable of producing a lethal area five times the size of that produced by the old 2-in mortar bombs, as a result mainly of the pre-notched wire fragments.

One of the primary uses of the 51-mm mortar in British service is to provide illumination for Milan anti-tank missile teams for nocturnal operations. The smoke bomb provides screening for all manner of infantry operations, while the HE bombs are used in the time-honoured manner.

The basic man-carried satchel contains five bombs, and one man can carry the mortar and a satchel without impeding his normal combat load-carrying ability to any marked extent.

A product of Sweden's small but advanced armaments industry, the **Lyran** is a special form of infantry support weapon for it fires only an illuminating round. The use of infantry support weapons to fire illuminating rounds is not new, but it has become increasingly important with a host of applications. Mortars have long been used to fire special bombs that eject a small parachute at the apogee of their trajectory and then descend as high-power flares spreading their light on the ground below. This light can be used to illuminate an attacking enemy or to reveal an armoured target for missile teams to tackle, and these are only two applications.

## Man-portability

The Lyran was designed, developed and produced by Bofors, and in its infantry version (there is also a variant designed for use on combat vehicles) is based on two polyethylene packs: one contains the barrel and two flare shells, and the other four flare shells. For use the barrel is taken out of its pack and screwed into a housing on the pack itself. The firer actually sits on the pack and uses a spirit level to set the barrel at an angle of 47 degrees. A flare shell is then taken and its simple nose fuse set to operate at a range of 400 or 800 m (440 or 875 yards). The shell is then allowed to fall to the base of the barrel and is fired in the normal manner, rising to a height of between 200 and 300 m (655 and 985 ft) before the parachute emerges to give the flare a burn time of about 25 seconds. At a height of 160 m (525 ft) the flare illuminates an area about 630 m (689 yards) in diameter.

For many years the US Army used the 81-mm (3.2-in) Mortar M29 as its standard weapon of this class, and although this weapon was successful it was latterly seen as lacking adequate range and, by the standards that emerged in the Vietnam War, as also being too heavy. The US Army therefore decided to revert to the 60-mm calibre as used in World War II but now updated for additional range. This led to a lengthy and involved programme of development to create the **60-mm M224 Lightweight Company Mortar**. This has been issued to infantry, airborne and air-mobile infantry units, and is a long-barrelled weapon that can be fitted with either a conventional bipod or a simple baseplate for use in the 'commando' configuration. Much use is made of aluminium alloys for components such as the large baseplate, and the entire weapon can be broken down into two loads for manpack transport. It is also possible to mount the weapon on some vehicles.

The main elements of the M224 are the 6.53 kg (14.4 lb) M225 cannon assembly, 6.9 kg (15.2 lb) M170 bipod assembly, 6.53 lb (14.4 lb) M14 baseplate assembly, and 1.63 kg (3.6 lb) M8 auxiliary baseplate, to which must be added to items such as the M64 sight unit. The M224 has a maximum rate of fire of 30 rounds per minute and a sustained rate of fire of 20 rounds per minute.

## Advanced fuse

Perhaps the most important design feature of the M224 is the ammunition it fires, and especially the multi-option fuse involved. The M224 fires HE illuminating, smoke and practice rounds, and the multi-option fuse is known as the M734. This is an electronic unit, and was among the first of its type to reach service. The M734 has four detonating options: high air-burst, low air-burst, point detonation and delay. The fuse has inbuilt redundancy, in that if the chosen option does not operate the fuse automatically activates the next option. For instance, if low air-burst has been selected and does not operate, the fuse detonates on point contact i.e. when it strikes the ground; if that fails it switches itself to delay. Power to operate the microcircuits is generated inside the fuse by air passing through a miniature turbine in the nose.

The ability to select high or low air-burst combines with a reasonable certainty that the fuse will operate as selected to enhance the destructive effect of the bomb. Moreover, the number of fragments spread over a wide area comes close to the destructive and anti-personnel effects of 81-mm bombs. The electronic fuse is expensive to produce, however, and has to be churned out in very large numbers to enable the economics of scale to bring the costs down to reasonable levels.

## Laser aid

To go with the M224 and its electronically fused bombs, the US Army uses a laser rangefinder to determine target ranges with great accuracy and so allow the first bombs to arrive right on target for maximum effect. Thus the M224 lightweight company mortar has elevated the mortar from its original stage of being a humble weapon to the level at which it can be regarded as virtually a weapon system.

There are, of course, a number of other light mortars. Typical of these are the Chinese 60-mm Type 31 and Type 63 mortars, three French 60-mm Hotchkiss-Brandt mortars, Israeli Soltam 52- and 60-mm mortars, two Spanish ECIA 60-mm mortars, sundry Soviet (now Russian) 50-mm mortars and the Yugoslav 50-mm M8 mortar.

### SPECIFICATIONS

**M224 Lightweight Company Mortar**
**Calibre:** 60-mm (2.36-in)
**Length:** 1.106 m (40 in)
**Weight:** 21.11kg (46.5 lb)
**Maximum range:** 3475 m (3,800 yards)

**Hotchkiss-Brandt 60-mm Light Mortar**
**Calibre:** 60-mm (2.36-in)
**Length:** barrel and breech 0.724 m (28.5 in)
**Weights:** overall 14.8 kg (32.63 lb); 1.65 kg (3.64 lb)
**Maximum range:** 2000 m (2,185 yards)

**60-mm Soltam Mortar**
**Calibre:** 60.75-mm (2.39-in)
**Length:** barrel and breech 0.74 m (29.13 in)
**Weights:** complete with bipod 14.3 kg (31.53 kg) in firing position; bomb 1.59 kg (3.51 lb)
**Maximum range:** 2555 m (2,975 yards)

***The Lyran system in assembled form reveals the essentially simple nature of this useful illuminating system with the launcher attached to the carrying case that also contains two flare bombs. The other case carries four bombs.***

# Medium mortars

The medium mortar is generally defined as having a calibre in the range between 60- and 102-mm (2.36- and 4-in), resulting in a weapon weighing between 35 and 70 kg (77 and 154 lb) and firing a 3.5- to 7-kg (7.7- to 15.4-lb) bomb out to a range in the order of 1850 to 5500 m (2,025 to 6,015 yards).

While the light mortar provides small units, up to company size, with an organic weapon for the generation of their own tactical fire support, the medium mortar is a more ambitious weapon. It is generally allocated at battalion or regimental level, at which there is the possibility of vehicular transport, and offers a more effective blend of lethality and range.

The medium mortar designed, developed and manufactured by the Austrian SMI organisation is the 81.4-mm (3.2-in) **M8**. The design of this weapon was influenced by that of a British mortar, but much use is made of aluminium alloy for the baseplate and high-quality steel for the barrel. As with SMI's M6 light mortar, the M8 is produced in subvariants, the **M8/122 Standard** and the **M8/222 Long Range,** the latter with a longer barrel and greater weight. As with the company's light mortars, it is intended that best results should come from the use of a special bomb, in this case the HE-70 that can be fired to a range of 6500 m (7,110 yards) by the M8/222. The mortars were developed to replace the British 81-mm weapons in service with the Austrian army, and SMI also offers the series on the export market, and also in 82-mm (3.23-in) calibre to use ammunition developed in the former Warsaw Pact.

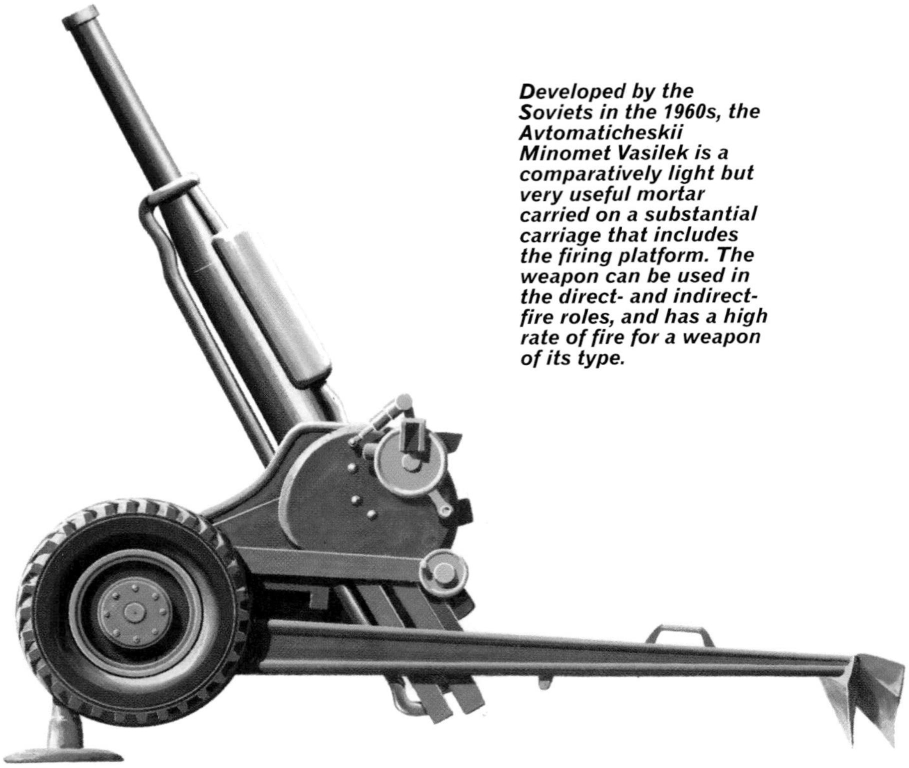

***Developed by the Soviets in the 1960s, the Avtomaticheskii Minomet Vasilek is a comparatively light but very useful mortar carried on a substantial carriage that includes the firing platform. The weapon can be used in the direct- and indirect-fire roles, and has a high rate of fire for a weapon of its type.***

***The threat of nuclear, biological and chemical agents has long been present in battle conditions, and this L16 mortar crew is seen under training conditions wearing their NBC 'noddy' suits.***

## Excellent British type

The **Mortar L16** has been one of the major British success stories of the era after World War II, for it is used not only by the British army but also by many other nations including the USA, where it is operated by the US Army as the **Mortar M252**. One of the main reasons for the success of the 81.4-mm (3.2-in) L16 has been its ability to fire bombs using powerful propellant charges that would normally make the barrel too hot for sustained use. The barrel of the L16 is much thicker than normal and equipped with cooling fins around its lower portion. These allow the L16 to fire the really hot charges that provide the weapon with remarkable range capability: some types of bomb can be delivered to 6000 m (6,560 yards) or more. This capability is counterbalanced by disadvantages such as an uncomfortable level of muzzle blast.

## Advanced features

Other features of the L16 are no less advanced than the barrel. The mounting is of a type known as a 'K' mount from its shape, and this allows rapid and easy levelling and elevation. The baseplate and sight are of Canadian design, the former made by a special process in which the aluminium alloy is blown into its mould by a controlled explosion. The baseplate provides 360-degree traverse without any need to uproot and then re-bed the base plate.

***This American mortar team was caught on camera during the Vietnam War. Medium mortars provided excellent fire support in this conflict, which nonetheless revealed the need for lighter weapons.***

The ammunition used by the L16 can be quite varied, for the weapon is capable of firing any 81-mm bomb in service with NATO. As always, the best results are obtained with matching ammunition, and the latest HE fragmentation bomb is the 4.2-kg (9.2-lb) L36A2 with a maximum range of 5650 m (6,180 yards). Other bombs include smoke, short-range practice and Brandt illuminating types.

The L16 has seen combat during the Falklands and Gulf wars. In the Falklands campaign it was so effective that some Argentine reports suggested that the L16's bombs were fitted with heat-seeking guidance packages able to make the bomb home in on soldiers.

A special mounting allowing the L16's use on APCs such as the FV432 and M113 series has been developed, but for normal infantry use the L16 is broken down into a number of loads that can be man-packed into action.

## Classic design

The name Brandt has been associated with the design, development and manufacture of mortars since World War I. Much of the detail development work carried out between the two world wars was undertaken by Stokes Brandt, a French company which became part of Brandt Armements. Today the range of mortar types produced by the company is prodigious in the light, medium and heavy mortar categories. Brandt medium mortars are of the 81-mm calibre and are available in several models, ranging from the basic **Mortier MO 81-61 C** to special models with long barrels, such as the **Mortier MO 81-61 L**, to obtain the maximum possible range.

## Sturdy and effective

In design terms all of them are fairly orthodox, and all have been sold to many land forces around the world. To go with them, Brandt also produces a wide range of bombs and associated propellant charges. The bomb types include HE, HE fragmentation, smoke, illuminating and target-marking bombs, the last for indicating targets to aircraft.

The army of the USSR, now fragmented into the Russian Federation and a number of smaller states combined under the aegis of the Commonwealth of Independent States, controlled the development of a large number of mortar types over the years, and the surprising thing is that many of them dating from before World War II remain in large-scale service. These mortars are of the light, medium and heavy types in standard calibres such as 50-mm (1.97-in), 82-mm (3.23-in), 107-mm (4.21-in), 120-mm (4.73-in) and 160-mm (6.3-in).

Although it was the heavy mortar type, starting with a calibre of 107-mm (4.22-in), on which they later concentrated, the Soviets did make use of medium mortars. The first of these was the **82-PM 36**, which was introduced in 1936 as a copy of a Brandt muzzle-loaded and smooth-bore weapon. The following **82-PM 37** differed mainly in its use of a round rather than square baseplate, and in the introduction of recoil springs between the barrel and the bipod. The **82-PM 41** was intended to improve the basic weapon's mobility, and instead of the bipod had a stub axle arrangement with two pressed-steel wheels and, in its centre, the elevating rod. The **82-PM 43** differed from the 82-PM-41 only in having fixed rather than detachable wheels. Finally there appeared the **82-PM New 37** based on the 82-PM 37 but with a lighter baseplate and tripod to improve battlefield mobility.

## Decided oddity

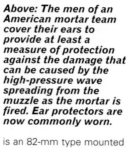

An oddity among these Soviet mortars is the weapon known as the **Avtomaticheskii Minomet Vasilek** (Little Vasili automatic mortar). Introduced in 1971, this weapon is otherwise known as the **2B9** and is an 82-mm type mounted on a mountain gun carriage that can be towed by a light vehicle. Once emplaced it can be used either in the direct-fire role as a conventional gun or in the high-angle mortar role. In action the carriage's wheels are raised off the ground and the weapon rests on a firing baseplate. The weapon is fed manually at the muzzle or automatically through the breech by four-round clip. The HE bomb weighs 3.23 kg (7.12 lb), and can be fired to a maximum range of 4750 m (5,195 yards).

There are several variants of the Vasilek for installation on light armoured vehicles, usually in some form of turret. Each infantry battalion of the Soviet (and now CIS) army should incorporate a battery of six Vasilek equipments, but in fact it is probably only the motorised and mechanised battalions of first-line divisions that are fully equipped.

The 81-mm mortar is used by the armies of most countries as it is affordable yet provides good firepower for its weight. It is also worth noting that several countries other than those detailed above have also manufactured and fielded weapons of this type. The Chinese **Type 53**, for instance, is a copy of the 82-PM 37. The Finnish company Tampella has produced two weapons, the **M-38** and **M-56**. Like Tampella, Israel's Soltam is another gun manufacturer which has branched into the mortar market, its primary offering in the medium calibre being the 81-mm **M-64**, which has been developed in versions with short, long and two-piece barrels. In Spain, ECIA offer the **Model L-N** and **Model L-L** 81-mm mortars.

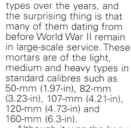

***Above: The men of an American mortar team cover their ears to provide at least a measure of protection against the damage that can be caused by the high-pressure wave spreading from the muzzle as the mortar is fired. Ear protectors are now commonly worn.***

***An American mortar team is seen in action during the Korean War of the early 1950s. The often static fighting of this conflict made it sensible to construct fire positions protected by piled sandbags or natural features.***

***The British L16 mortar is seen in two of its standard applications as a ground-based weapon (above left) and vehicle-carried type (left). The vehicle is the FV432 armoured personnel carrier, with many bombs stowed in the hull.***

***The two-man crew of an Austrian 81-mm (3.2-in) mortar prepare their weapon. While one man levels the weapon and takes preliminary sighting details, the other ensures that the spiked feet of the bipod are firmly fixed.***

### SPECIFICATION

**Mortar L16**
**Calibre:** 81.4-mm (3.2-in)
**Length:** barrel 1.28 m (50.4 in)
**Weights:** mortar 37.85 kg (83.45 lb); HE bomb 4.2 kg (9.26 lb)
**Maximum range:** 5650 m (6,180 yards)

**Brandt Mortier MO 82-61 L**
**Calibre:** 81.4-mm (3.2-in)
**Length:** barrel 1.45 m (57.09 in)
**Weights:** mortar 41.5 kg (91.5 lb); HE bomb 4.325 kg (9.53 lb)
**Maximum range:** 5000 m (5,470 yards)

**82-PM 41**
**Calibre:** 82-mm (3.23-in)
**Length:** barrel 1.22 m (48.03 in)
**Weight:** mortar 52 kg (114.6 lb)
**Maximum range:** 2550 m (2,790 yards)

# Heavy mortars

Heavy mortars are weapons with a calibre greater than 102-mm (4-in) and firing a bomb heavier than 7 kg (15.4 lb) to a range of more than 6000 m (6,560 yards). Such weapons hit hard at long battlefield ranges and yet are comparatively mobile in the tactical sense.

In Austria, the SMI organisation produces a large assortment of mortars in all sizes, and the largest of these is the 120-mm (4.72-in) **M12** designed for the Austrian army but also offered for export. Like many other weapons of this calibre, the design is based on that of the Soviet 120-HM 38, but much use is made of special metals both to lighten the weight and to enable larger charges to be fired for increased range.

The M12 is relatively easy to use in action as a result of a special bipod design with recoil absorbers. Once again a special bomb is produced: this the HE-78, which weighs 14.5 kg (31.97 lb) including 2.2 kg (4.85 lb) of explosive payload and can be fired to a range of 8500 m (9,295 yards).

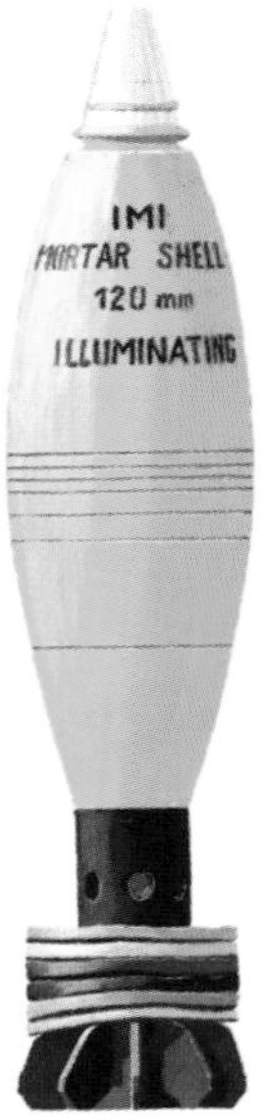


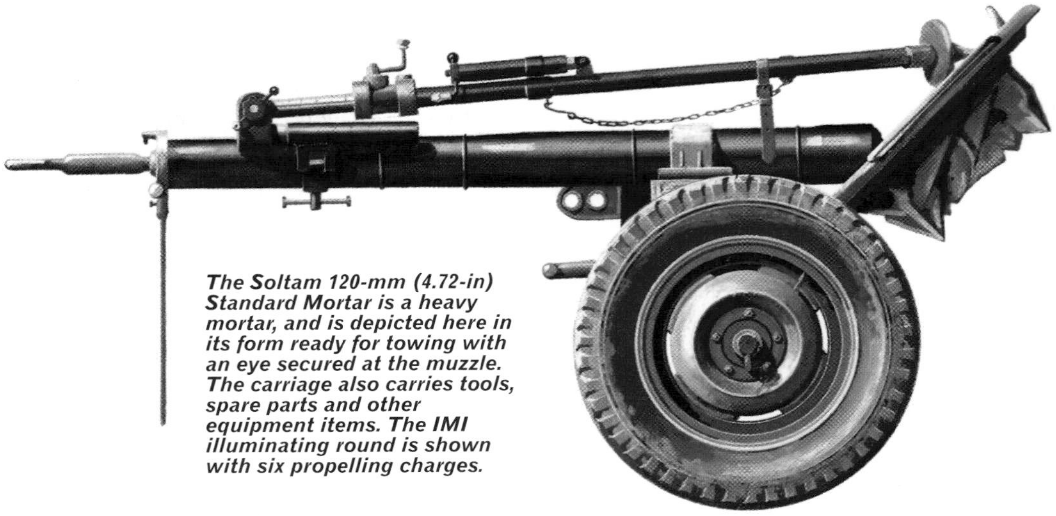

***The Soltam 120-mm (4.72-in) Standard Mortar is a heavy mortar, and is depicted here in its form ready for towing with an eye secured at the muzzle. The carriage also carries tools, spare parts and other equipment items. The IMI illuminating round is shown with six propelling charges.***

## French lead

In France, the Brandt company produces conventional light and medium mortars in 60- and 81.4-mm calibres, but as an organisation it is best known for its 120-mm heavy mortars. It is in this calibre that the mortar can become a highly versatile adjunct to conventional artillery, and many armies use 120-mm mortars in place of artillery. The smooth-bore models in this range are conventional mortars that can be used in exactly the same way as smaller-calibre models, but the rifled mortars are much more complex and in many ways resemble conventional high-angle guns. The rifled weapons fire pre-rifled projectiles whose range can be enhanced by the use of an auxiliary rocket unit that cuts in only when the bomb is at the top of its trajectory. A typical range with this rocket assistance is 13000 m (14,215 yards) for an HE bomb weighing 18.7 kg (41.23 lb). Despite their size and weight, the Brandt rifled mortars can thus have a very useful performance, and key weapons on the series include the **Mortier MO-120-60** light mortar, **Mortier MO-120-M65** strengthened mortar, **Mortier MO-120-AM 50** heavy mortar, **Mortier MO-120-LT** mortar and **Mortier MO-120-RT-61** rifled mortar.

The American 106.7-mm (4.2-in) mortars have been around for a long time as they were first developed to fire smoke bombs before World War II. Since then they have been the subject of many improvement programmes and general updating of weapon and ammunition to the point where the present-day version is no longer known as a 4.2-in mortar (except to the soldiers who use them), but instead as the 107-mm **Mortar M30**. This is a rifled mortar that fires a spin-stabilised projectile. In its present form the M30 uses not the original rectangular baseplate but rather a heavy circular unit with the barrel supported on a single column. The barrel can rotate on the baseplate and it is fitted with a recoil system to absorb what can be quite considerable firing forces. All this adds up to a considerable degree so that the complete weapon weighs no less than 305 kg (672 lb). This is quite a lot to get in and out of action in a hurry,

***A Brandt 120-mm (4.72-in) rifled mortar with its breech resting on the baseplate and the central part of the barrel on the wheeled carriage. The muzzle-loaded bombs weigh up to 18.7 kg (41.23 lb).***

***The great weight of the Soltam 160-mm (6.3-in) mortar inevitably suggested vehicles installations such as that seen here in the forward part of a converted M4 Sherman tank chassis of World War II vintage.***

### SPECIFICATIONS

**M12**
**Calibre:** 120-mm (4.72-in)
**Length:** barrel 2.015 m (79.33 in)
**Weights:** mortar 305 kg (672.4 lb); HE bomb 14.5 kg (31.97 lb)
**Maximum range:** 8500 m (9,285 yards)

**Brandt Mortier MO-120-RT-61**
**Calibre:** 120-mm (4.72-in)
**Length:** barrel 2.08 m (81.9 in)
**Weights:** mortar 582 kg (1,283 lb); HE bomb 18.7 kg (41.23 lb)
**Maximum range:** 13000 m (14,215 yards) with rocket-assisted bomb

**Mortar M30**
**Calibre:** 107.7-mm (4.2-in)
**Length:** barrel 1.524 m (60 in)
**Weight:** mortar 305 kg (672.4 kg); HE bomb 12.2 kg (26.9 lb); smoke bomb 11.32 kg (24.95 kg)
**Maximum range:** 6800 m (7,435 yards)

***Mortars do not change their elevation to increase or decrease range: instead, the crew increases or decreases the propellant charge. This American 4.2-in mortar has the relevant charges and ranges inscribed permanently on the barrel.***

so the size of the mortar crew and its carrying vehicle are correspondingly large. Many M30s are in fact not ground-mounted at all but are carried on special mountings inside M113 APCs to fire through roof hatches.

## Capable bomb

The ammunition used on the M30 more closely resembles an artillery round than a mortar bomb. It is of the type known as semi-fixed, for components of the charge can be added or removed as required. The range of projectile types has gradually been increased over the years and there are now no less than three HE, two smoke, one illuminating and two chemical rounds.

In Israel, Soltam produces a full range of mortars but it is with its heavy mortars that the company has made its name. Soltam produces two 120-mm models and one of a massive 160-mm (6.3-in) calibre. All these are large enough to warrant their own wheeled travelling carriages, although of the 120-mm mortars one is described as the **Light Mortar** and the other as the **M-65 Standard Mortar**.

The light model is designed for infantry use, is carried into action on its wheeled carriage and can be towed by manpower alone. The standard model is much more substantial and is towed into action. In range terms there is little to choose between the two Soltam 120-mm models, although the standard model has a slight edge. They both fire the same bombs and both can be mounted in APCs if required. The Soltam 120-mm bomb weighs 12.9 kg (28.44 lb), of which 2.3 kg (5.07 lb) is the HE payload.

## Super-heavy mortar

With the Soltam 160-mm **M-66** weapon, mortars cross the line from infantry support to artillery. Each M-66 has a crew of six to eight men, and as the barrel is too long for muzzle loading a breech-loading system has to be used. The M-66 fires a 40 kg (88.18 lb) bomb to a range of 9300 m (10,170 yards), and the 1700-kg (3,748-lb) overall weight of the M-66 means that the type is often carried by a converted tank.

The Soviet army and its successors have made extensive use of heavy mortars, including the 107-mm **107-PBHM 38**, 120-mm **120-HM 38** and **120-mm Model 43**, and **160-mm Model 1943** dating from before or during World War II. The large 160-mm weapon is used by divisional support batteries instead of conventional artillery. It is a breech-loaded weapon of great length and weight, and the latest model is known as the **M-160**. The 240-mm (9.45-in) **M-240** is a genuinely formidable weapon that was first revealed in public during 1953. In travelling configuration, the M-240 is 6.51 m (21 ft 4 in) long, and is towed on a two-wheeled carriage. The M-240 is in many respects similar to the 160-mm M-160. Thus the M-240 is a breech-loaded weapon, the barrel being hinged around its support point so that the muzzle can be lowered and thereby reveal the breech into which the bomb and its propellant charges are inserted before the muzzle is raised and the breech closed before being locked.

The M-240 is a massive item of equipment with a barrel that is 5.34 m (210.24 in) long, and in firing position the M-240 turns the scales at 3610 kg (7,959 lb). Such size and mass are reflected in the M-240 capabilities, which including the firing of a 100-kg (220.46-lb) HE bomb out to a maximum range of 9700 m (10,610 yards after leaving the muzzle at a velocity of 362 m per second).

This behemoth of a battlefield weapon is operated by a crew of nine men, and its maximum rate of fire is one round per minute.

Other countries that have produced heavy mortars include Finland, whose Tampella company created the **120-mm M-40** and **160-mm M-58**; Spain, whose ECIA organisation developed the **105-mm (4.13-in) Model L**, **120-mm Model L** and **Model SL**; Sweden, in which Bofors made the **120-mm M/41C**; and Switzerland, where the Waffenfabrikk manufactured the **120-mm Model 64** and **Model 74**.

***This Brandt mortar, of 120-mm (4.72-in) calibre, is typical of the more modern type of heavier mortar. The size and weight of the weapon mean that battlefield mobility can be provided only by the use of a wheeled carriage.***

***The Soviet 160-mm Model 1943 mortar is a large weapon of elderly design, yet offers good fire-support capabilities for battlefield purposes. Often used in place of more conventional artillery, the weapon fires an HE/fragmentation bomb weighing 40.8-kg (89.5-lb).***

### SPECIFICATIONS

**Soltam 120-mm Standard**
**Calibre:** 120-mm (4.72-in)
**Length:** barrel 2.154 m (84.8 in)
**Weights:** mortar 245 kg (540 lb) in action; HE bomb 12.9 kg (28.44 lb)
**Maximum range:** 8500 m (9,295 yards)

**Soltam M-66**
**Calibre:** 160-mm (6.3-in)
**Length:** barrel 3.066 m (120.7 in)
**Weights:** mortar 1700 kg (3,748 lb) in action; HE bomb 40 kg (88.18 lb)
**Maximum range:** 9600 m (10,500 yards)

**120-mm Model 1943**
**Calibre:** 120-mm (4.72-in)
**Length:** barrel 1.854 m (73 in)
**Weight:** mortar 275 kg (606.3 lb) in action; HE fragmentation bomb 16 kg (35.27 lb)
**Maximum range:** 5700 m (6,235 yards)

# Gun-mortars

***The Brandt 60-mm Model LR gun-mortar is a gun/smooth-bore mortar hybrid. It can be loaded at the muzzle, or alternatively can be breech-loaded from within the confines of a vehicle. This long-range weapon fires a special bomb to 5000 m (5,470 yards).***

With its gun-mortars the French Brandt company introduced a class of ordnance that has no real counterpart anywhere else in the world. This results from the fact that Brandt combined into a single weapon the attributes of the high-angle mortar and the conventional gun. The object was the creation of a versatile close-support weapon. The concept is simple: a breech- as well as muzzle-loaded mortar is disposed in the fashion that allows the mortar bombs to be loaded into the barrel from the breech for low-trajectory firing and from the muzzle for high-angle fire.

This type of weapon was initially developed for mounting on light AFVs, but the gun-mortar has proved so attractive an option that several other applications have been evolved. The gun-mortar cannot be used from a bipod or other ground mounting, however.

## Two weapon types

There are two calibres in Brandt's range of gun-mortars, namely 60-mm (2.36-in) and 81.4-mm (3.2-in). The 60-mm weapon is the one more likely to be used for infantry support, while the 81-mm weapon is generally installed in large armoured cars and APCs. (The 60-mm versions are also used as turret weapons on light armoured vehicles, and some have been mounted on light patrol craft, including inflatable Zodiac-type boats.) These turret-mountings are designed for the close support of infantry operations.

The smooth-bore barrel is mounted so that a spring around the barrel absorbs most of the recoil forces and thus reduces the trunnion forces to a great degree. Conventional mortar projectiles can be fired, but for direct-fire use special canister rounds or hollow-charge armour-piercing projectiles can be fired. When fired in the low-trajectory mode, the standard 60-mm gun-mortar has a range of about 500 m (547 yards), increasing to 2050 m (2,240 yards) in the conventional mode. When the weapon is employed in the mortar role, the bombs are muzzle-loaded to fall and strike a fixed firing pin, but in the low-trajectory role they are loaded via the breech mechanism. Brandt also produced a special long-range version of the 60-mm gun-mortar with direct- and indirect-fire ranges of 500 m and 5000 m (5,470 yards) respectively, the latter with a special bomb.

***This is a Brandt 60-mm (2.36-in) gun-mortar on a Zodiac inflatable craft to highlight the low trunnion loadings of this weapon type. The gun-mortar can be breech- or muzzle-loaded, only the former being possible in this application.***

## Greater capability

The 81-mm weapon is more complicated. This is intended as the primary weapon for armoured vehicles, and is therefore fitted with a recoil mechanism and is proportionally much heavier than the 60-mm models. However, the larger gun-mortar can fire the entire range of 81-mm projectiles, and even has one that is unique to its type. This is an armour-piercing 'arrow' projectile fired, with a special charge, only in the direct-fire role. It is capable of piercing up to 50 mm (1.97 in) of armour at 1000 m (1,095 yards).

Development of both gun-mortar types continues, and both weapons are in widespread service, especially in less advanced countries of the world.

**SPECIFICATIONS**

| Brandt 60-mm gun-mortar (standard model) | Brandt 81-mm gun-mortar (standard model) |
|---|---|
| **Calibre:** 60-mm (2.36-in) | **Calibre:** 81.4-mm (3.2-in) |
| **Length:** 1.21 m (47.64 in) | **Length:** barrel 2.3 m (90.55 in) |
| **Weights:** gun-mortar 42 kg (92.6 lb); HE bomb 1.72 kg (3.79 lb) | **Weights:** gun-mortar 500 kg (1,102 lb); HE bomb 4.45 kg (9.8 lb) |
| **Maximum range:** 500 m (545 yards in the direct-fire mode and 2050 m (2,240 yards) in the indirect-fire mode | **Maximum range:** 1000 m (1,095 yards) in the direct-fire model and 8000 m (8,750 yards) in the indirect-fire mode |

***Above: This SIBMAS 6x6 APC features a turret carrying a 60-mm (2.36-in) Brandt gun-mortar of the long-barrel type for additional range. In this type of application, the weapon is normally breech-loaded and fired using a percussion trigger.***

***Right: A gun-mortar in a turret can provide light vehicles with a potent armament capability for the shorter-range direct and longer-range indirect fire roles. On this SIBMAS APC the 60-mm gun-mortar replaces a 20-mm cannon.***

# Grenade launchers

The rifle-launched grenade is still used, but is not a fashionable weapon for several reasons. Two of these are that the firing of a rifle grenade can often cause sufficient recoil to damage the rifle, and that accurate aiming is difficult. In recent years the use of special propellant cartridges has been partially replaced by bullet traps in the tails of grenades to absorb the forces of a fired bullet and use them to propel the grenade.

In Italy this has led to the development of a special infantry support weapon known as the **AP/AV700**. In effect this is a trio of rifle-grenade launchers set side by side on a common baseplate or launcher. The finned rifle grenades fit over spigots, and are launched by standard ball cartridges loaded into the breech mechanism at the base of each spigot. The bullets are fired directly into the grenades' tails, the flash of their ignition being used to light a delay unit that in turn ignites a small rocket motor to increase range to 700 m (765 yards). Moreover, it is possible to aim fairly accurately and consistently, for in flight the grenades are stabilized by their fins and also by gases vented from the rocket to add further spin.

It is possible to fire the grenades using either the standard NATO 7.62-mm (0.3-in) or 5.56-mm (0.219-in) ball cartridges, but the spigot will accept only one or the other. The grenades can also be fired from conventional rifle launchers.

The grenades have hollow-charge warheads able to penetrate up to 120 mm (4.72 m) of armour, but they also have a considerable blast and anti-personnel effect. The three-spigot launcher can fire the grenades one at a time or in one salvo, and it is possible to fire six or seven salvoes per minute.

### Multiple roles

Possible applications include its use in place of orthodox light mortars by infantry units, and its mounting on light armoured or soft-skinned vehicles. It could also be used on light patrol or landing craft, and applications at outlying or guard blockhouses can be foreseen. The launcher can be carried on a special backpack, with another carrying the grenades.

The 30-mm **AGS-17 Plamya** (flame) is an automatic grenade-launcher that first appeared in the USSR in 1975, and is now widely employed down to company level (two weapons) on the forces of what is now the Commonwealth of Independent States. When it first appeared, the AGS-17 caused a stir in Western weapon design circles, for then there was no Western equivalent, although one has appeared since.

The AGS-17 fires small HE grenades at a rate of just one per second. The grenades are fed into the weapon from a 29-round belt, usually from a belt drum attached prominently on the right-hand side of the weapon. For firing, the AGS-17 is mounted on a tripod, and can be aimed with the aid of a dial sight at the rear of the weapon body. The weapon works on the simple blowback system, part of the action operating a pawl mechanism to move the ammunition belt. Firing can be of either the direct or indirect types, the latter providing more range.

### Afghan service

The AGS-17 was used in action in Afghanistan, and has been seen not only on a tripod mounting but also on special helicopter mounts. In Afghanistan the AGS-17 was used widely for fire suppression. However, the weapon's aspect which has impressed Western observers most is its range, which can be as much as 1750 m (1,915 yards) although operationally it is not often used at ranges greater than 1200 m (1,315 yards). This means that the weapon has a much higher potential for fire response than a mortar, and its automatic rate of fire can quickly compensate for the small projectile payload. The main drawback of the AGS-17 seems to be its weight, for the launcher and tripod together weigh more than 53 kg (117 lb), which means it has to have a crew of at least two men, and probably more, to carry the extra ammunition required for sustained use.

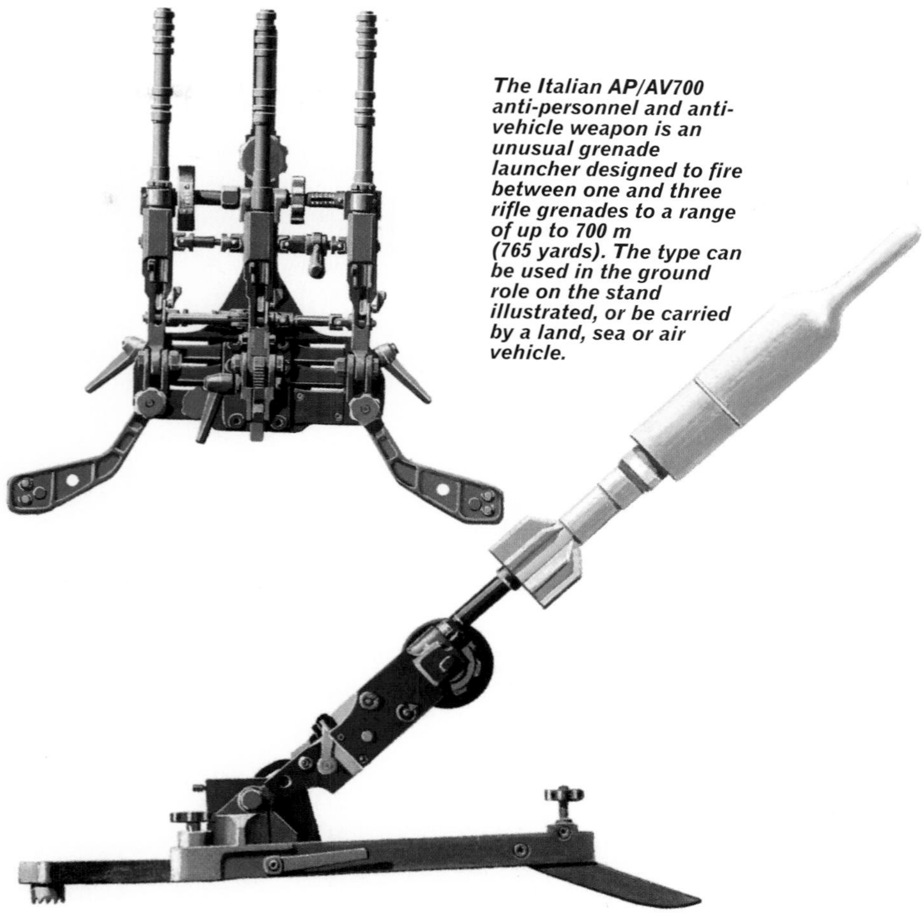

***The Italian AP/AV700 anti-personnel and anti-vehicle weapon is an unusual grenade launcher designed to fire between one and three rifle grenades to a range of up to 700 m (765 yards). The type can be used in the ground role on the stand illustrated, or be carried by a land, sea or air vehicle.***

**SPECIFICATIONS**

| AP/AV700 | AGS-17 Plamya |
|---|---|
| **Length:** spigot 300 mm (11.81 in)<br>**Weights:** launcher 11 kg (24.25 lb); grenade 0.93 kg (2.05 m); grenade warhead 0.46 kg (1.01 lb)<br>**Maximum range:** 700 m (765 yards) | **Calibre:** 30 mm<br>**Length:** 840 mm (33 in)<br>**Weights:** launcher about 18 kg (39.7 lb); tripod about 35 kg (77.2 lb); grenade 0.35 m (0.77 lb)<br>**Maximum range:** 1750 m (1,915 yards) |

***The AGS-17 operates on the blowback principle, the propellant forcing the bolt back and working the reloading cycle as well as driving the grenade up the barrel.***

***The AGS-17 Plamya is not light, but turns the scales at less than a heavy machine-gun and can provide a very considerable volume of fire support, albeit with less pinpoint accuracy than the heavy machine-gun but with greater area saturation.***

# Rifle grenades and launchers

The rifle grenade was developed as a means of bridging the range and firepower gap between the hand-thrown grenade and the light mortar. Moreover, the low velocity of the rifle grenade combined with its high trajectory to suggest the weapon's use in the anti-tank role: the steeply falling final trajectory opened the possibility of attacks on the thinner armour of any tank's upper surfaces with a small yet effective hollow-charge warhead. From these simple beginnings, and despite the major problems of having it land with any real accuracy, the rifle grenade gained a modest level of endorsement as a simple and cheap method of boosting the firepower of the infantryman.

The American 40-mm (1.575-in) grenade family was originally the **M406** series, and there are dozens of different types in this series. The grenade looks like a squat rifle round of large calibre. The firing system is such that the propellant gases are allowed to flow through a series of vent holes into a chamber in which they are allowed to expand at a relatively low pressure, thus allowing quite light weapons to fire the grenades.

## Special launcher

The M406 was designed to be fired from a dedicated launcher rather than a rifle, and the first launcher was the notably simple **M79**. To all intents and purposes this is a special single-round shotgun into which a grenade is hand-loaded after the action has been broken. The weapon is then fired from the shoulder in the normal way The main limits of the M79, which is fairly widely used (and was indeed employed by the Royal Marines in the Falklands Islands campaign of 1982), are that its single-role purpose and bulk means that it has to be carried and operated by a soldier who cannot use his rifle at the same time.

This led to the design, development and introduction of the **M203** launcher. This is again a single-shot launcher, but in this instance attached under the fore grip of an M16A1 or M16A2 rifle. The M203 was selected for service during the late 1960s, and has been in service ever since. The M203 clips under the rifle in a fashion that ensures that the launcher interferes in no way with the rifle's normal function, and the weight of the M203 is a comparatively modest 1.63 kg (3.59 lb) loaded. Almost every US Army section has at least one man (and often more) with an M203 launcher fitted to his rifle. The grenades fired are usually the HE type of the M406 series, but also available are smoke, marker smoke, flare, CS riot control and others.

***Grenade launchers like the M203 give the infantry rifleman the ability to provide his own fire support, independent of mortars and artillery.***

***A US army recruit receives instruction on the use of the 40-mm (1.57-in) M203 grenade launcher attached to an M16A1 rifle. The grenade launcher sights can be seen, as can the method of attaching the launcher to the rifle's fore stock.***

## Modest accuracy

The M203 offers levels of accuracy that make it feasible to engage point targets at ranges up to about 150 m (165 yards) and area targets beyond this distance up to the weapon's maximum range of between 350 and 400 m (385 and 435 yards), depending on the type of grenade fired. At these ranges the performance of the grenades (especially those of the HE type) is limited by the amount of volume required for the impact fuse, whose requirements each fit into the space available for the explosive payload proper. The fuse has to be relatively large to be fully effective and reliable, so the reduction in the explosive payload has to be offset by an increase in the number of grenades fired at any particular target.

## Automatic launcher

This requires the use of multiple rounds, and as the M79 and M203 are both single-shot weapons, a great deal of design and development effort was begun on automatic weapons to fire the 40-mm grenades.

One early effort in this field was the **XM174**, which was not taken into service as there became available the **M384** grenade, a development of the M406 with a heavier explosive payload and a more powerful propellant. To fire this improved grenade the Americans adopted an automatic

### SPECIFICATIONS

**Mk 19**
**Calibre:** 40-mm (1.57-in)
**Length:** overall 1.028 m (40.5 in)
**Weight:** launcher 35 kg (77.2 lb)
**Rate of fire:** 375 rounds per minute
**Maximum range:** 1600 m (1,750 yards)

**M79**
**Calibre:** 40-mm (1.57-in)
**Length:** overall 737 mm (29 in)
**Weight:** launcher 2.72 kg (6 lb)
**Maximum range:** 350 m (385 yards)

**M203**
**Calibre:** 40-mm (1.57-in)
**Length:** overall 389 mm (15.3 in)
**Weight:** launcher 1.36 kg (3 lb)
**Maximum range:** 350 m (385 yards)

***The single-shot M203, a pump-action launcher attached to an M16 series assault rifle, represents a great advance over the M79 dedicated launcher as it leaves the firer with a usable rifle already in his hands.***

launcher known as the **Mk 19**. The mechanism of this launcher is based loosely on that of the 0.5-in (12.7-mm) Browning M2 heavy machine-gun in combination with a very short barrel. A belt-feed mechanism is employed to feed the grenades into the Mk 19's mechanism, and a rate of fire as high as 375 rounds per minute can be achieved. For tactical use the Mk 19 can be mounted on a tripod, or alternatively on a pedestal mount carried by a vehicle or light vessel. Another advantage, other than the rate of fire, offered by the Mk 19 over the M79 and M204, is a considerably longer range.

Reverting to the basic concept of the rifle grenade, it is worth noting that the low cost and simplicity of the weapon, in combination with the universal availability of the rifle as the means to launch these weapons, has made it feasible for any country with even the most limited facilities for the manufacture of small arms ammunition and other light ordnance to undertake the design and manufacture of rifle grenades. Some of these grenades, especially those carrying the type of hollow-charge warhead providing a capability against armoured fighting vehicles, bunkers and light vessels, are purpose-designed for the task. Others, intended for use against troops in the open, are straightforward adaptations of standard hand-thrown HE fragmentation grenades with a finned body carrying the grenade as its warhead.

## Grenade adaptation

Typical of the adapted standard hand grenade is the **GME-FMK2-MO** grenade designed and made in Argentina. This is an orthodox hand grenade with a pre-fragmented steel body weighing 165 g (5.8 oz) and carrying 75.8 g (2.67 oz) of explosive triggered by the charge in a fuse mechanism, whose body weighs 44.79 g (1.44 oz), after a delay that varies between 3.4 and 4.5 seconds. On the detonation of its HE charge, the grenade body shatters into a large number of fragments each weighing between 3 and 5 g (0.11 and 0.18 oz) and providing a useful effect against any person within 5 m (16.4 ft). For use as a rifle grenade, the weapon is seated on top of its launcher, which comes complete with the special propellant cartridge, and these two elements are located on to the barrel and into the breech of the rifle respectively. After the grenade's safety pin has been removed, the firer aims and discharges his rifle, propelling the grenade into a trajectory offering a maximum range of some 350 to 400 m (385 to 435 yards) and the possibility of an air or ground burst depending on the firer's expertise.

*The Mk 19 automatic grenade launcher, seen here with a belt of 40-mm (1.57-in) armour-piercing grenades, has a rate of 375 rounds per minute and offers the possibility of saturating a large area with any of several types of round.*

*The first launcher made specifically to fire spin-stabilised grenades was the M79. This is a single-shot dedicated launcher that can fire its grenade to a maximum range of 400 m (435 yards). Its main limitation was that the firer had no rifle.*

*Reconnaissance specialists of the US Army, clad in distinctive 'tiger stripe' fatigues, fire M79 launchers in Vietnam, where the launcher was nicknamed the 'Blooper' gun after a children's toy of the period.*

## Special grenade

Typical of the purpose-designed rifle grenade is a Belgian offering, the **ARP-RFL-40 BT**, designed and made by the MECAR organisation in variants to be fired from standard 7.62- and 5.56-mm (0.3- and 0.219-in) rifles. The weapon has a maximum diameter of 40 mm and an overall length of 243 mm (9.57 in), and weighs 264 g (9.31 oz). The launching method is of the bullet trap rather than gas propellant type: at the muzzle the standard ball projectile fired by the rifle is caught by a ladder of five discs of metal inside the rear of the rifle grenade, its energy thereby being transferred to the grenade for a trajectory out to a maximum range of 275 m (300 yards) but a practical range of 100 m (110 yards) at a launch elevation of +45 degrees.

The grenade is armed 8 m (26.25 ft) after leaving the rifle at a nominal velocity of 60 m (197 ft) per second, and the penetrative capabilities of its warhead include 125 mm (4.92 in) of steel armour or 400 mm (15.75 in) of concrete after a descent at an angle of 70 degrees.

### SPECIFICATIONS

**Heckler & Koch HK 69A1 (Germany)**
**Type:** single-shot grenade launcher
**Calibre:** 40-mm (1.57-in)
**Length:** overall 610 mm (24 in) with the stock extended
**Weight:** launcher 1.8 kg (3.97 lb)
**Maximum range:** 300 m (330 yards)

**Grenade Discharger L1A1 (UK)**
**Type:** single-shot grenade launcher
**Calibre:** 66-mm (2.6-in)
**Length:** overall 695 mm (27.4 in)
**Weight:** 2.7 kg (6 lb)
**Maximum range:** 100 m (110 yards)

# Shotguns

**As a close-quarter weapon the shotgun has few equals. It proved a superb anti-ambush weapon in the jungles of Malaya and Vietnam, yet many armies remain uneasy about the combat shotgun. Sub-machine guns were once derided as 'gangster weapons' by traditionally minded soldiers, and shotguns have met with similar criticism.**

*Although the pump-action combat shotgun can provide excellent short-range firepower in jungle conditions, its ammunition is prone to moisture damage and its tubular magazine is slow to load.*

World War I broke a lot of barriers in the matter of weapons, and the close-quarter fighting of trench raids gave short-range weapons a value they had never had before. The Americans soon adopted a number of pump-action 12-bore guns for trench fighting; these were commercial sporting weapons which had their barrels cut down and fitted with bayonet lugs. Loaded with seven or eight 00 Buck cartridges, they were a formidable method of clearing trenches and dug-outs. There were complaints from the Germans about 'barbarous' methods of warfare, but these remarks did not sit well from the people who had introduced poison gas, so nobody took much notice of their complaints.

### World War II

The Americans kept their shotguns during the peace between the world wars, principally as guard weapons, and then brought them out again during World War II, in which the US Marine Corps putting a number of them to use in the island campaigns of the Pacific war. But they saw little action elsewhere, and it was not until the Malayan emergency in the 1950s that the shotgun began to make some impression on military circles outside the USA.

The Malayan police were using pump and automatic shotguns, and the British army began to adopt these weapons as patrol armament. The principal threat to patrols in the jungle was, and always will be, the ambush, and it was found that two or three shotguns could put down a blast of return fire as soon as an ambush opened, giving the remainder of the patrol time to take cover and begin returning fire from the more conventional rifles and machine-guns. The cloud of shot from a burst of shotgun fire covered the whole ambush area and was enough to put the ambushers off their stroke for enough time to give the patrol a chance to begin retaliatory action.

### Jungle experience

In the early 1950s the British army in Malaya made a very thorough examination of the use and effectiveness of shotguns in jungle warfare. Its conclusions were embodied in a report which has never been made public in Great Britain, though it seems to have been fairly well read in other countries. One conclusion was that an automatic shotgun ought to replace the light machine-gun as a patrol weapon because it provided a substantially better chance of securing a lethal hit.

Nothing came of this report. The official attitude was that this was simply a response to a unique tactical situation which was unlikely to be repeated, so the implications could be ignored.

### The Vietnam War

The next major use of shotguns came in Vietnam. The only weapons suitable for military service were the pump-action repeater and the automatic. Of those two the automatic was looked at with some suspicion since it has a failure rate of about one stoppage for 250 shots fired, a rate far too high for the military.

The pump-action gun also has drawbacks, primarily the reloading problem. Pump guns have tubular magazines under the barrel, which must be reloaded one cartridge at a time, which is not the easiest thing to do in the heat of an ambush. Moreover, tubular magazines are easily dented, which causes stop-

*The shotgun is an ideal weapon for maritime boarding parties, which face the possibility of ambush as they make their way on to the vessel being boarded. The shotgun can help to counter the boarding party's tactical disadvantages.*

*The case for the combat shotgun, already demonstrated by the British during the Malayan Emergency of the 1950s, was fully confirmed by the americans in the Vietnam War. Here the shotgun was often a decisive tactical weapon.*

pages.

The third problem is ammunition. Although effective, ordinary shotgun ammunition is not ideal for coping with human targets, and commercial shotgun ammunition could not stand up to the humidity of jungle conditions in Vietnam.

All these problems were amenable to solution, given one thing: money. The manufacturers of shotguns were not stupid. They could doubtless solve the various military requirements – but they were not going to spend large sums of cash on something with a very doubtful element of profit in it. The Vietnam War was the catalyst which loosened the purse strings and got a little cash flowing into shotgun design.

### Designed for the task

In 1979 the decision was taken by the US Navy to put some work into developing a purpose-built combat shotgun for the US Marine Corps. The idea was taken up by the US Joint Services Small Arms Panel, and the programme was known as RHINO (Repeating Handheld Improved Non-rifled Ordnance). Apart from a very broad specification on the length of cartridge and the amount of recoil to be felt by the firer, very little restraint was placed upon the design.

Contracts were put out for development, and the resulting weapon was to be known as the CAWS – Close Assault Weapon System.

What emerged was a selective-fire shotgun with better lethal range than existing weapons. Box magazines, improved reloading time and cartridges were developed that could take a variety of loadings, including buckshot and flechette, with sufficient propellant to give them lethal effect out to 185 m (200 yards) or so.

The RHINO programme stimulated designers elsewhere. The police in Europe were suddenly becoming very shotgun-minded, seeing it as a useful weapon in counter-terrorist work and also as a formidable riot-control weapon.

The Pentagon was not satisfied with the progress of CAWS development, however, performance of the weapons being considered unsatisfactory. The result was that the programme was abruptly terminated.

Nevertheless, there remain several private ventures which are showing considerable promise and which may well find their way into military service. They have been developed with military or police use in view, so that they are all robust and practical weapons, and they all promise better performance than an adapted commercial weapon. Whether or not they will succeed still remains to be seen.

## SCATTER GUNS

Faced with ambush at short range, troops operating in jungle conditions need a means to redress the balance with a few powerful 'area-saturation' rounds fired from a shotgun to keep the ambushers' heads down and buy the few seconds needed for the ambushed party's men to find cover and start fighting back. The key to the shotgun's capability in this regard is its ability to fire a spread of shot, each capable of wounding if not killing the person it hits, with each round. The choke of the barrel, sometimes variable, dictates how the shot of such a 'scatter gun' spreads, a typical figure being a shot-pattern diameter of about 0.9 m (3 ft) at a range of 45 m (50 yards). Thus a snap shot stands a good chance of hitting and wounding an attacker, as indicated by the spread of shot over the upper part of the illustration (right). The shotgun can also be used to fire a single heavy slug of metal, albeit to a considerably shorter range than a rifle, but nevertheless with sufficient kinetic energy to completely check and kill an attacker at short range (lower part of illustration). The unitary slug also possesses considerable capability against vehicles and other light equipment.

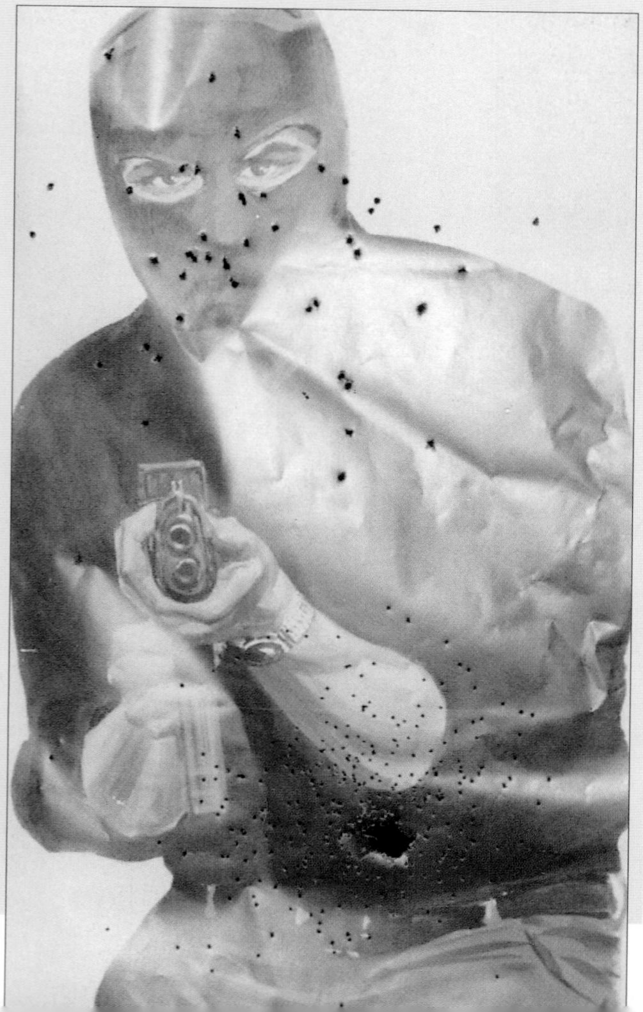

# Browning Automatic Shotguns

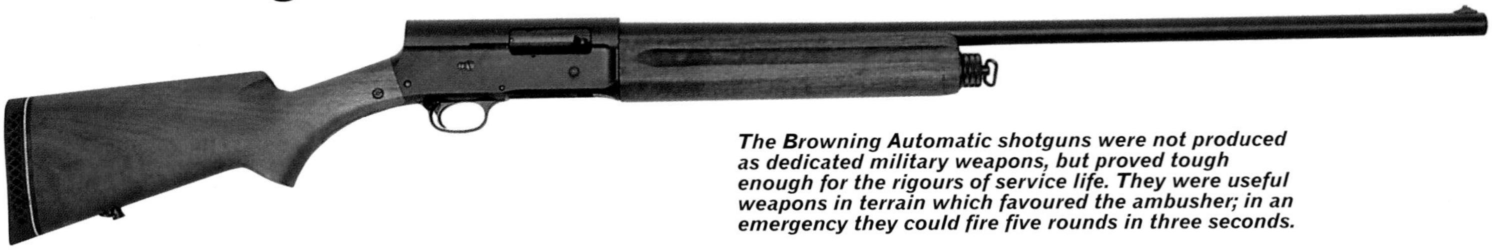

***The Browning Automatic shotguns were not produced as dedicated military weapons, but proved tough enough for the rigours of service life. They were useful weapons in terrain which favoured the ambusher; in an emergency they could fire five rounds in three seconds.***

***A British soldier of the 18th Independent Brigade, on patrol in the jungle during the Malayan Emergency, carries a Browning A5, which gave him formidable short-range firepower.***

Any description of the **Browning Automatic** shotgun as a combat weapon is beset by the difficulty that there has never been a purpose-produced military version of any of these designs. The first Browning Automatic (actually semi-automatic or self-loading) shotgun was conceived as early as 1898, but it was left to the Belgian Fabrique Nationale (FN) to start production and many of the guns still in use are Belgian-made. They were all conceived primarily as sporting weapons, but it was not long before substantial numbers were in military hands, often as security guard weapons or for similar duties. John M. Browning also negotiated a production licence with the American Remington concern and many Remington guns used by the US Army and others during World War II were in fact Browning Automatics, typical weapons being the **Remington Model 11A** and **Remington Model 12**.

## Good jungle weapon

After World War II Browning sporting guns were widely used as military weapons in regions such as Central and South America, but it took the Malayan Emergency of 1948–1960 to make the Browning Automatic an established military weapon. The British army used Greener GP guns and Browning Automatics throughout that long campaign, often (but not always) with the long sporting barrel cut back to as short a length as possible. Most guns used by the British were 12-gauge weapons with five-round magazines, and fired commercial heavy shot cartridges.

It was not long before the British relearned the old lesson that the automatic shotgun is an almost perfect weapon for the close-quarter combat of jungle warfare. As an ambush or counter-ambush gun the Browning Automatic was ideal as it could be used to get off five rounds in as few as three seconds. At the time little publicity was given to the combat use of these shotguns (the **Remington Model 870R** was also employed) but many soldiers who served in Malaya during the Emergency probably carried a Browning Automatic at some time or another.

After 1960 the British army set aside the Browning for more conventional weapons, but doubtless some are still retained for 'special purposes'. Despite the type's Malayan popularity, soldiers found that the weapon was slow to reload and took considerable care, especially when shortened barrels imposed excessive firing loads on the self-loading components.

Brownings popped up again during the Rhodesian anti-guerrilla/freedom fighter campaigns, and the gun is still a widely used 'small campaign' weapon. But there is still no sign of a combat version of the Browning Automatic, despite a brief flurry of design activity during the 1960s.

**SPECIFICATION**

**Browning Automatic (standard model)**
**Calibre:** 12 gauge

**Length:** barrel 711 mm (28 in)
**Weight:** loaded 4.1 kg (9 lb)
**Feed:** 5-round tubular magazine

# FN Riot Shotgun

As its name implies, the **Fabrique Nationale Riot Shotgun** is primarily a police and para-military weapon. In design terms it is relatively unremarkable as a manually operated pump-action shotgun with a tubular magazine holding five rounds. FN is no stranger to shotgun design, for it was among the first to produce the many John M. Browning Automatic shotgun designs in the 1920s, and since that time the company has been among the world leaders in the manufacture of these weapons. Many of FN's designs are intended for sporting purposes, but it takes little to transform a sporting shotgun into a law enforcement weapon and FN has never been slow to commit itself to any such undertaking.

The Riot Shotgun first appeared in 1970 and was based on the widely used FN automatic sporting gun of the period. It was at one time available with three interchangeable barrel lengths. The first models had rear and fore sights, but on later production models these have been removed and the standard barrel length is now 500 mm (19.7 in). Rubber butt pads and sling swivels are fitted as standard.

## Rugged design

The main difference between the Riot Shotgun and the FN sporting models is that the riot version is much more rugged than the civilian shotguns. There is, for instance, a bolt that runs right through the buttstock to strengthen that component, and all metalwork has been 'beefed up' to withstand the rigours of hard use. The metal surfaces have also been specially plated so that they require only the minimum of care and maintenance.

***Shotgun ammunition comes in a bewildering variety of forms, which different countries unhelpfully divide into different categories. On the left is a conventional birdshot round for the FN shotgun; in the centre a flechette round; and on the right a brenecke rifled slug.***

For reasons of maintaining an overall high standard of reliability, FN even decided to retain the original five-round tubular magazine and has thus never introduced the extension magazines used on many other contemporary paramilitary shotguns. FN instead decided to retain the simple manual action in which each 'pump' motion ejects a spent case and loads a fresh round. FN once tried to create an automatic version of the Riot Shotgun, but this was made only as a prototype with a six-round magazine.

FN has produced its Riot Shotgun in a form suitable for firing full-calibre slugs, but the majority of guns in regular service are used to fire 12-gauge shot only: in fact there has never been a Riot Shotgun in any other calibre. The type is used by the Belgian police and some para-military units, and it has been sold to some overseas police forces. It is a very reliable and rugged weapon and is more than adequate for its paramilitary role.

***Pump-action shotguns like the FN are used by police forces all over the world. They are reliable weapons with high short-range hit probability, and do not produce stray bullets which can be lethal to bystanders hundreds of yards away.***

**SPECIFICATION**

**FN Riot Shotgun**
**Calibre:** 12 gauge
**Weight:** 2.95 kg (6.5 lb)
**Lengths:** overall 970 mm (38.19 in); barrel 500 mm (19.7 in)
**Feed:** 5-round tubular magazine

# Beretta RS200 and RS202P Shotguns

A company based firmly in Italy but with outlets all over the world, Armi Beretta SpA is without doubt one of the most respected names in small-arms design and manufacture, and is also no stranger to the manufacture of shotguns. Although the company's first such weapons were directed mainly toward the civil market as sporting guns, Beretta soon followed the tendency toward the manufacture of more robust shotguns intended for police and paramilitary purposes. The first result of this process was the introduction of the 12-gauge **Beretta RS200 (Police Model)** as a manually operated pump-action shotgun.

***The RS202-MI is the folding-stock version of the successful RS202P 12-gauge shotgun. Loading is marginally easier than on the original weapon, and the bolt mechanism has been altered.***

## Excellent finish

As with all other firearms from the Beretta company, this RS200 (Police Model) is a well designed and superbly finished weapon notable for the degree to which it has been strengthened for the type of rough handling it can expect to receive in police and para-military hands.

Beretta introduced no innovations with the RS200 other than a special safety sliding-block breech locking device that prevents the possibility of the weapon being discharged before the breech locking process has been completed. The hammer also has a special safety lug feature, and there is a bolt catch that enables a cartridge to be safely removed from the chamber without having to fire it. Another interesting feature of the RS200 for police and paramilitary use is the fact that it can be used to fire small tear gas cartridges, to a maximum range of about 100 m (110 yards), as well as the usual shot or slug loadings.

## Advanced design

Although now out of production, the RS200 is used by many police and other forces. It was replaced in manufacture by the **RS202P**, which differs from its predecessor mainly in its loading procedure, which by comparison with that of the RS200 (Police Model) was made much easier, and in slight variations to the bolt mechanism. With the introduction of the RS202P came two variants. The first was schemed to reduce the overall length of the weapon as a means of facilitating its stowage and handling: this **RS202-MI** variant has a skeleton-type folding buttstock that can be stowed along the left-hand side of the body. The second of the variants carries over this folding buttstock, but in addition has a variable choke device over the muzzle to allow the alteration of the spread of shot, and also a perforated barrel jacket to make handling easier, as it is is impossible to hold the barrel once it has become hot after the firing of several rounds. To assist the firer in rapid aiming, special sights have been fitted to this second variant, which is known as the **RS202P-M2**.

The RS202P shotguns have followed the overall acceptance of the RS200, but the rate of sales has not been remarkable, mainly because the Beretta shotguns seem to lack the aesthetic, or perhaps futuristic, visual appeal of some of the more modern designs that have entered the market. The RS202P is now apparently being produced to order only. For all this it is a reliable and well-made gun that seems set to remain in use for many years to come.

***This RS202-M2 has a perforated barrel jacket, which makes for easier handling of the gun after the barrel has become hot from repeated firing. Beretta provides a variable choke unit to give a choice of shot spread patterns.***

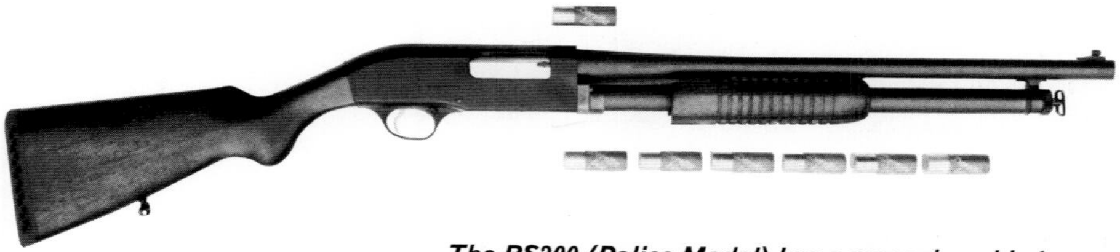

***The RS200 (Police Model) has a magazine able to take six rounds, and a seventh round can be carried in the chamber. The inertia-operated firing pin on the RS200 (Police Model) prevents the gun from being fired until the bolt is fully locked.***

**SPECIFICATION**

**RS200 (Police Model)**
**Calibre:** 12 gauge
**Lengths:** overall 1030 mm (40.55 in); barrel 520 mm (20.47 in)
**Weight:** about 3 kg (6.6 lb)
**Feed:** 5/6-round tubular magazine

# SPAS Model 12 Shotgun

***Many military and police shotguns are modified sporting weapons, but Luigi Franchi SpA designed the SPAS 11 and SPAS 12 (seen here) from the outset as combat weapons. This formidable weapon can be operated in the pump-action single-shot mode, or be set to the semi-automatic mode, in which up to four rounds per second are possible.***

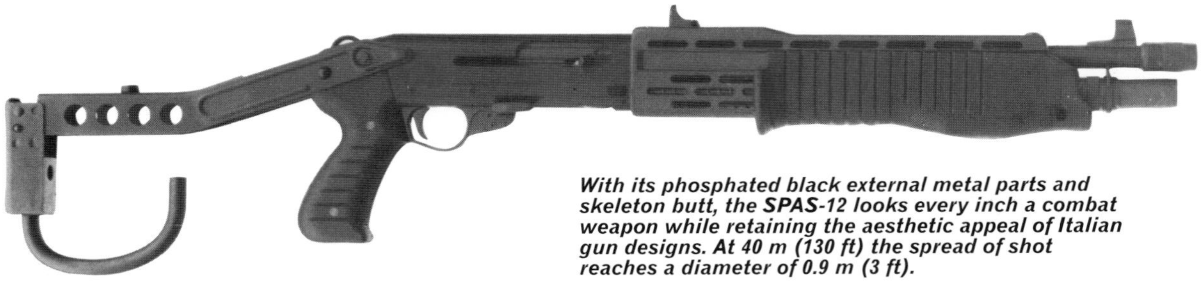

***With its phosphated black external metal parts and skeleton butt, the SPAS-12 looks every inch a combat weapon while retaining the aesthetic appeal of Italian gun designs. At 40 m (130 ft) the spread of shot reaches a diameter of 0.9 m (3 ft).***

The **SPAS Model 12** (SPAS standing for Special-Purpose Automatic Shotgun or, in civilian hands, Sporting Purpose Automatic Shotgun) is one of the most interesting and influential combat shotgun designs to have appeared for a long time. The new type was designed and has since been produced by Luigi Franchi SpA, an Italian firm which had specialised in the creation of sporting shotguns for many years. When the demand for a shot-firing combat weapon became apparent in the early 1970s, the Franchi team decided to design a new weapon using a novel approach: it opted to create a true combat weapon, not a conversion of an existing sporting model, and the result is the **SPAS Model 11**. This is optimised for the combat role in a number of its features as detailed below, but was also made as short as possible, optimised for reliability and low maintenance, and purposely made as 'pointable' as possible so that the firer, after only a short period of training, had a good chance of securing a first-round hit.

### Heavy and strong

Like its Model 12 development, the Model 11 is a heavy weapon that is so robust it can be used as a club. It has a distinctive appearance: there is no orthodox butt, but rather a fixed skeleton metal butt on the Model 11 or a folding stock on the Model 12. The mechanism at first sight appears to be a bulky manual pump action, but is in fact a combination of semi-automatic and pump-action features, the change between semi-automatic and pump-action operation being controlled by pressure on a button in the fore end and then movement of this fore end backward for pump action or forward for semi-automatic. In the semi-automatic mode, gas tapped from the barrel impinges on an annular piston round the under-barrel magazine. To work the action, which includes a vertically tilting locking lug that engages in the barrel extension to lock the bolt. The receiver is made of light alloy, while the barrel and gas piston are manufactured of steel hard-chromed to reduce the chances of corrosion. All the exterior surfaces are sand-blasted and phosphated black, and the pistol grip and fore end are of plastic.

### Tubular magazine

The tubular magazine under the short barrel can accommodate up to seven rounds. These rounds can vary from light bird shot to heavy metal slugs that can penetrate steel plate.

The rest of the SPAS is well provided with novel features. The variant most likely to be encountered is the Model 12, which has a bulky front handguard and a folding stock. The stock has a piece of curved metal under the 'butt plate' that loops around the forearm and allows the weapon to be held and fired with one hand, although anyone firing the weapon in such a way will soon learn what a handful the Model 12 can be. There is a pistol grip, the muzzle can be fitted with a shotspreading choke device and another muzzle attachment is a grenade launcher. Small tear gas and CS projectiles can also be fired out to a range of 150 m (165 yards). Sights are provided but the spread of shot from a normal 12-gauge cartridge is such that at 40 m (45 yards) the shot pellets cover a circle with a diameter of 900 mm (35.4 in), so accuracy of aim is not vastly important at this type of typical combat range.

The SPAS is a true combat shotgun and in the hands of a fully trained operative can be a formidable weapon. The Model 12 has been sold to several military and paramilitary armed forces, and some have appeared on the civilian market. Many of these have been snapped up by shotgun enthusiasts, but in many countries the short barrel breaks legal regulations and so needs a barrel extension.

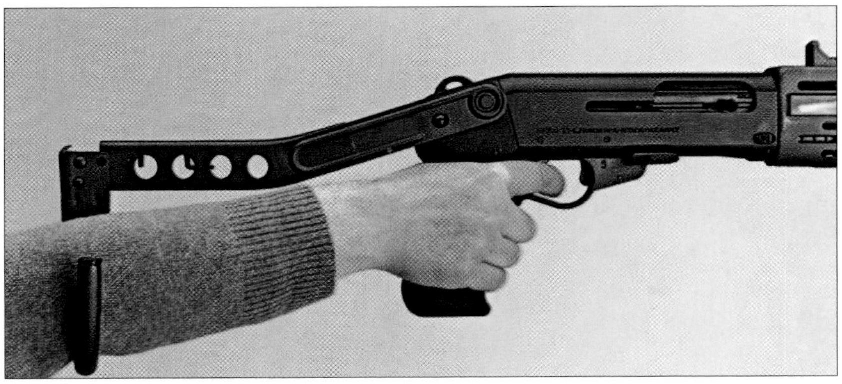

***A key feature of the SPAS-12 is the provision of a hook under the rear of the butt to hold the forearm of the firer, which allows the weapon to be fired with just one hand. However, control is distinctly limited.***

**SPECIFICATION**

**SPAS-12**
**Calibre:** 12-gauge
**Length overall:** 1041 mm (40.98 in) with butt extended and 710 mm (27.95 in) with butt folded
**Length of barrel:** 460 mm (18.11 in)
**Weight:** 4.2 kg (9.26 lb)
**Feed:** 7-round tubular magazine

# SPAS-15 Shotgun

**SPECIFICATION**

**SPAS-15**
**Calibre:** 12-gauge
**Length overall:** 1000 mm (39.37 in) with butt extended and 750 mm (29.53 in) with butt folded
**Length of barrel:** 450 mm (17.72 in)
**Weight:** empty 3.9 kg (8.6 lb)
**Feed:** 6-round detachable box magazine

The **SPAS-15** shotgun is a further development of the earlier SPAS-12 shotgun, and is intended as police and military weapon offering considerable firepower through the use of a gas-operated semi-automatic action and a detachable single-stack box magazine. Thus multiple shots can be fired in quick succession from a magazine that can be changed more quickly than a tubular magazine can be reloaded. Versatility is offered by the provision of a manually selected single-shot pump action to complement the semi-automatic action, this allowing the weapon to fire low-pressure non-lethal ammunition such as tear gas and rubber slug projectiles. The firing modes are chosen in the fashion of the SPAS-12.

The SPAS-15 is based on an action with a rotary bolt and a short piston stroke, the latter located above the barrel. The bolt group is mounted on dual guide rods together with the recoil springs, and can be removed as a single unit.

The cocking handle is located on top of the receiver under the carrying handle, and can be operated with either hand. The SPAS-15 has a manual safety located inside the trigger guard to lock the trigger, and an automatic grip safety on the pistol grip under the trigger guard.

The SPAS-15 has open adjustable sights, and can be fitted with additional sighting devices such as red dot sights or laser pointers. The receiver of SPAS-15 is made from aluminum alloy and its furniture from polymer plastics. Earlier models had a fixed plastic or folding metal skeleton butt, but recent models have a side-folding, solid plastic butt. The magazine is plastic.

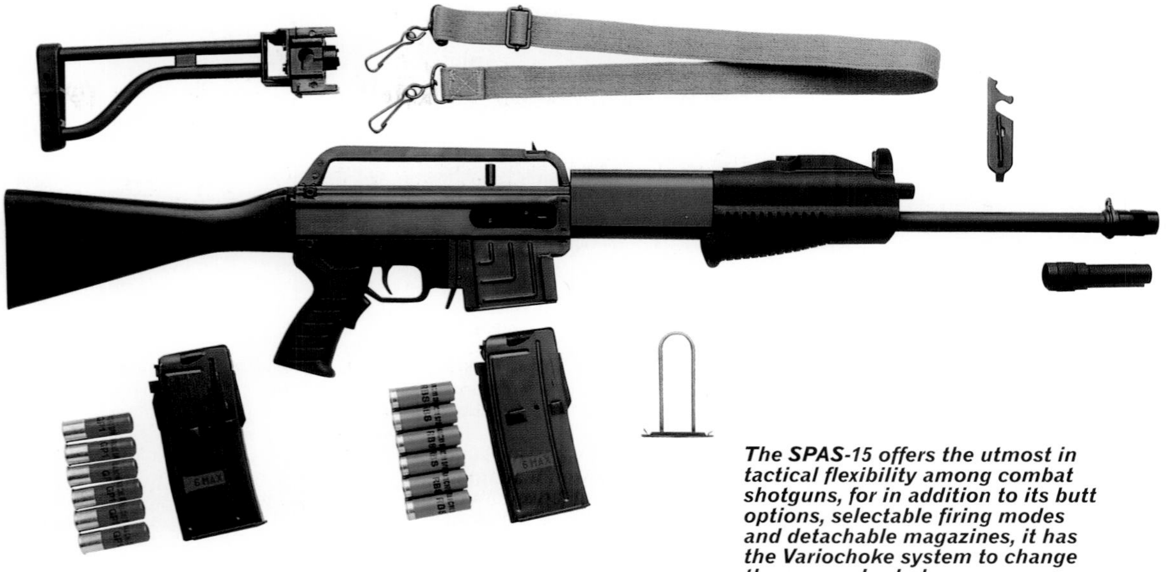

***The SPAS-15 offers the utmost in tactical flexibility among combat shotguns, for in addition to its butt options, selectable firing modes and detachable magazines, it has the Variochoke system to change the weapon's choke.***

# Striker Shotgun

Developed by the South African company Armsel, the **Striker** is a semi-automatic 12-gauge shotgun that appeared on the market in the mid-1980s. The Striker is an indigenous South African design that is now being manufactured by Reunert Technology Systems near Johannesburg, although initial production was by Armsel; the weapon is also made under licence in the USA, where the Striker has been adopted by many law enforcement agencies for use by their weapons teams, and also been developed into other forms. The Striker was designed for a wide range of operational roles ranging from civilian self-protection to full military combat applications.

## Rotary magazine

The Striker's most important single feature is its 12-round rotary magazine. This is loaded with cartridges through a trap on the right rear of the drum, which is rotated by a spring tensioned by a key at the front of the magazine. Once the weapon is loaded, one pull of the trigger fires a round and rotates the next round into line with the firing pin, it being impossible to fire the weapon until the firing pin is exactly in line with the next cartridge. The recoil is claimed to be less than that of a normal shotgun, although exactly why this should be is not clear for the barrel is certainly shorter than those of most other similar weapons. It is possible that the recoil is masked by the fact that the Striker has a foregrip under the barrel and a pistol grip; there is also a metal stock that can be folded up and over the barrel. The barrel has a perforated metal sleeve to dissipate heat produced by prolonged firing and to prevent the hot barrel being touched by the firer's hand, for the rapid firing of the full 12 rounds would certainly produce a very hot barrel.

## Gas ejection

Other features of the Striker are a double-action trigger and a gas ejection system to remove a spent cartridges from the system as the next round is fired.

The Striker can fire a wide range of 12-gauge ammunition ranging from bird shot (often used in ancien-regime South Africa for the dispersal of crowds) to heavy metal slugs. The weapon can be fired with the butt folded, although the discharge of the heavier loads without use of the butt could prove somewhat too lively for comfort.

## Short-range use

The sights are very simple, for the Striker is obviously not meant as anything other than a very short-range weapon for clearing crowds or perhaps in close-quarter combat in built-up areas. It could also prove to be very useful in bush warfare where infantry engagements and ambushes are often at very close ranges as a consequence of the overall lack of visibility resulting from the prevalent short scrub vegetation.

As well as its widespread service with American law enforcement bodies, the Striker has been adopted by the South African army and police, and has also found an operational niche with the Israeli armed forces and police.

***It would have been surprising if a nation in arms such as South Africa in its apartheid days had not come up with some interesting small arms developments. The semi-automatic Armsel Striker is a case in point, its 12-shot rotary magazine giving considerably more firepower than conventional guns.***

***With its short overall length and seemingly massive rotary magazine, holding a very useful 12 rounds of 12-gauge ammunition, the Striker is a weapon of impressive appearance. It is also highly capable and could be a decisive short-range weapon.***

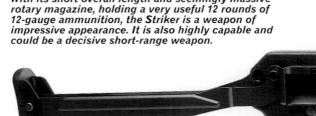

# Mossberg 500 Shotguns

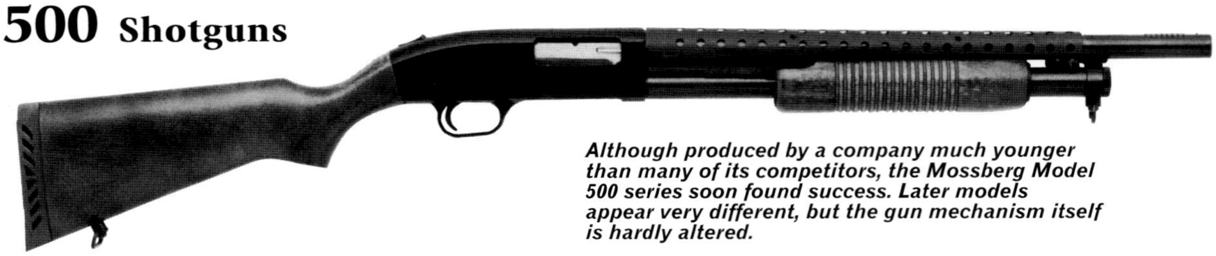

***Although produced by a company much younger than many of its competitors, the Mossberg Model 500 series soon found success. Later models appear very different, but the gun mechanism itself is hardly altered.***

O.F. Mossberg and Sons Inc. is a relative newcomer to combat as opposed to sporting shotguns, for its first such weapon, the **Mossberg Model 500**, appeared in 1961. After a while Mossberg made its market breakthrough and the Model 500 remains the company's 'base' product.

The Model 500 is a manual slide-action 12-gauge weapon. The receiver body is forged from high-grade aluminium and the steel bolt locks into a barrel extension to take the firing loads off the receiver. Most components such as the extractors and action slides are 'doubled' to produce strength and reliability, and this makes the Model 500 a very robust weapon despite its low overall price. These points have made the Model 500 and its variants widely used police weapons, but Mossberg has also produced combat versions.

One is the **Model ATP-8SP**. This is basically a police Model 500 with a non-reflective finish and extra attention given to the protective finish of every component. A bayonet mount is provided, and there is even provision for mounting a telescopic sight for use when firing slugs, although this feature would appear to be little used. A perforated handguard may be fitted over the barrel and, as with most of the Model 500 range, an up-and-over folding metal buttstock may be used in place of the normal hardwood fixed component. The Model 500 ATP-8SP has sold well but has been replaced by an updated combat model.

## Bullpup design

This is the **Model 500 Bullpup 12**. As its name implies, this is a bullpup design with a pistol grip assembly placed forward of the receiver. This makes the weapon considerably shorter than its conventional equivalent, and thus much easier to handle and stow in confined spaces, a considerable selling point for many police and military authorities. On the Bullpup 12 the receiver and much of the weapon body are entirely enclosed in a strong thermoplastic material so there are few components to catch on clothing or anything else This is partly negated by the all-inline bullpup layout that dictates that the rear and fore sights have to stick up on posts, but these can be folded down when not required.

The Bullpup 12 can be manufactured 'from new', but Mossberg produces a kit to convert existing Model 500 weapons to the revised configuration.

Another Mossberg shotgun with military potential is the **Model 590** developed in the 1970s with a strengthened structure.

**SPECIFICATION**

| | |
|---|---|
| **Mossberg Model 500 Bullpup 12**<br>**Calibre:** 12 gauge<br>**Lengths:** overall 784 mm (30.87 in); barrel 508 mm (20 in) | **Weight:** 3.85 kg (8.49 lb)<br>**Feed:** 6- or 8-round tubular magazine |

# Ithaca 37 M and P Shotguns

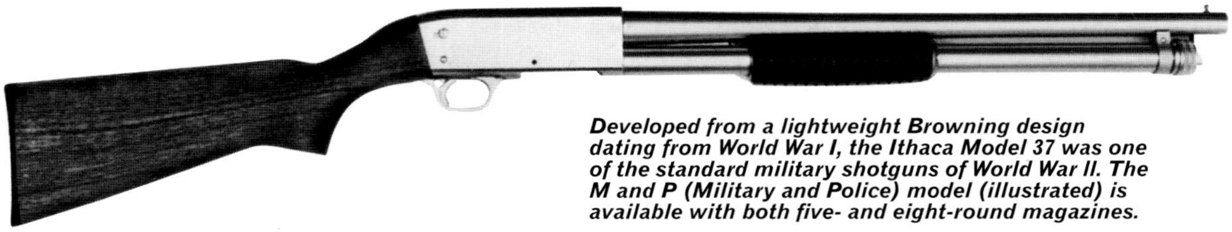

***Developed from a lightweight Browning design dating from World War I, the Ithaca Model 37 was one of the standard military shotguns of World War II. The M and P (Military and Police) model (illustrated) is available with both five- and eight-round magazines.***

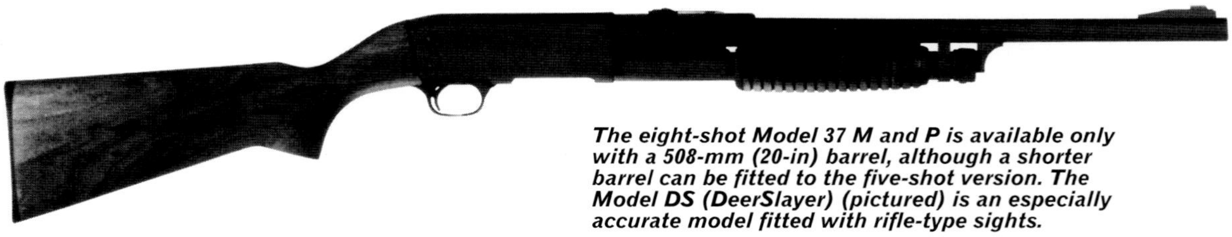

***The eight-shot Model 37 M and P is available only with a 508-mm (20-in) barrel, although a shorter barrel can be fitted to the five-shot version. The Model DS (DeerSlayer) (pictured) is an especially accurate model fitted with rifle-type sights.***

In the USA the shotgun is a well established police and prison service weapon, to the extent that many shotgun manufacturers find it well worth their while to produce weapons tailored to individual police department specifications. Some of these weapons come very close to military specifications, and such is the **Ithaca Model LAPD** shotgun, a weapon based on the **Ithaca Model DS** (DeerSlayer, from the company's trademark). In its turn the Model DS was based on a very well established design known as the **Ithaca Model 37 M and P**, very robust and well-made weapons produced for policing requirements.

## Long pedigree

The Model 37 series has been around for some time: during World War II it was one of the shotguns selected by the US Army for military use. It was used during that period for general shotgun purposes, including riot control and guard duties, and was then available in three barrel lengths. The current Model M and P models are not significantly dissimilar from the World War II versions, but are now made that much more rugged. The current shotguns are produced in several forms and with a range of options available. Two important variants are the **Model 37 Homeland Security** for self-defence and police use, and the **Model 37 Stakeout** compact weapon with a shorter barrel and a pistol grip in place of the conventional stock. Model 37 weapons may be fitted with a five- or eight-round tubular magazine, and the two barrel lengths are 470 mm (18.5 in) and 508 mm (20 in). Both are used to fire the usual range of 12-gauge shot cartridges using a cylinder choke barrel whereas the Model DS has a precision-bored cylindrical barrel that can be used to fire heavy slugs. The Model DS has only the 508-mm barrel, and sights are provided. The option of a five- or eight-round magazine is carried over.

The Model LAPD for the Los Angeles Police Department is the Model DS with a rubber butt pad, special sights, sling swivels and a carrying strap. It has a 470-mm barrel, a five-round tubular magazine and, like all the other models in the Model 37 range, a robust manual slide pump action. Some of these weapons are used by the special forces of several nations.

All the weapons in the Model 37 M and P range have Parkerized finishes to reduce wear and the need for constant cleaning.

**SPECIFICATION**

| | |
|---|---|
| **Model P and M**<br>**Calibre:** 12 gauge<br>**Lengths:** overall 1016 mm (40 in) with the 508-mm barrel; barrel 470 or 508 mm (18.5 or 20 in) | **Weight:** 2.94 kg (6.48 lb) or 3.06 kg (6.745 lb) depending on barrel length<br>**Feed:** 5- or 8-round tubular magazine |

***The more highly finished appearance of this Ithaca Model 37DS Police Special attests to its original role as a civilian hunting weapon. Nevertheless, its light weight, accuracy and reliable action make it effective as a paramilitary and law enforcement weapon.***

# Winchester Shotguns

The US Repeating Arms Company, usually known as Winchester, is best known for its rifles, but also produces shotguns for the sporting market and for police and para-military use. In the past Winchester shotguns were produced in a wide variety of models, including the classic Model 12 used during World War II and some of the few box-magazine combat shotguns ever produced, but current models are limited to a few manual slide-action models.

The basic Winchester shotgun model is a 12-gauge design known as the **Winchester Defender**. This was specifically created, developed and manufactured for use by conventional police forces, but the weapon has also found its way into the hands of several purely military forces. In overall terms, the Defender is of perfectly conventional design, but the action is notably compact and, as is always the case with Winchester weapons, the standard to which the weapons are manufactured and finished is very good.

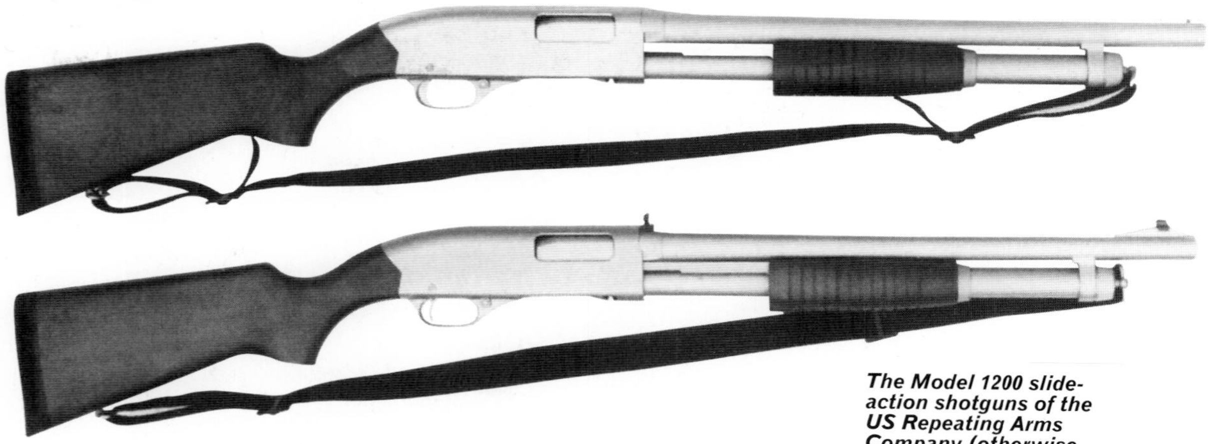

***The Model 1200 slide-action shotguns of the US Repeating Arms Company (otherwise known as Winchester) have 457-mm (18-in) barrels and are finished in a satinised chrome which minimises reflected light and resists corrosion.***

## Rotary bolt action

Operating the slide action opens and closes a rotary bolt of the type that provides a very positive and safe lock, and the unlocking is recoil-assisted to speed the action considerably, placing the weapon almost into the semi-automatic class.

The tubular magazine extends to just under the muzzle and can hold six or seven cartridges, depending on whether they are normal shot cartridges or the longer heavy slug type. The finish is usually blued or Parkerized, but there is a version produced specially for police use, all the metalwork being stainless steel. This version may be fitted with rifle-type sights for firing slugs, and the magazine is slightly shorter than that of the standard Defender. Sling swivels are provided.

## Navalised model

Perhaps the most unusual of the current Winchester shotguns is the **Model 1300 Marines** produced specially for use by naval and marine forces. This is based on the Defender but is more akin to the stainless steel police model for it has been designed to be corrosion-resistant. All weapons in a naval environment are subject to the effects of corrosive salts, and stainless steel is proof against many of them. To ensure virtually complete protection the 'marine' Winchester also has all its external metal parts chrome-plated. The result is a weapon of notably striking appearance, but one which would also seem to have some eye-catching drawbacks in combat situations. However, this model has been sold, usually to para-military forces such as coast guards who feel the need for a shotgun with which to arm their boarding parties.

***British police increasingly follow this Winchester-armed American model, with fireproof overalls, bulletproof vest and visored helmet. Shotgun-armed policemen are now seen on the streets of London when the Metropolitan Police's specialist weapons officers are on duty.***

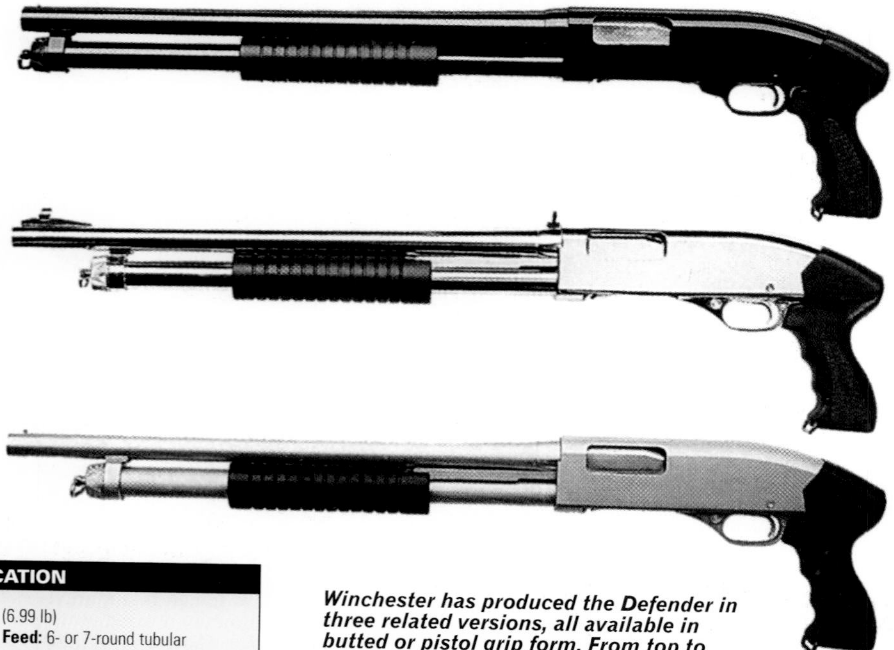

***Winchester has produced the Defender in three related versions, all available in butted or pistol grip form. From top to bottom, these are the Pistol Grip Defender, Pistol Grip Stainless Marine, and Pistol Grip Stainless Police. The last has a smaller magazine.***

**SPECIFICATION**

**Winchester Defender**
**Calibre:** 12 gauge
**Length:** barrel 457 mm (18 in)
**Weight:** 3.06 kg (6.74 lb) or (stainless steel models) 3.17 kg (6.99 lb)
**Feed:** 6- or 7-round tubular magazine or (stainless steel models) 5- or 6-round tubular magazine

# Pancor Jackhammer Shotgun

The **Pancor Jackhammer** is a recent arrival on the combat shotgun scene, but uses an operating mechanism that has been around for some time. The weapon was designed by John Andersen, who began to seek patent protection for his design in 1984, and has many original features, not the least its ability to fire on full automatic and its use of a pre-loaded 10-round rotary magazine.

The Jackhammer is a gas-operated weapon, has an unusual appearance and is based on a 'bullpup' configuration with the rotary magazine therefore located behind the trigger group. The plastic magazine holds 10 rounds and is clipped into the weapon before the fore-end of the stock is moved to and fro to cock the weapon. On firing, the barrel moves forward. As it does so, a gas-operated stud moves in an angled groove on the magazine to start the rotation to the next round. Once it has reached the forward limit of its movement, the barrel is pushed back by a spring and the magazine rotation is completed. (This system was used in a British weapon of World War I, the Webley-Fosbery revolver.) Once the barrel has returned, the weapon is ready for the next shot.

**SPECIFICATION**

| | |
|---|---|
| **Jackhammer** | **Weight:** loaded 4.57 kg (10.1 lb) |
| **Calibre:** 12-gauge | **Rate of fire, cyclic:** 240 rounds per minute |
| **Length overall:** 762 mm (30 in) | **Feed:** 10-round rotary magazine |
| **Length of barrel:** 457 mm (18 in) | |

Firing in fully automatic mode the weapon has a cyclic rate of fire of 240 rounds per minute, and barrel jump is partially offset by a downward-angled muzzle compensator that doubles as a flash eliminator.

## Little metal

The Jackhammer makes much use of tough plastics throughout its construction. In fact only the barrel, return spring magazine rotation mechanism and muzzle flash eliminator are steel. The magazines, known as 'ammo cassettes', are delivered pre-loaded and sealed in plastic film (removed before loading) colour-coded to indicate the type of cartridge enclosed. It is not possible to load single cartridges, but single-round fire can be selected.

The sights are contained in a channel on the long assembly that acts as a carrying handle. Firing the Jackhammer is not a problem for left-handed firers as no spent cartridge cases are ejected: these remain in the rotary magazine discarded once all the rounds have been fired. When the magazine is empty, a retaining catch opens and allows the component to fall free.

The Jackhammer is an interesting weapon with considerable potential, but has not yet been placed in production.

***The unusual Pancor Jackhammer uses an action similar to that of the Webley-Fosbery self-loading revolver of World War I. When firing, the gas pressure in the annular cylinder round the barrel drives back a piston that operates the action, engaging a groove in the cylinder which turns it and presents a new shell for firing. Because used cases remain in the cylinder, the Jackhammer avoids the problems associated with bullpup designs, notably the ejection of cartridges close to a shooter's face. On full automatic, the magazine is emptied in 2.5 seconds. The compensator holds the weapon down when firing at that rate.***

# Remington Model 870 Mk 1 Shotgun

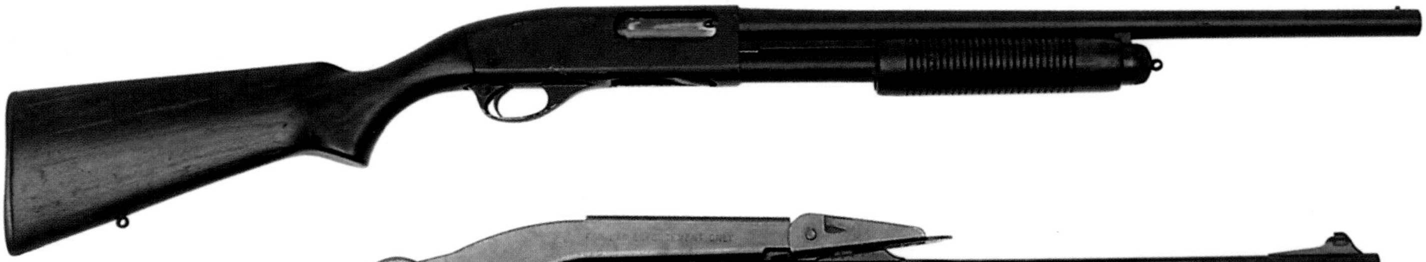

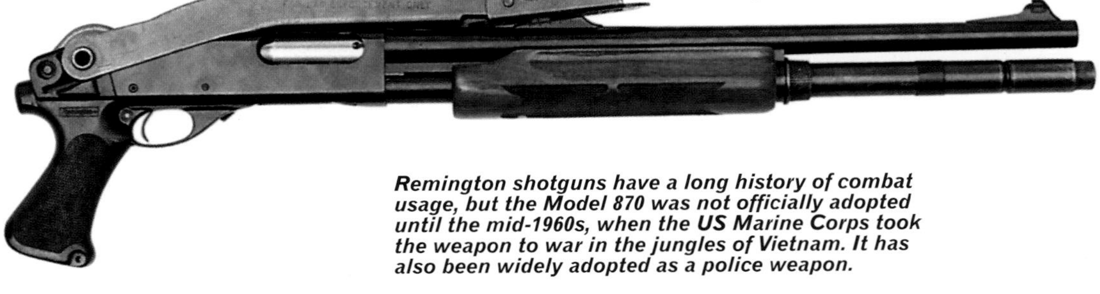

***Remington shotguns have a long history of combat usage, but the Model 870 was not officially adopted until the mid-1960s, when the US Marine Corps took the weapon to war in the jungles of Vietnam. It has also been widely adopted as a police weapon.***

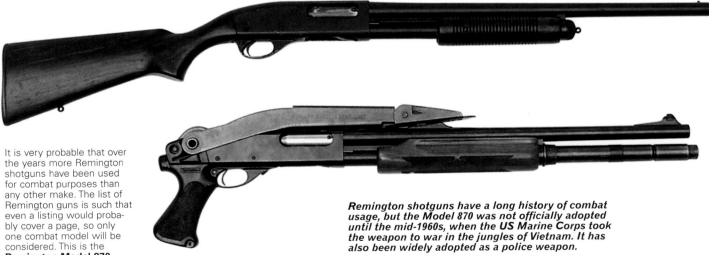

It is very probable that over the years more Remington shotguns have been used for combat purposes than any other make. The list of Remington guns is such that even a listing would probably cover a page, so only one combat model will be considered. This is the **Remington Model 870** modified for use by the US Marines Corps and known formally as the **Shotgun, 12-gauge, Remington, Model 870, Mk 1**.

The Model 870 has been one of the most widely-used of all shotguns for some time. It has been produced in basic models such as the **Model 870R** (Riot) and **Model 870P** (Police), but there have been many other types and an equally large number of conversions and adaptations. The Model 870 is a slide-action weapon, and when the US Marine Corps conducted prospective combat shotgun trials during 1966 it decided that, for reasons of reliability in combat, such a weapon would be preferable to one of the many semi-automatic actions available, and the Model 870 thus became the US Marine Corps' main choice. After a few modifications had been effected to make the weapon an exact fit to the service's requirements, the Model 870 Mk 1 was placed in production and has remained in USMC service ever since. These modifications included a longer magazine, a heat-shield round the barrel to prevent the firer from burning his hands, and a protective non-glare finish that also protects the weapon from the inroads of corrosive rust.

## Orthodox action

The Model 870 Mk 1 is a pump-action weapon with dual action bars and a tilting breech block that locks directly onto the barrel extension, and has a seven-round tubular magazine below the barrel. The barrel can be changed in a matter of minutes, and the weapon is used to fire a wide range of ammunition types ranging from light shot to flechettes. The gun has many 'extras', such as sling swivels, to meet the requirements of the US Marine Corps, and the holding bracket for the

magazine extension (added to increase the magazine's capacity) has a lug to mount a bayonet, which is exactly the same as that used on the M16 assault rifle. The ventilated hand-guard over the barrel and the rubber butt pads found on many civilian Model 870s are not fitted to the Model 870 Mk 1 as they were deemed unnecessary for a shotgun used in the combat role.

The US Marine Corps has used its Model 870 Mk 1 shotguns quite frequently since they were introduced.

***Such is the utility of the shotgun in the jungle that the British army made extensive use of the weapon in counter-terrorist operations in Malaya, both against Communists and during the Indonesian confrontation. The fully stocked Model 870 is one used in the Far East; the other is a folding stocked riot gun with extended magazine.***

The weapon is not one that is usually carried during large-scale amphibious operations, but the US Marines Corps has many other combat tasks including the creation and despatch of boarding parties during actions such as that carried out during the 'Mayaguez incident' of May 1975, when an American merchant ship was in effect 'cut out' of an anchorage near the Cambodian port of Sihanoukville after being detained illegally. The guns were used widely during the Vietnam War (often by SEAL teams) and are still in gainful service.

At one point there was a project to convert the Model 870 Mk 1 to accommodate a 10- or 20-round box magazine, with obvious tactical advantages, but the end of the Vietnam War terminated the scheme at the advanced development stage.

The Model 870 has also found favour with police, security and para-military organisations, who generally opt for a model with its magazine lengthened to take eight rounds, fixed or folding stocks with or without a pistol grip, a 551- or 709-mm (14- or 18-in) barrel with cylinder or improved cylinder chokes, rifle-type or ghost ring (peep) sights, tactical flashlight, laser aiming spit and provision for firing a number of non-lethal special-purpose rounds (including tear gas grenades and rubber bullets) as well as the more conventional lethal types such as buckshot and unitary slug.

**SPECIFICATION**

**Model 870 Mk 1**
**Calibre:** 12-gauge
**Length overall:** 1060 mm (41.73 in)
**Length of barrel:** 533 mm (21 in)
**Weight:** 3.6 kg (7.94 lb)
**Feed:** 7-round tubular magazine

# Advanced combat shotguns

Designed by Maxwell G. Atchisson in 1972, the **Atchisson Assault Shotgun** gas-assisted recoil-operated prototype paved the way for a new type of weapon, the assault (as opposed to combat) shotgun. Based on M16 rifle components, the Atchisson had about the same dimensions and configuration as the M16 rifle but was designed to fire buckshot or solid slug ammunition. Of simple design, its barrel screwed into a long, tubular receiver which housed the bolt and the recoil spring. A BAR M1918 trigger mechanism combined with the pistol grip of the Thompson submachine gun constituted the trigger assembly. The weapon was capable of semi-automatic and automatic fire, and fired from a five-round box or 20-round drum magazine.

***The Atchisson selective fire, 12-gauge assault shotgun. It features a gas-operated mechanism, a heavy bolt and interchangeable 20 round drum or 8 round box magazine.***

With the concept proved, Atchisson spent the period between 1973 and 1979 creating an improved version. The most obvious change was the enclosure of the entire mechanism in two clamshell stock halves. Production was undertaken in modest numbers from 1981 in the US and Korea, and in 1984 the standard was revised to include a bayonet mounting, and the non-slip patterning was omitted from the fore end of the clamshell. All the Atchisson weapons could fire NATO standard rifle grenades, and the magazine options were a seven-round single-row box magazine and a 20-round drum magazine.

## New generation

In the early 1980s the USA began the CAWS (Close Assault Weapon System) programme to develop a weapon able to fire high-impulse multiple projectiles to an effective range of 100-150 m (110-165 yards). One of the teams was Heckler & Koch and Winchester/Olin, the former responsible for the weapon and the latter for the ammunition.

***Long and short variants of the Heckler & Koch/Winchester CAW. The operation was short recoil with a cyclic full-automatic rate of 240 rounds per minute.***

The **Heckler & Koch CAW** emerged as a selective-fire smooth-bore weapon using high-pressure ammunition to fire tungsten shot and flechettes. The CAW was based on a gas-assisted recoil-operated action with a moving barrel, and in appearance was similar to the G11 assault rifle in its bullpup layout with an integral carrying handle. The cocking handle was located under the carrying handle, over the receiver, and was ambidextrous, and the safety/fire-selector's three positions were safe, semi-automatic and three-round burst. The CAW was tested by the US services, but then the whole CAWS programme was closed and development ceased.

**SPECIFICATIONS**

**Atchisson Assault Shotgun**
**Calibre:** 12-gauge
**Length overall:** 991 mm (39 in)
**Length of barrel:** not available
**Weight:** 5.45 kg (12 lb)
**Rate of fire, cyclic:** 360 rpm
**Feed:** 7-round tubular magazine

**Heckler & Koch CAW**
**Calibre:** 12-gauge
**Length overall:** 988 or 762 mm (38.9 or 30 in)
**Length of barrel:** 686 or 457 mm (27 or 18 in)
**Weight:** 3.86 kg (8.5 lb)
**Feed:** 10-round box magazine

# Riot control

**Riot control is an increasingly important mission for modern armies. In democratic countries, it is the right of every citizen to protest peacefully, but even in the best ordered societies, such gatherings can get out of hand and security forces are forced to intervene. It is only when the police are unable to cope with the scale of the violence – as happened in Northern Ireland in the late 1960s – that they are compelled to ask the military for help.**

*Troops with good training in riot-control techniques should generally seek to avoid direct contact with rioters, and also avoid the use of excessive violence that may exacerbate the situation.*

During a riot, troops or police must try to keep a reasonable distance between themselves and the crowd. This prevents the security forces from being outflanked or overwhelmed, and tempers tend to remain cooler if a distance between the two sides is maintained. However, these measures are not always possible.

When contact is unavoidable, the most common and simplest means of crowd control is the plain wooden baton or truncheon. Security forces will also have CS gas (the most commonly used type of gas) grenades, which can be thrown by hand or fired from a variety of anti-riot weapons, including shotguns, grenade launchers and conventional rifles.

Many of these weapons can also fire anti-riot projectiles of various sizes and lethality. Most commonly these are rubber or plastic 'bullets', designed to counter petrol bombers or stone-throwing crowds up to a range of about 60 m (65 yards). Intended to cause no more than bruising or shock, such rounds can be lethal when used at very close range. Baton rounds, as they are called, do have the advantage of being selective: if a youth is seen to be on the verge of hurling a petrol bomb, he can be targeted directly without any significant threat to possibly innocent bystanders on either side of him.

Gas, on the other hand, is indiscriminate. CS causes extreme discomfort to the eyes, nose and breathing passages, yet rarely has serious or lasting effects. Many armies in countries prone to riot use it freely, though in European countries it is normally used only in very serious disturbances.

Although it can be a very effective crowd disperser, CS can affect rioters, innocent bystanders and security forces alike. Crowds all over the world have learned that the wearing of wet handkerchiefs over the face combats the effect of the gas, and have learned to throw or kick the grenades back at the security forces.

## Riot vehicles

All over the world, a wide variety of wheeled vehicles have been adapted or manufactured specifically for riot control. They range from modified light commercial vehicles to fully equipped armoured personnel carriers.

Riot control vehicles provide protection and support. Vehicles often have large unfolding fenders on each side that provide troops with protection from thrown missiles and, if the vehicle is parked in the middle of a relatively narrow road flanked by buildings, can block most of the road off and prevent rioters from progressing further.

At the same time, the vehicle is a refuge for anyone who is injured, and it can house reliable radio communications. Other attachments may include roof- or turret-mounted searchlights, loudspeaker systems, cowcatchers for the removal of illegal street barricades and water cannon for dampening the enthusiasm of crowds. It is even possible to electrify the outer surface of such vehicles to prevent rioters from climbing on to them.

*Police and troops in riot-control equipment have a distinctly threatening appearance. However, they must try to avoid being provoked into excessive action by rioters, who see over-reaction by the authorities as a major propaganda victory.*

### Helicopters

Increasingly, helicopters are used to monitor crowds. This technique was widely used by the British army in Northern Ireland, and has been adopted by police forces all over the world. Police helicopters are generally fitted with video cameras, thermal imagers and powerful searchlights. Some have datalinks which allow live television pictures to be transmitted back to a headquarters on the ground, where the information can be evaluated and acted upon.

### A choice of tactics

Police forces around the world use varying degrees of force to disperse a riot. In some countries the army is automatically called out; elsewhere, the army is committed only as a last resort.

Many countries have formed special so-called 'third force' organisations, specifically to deal with riots and other public order problems: examples are the Compagnie Républicaine de Sécurité (CRS) in France, and the Bundesgrenzschütze, or Federal Border Guard, in Germany. The philosophy of the CRS is diametrically opposed to that of the British security forces or most US police forces. In France, maximum force is used at an early stage, to show rioters that the authorities mean business and to deter further misbehaviour. The CRS put down the May 1968 student riots in Paris ruthlessly.

The German police and other European forces tend to use much the same tactics. The British, however, use only the degree of force necessary to meet any given situation, relying on good intelligence, observation and communication to effect the channelling of a demonstration, only escalating their reaction as appropriate.

### Different perspectives

There are arguments in terms of pure efficiency for both approaches. The fierce reputation of the CRS must give any would-be rioter pause for thought. However, the more measured approach, while slower to resolve a difficult situation, offers the chance to control matters before too much damage or injury occurs.

When British troops were first sent to Northern Ireland, inexperienced soldiers often found themselves in the middle of riots. Initially, the frightened and confused young men reacted violently, but in 25 years of operations the army developed effective methods of dispersing crowds and cooling the situation.

Ideally, soldiers should never get involved in crowd or riot control, but history has shown that the police are not always able to cope. When that happens, soldiers are expected to act 'in support of the civil power', i.e. the police. It is often an unpleasant business, but it is one that the modern soldier must expect to encounter and cope with.

*Above: Water cannon are an excellent 'weapon' with which to cool the ardour of rioters, both literally and metaphorically. The force of a cannon's jet can knock a man flat and drive him along the road.*

*Below: There are several types of specialist riot-control munitions, one of the most common being the baton round. This is designed to inflict a severe, bruising blow, but can sometimes be lethal.*

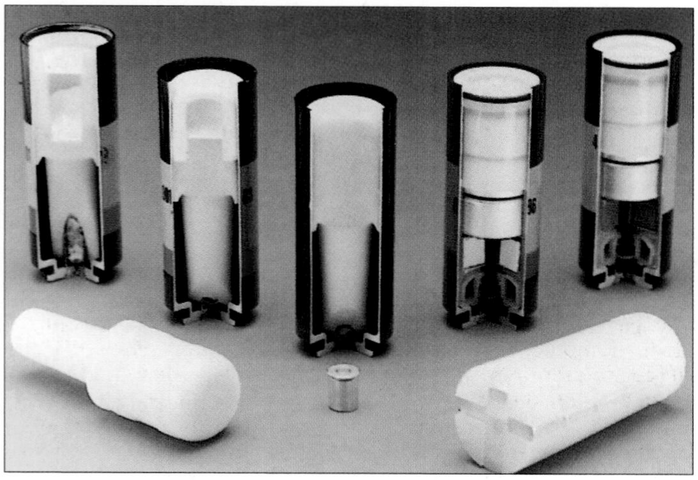

## SUCCESSFUL RIOT CONTROL

Before taking part in riot control operations, all troops involved must be clearly briefed on:

1. The background of the situation and the specific mission of their unit.

2. The rules governing the application of force.

3. The psychological aspects of the local situation, e.g. the types of response likely from the local population and the proper counter to these responses.

4. Identification to be used by the news media representatives and civil officials.

*Armoured vehicles with side screens are very useful in channelling or halting the movement of rioters, but the appearance of troops with conventional firearms often indicates the descent of a mass demonstration into a violent riot.*

# Non-lethal weapons

In riot and crowd-control operations, the task of the security and police forces involved is to bring the situation under control with the minimum use of force, without fatalities and preferably without injuries. This dictates the use of special 'weapons' that fall into two basic categories: less-than-lethal and non-lethal. The less-than-lethal weapon is designed to minimise the chances of any fatalities, and include projectile weapons firing bean bag, rubber bullet and sticky foam projectiles, while the non-lethal weapon is designed to incapacitate without causing fatalities, injuries and aftereffects. The primary occasions for the use of non-lethal weapons, other than riots and major disturbances, include close-quarter operations (generally of a small size such as bar and domestic situations), the halting of a fleeing person, the immobilisation of persons involved in hostage situations and barricade situations without hostages.

***The FN 303 is a weapon to fire a considerable assortment of non-lethal projectiles to long range. The weapon is powered by compressed air in a cylinder attached to the right-hand side of the weapon alongside the barrel.***

***The FN 303 is aimed and fired in much the same way as a conventional firearm, and its ammunition drawn from a 15-round magazine located just to the rear of the fore grip***

***The FN 303 is also produced in a form that can be attached to most types of modern assault rifle, such as the M16 illustrated here.***

## Bean bag round

The **bean bag round**, which is effective to a range of some 15 m (50 ft) but is notably inaccurate, comprises plastic beans in a flexible nylon bag, and is fired at some 280 m (919 ft) per second to strike the target person with great force. For this reason, at firing ranges of less than 6 m (20 ft), the firer should not aim at the target figure's head, neck and areas containing the spleen, liver and kidneys. The same strictures apply to the use of rubber and plastic bullets.

Much the same capability is provided by special hand-thrown grenades such as the **Hornet's Nest Sting Grenade** from Ramo Defense. This combines the concussive effect of a low-power explosive charge and the painful impact of hard rubber balls. The grenade typically carries a load of 60 0.45-in (11.4-mm) or 15 0.69-in (17.5-mm) rubber balls, which fly out from the explosion in a 360-degree pattern out to an effective radius of between 2.1 and 7.6 m (7 and 25 ft).

***The TRGG is a crowd-control 'weapon' that has been in service with the German civil security forces for some time, and is a projector that fires irritant or marker agents.***

## Rubber disc round

Another round of the same basic concept, designed to be fired from a special launcher attached to the muzzle of an M16 assault rifle, is the **Sting-RAG**. This is a pliable ring of soft rubber some 6.35 cm (2.5 in) in diameter, and on firing rotates at 2,500 revolutions per minute to strike its target at about 60 m (200 ft) per second at a range of 60 m (200 ft). The Sting-RAG's accuracy is highly susceptible to wind effects, and the round is rendered generally ineffective if the target is wearing thick clothing. The round can also damage the eyes. Basically similar rounds also fired from a rifle include small water balloon and 'splat' rounds.

## Pellet launcher

Developed by Fabrique Nationale in Belgium, the **FN 303** is a semi-automatic system worked by compressed air and designed to fire a wide assortment of 12-gauge impact, marking, malodorant and illuminating projectiles each weighing in the order of 8 g (0.28 oz). The FN 303 'gun' possesses a very futuristic appearance, and is the core of a long-range system created specifically to provide good capabilities against individuals as well as crowds. The 'gun' is available as a stand-alone weapon or in a form allowing it to be attached under the barrel of most modern assault rifles.

Another type of restraint, developed by the Sandia National Laboratory in Albuquerque, New Mexico, is a **sticky foam** dispensed from a special sling-carried container and so sticky that it can stop a target in its tracks. The two primary disadvantages of this sticky foam are its potential for killing the target should it cover the mouth and nose, thereby causing suffocation, and the fact that while the foam itself is non-toxic, all the known solvents to free the target person are potentially toxic. The alternative to a solvent is to cut the foam free with scissors.

## Irritant-filled sphere

Another American development, now widely used by police forces, is the **PepperBall**, created, made and marketed by PepperBall Technologies Inc. Delivered from a special launcher of the semi-automatic type using compressed air as its power source, the PepperBall is a hard plastic sphere that bursts on impact, which is itself sufficient to hinder the target.

The bursting sphere releases a quantity of pharmaceutical-grade PAVA (capsicum II) powder, a strong irritant that affects the target's eyes, nose, throat and lungs, rendering him or her incapable of anything but trying to breathe.

### Irritant sprayer

A notable non-lethal weapon, in this instance created by the Heckler & Koch company of Germany, is the **TRGG** portable irritant agent projector, which in configuration resembles a flamethrower: it is carried on a backpack bearing flamethrower-type tanks, and the operator aims and fires the irritant agent using a hand-held projector that looks very like a flamethrower gun. In fact the analogy is quite close, but the TRGG is designed to project an irritant agent instead of a gout of flame.

The backpack of the TRGG has two tanks: one contains the agent and the other a pressurising gas, usually carbon dioxide. When the operator pulls a trigger on the projector, the pressurised gas forces out the agent from its tanks and along a flexible tube leading to the projector. The agent concerned can be any one of a number of types ranging from tear gas to CS. The weapon can also project powerful dyes to mark rioters for later seizure.

The TRGG has a maximum operational range of 20 m (22 yards), and the contents of the tanks are sufficient for about 80 jets of agent, each jet usually being monitored on an automatic basis to prevent waste or excessive concentrations of agent. When refills are required, the tanks can be changed easily and within a time of just a few seconds without recourse to tools. This is usually done by a person other than the operator, who would otherwise have to remove the carrying frame for reloading.

Riot-control devices such as the TRGG are not favoured by some police and para-military forces. The very appearance of the TRGG is distinctive and makes it and its user a target for possible retaliation, while the weight of the equipment is sufficiently great to make it impossible for the operator to move very rapidly should circumstances demand it.

The device also has a relatively restricted range. The 20 m mentioned above may not be achieved against even a slight headwind, and at longer ranges the irritant agent can be dispersed to such an extent that it may have little effect on determined rioters. At closer ranges, however, it is a formidable deterrent. But again, at these short ranges the TRGG requires a considerable degree of protective support and many police or para-military forces might not think that it deserves such an outlay of manpower. To date the TRGG has seen little use outside Germany, although organisations elsewhere have looked into its possibilities.

***One of the longest-established and most effective non-lethal weapons for crowd control is the water cannon. The 'fire' from such a vehicle generally knocks down pedestrians and cools their ardour.***

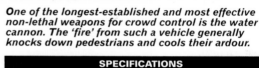

**SPECIFICATIONS**

| | |
|---|---|
| **FN 303** | |
| **Calibre:** | 12-gauge |
| **Length overall:** | 740 mm (29.13 in) for the stand-alone model and 425 mm (16.7 in) for the under-barrel model |
| **Weight:** | 2.3 kg (5.1 lb) for the stand-alone model and 2.2 kg (4.85 lb) for the under-barrel model |
| **Propellant capacity:** | sufficient for about 65 shots |
| **Feed:** | 15-round magazine |
| **Effective range:** | 100 m (110 yards) |
| **TRGG** | |
| **Weight:** | empty 10.5 kg (23.15 lb) and full 20.5 kg (45.2 lb) |
| **Propellant capacity:** | sufficient for about 80 jets |
| **Maximum range:** | about 20 m (22 yards) |

### Flash-Ball

Produced by Verney-Carron, a leading French manufacturer of hunting weapons, the **Flash-Ball** generates the stopping power of a 0.38-in Special bullet. Even at short range the projectile does not penetrate clothing, but nonetheless effectively knocks out the target. This major advantage has been proved in action by security forces already using the weapon. The Flash-Ball launcher itself looks threatening, is capable of being brought into action rapidly and is available in single- and double-barrelled forms. The weapon is light in weight yet robust, and is adaptable to all situations requiring the use of non-lethal force.

The items mentioned above are typical of the modern generation of non-lethal and less-than-lethal weapons for the control of riots and major disturbances at the upper end of the scale, and single individuals at its lower end. The lethality of these weapons is low, but from the later part of the 20th century there has been considerable public and political pressure, largely as a result of the growing incidence of crowd disorder, for the creation of still safer weapons. An experimental development by the US Air Force Research Laboratory, is an '**active-denial technology**' weapon that operates by discharging micro-millimetre waves that penetrate the target's skin to raise the temperature of the flesh below it by a few dozen degrees and thereby cause extreme pain without actually inflicting a burn.

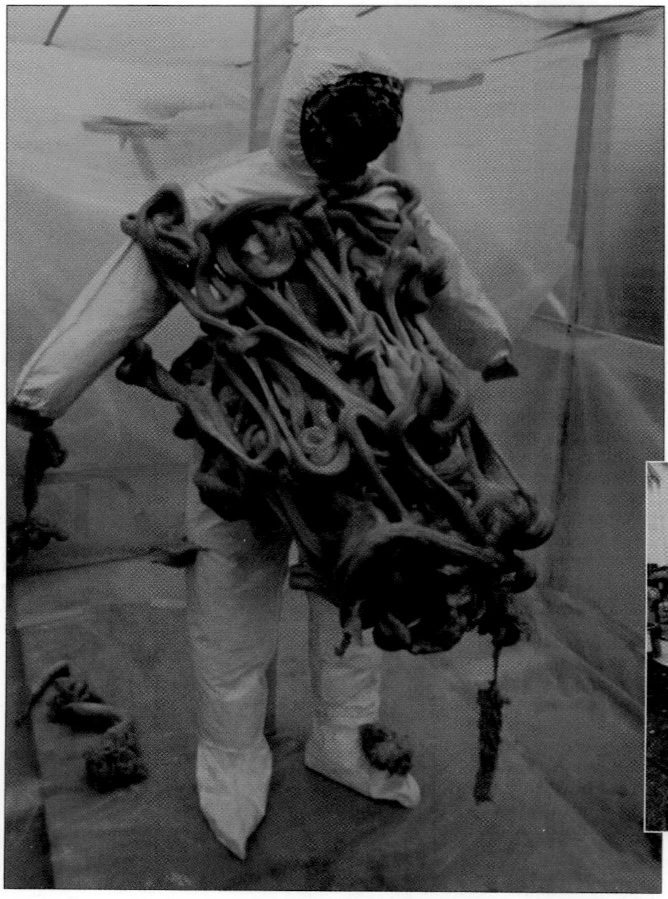

***The programme to develop sticky foam at the Sandia National Laboratory was sponsored by the US National Institute for Justice as a means of restraining subjects until handcuffs could be be applied. The foam is then cut off.***

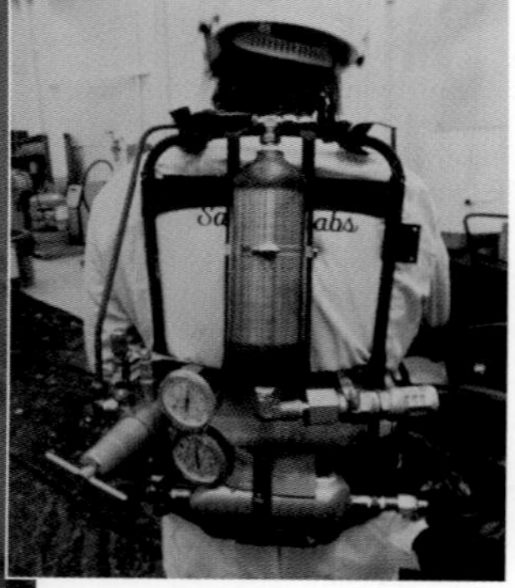

***Sticky foam is dispensed from a back-pack arrangement carrying pressurised gas and the foam agent. The system's range is not great, so sticky foam is best employed inside buildings rather than in the open.***

# Riot control vehicles

The use of APCs on urban streets leads invariably to 'tanks quell riot' headlines in the media, and thus a spate of public unease. Moreover, both tracked and wheeled APCs are very expensive to maintain and not optimised for internal security (IS) operations. It was this and other reasons that persuaded the British army to retain obsolete wheeled APCs for use in Northern Ireland, and wheeled APC manufacturers also offer specialised IS variants of battlefield vehicles.

For a variety of reasons tracked APCs are not suited to the IS role, so many companies have designed wheeled vehicles for use in IS operations. The hull of such vehicles must provide protection against attack with 7.62-mm (0.3-in) rifle projectiles. In some countries the terrorist's most commonly employed weapon is the mine, often laid in culverts under roads in remoter areas and intended for detonation when a military or para-military vehicle runs over it. If the mine is a standard anti-personnel mine or small anti tank mine, the vehicle designer can help to minimise the amount of damage inflicted on the vehicle by careful design of the hull armour. The design ensures that the blast is deflected sideways and upward, and thus not contained under the hull of the vehicle, which would lead to the vehicle being lifted and turned over, or alternatively to having its lower surface penetrated by the blast. For example, the British **Saxon** vehicle has an integral hull with the areas above the wheels manufactured of sheet steel so that they blow off should a mine detonate under the vehicle. The South African **Rhino** and **Bulldog** have a V-shaped lower hull raised well above the wheels so that if the vehicle runs over a mine it is the wheels and suspension that take the blast.

***Many wheeled APCs serve in the IS role with various degrees of modification. The Vickers Valkyr can carry a wide variety of equipment for this task, including a barricade removal device, smoke grenade launchers and tear gas bottles as well as the men's equipment.***

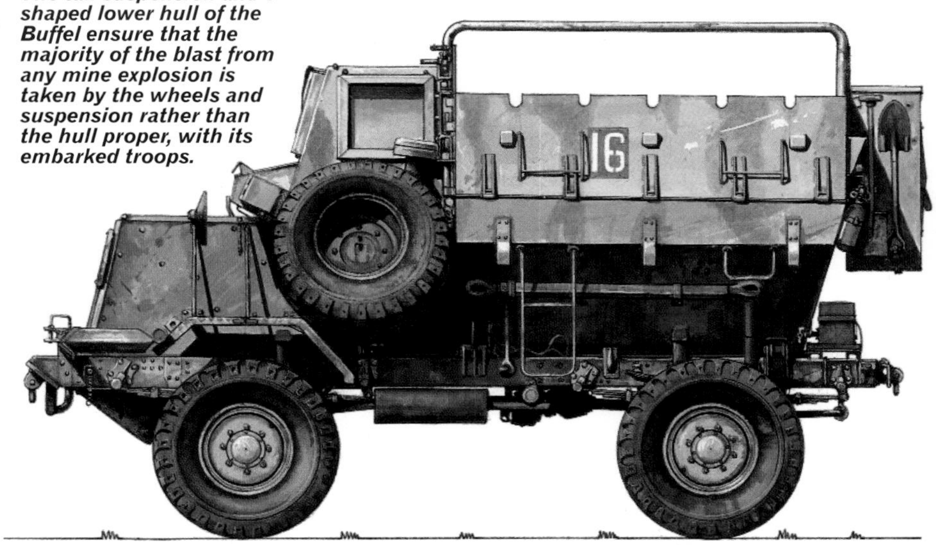


***The tall suspension and V-shaped lower hull of the Buffel ensure that the majority of the blast from any mine explosion is taken by the wheels and suspension rather than the hull proper, with its embarked troops.***

## Preference for diesel

The designers and users of IS vehicles prefer diesel engines to petrol engines because diesel fuel is of lower volatility than petrol and therefore does not catch fire as easily. The commander, driver and troops must have all-round fields of vision through windows providing the same degree of protection as the rest of the hull. The commander's and driver's windows must have wipers and a reservoir of special cleaning liquids to ensure that paint thrown by demonstrators is removed speedily.

The means of entry and exit must be as numerous and large as possible. If the main door is at the rear and the vehicle is ambushed from the rear, for example, the occupants cannot leave the vehicle in safety unless they also have access to side doors. Moreover, the doors and handles must be designed so that unauthorised entry is not possible, and there should be no external fittings that rioters could use to help them climb onto the vehicle.

The tyres must be of the run-flat type to enable the vehicle to be driven some distance after the tyres have been damaged by bullets. The vehicle should also have a fire detection and suppression system, especially around the wheel arches as rioters often throw petrol bombs at any IS vehicle's rubber tyres. The roof must be sloped so that grenades roll off before exploding. The openings around the doors and the engine compartment must be carefully designed so that any flaming liquid from petrol bombs runs down to the ground and not into the vehicle.

***The Buffel is one of South Africa's increasing range of home-produced military vehicles, and its design reflects South African combat experience both at home and in operations in Namibia and Angola.***

## Creature comforts

As the troops or police may have to stay inside the vehicle for considerable periods, the interior must be insulated and provided with a heating/cooling system. The seats must have belts because if the vehicle does run over a mine, many of the casualties could result from occupants being thrown around the vehicle's interior. Adequate stowage space must be provided for riot shields, weapons and other essential equipment.

***The Vickers Valkyr can serve in a variety of roles from APC to weapons carrier, command post, ambulance and internal security vehicle. The last is becoming a standard variant to wheeled personnel carriers, which are costlier and less effective in the IS task.***

**SPECIFICATION**

**Alvis OMC Casspir Mk III**
**Crew:** 2+10
**Weight:** 12.58 tonnes
**Dimensions:** length 6.87 m (22 ft 6½ in); width 2.45 m (8 ft ½ in); height 3.125 m (10 ft 3 in)
**Powerplant:** one ADE-352T liquid-cooled 6-cylinder diesel developing 127 kW (170 hp)
**Performance:** maximum road speed 90 km/h (56 mph); maximum road range 850 km (528 miles); fording 1 m (3 ft 3¾ in); gradient 65 per cent; vertical obstacle 0.5 m (1 ft 7½ in); trench 1.06 m (3 ft 5¾ in)
**Armament:** between one and three 7.62-mm (0.3-in) machine-guns

Some IS vehicles are fitted with turret-mounted 12.7- or 7.62-mm (0.5- or 0.3-in) machine-guns, while others have a simple armoured observation cupola for the commander. Specialised equipment such as a barricade remover at the front of the vehicle is standard on some vehicles, while others have provision to be outfitted as command post vehicles or ambulances. The type can also be used to carry EOD (explosive ordnance disposal) teams and their equipment, and it is common for IS vehicles to carry water cannon or gas grenade launchers.

Some countries use standard military wheeled APCs for the IS role while others prefer to operate cheaper vehicles based on standard light truck chassis such as those from Mercedes-Benz and Land Rover.

***The Transaif multi-role internal security vehicle, which appeared in 1985, offers most of the abilities of a military APC, but at a much more modest cost.***

***The AT 105 Saxon, procured by the British army, is a type that has also been bought by other countries for the para-military role. These are Saxon vehicles in Malaysian service.***

## APCs for the IS role

Some wheeled APCs are used in an internal security role. These include the **MOWAG Roland**, **MR 8** and **Piranha** ranges of 4x4, 6x6 and 8x8 vehicles, AV **Technology Dragoon**, **Cadillac Gage Commando** family and **Commando Ranger**, **Humber 'Pig'**, **Alvis Saracen**, **GKN Sankey AT 105 Saxon**, **ENGESA EE-11 Urutu**, **SIBMAS**, **Vickers Defence Systems/BDX Valkyr**, **Fiat Tipo 6614**, **Renault VAB**, **Berliet VXB-170**, **Panhard VCR** and **MS**, **ACMAT**, **BMR-600** and **BLR-600**, **Ratel**, **Transportpanzer**, **Condor** and Soviet **BTR** series.

IS vehicles based on a Mercedes-Benz chassis from Germany include the **UR-416** delivered from 1969, and also the more recent **TM 170** and **TM 125**. Since 1965 Shorts of Northern Ireland has built very substantial numbers of its **Shorland** armoured patrol car, and 1974 introduced the **Shorland SB 401**. Hotspur of Wales has also developed APCs in 4x4 and 6x6 configurations on the Land Rover chassis.

The Fiat 11A7 A Campagnola 4x4 light vehicle is used by many countries, so the Advanced Security Agency SpA of Milan developed the **Guardian** range of 4x4 IS and now offers such vehicles on the original Fiat chassis and also on those of the Land Rover One Ten and Mercedes-Benz 280 GE.

In addition to making the Piranha range of 4x4 and 6x6 vehicles under licence, Chile also builds the **VTP 2** which is similar in some respects to the German Thyssen IS vehicle, and the **Multi 163** APC that is also used to patrol airports and other high-risk areas. The Bravia company of Portugal has built the **Chaimite** range of 4x4 APCs in variants almost identical to the V-100 family by Cadillac Gage, which has built for the US Army National Guard the **Commando Mk III** APC that is similar in basic concept to the Shorland vehicles, although somewhat larger.

While Western countries have, over the years, developed many types of vehicle suitable for use in IS operations, up to the time of its collapse the Warsaw Pact countries in general and the USSR in particular did not develop vehicles specifically for this role.

Events in Afghanistan then revealed that the BTR-60 and BTR-70 series of 8x8 APCs suffered from a number of drawbacks in the IS role. Some of the vehicles were fitted with additional armour protection and more firepower, including an AGS 17 grenade launcher.

Some time ago East Germany built two types of vehicles for IS operations in the form of the **SK-1** armoured car and the **SK-2** armoured water cannon. The SK-1 was armed with a turret-mounted machine-gun. The SK-2 armoured water cannon was built on the chassis of the G5 6x6 truck, and on its roof to the rear of the cab had a high-pressure water cannon.

***A Buffel heads purposefully into the terrain for which it was designed. Although APCs can often double as internal security vehicles, the reverse is not often the case. As with all military procurement, 'you pays your money and you takes your choice'.***

***An interior view of the Transaif shows the good visibility through armoured glass. A monitor on the dashboard allows the driver to see what is behind the vehicle.***

***On patrol in Northern Ireland with a Humber 1-ton APC. Five hundred 'Pigs' were retained by the British army as IS vehicles.***

# Riot control grenades

***Theoretically, baton rounds should not be fired at individuals at close range, but the new generation of riot-control weapons offers the accuracy to make this feasible should it prove necessary.***

Riot-control grenades take two basic forms, chemical and kinetic. Chemical grenades are designed to emit fumes that irritate or disable to the extent that they prevent persons from carrying out a chosen course of action, i.e. they quell rioters. The primary requirement demanded of such agents is that they irritate or disable, but also that they do no permanent damage.

For many years the chosen irritant agent in riot control was tear gas, a relatively harmless substance that does little more than bring tears to the eyes and impart a general feeling of choking and helplessness. Tear gas is now generally known as CN, but its proper chemical name is alpha-chloroacetophenone.

## Easily dispersed

The most significant failing of tear gas, soon discovered once it had entered service as a riot-control agent, was found to be that in open areas its vapour cloud generally dispersed so readily and so quickly that the tear gas mist easily lost its disabling properties. Tear gas was also relatively easy to tolerate, especially after some experience of the substance, and many fit young people could therefore carry on their disorderly activities after exposure to CN with only a minimum of inconvenience.

Inside a building it was often another matter entirely as the walls, roof and floor of the building helped to contain the tear gas mist at a concentration that was still incapacitating, but in the open tear gas was soon seen to be relatively inefficient in its primary task as an anti-riot weapon.

During the early 1950s, therefore, a new and more effective and persistent agent was demanded as a successor to tear gas. This led to the suggestion that a new chemical, rejoicing in the chemical name of orthochlorobenzalmalononitrile, be employed as an alternative to tear gas with superior disabling capabilities. It was not long before this new substance was given the handier appellation CS.

CS is normally a solid substance, but on contact with air forms a white or light grey vapour cloud with a general odour of pepper, and for this reason CS is sometimes known as pepper gas. The vapour can induce the usual tears, but with the addition of a general choking sensation and a difficulty in breathing. The effect is distinctly unpleasant, and experience has revealed that high concentrations of CS can cause nausea and vomiting. To add to its effects, CS can be persistent, especially if vapour droplets adhere to clothing. CS is not totally disabling, however, and there are no long-term physical effects.

CS was first used during the late 1950s, and was soon found to be a remarkably efficient method of breaking up mobs.

At first the prime method of delivering the agent was the hand grenade, in exactly the same fashion that had been used previously for tear gas and smoke. While these grenades were easy to manufacture and use, they suffered from the same drawbacks as the earlier grenades: it took time for the vapour cloud to build up, range was limited by the strength of the thrower (who thereby came well into missile range of the offending crowd), and the grenades could readily be picked up by an adventurous rioter and thrown back. A redesign of the basic CS grenade has therefore taken place.

## New grenade design

Modern CS grenades nearly all contain small multiple containers or pellets to emit the CS fumes. As it lands, the grenade body scatters these small containers or pellets (the British L11A1 grenade releases 23 pellets, for example) over a wide

***The US Marines Corps provides security for US embassies around the world, and must be able to defend them against hostile crowds without immediate recourse to firearms. Seen here in Manila, this Marine has a projector for tear gas grenades attached to his Remington 870 shotgun.***

area, and the emission period is usually short so that any container or pellet thrown back by a rioter has little or no effect. The other design point is that it is now very rare for CS grenades to be thrown, for they are generally projected using a small propellant charge from a launcher to a range of 100 m (110 yards) or more, the launcher usually being some type of riot gun. When riot guns are used, the usual diameter of the grenade is 37-mm (1.456-in), but this is now generally regarded as being too small and the British army has opted for a grenade diameter of 66-mm (2.6-in) and uses a specialised launcher, the Grenade Discharger L1A1, rather than a riot gun to fire the grenade.

CS is not the only modern form of irritant agent, but it is certainly the type that is most widely used. Other irritant agents include mild hallucinogenic agents that impart a temporary feeling of panic or fear, but the use of such agents is disapproved by many on humanitarian grounds, and such weapons may thus be of the double-edged type, generating adverse publicity of more significance than any real advantage gained in basic riot-control terms. Moreover, some of these 'mind' agents have a nasty habit of being just as effective on their users as on their intended targets, even when a respirator is being used. Most police and paramilitary respirators are limited in their effectiveness, providing protection only against CS and CN, and some powerful modern agents could overcome the protective properties of such equipment.

## Kinetic grenades

Humanitarian considerations also come to the fore when kinetic grenades are considered. These are usually the baton rounds or the infamous 'rubber bullets' that are used to disable by stunning. Kinetic projectiles of this type were first mooted during the 1950s, when it started to become clear to authorities in several countries that the last-ditch but yet effective control of riots demanded not conventional firearms, whose use would lead to severe wounds and deaths, and therefore to a mass of adverse publicity, but rather something that was more powerful than the standard irritant agents in use at that time. At first disabling missiles of several types were considered, these ranging from lead shot in thick bags to heavy rubber rings. Such munitions were usually fired from ordinary riot guns, but it was not long before the baton round in its present form appeared. At first wooden projectiles were used, but these were soon discarded as they were prone to splintering and causing the type of nasty wounds that drew adverse publicity. Then for some time rubber was used before it was discovered that under certain circumstances rubber was also likely to cause injuries that were too severe.

The current baton rounds are flat-ended PVC slugs that are not as heavy as rubber but are nonetheless likely to impart a powerful blow on the recipient.

## Occasional lethality

It cannot be denied that baton rounds can and indeed do cause serious injuries if used at very close ranges, and have also caused a number of deaths. They are also very inaccurate and often have to be used as area weapons rather than as point target weapons. But rounds of this type can prove effective in breaking up hostile crowds, and when used with extreme care they can even disable ringleaders of a riot or other troublesome individuals. They can certainly keep crowds out of hand-thrown missile range. Despite this, the use of baton rounds has often resulted in a great public outcry against their employment. But in the absence of anything better the baton round is an established anti-riot munition.

***Above: The Hilton multi-purpose gun can fire an impressive variety of projectiles ranging from gas shells to single and multiple baton rounds.***

***Right: A police officer in Washington, DC, during the 1970s carries a riot gun with reload rounds from the satchel stuffed into his shirt front.***

***Right: The Fabrique Nationale company of Belgium has produced this grenade-launcher to fit on to the FNC 5.56-mm (0.256-in) light assault rifle or, fitted with a stock, to be used as a weapon in its own right.***

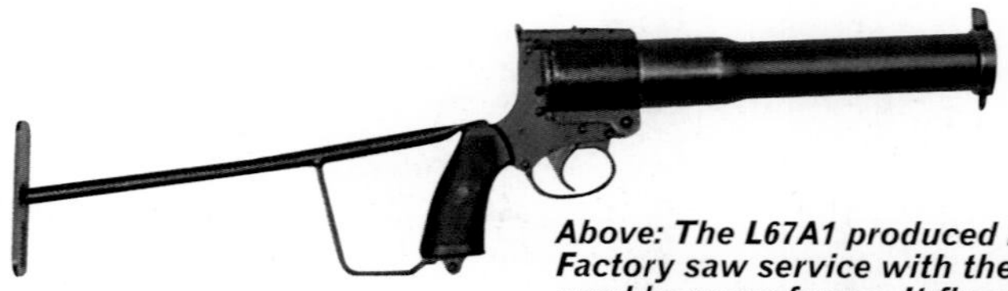

***Above: The L67A1 produced by the Royal Ordnance Factory saw service with the British army and is still used by some forces. It fires the L18A1 CS gas round, which holds four gas pellets designed to burst 6 m (20 ft) above the ground so that members of the crowd cannot pick up the gas canister and throw it back.***

# Arwen Riot-control weapon

The **Arwen** (Anti-Riot Weapon Enfield) is something of an innovation and certainly an advanced design in comparison with many contemporaries. It is a very sophisticated piece of engineering that can perhaps be called a weapon system, as it is a riot munition launcher allied to a novel range of ammunition. It was developed by the Small Arms division of Royal Ordnance at Enfield Lock in Middlesex.

The Arwen has a calibre of 37-mm (1.456-in) and may be considered as two tubes joined together by a rotary magazine. The rear tube holds a butt plate and can be adjusted telescopically to suit the firer. The rear tube is joined to a firing mechanism, complete with pistol grip, while the forward tube is the barrel with its corrugated cooling profile. The barrel is fitted with a foregrip, also adjustable in position to suit the firer. Between these sections is the five-round rotary magazine. The firing mechanism is simple and controlled by the trigger. Pulling the trigger rotates the magazine until a round is in line with the chamber, and further trigger pressure then fires the round. Leaf sights are provided, for the Arwen is more accurate than most weapons of its type.

## Ammunition options

Five types of round can be fired from the Arwen, although not all may be encountered operationally. The main anti-riot munition is a baton round with a mushroom-shaped head that provides the PVC projectile with a good ballistic trajectory, allowing deliberate aim at point targets to be made. The other rounds that have been developed include a CS round, a screening smoke round, a baton round with a CS element and a round that fires a projectile to penetrate thin barricades while carrying some form of irritant agent. The main design point regarding all these rounds is that their aluminium cases act as their own firing chambers. At the instant of firing each round has it own internal charge and is fired with support provided by sprockets at the front and rear of the rotary magazine – the rest of the case is quite unsupported as only relatively small propellant charges are used.

## Good rate of fire

The Arwen can be fired with accuracy up to a range of about 100 m (110 yards) using the baton round. The usual rate of fire, including ejection of spent cases and reloading through a rim on the right-hand side of the magazine, is about 12 rounds per minute. These two factors make the Arwen a formidable anti-riot weapon. It has been purchased by many police and security forces, especially in North America, where it is now a favoured weapon for guards in maximum-security penal establishments.

**SPECIFICATION**

**Arwen**
**Calibre:** 37-mm (1.456-in)
**Length:** adjustable from 760 to 840 mm (29.9 to 33 in)
**Weight:** empty 3.1 kg (6.83 lb); loaded 3.8 kg (8.36 lb)
**Feed:** 5-round rotary magazine
**Typical range:** baton round 100 m (110 yards)

***Above: This 37-mm (1.456-in) XL77 automatic weapon was one of the prototype designs made and tested at the Royal Ordnance Factory at Enfield.***

***Above: The Arwen is one of the most advanced and capable riot-control weapons in service anywhere in the world, and offers a high rate of fire as well as considerable accuracy with several types of ammunition.***

***Below: Another prototype leading to the Arwen was this pump-action shotgun with a notably threatening appearance and also an action of menacing sound.***

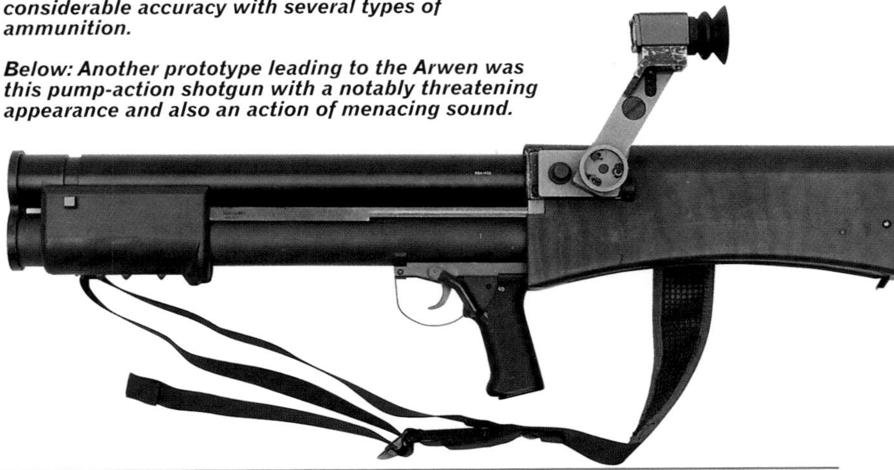

# Schermuly Multi-purpose gun

The **Schermuly Multi-Purpose Gun** is a single-shot weapon with a calibre of 37-mm (1.456-in) to enable it to fire a wide range of anti-riot and other munitions, thereby warranting its multi-purpose designation. The weapon can fire all manner of baton, smoke, irritant agent and other rounds of the right calibre, and can be fitted with an adapter to fire 12-gauge shotgun cartridges.

The Schermuly gun is manufactured by Webley and Scott but marketed by Schermuly. The basis of the weapon is a signal pistol, essentially a much-updated version of a World War II design that now makes use of high-tensile aluminium alloys for greater strength in combination with lower weight. As such, the gun may be regarded as an enlarged version of the signal pistol adapted with a wooden butt, a long smooth-bore barrel and a foregrip. Loading is based on the conventional shotgun break-open system, and there is a large interlock device over the chamber to ensure the barrel is securely locked for firing, which ensures that the weapon cannot be fired unless closed properly. The double-action trigger demands a long and firm pull to ensure it does not go off accidentally, and there is also an automatic rebound device in the striker mechanism to

***Riot guns tend to be fired like shotguns, i.e. from a standing posture, and for this reason the Schermuly was deliberately designed to handle like a shotgun. The hardwood butt attached to the pistol grip assembly also mounts the back sight.***

**SPECIFICATION**

**Schermuly multi-purpose gun**
**Calibre:** 37-mm (1.456-in)
**Length overall:** 828 mm (32.6 in)
**Weight:** 3.18 kg (7 lb)
**Typical range:** up to 150 m (165 yards)

prevent the accidental discharge of the weapon should it be dropped when loaded.

### Shotgun feel

As noted above, the Schermuly Multi-Purpose Gun makes extensive use of aluminium (including high-grade aluminium castings) in its construction to keep down weight, but the result is a quality weapon that has been deliberately designed to have the feel of an expensive shotgun, though it is arguable that the shotgun analogy is spoiled somewhat by the fact that leaf sights are fitted and a foregrip is provided under the barrel. Various barrel lengths can be produced, but one special feature of the Schermuly is that it can be fitted on the machine-gun weapon mounts of many armoured vehicles used in the internal security role, such as the Saracen armoured personnel carrier and the Shorland armoured car. Anti-riot guns can often be of very much more use than machine-guns in internal security operations, so this capability provides the Schermuly gun with a valuable 'extra'. As mentioned above, the Schermuly gun can fire a wide range of munition types. It fires not only the usual British army rounds, but also many commercial products manufactured for a wider market. Schermuly is also known as Pains-Wessex, so it is not surprising that the company also makes anti-riot munitions to go with its gun. Available are irritant agent and other rounds, some of which are used by the British army, which has also made use of the Schermuly gun.

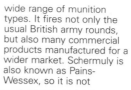

***Right: The Schermuly is made of light alloy, and different barrels and calibres are possible. The foregrip helps the firer to achieve accuracy and keeps his hand away from a hot barrel; it is also adjustable.***

***Far right: The Schermuly gun is made by Webley and Scott. It fires 37-mm (1.45-in) projectiles to a maximum range of 150 m (165 yards) and can be fitted to the machine-gun mounts on vehicles such as the Saracen APC.***

# MM-1 Multi-round projectile launcher

The **MM-1 Multi-Round Projectile Launcher** is one of a recent breed of anti-riot weapons that uses a rotary magazine to hold a number of anti-riot rounds ready to fire: in the case of MM-1 this magazine holds 12 rounds. The MM-1 has been designed for situations where a single anti-riot round would be inadequate. In the face of a mob rushing directly at a firer, a single round is often insufficient to deter everyone in the mob, and the firer can easily be overwhelmed.

With the MM-1 this is far less likely to happen. Using the MM-1 it is possible to fire 12 rounds in as few as six seconds, something that might make even the most determined mob have second thoughts. The rounds are held in 12 chambers on a rotating plate; as each round is fired a spring mechanism brings the next chamber into line with the barrel, ready for another pull of the trigger. The MM-1 has no butt, being held by the firer by a foregrip and a pistol grip behind the large and bulky magazine. After each loading the chamber plate is wound up by turning it in a counter-clockwise direction to tension its rotary spring mechanism.

The MM-1 can fire either 37-mm (1.456-in) or 40-mm (1.575-in) anti-riot munitions of all kinds, and adaptors can be fitted to allow the weapon to fire conventional shotgun cartridges. Flares can also be fired. The maximum range is about 120 m (130 yards), but this capability is less important to most users than the shock effect of a number of rounds being fired in rapid succession.

This is not the only advantage of the MM-1, for with this weapon one man can lay down a wide CS or smokescreen from a range of over 100 m (110 yards). This fact has been fully appreciated by many police and special forces in the Middle East, the USA, Europe and Africa, and the MM-1 is now a widely used weapon. The only problems that arise with this capable weapon are its bulk and the time its takes to reload the feed arrangement. The MM-1 is produced by Hawk Engineering, Inc. of Northfield in the state of Illinois.

***The MM-1 is not a light piece of kit, but offers a number of advantages over more conventional designs. One man can lay a large smokescreen or generate a big cloud of CS gas amongst a crowd from outside the range of hand-thrown missiles.***

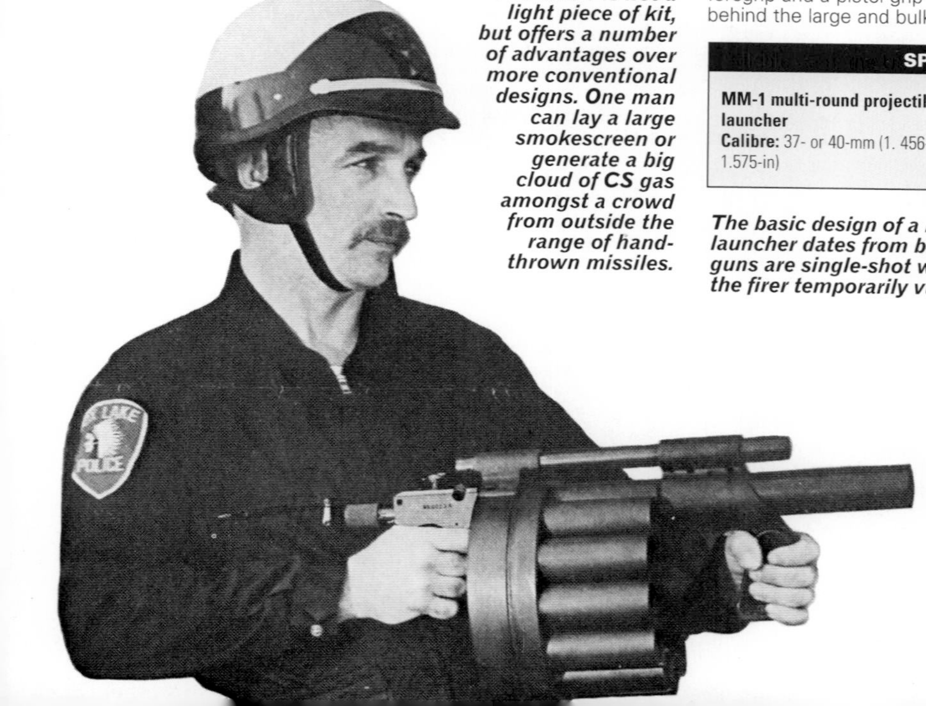

**SPECIFICATION**

| | |
|---|---|
| **MM-1 multi-round projectile launcher** | **Length overall:** 546 mm (21.5 in) |
| **Calibre:** 37- or 40-mm (1. 456- or 1.575-in) | **Weight:** loaded 9 kg (19.84 lb) |
| | **Feed:** 12-round revolver cylinder |
| | **Typical range:** 120 m (130 yards) |

***The basic design of a rotary-magazine grenade-launcher dates from before World War II. Most anti-riot guns are single-shot weapons, which obviously render the firer temporarily vulnerable while he reloads.***

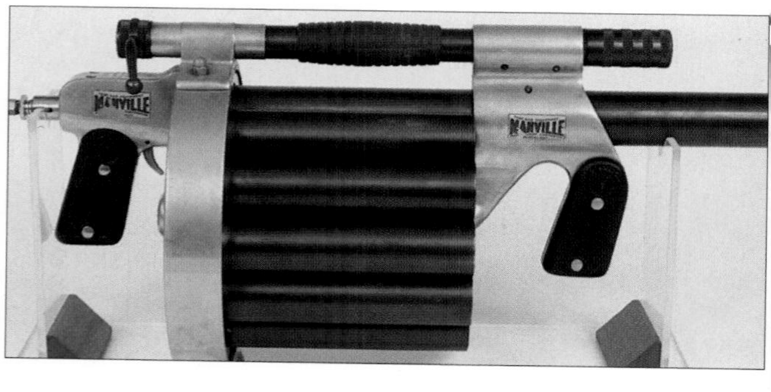

# Smith & Wesson No. 210 Shoulder gas gun

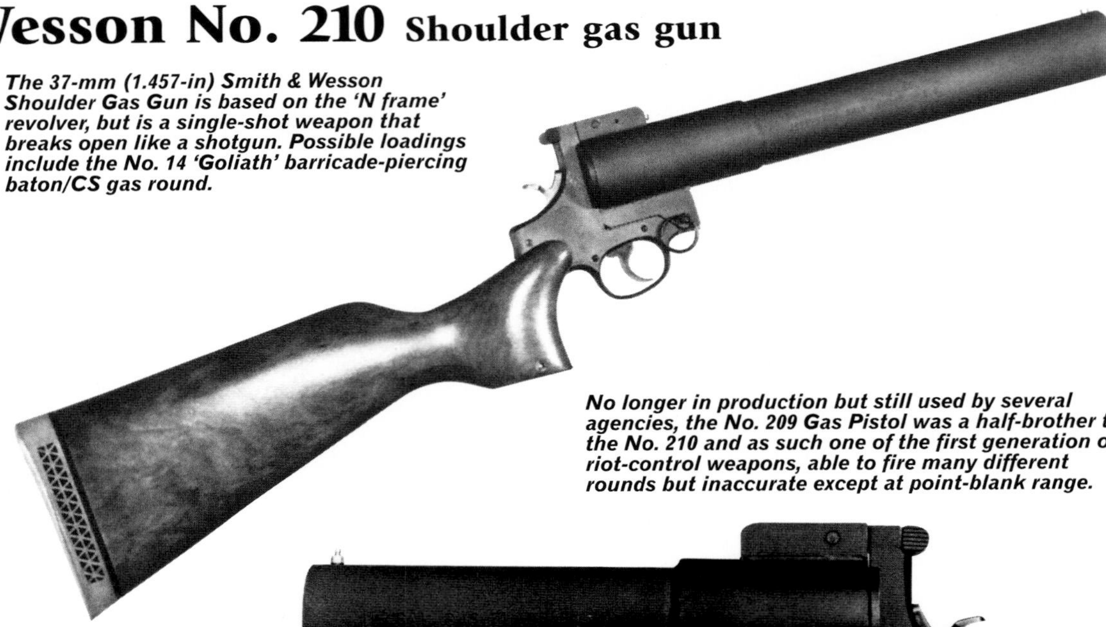

***The 37-mm (1.457-in) Smith & Wesson Shoulder Gas Gun is based on the 'N frame' revolver, but is a single-shot weapon that breaks open like a shotgun. Possible loadings include the No. 14 'Goliath' barricade-piercing baton/CS gas round.***

In addition to its well-known hand gun activities, the great American small arms manufacturer Smith & Wesson has also made considerable inroads into the steadily growing international market for riot-control weapons and their associated munitions. Thus the company has produced a wide range of munitions filled with everything from irritant agents to smoke, and has also manufactured the weapons to fire these munitions. One of the most widely used of the company's launchers is the **Smith & Wesson No. 210 Shoulder Gas Gun**.

The No. 210 has a calibre of 37-mm (1.456-in), which is a riot-control munition calibre established in the USA, mainly as a result of the efforts of Smith & Wesson, and now universally accepted as the primary calibre for the riot-control task. The basis of the weapon is the frame of the company's 'N frame' revolver, but instead of using a revolving cylinder carrying several rounds, the No. 210 is a single-shot weapon. The barrel breaks down in a shotgun fashion, using the lower front corner of the frame to accommodate the pivot point. The outline of the pistol butt can still be discerned as the forward edge of what is now a wooden butt that is fitted with a much-needed rubber recoil pad to help absorb the heavy recoil forces of firing this large-calibre round and so reduce the impact on the firer.

The firing mechanism can be of either single- or double-action type, and the weapon has an external hammer. The barrel of the No. 210 can be removed for carriage or storage, and the weapon is sufficiently long and bulky that it is usually issued with a shoulder sling. Aiming is effected with the aid of fixed sights.

## Varied ammunition

The No. 210 Shoulder Gas Gun can be used to fire a wide range of munitions. Most of these are of the conventional type, but some are rather unusual. An example of the latter is the No. 14 Goliath projectile, which is a multi-capable projectile comprising a CS-carrying baton section that can be fired through thin barricades.

There are two types of No. 17 baton round, both cased in thin metal, the longer-ranged version being fired to about 135 m (150 yards). The No. 18 baton round is similar to the No. 17 but uses a rubber slug with no metal casing. The No. 21 is intended for closer-range situations and fires a dense cloud of CS to a range of about 11 m (35 ft).

Some of these rounds can be produced in a more accurate 'Tru-Flite' form with tail-mounted fins that impart better directional stability. Given their weight and the greater drag of the fins, these rounds also use a slightly heavier propellant charge. The heavier charge means that 'Tru-Flite' rounds cannot be fired from the No. 210 Shoulder Gas Gun's stable-mate, the **No. 209 Gas Pistol**. This has a much shorter barrel than the No. 210, and has a standard revolver butt and frame. In overall appearance, the No. 209 weapon is distinctly disconcerting.

***No longer in production but still used by several agencies, the No. 209 Gas Pistol was a half-brother to the No. 210 and as such one of the first generation of riot-control weapons, able to fire many different rounds but inaccurate except at point-blank range.***

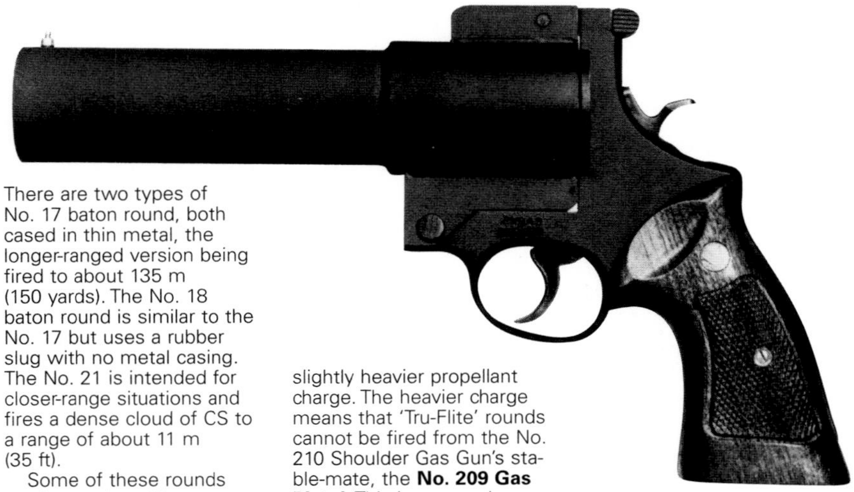

## Old but still capable

The No. 210 is a classic example of the first generation of riot-control weapons and remained in production for many years before finally being discontinued. Even so, the weapon is still in some demand as it is capable and thoroughly proved in service. Even its strongest advocate cannot claim, however, that the No. 210 Shoulder Gas Gun is an easy launcher to fire: some of the rounds used with the No. 210 have considerable 'kick' in terms of their recoil, and like many weapons of its kind the No. 210 is not particularly accurate except at very close ranges.

Typical of the type of modern baton round fired by the No. 210 Shoulder Gas Gun is the ALS Technologies Interlocking Rubber Baton Projectile. Offered in 40-mm (1.575-in) as well as 37-mm calibre, the IRBP round is 127 mm (5 in) long and weighs 114 gr (4 oz), and fires three 21-gr (0.74-oz) rubber discs to produce what the company describes as 'controlled and directed incapacitation by blunt impact trauma and excruciating pain', causing loss of breath as well as pain. The effective range is between 9 and 30 m (10 and 33 yards).

The British army used the type in Northern Ireland in the early years of the 'troubles', but then switched to the Grenade Discharger L1A1, but several British police forces still retain the No. 210 in their limited armouries. Smith & Wesson decided in the mid-1980s to leave the riot-control munitions market.

***The No. 210 Shoulder Gas Gun was used by the British army in Northern Ireland until it decided to switch to the larger-calibre and more modern and capable Grenade Discharger L1A1.***

| SPECIFICATION | |
|---|---|
| **No. 210 Shoulder Gas Gun** | **Weight:** about 2.7 kg (5.95 lb) |
| **Calibre:** 37-mm (1.456-in) | **Maximum range:** long-range baton round 135 m (150 yards) |
| **Length overall:** 736.6 mm (29 in) | |

# Federal Riot Gun

The **Federal Riot Gun** is now one of the most widely used riot-control guns ever produced, and is in service with army, para-military, security, police and prison forces all round the world. The weapon was originally developed by the Federal Laboratories, Inc. (of Saltsburg in the American state of Pennsylvania) to fire the extensive range of anti-riot munitions produced by the same organisation. At first most of these products were used by American penal institutions with a constant need to keep large and potentially very unruly populations under control, but over the years the use of the weapon and its munitions steadily spread to many other organisations.

***The Federal Riot Gun is one of the most widely used weapons of its type, and serves with armies and police organisations throughout the world. Manufactured in non-rusting alloys, it is a double-action, single-shot gun with no exposed hammer.***

## Robust strength

The Federal Riot Gun is a simple single-shot weapon with few frills. As a result of its simplicity and manufactured from a number of non-rusting alloys, it is extremely robust and reliable, and can be maintained and repaired under most operational conditions without undue difficulty or problem.

***The Federal Riot Gun is handled, loaded and aimed in the manner of a shotgun, and is a single-shot weapon loaded (here with a baton round) after the frame has been 'broken'.***

***The British army used the Federal Riot Gun in Northern Ireland and found it to be a reliable weapon, but its monstrous recoil and inherent lack of accuracy did not endear it to the troops. It has been superseded by the L1A1.***

| SPECIFICATION | |
|---|---|
| **Federal Riot Gun** | **Weight:** not recorded |
| **Calibre:** 37-mm (1.456-in) | **Typical range:** up to 100 m (110 yards) |
| **Length overall:** 737 mm (29 in) | |

The latest version is the **Riot Gun Model 203A** which has an in-line barrel and butt disposition, and a very strong mechanism to lock the barrel and frame: this mechanism is located just forward of the weapon's large pistol grip.

The firing mechanism is of the double-action type with no capability for single-action use and, given the weapon's original use in prison control situations, it was a very sensible decision to design the weapon without an external hammer of the type that inevitably would snag in clothing or other equipment at a crucial moment.

There is a foregrip with a connection for a sling, attached at the other end to the high-quality wooden butt. The sights are fixed at 45 m (50 yards). Most other models of the Federal Riot Gun are basically similar to the Model 203A except in details.

## Attractive sales pack

One of the primary reasons for the Federal Riot Gun's widespread use is that the basic weapon often comes as part of a package deal associated with Federal anti-riot munitions. These come in the standard 37-mm (1.456-in) calibre, and can be fired by riot-control weapons other than the Federal Riot Gun. As usual there are many types of munition, but two of these deserve special mention.

The first of these is the Federal 'Spedeheat' CS round that can be fired to a range of about 100 m (110 yards). The round has a thin bullet-shaped casing of aluminium alloy, can emit CS fumes for up to 30 seconds, and possesses the strength for secondary use as a baton round. The second notable round is another CS round, the Federal SKAT round that fires a cluster of five small CS grenades at the same time. These small CS grenades are designed for skip delivery, the firer aiming at the ground in front of the rioting crowd so that the small grenades land in front of the rioters and then ricochet back into the air in an erratic fashion. In general the grenades bounce outward in a fan-shaped arc to disperse their CS contents in an intense cloud. As they emit fumes for only about 15 seconds it is not a matter of any great moment if a rioter manages to pick up any of the grenades and throw them back at the security forces.

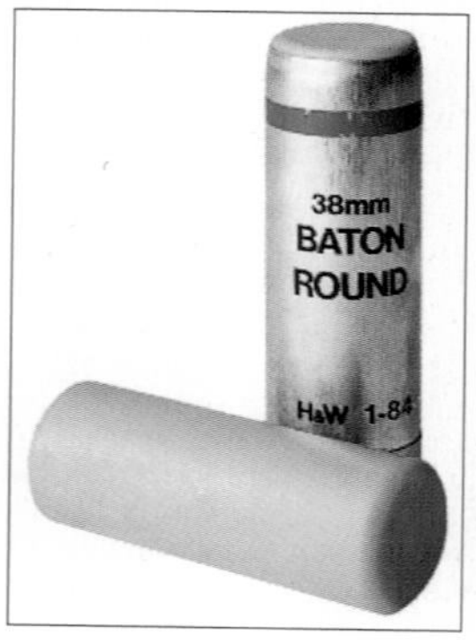


***The baton round is one of the most feared rounds fired by small-calibre riot-control weapons, as its high-energy impact causes great short-term pain and severe long-term bruising.***

## British experience

The Federal Riot Gun was one of the weapons obtained by the British army at the start of the 'troubles' in Northern Ireland. The army found the Riot Gun to be a serviceable weapon, but also that it was difficult to fire accurately, especially as it has quite a powerful recoil. The Riot Gun had been replaced by the Grenade Discharger L1A1 by the mid-1980s, but many British police forces still keep the Federal Riot Gun in reserve in their armouries for use in emergency situations.

# Land warrior

## 21st century soldier

**The infantryman has changed more in the last decade than at any time in the previous century. What would have seemed like science fiction only 10 years ago is about to go into service for real. Many of the world's armies are developing systems to integrate the individual foot soldier into the digital battlefield. The French FELIN (*Fantassin a Equipements et Liaisons Integre*) and the British FIST/Crusader 21 are programmes which will see high-tech equipment applied to the ordinary soldier over the next decade, but it is the American Land Warrior System which is the first to go into large-scale service.**

*Above and below: Currently being fielded by the US Army, the Land Warrior system incorporates one-man computerised navigation, communications, weapons and sighting systems. Land Warrior will give the ordinary infantry soldier more information about the battlefield than he has had at any time in history.*

The new systems being developed are intended to enhance the capabilities of traditional visual recognition and sighting systems. This will enable the infantryman to engage at maximum range and with maximum accuracy in all weathers, by day or by night.

### Land Warrior

Land Warrior is currently being fielded and is the US army's program for enhancing the infantry soldier's battlefield capabilities. It is a modular, integrated fighting system for dismounted combat soldiers, designed to allow the individual to play a full part in the 21st century battlefield.

Land Warrior, providing enhanced capabilities, increases the combat effectiveness of infantry teams, squads, crews, and platoons as well as the individual dismounted soldier. As the first truly integrated one-man fighting system, Land Warrior is the precursor to many radical changes for the soldier of the near future. Land Warrior will significantly increase situational awareness, lethality and survivability. The enhanced sensor capabilities give suitably equipped troops the kind of all-weather ability previously reserved for vehicle or aircraft crews, allowing the ordinary infantryman to truly 'own the night.'

### Information war

The key to Land Warrior's enhanced capability is the integrated computer/radio system. Information collection and dissemination up and down the chain of command will be enhanced through real-time digital reporting and still frame video capture and transmission.

Each soldier can view a map in his helmet mounted display which shows his location, the position of other squad and platoon members and known enemy sites. Other capabilities make the soldier even more combat effective; the use of an embedded Global Positioning System takes away any uncertainty about where he is, and an integrated image intensifier makes night operations almost as easy as day.

### Protect the force

Survivability will be increased as a result of the data connection between the soldier and his weapon. He will have the ability to engage the enemy with only his hands and arms exposed, through the integration of the thermal weapon sight and video camera with a modular weapon and helmet-mounted display.

Improved body armour, a laser detector, improved chemical protection and ballistic/laser eye protection will further enhance soldier survivability. Vastly increased situational awareness and integration of combat ID – a kind of one-man IFF system – will help prevent the fratricide or 'Blue on Blue' kills which are always a risk in night engagements.

## WEAPON SUBSYSTEM

The modular weapon subsystem is designed to improve hit probability without loss of mobility. It is fitted onto a rail on a modified M16 rifle or M4 carbine. The main components of the weapon subsystem include a Light or Medium Thermal Weapon Sight (TWS) for target detection in all weathers and visibility, a Multi-Functional Laser providing range and direction finding, aiming points and third-party target illumination. The weapon also carries an Integrated Inertial Guidance Dead Reckoning Module (DRM), which maintains accurate location when GPS signals are temporarily unavailable. 'On Weapon' Controls allow a soldier to maintain weapon firing position while controlling all components of the Land Warrior system.

## HELMET

The Integrated Helmet Assembly Subsystem (IHAS) provides the soldier with ballistic protection as well as high-fidelity visual and audible battlefield information. The IHAS provides for operation in day, night, and NBC environments. The Helmet Shell uses advanced materials to reduce weight. An innovative new suspension system provides a stable platform for optical components. The Helmet-Mounted Display provides primary visual information output and complete access to the computer database. The Map Display feature allows a soldier to see his location, and the location of other members of his squad and platoon.

## COMPUTER

The Computer/Radio Subsystem (CRS) integrates the Land Warrior soldier into the digitised battlefield. The CRS consists primarily of commercial and existing government equipment. The Communications/Navigation Module provides voice and data transmit/receive capability. A GPS Receiver provides location data for navigation and situational awareness. An Integrated Inertial Guidance Dead Reckoning Module (DRM) maintains accurate location when GPS signal is temporarily unavailable. The CRS can capture and transmit still-frame video. It also integrates with the Multifunctional Laser to provide automated indirect fire support designation. The computer equipment is completely integrated into the load carrying system. The software subsystem is the heart of Land Warrior, and is designed to meet the soldier's tactical needs. It greatly improves his mission effectiveness and performance capability.

## PROTECTIVE CLOTHING

The Protective Clothing and Individual Equipment (PCIE) Subsystem provides the mechanical means of integrating the Land Warrior System. This integrated, modular subsystem enhances soldier mobility and survivability and redefines soldier comfort. The Interceptor Body Armor comes in five sizes, with front and back ergonomically-designed plates. The Outer Tactical Vest without plates weighs 3.8 kg (8.4 lb) and protects against fragmentation and 9-mm rounds. The Small Arms Protective Insert Plates weigh 1.8 kg (4 lb) each and withstand multiple hits from 7.62-mm (0.3-in) ball rounds. The total system weight is 7.4 kg (16.4 lb), a 4.5-kg/10-lb saving from the current PASGT Vest/ISAPO combination. There are attachable throat and groin protectors for increased protection and webbing attachment loops on the front of the vest which accommodate the same pockets used in the Load Carrying Equipment.

# FN2000 Modular system

*The FN2000 is a fully modular assault weapon system. The basic weapon can be modified by the addition of external modules to increase its versatility: this example has been fitted with a 40-mm grenade launcher and an advanced electronic fire control system.*

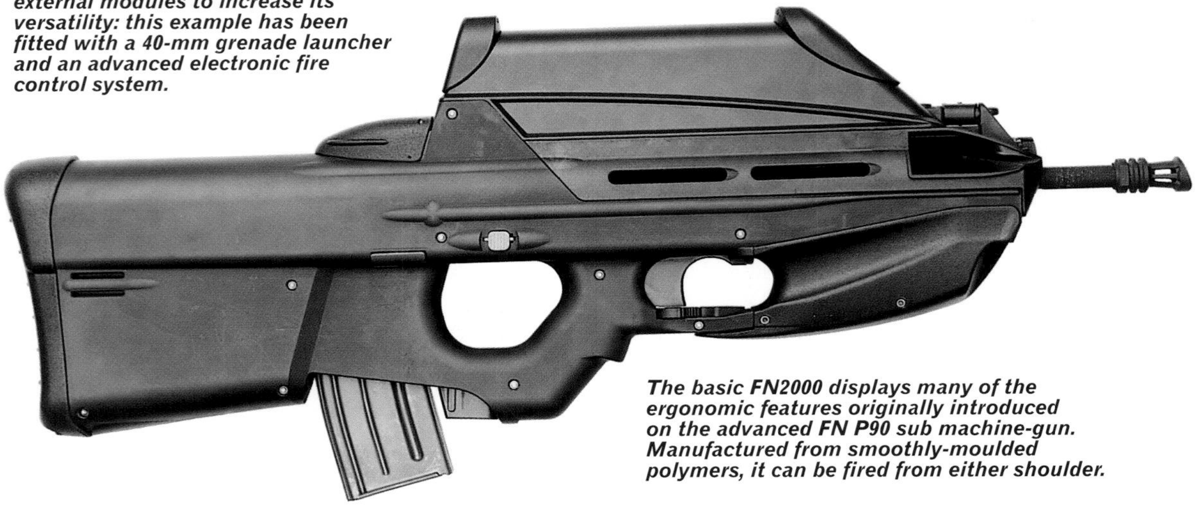

*The basic FN2000 displays many of the ergonomic features originally introduced on the advanced FN P90 sub machine-gun. Manufactured from smoothly-moulded polymers, it can be fired from either shoulder.*

FN Herstal offered a succession of 5.56-mm assault rifles to replace the magnificent 7.62-mm FN FAL (known to the British Army as the SLR – Self Loading Rifle) that made the company's post-war reputation. None of them achieved great success: in a crowded market, most armies either bought American (the M16) or developed their own (the French FA MAS, the Italian Berettas, the quixotic British SA 80). So Belgian equivalents like the 5.56-mm FNC had limited impact. Whether the FN 2000 will achieve major export sales is too early to tell, but it is an interesting design from a company with an eye for innovation – its P90 personal weapon certainly caught the world's attention when touted in the late 1980s. One look at the FN 2000 suggests that the ergonomic lessons of the P90 have not been forgotten. The FN 2000 is a very easy weapon to learn to shoot, and its construction lends itself to a quick and simple field-strip.

## Weapon design

The FN 2000 is a 'bullpup' design – the magazine is located behind the trigger group to reduce the overall length of the gun to under 700 mm. This is useful for troops who will go to war in armoured personnel carriers who, when they dismount for battle, will often find themselves fighting in built-up areas.

The FN 2000 addresses one of the most serious drawbacks of the British bullpup rifle, the SA 80. The latter can only be fired from the right shoulder: if you try to fire it from the left, the spent cases will fly straight into your face. Since one in 20 soldiers are left-handed, this is not terribly helpful. More critically, when fighting in built-up areas, soldiers often need to be able to shoot around a left hand corner. To do so with an SA 80 forces you to expose far more of your body to return fire than is necessary.

The FN 2000 has a unique ejection system that funnels the ejected case along a tunnel, sending it forwards rather than sideways. A soldier can shoot left-handed without the risk of cases, gas or other debris striking the face. In addition, the fire selector, safety catch and magazine release are all positioned to they can be operated without difficulty with either hand.

Chambered for 5.56-mm x 45 NATO rounds, the FN 2000 is a conventional gas-operated, rotating bolt design. The high cyclic rate (over 800 rpm) produces accurate short bursts. The weapon is of modular construction. This enables users to quickly and easily modify the weapon for specific requirements. (In truth, this is more relevant to law enforcement usage than the military, but with the growth of 'peacekeeping' missions, there is increasing cross-over between the two.) The stock is a tough polymer and the sighting rail can be fitted with whatever sighting system the user prefers (or army can afford). The standard option is a x1.6 optical sight: enough to make an aimed shot easier but not so strong that both eyes need to be closed to aim. There is a mounting point ahead of the trigger guard so it can carry a grenade launcher, torch or other useful 'add on'.

Unlike traditional rifle

*The mounting rail on top of the FN2000 can accept a variety of sighting equipment. The standard x1.6 optical sight seen here can be replaced by night sights or the grenade FCS.*

designs, the FN2000 has a pistol grip designed from the beginning to be equally comfortable when firing either rifle rounds or grenades. With a nod to developments across the Atlantic, FN do offer a computerised fire control module with laser rangefinder to calculate the point of aim and set the sights for the 40-mm grenade launcher. All such devices are open to the criticism that they are not truly 'soldier proof' i.e. robust enough for hard service in the field, as opposed to demonstration shoots for visiting media. They also require power sources – batteries – that do not last long and the whole thing adds up to yet more weight for troops to carry. The fate of the famous SAS patrol 'Bravo Two Zero' should stand as a warning to even the fittest troops who attempt to go into action carrying extremely heavy loads.

### Grenade launcher

The grenade launcher is a pump action, rotary locking weapon. It fires a wide range of 40-mm munitions: the basic high explosive round is fired with a muzzle velocity of 76 metres per second (249 ft/sec). The grenade launcher barrel is 230 mm (9.05 in) long and it increases the overall length of the weapon to 727 mm (28.6 in). This is still handy enough, especially compared to the older generation of 7.62-mm rifles than exceeded a metre in length.

### Future prospects

Like all of today's advanced infantry weapons, the FN 2000's prospects depend on the willingness of western governments to invest large sums of money on their infantry units. Whether any defence ministry will conclude the FN 2000 offers such a significant advantage over the M16 (or similar) that it can persuade its political masters to supply the necessary funds remains to be seen.

The other stone in the road ahead is the continued commitment to 5.56-mm calibre: both the 1991 Gulf War and recent operations in Afghanistan have highlighted its limitations in a combat environment where long range fire-fights are the rule rather than the exception. Some soldiers would like to see a return to 7.62-mm weapons; all armies involved in these actions have increased the number of 5.56-mm machine guns in their infantry companies.

***To allow for ambidextrous fire, spent cases are not ejected sideways as on a more conventional weapon: they are projected forwards from a port just behind and to the right of the muzzle.***

**SPECIFICATION**

**FN 2000**
**Calibre:** 5.56 x 45 mm NATO
**Length overall:** 694 mm
**Barrel length:** 400 mm
**Magazine capacity:** 30 rounds
**Weights:** 3.6 kg empty; 4.6 kg with 40 mm grenade launcher

## A BRIEF HISTORY OF FABRIQUE NATIONALE

Fabrique Nationale d 'Armes de Guerre has a long history of producing high quality military firearms. Established in 1889 to manufacture 150,000 Mauser rifles ordered by the Belgian Government, the company entered into a significant relationship with John Moses Browning, probably the most innovative firearms designer in history.

In the 1930s, under the design leadership of Dieudonne Saive, the company began the development of a series of self-loading rifles which would provide the foundation of the company's postwar success.

The FN Model 49 was followed by the superb FN FAL, a classic battle rifle designed to make use of the new NATO standard 7.62-mm round. One of the most successful weapons of all time, the FAL was sold to more than 90 countries.

With the introduction of smaller calibre weapons in the 1960s and 1970s, FN introduced a derivative of the FAL which was redesigned to take the new NATO 5.56-mm round. The FNC was a fine weapon, being both accurate and reliable, but it did not achieve the export success of its famous progenitor.

***Above: A version of the FN FAL was the standard British battle rifle for three decades.***

***The FN Model 49 was the company's first auto rifle.***

***The FNC is a light assault rifle based on the FN FAL.***

# FA MAS FELIN Rifle

France introduced a bullpup rifle in 5.56-mm (0.256-in) calibre as the **FA MAS** in the course of the early 1980s after being formally adopted in 1978 following a development programme launched in 1972. The weapon's designation stands for Fusil d'Assaut de la Manufacture d'Armes de St Etienne (assault rifle from MAS), this last being a division of the state-owned GIAT Industries armaments organisation.

Dubbed *le clairon* (the bugle) by the troops because of its unusual appearance, having a general similarity to this musical instrument much favoured by the armed forces, the FA MAS has gained a considerable measure of popular and operational success. This is in marked and dramatic contrast to the dismal reputation of the British SA80 (more formally the L85), which has somehow contrived to be as heavy as the 7.62-mm (0.3-in) semi-automatic rifle it replaced.

Unlike the SA80, the FA MAS can easily be switched to fire from either shoulder (the cheekpiece and ejector mechanism being switchable from one side to the other), and its integral folding bipod makes a long-range shot a rather more practical proposition. It is recommended that the change from left- to right-hand use, or vice versa, should not be attempted in the field as the process requires the removal and later the reinstallation of several small components that could well be lost and thereby render the weapon inoperative.

The latest version of this useful French weapon, which operates on the delayed blowback principle not commonly used for assault rifles and the like, is the **FA MAS G2**. This features a number of incremental improvements over the original FAS MAS F1 and FA MAS F2 standards. Similar to the original FA MAS, the FA MAS G2 is designed with single-shot, three-round burst (for one pull of the trigger) and fully automatic firing capabilities controlled by a combined safety switch and selector inside the trigger guard with safe, single-shot and automatic positions. The selection between three-round burst and fully automatic fire modes is controlled by an automatic fire mode selector located beyond the magazine housing on the bottom of the stock. Other changes incorporated in this weapon include the replacement of the folding bipod (which can be reattached) by sling swivels, the omission of the inbuilt grenade launcher, the extension of the trigger guard to cover the whole of the grip, the modification of the magazine housing to accept NATO standard 30-round M16-type box magazines as well as the FA MAS's own particular 25-round magazine, and provision for the installation under the barrel of the M203 40-mm (1.575-in)

***This artwork suggests the possible look of French infantrymen of the next generation debussing from their infantry fighting vehicle with FA MAS FELIN rifles and PAPOP personal kit.***

***The PAPOP concept is designed to produce a more capable type of French infantryman with considerably greater quantities of information available to him for both tactical and targeting purposes.***

grenade launcher. The FA MAS G2 can still be used to launch the 400-g (14.1-oz) rifle grenade, a type of weapon for which the French have shown great enthusiasm since World War I. The weapon's cyclic rate of fire is also adjustable in the range between 1,000 to 1,100 rounds per minute.

## Recent developments

The **FA MAS FELIN** is a modified FA MAS F1 currently undergoing trials as part of France's future infantryman programme. The weapon is known by the acronym PAPOP (Polyarme Polyprojectiles) and the FA MAS FELIN is similar in concept to the US Army's 'Land Warrior', the Australian Army's LAND 125 System and Britain's 'FIST'.

The French programme involves GIAT Industries, Thomson-CSF Texen and six other companies. It also follows the basic requirements laid down in NATO Document AC225. This involves the development of the infantryman into a virtual 'weapon system' that must be able to operate at night with considerably greater efficiency and capability than are currently accepted for the infantryman; make extensive and effective use of a wide range of visual aids for the assimilation and exploitation of tactical information; and provide a considerably superior capability in the engagement of targets behind cover than the current generation of conventional infantry armed with current in-service weapons of the rifle, machine-gun and grenade launcher types.

## Attributes

The FA MAS FELIN rifle thus carries equipment to facilitate day and night firing, offset firing using data received from another member of the team, range- finding, instinctive aiming and firing, and combat identification friend or foe. The weapon also carries the controls for the infantryman's communications system (radio, data and image). This combination of attributes is designed to provide a daylight 90 per cent hit probability on a standing and stationary man at 300 m (330 yards), declining to 50 per cent at 500 m (545 yards), and by night the same hit probabilities against the same type of target at 200 and 400 m (220 and 440 yards) respectively.

Ultimately this 'weapon system' concept will require a specialised and dedicated weapon that combines rifle and grenade launcher capabilities of an advanced order. The intention is to develop and manufacture a weapon that provides its firer with significantly enhanced reach and a much higher level of lethality than the current range of personal weapons. Another feature that is required is improved NBC protection providing full levels of protection against the effects of nuclear, biological and chemical weapons together with far greater user 'friendliness' than is provided by today's protective outfits. This is designed to ensure that the wearer has greater mobility (through reduced weight and greater flexibility, among other features) without any sacrifice in levels of protection. It is hoped that this integrated system will begin to enter service with the troops of the French army by the beginning of 2010, but this may be an overly optimistic date given the complexity of the tasks facing designers and also manufacturers.

***The French army is currently at a high level of operational capability, but the high command wants to transform these capabilities with more effective and versatile weapons operated by better informed troops.***

| SPECIFICATION | |
|---|---|
| **FA MAS G2**<br>**Calibre:** 5.56-mm (0.219-in)<br>**Length overall:** 757 mm (29.8 in)<br>**Length of barrel:** 488 mm (19.2 in) | **Weight:** empty 3.5 kg (7.7 lb); 3.97 kg (8.8 lb) loaded with 30-round magazine<br>**Feed:** 20- or 30-round box magazine |

## Weapon configuration

The current PAPOP combines a rifle, firing the now-standard 5.56-mm (0.219-in) x 45 cartridge, with a grenade launcher that fires a grenade with a diameter of 35-mm (1.38-in) rather than 40-mm as featured in current American weapons as well as on the OICW. The reduction in calibre reduces weight and thereby improves portability and range, but care is being taken to ensure that the reductions in diameter and weight do not compromise operational capability.

Like the OICW, the French weapon has a digital 'support system'. This is designed to provide the facility for the detection of targets, by night as well as day, at ranges of up to 300 m (330 yards) and, importantly, for the discrimination between 'friendly' and 'hostile' troops. The French weapon utilises a remote sighting system to fire from cover, and can designate targets for other weapons. Video data are transmitted to a head-up display on the soldier's visor in a fashion similar to that employed by modern warplanes to provide the pilot with tactically important information in a readily assimilated fashion that does not require the user's eyes to be taken off the target or terrain ahead of him or her. In the land-based system, the data can be transmitted so that commanders can literally 'see' what their men are seeing.

## Grenade programming

The French 35-mm grenade can be programmed at the moment of firing to optimise its fragmentation pattern for maximum effect on a specific target; in a fashion analogous to the adjustment of the choke of a shotgun, the fragmentation pattern of the grenade can be concentrated or dispersed. The 35-mm grenade weighs 200 g (7.055 oz) and is of the smallest size and mass that the French believe will achieve the intended task effectively.

***The FA MAS FELIN rifle adds a mass of targeting equipment and a small grenade launcher to the current FA MAS weapon, transforming the ability of the infantryman to fight with maximum effect by day and night.***

# Appendices

## Annual Allied and Axis Artillery Production (including AT and AA) 1939–45 (units)

| Nation | 1939 | 1940 | 1941 | 1942 | 1943 | 1944 | 1945 | Total |
|---|---|---|---|---|---|---|---|---|
| USA | n/a | n/a | n/a | n/a | n/a | n/a | n/a | 257,390 |
| USSR | 17,348 | 15,300 | 42,300 | 127,000 | 130,000 | 122,400 | 62,000 | 516,648 |
| UK | 538 | 4700 | 16,700 | 43,000 | 38,000 | 16,000 | 5939 | 124,877 |
| Canada | n/a | n/a | n/a | n/a | n/a | n/a | n/a | 10,552 |
| Other Allies* | n/a | n/a | n/a | n/a | n/a | n/a | n/a | 5215 |
| **Allied Total** | n/a | n/a | n/a | n/a | n/a | n/a | n/a | **914682** |
| Germany | 1214 | 6730 | 11,200 | 23,200 | 46,100 | 70,700 | n/a | 159,144 |
| Italy | n/a | n/a | n/a | n/a | n/a | n/a | n/a | 7200 |
| Hungary | n/a | n/a | n/a | n/a | n/a | n/a | n/a | 447 |
| Japan | n/a | n/a | 2250 | 2550 | 3600 | 3300 | 1650 | 13,350 |
| **Axis Total** | n/a | n/a | n/a | n/a | n/a | n/a | n/a | **180,141** |

## Total Allied and Axis Production of Mortars 1939–45 (units)

| USA | USSR | UK | Canada | Other Allies* | Total | Germany | Italy | Japan |
|---|---|---|---|---|---|---|---|---|
| 105,054 | 403,300 | 102,950 | 20,619 | 25,395 | 657,318 | 73,484 | n/a | n/a |

## Total Allied and Axis Machine-Gun Production (not SMGs) 1939–45 (units)

| USA | USSR | UK | Canada | Other Allies* | Total | Germany | Italy | Hungary | Japan |
|---|---|---|---|---|---|---|---|---|---|
| 2,679,840 | 1,477,400 | 297,336 | 251,925 | 37,983 | 4,744,484 | 674,280 | n/a | 4583 | 380,000 |

*Other Allies: Australia, India, New Zealand, South Africa

# Further Reading


Bishop, Chris (ed.) (2002) *Firepower – Infantry Weapons* (Kent: Grange Books)

Bishop, Chris (ed.) (1996) *Combat Guns and Infantry Weapons* (Shrewsbury: Airlife Publishing)

Ellis, John (1988) *The World War II Databook* (London: Aurum Press Ltd.)

Ford, Roger (1998) *The World's Great Rifles* (London: Brown Packaging Books Ltd.)

Gander, Terry J and Hogg, Ian V. (1995) *Jane's Infantry Weapons – Twenty-first Edition* (Surrey: Jane's Information Group Inc.)

Hogg, Ian V. (1979) *The Complete Machine-Gun – 1885 to the present* (London: Phoebus Publishing)

Hogg, Ian V. and Weeks, John (1985) *Military Small Arms of the 20th Century* (London: Arms and Armour Press)

Hogg, Ian and Weeks, John (1992) *Pistols of the World – The definitive illustrated guide to the world's pistols and revolvers* (London: Arms and Armour Press)

Hogg, Ian V. (1994) *Small Arms – Pistols and Rifles* (London: Greenhill Books)

Hogg, Ian V. (1995) *Jane's Police and Security Equipment – Eighth edition* (Surrey: Jane's Information Group)

Hogg, Ian (2000) *Jane's Guns Recognition Guide – Second Edition* (Glasgow: Harper Collins Publishers)

Ingram, Mike (2001) *The MP40 Submachine Gun* (Kent: Spellmount)

McNab, Chris (2001) *Twentieth-Century Small Arms* (Kent: Grange Books)

Markham, George (1987) *Guns of the Elite – Special forces firearms, 1940 to the present* (London: Arms and Armour Press)

Myatt, F (1979) *The Illustrated Encyclopedia of 19th Century Firearms* (London: Tiger Books International)

Myatt, Frederick (1980) *The Illustrated Encyclopedia of Pistols and Revolvers – An illustrated history of hand guns from the sixteenth century to the present day* (London: Salamander Books Ltd.)

Philip, Craig (1993) *The World's Great Small Arms* (London: Brown Books Ltd.)

Stevenson, Jan (ed.) (1988) *Modern Sporting Guns* (London: Salamander Books)

Zhuk, A.B, (1995) *The Illustrated Encyclopedia of Handguns – Pistols and revolvers of the world, 1870 to the present* (London: Greenhill Books)

# Glossary

**Battery** – Descriptive term for when a cartridge is in place and the gun is ready for firing.

**Bolt** – The part of a firearm which usually contains the firing pin or striker and which closes the breech ready for firing.

**Blowback** – Operating system in which the bolt is not locked to the breech, thus it is consequently pushed back by breech pressure on firing and cycles the gun.

**Breech** – The rear of the gun barrel.

**Breech-block** – Another method of closing the breech which generally involves a substantial rectangular block rather than a cylindrical bolt.

**Bullpup** – Term for when the receiver of a gun is actually set in the butt behind the trigger group, thus allowing for a full length barrel.

**Carbine** – A shortened rifle for specific assault roles.

**Chamber** – The section at the end of the barrel which receives and seats the cartridge ready for firing.

**Closed Bolt** – A mechanical system in which the bolt is closed up to the cartridge before the trigger is pulled. This allows greater stability through reducing the forward motion of parts on firing.

**Compensator** – A muzzle attachment which controls the direction of gas expanding from the weapon and thus resists muzzle climb or swing during automatic fire.

**Delayed Blowback** – A delay mechanically imposed on a blowback system to allow pressures in the breech to drop to safe levels before breech opening.

**Double action** – Relates to pistols which can be fired both by cocking the hammer and then pulling the trigger, and by a single long pull on the trigger which performs both cocking and firing actions.

**Flechette** – An bolt-like projectile which is smaller than the gun's calibre and requires a sabot to fit it to the barrel. Achieves very high velocities.

**Gas Operation** – Operating system in which a gun is cycled by gas being bled off from the barrel and used against a piston or the bolt to drive the bolt backwards and cycle the gun for the next round.

**GPMG** – An abbreviation for General Purpose Machine Gun.

**LMG** – An abbreviation for Light Machine Gun.

**Locking** – Describes the various methods by which the bolt or breech block is locked behind the chamber ready for firing.

**Long Recoil** – A method of recoil operation in which the barrel and bolt recoil for a length greater than that of the entire cartridge, during which extraction and loading are performed.

**Muzzle Brake** – A muzzle attachment which diverts muzzle blast sideways and thus reduces overall recoil.

**Open Bolt** – A mechanical system in which the bolt is kept at a distance from the cartridge before the trigger is pulled. This allows for better cooling of the weapon between shots.

**Receiver** – The body of the weapon which contains the gun's main operating parts.

**Recoil** – The rearward force generated by the explosive power of a projectile being fired.

**Recoil Operated** – Operating system in which the gun is cycled by the recoil-propelled force of both barrel and bolt when the weapon is fired. Both components recoil together for a certain distance before the barrel stops and the bolt continues backwards to perform reloading and rechambering.

**SAW** – Abbreviation for Squad Automatic Weapon.

**Self-loading** – Operating system in which one pull of the trigger allows the gun to fires and reload in a single action.

**Short Recoil** – A compressed version of recoil operation in which the barrel and bolt move back less than the length of the cartridge before the bolt detaches.

# Index

Page numbers in *italics* refer to picture captions.


0.38/200, Smith & Wesson *30*
2B9 (Avtomaticheskii Minomet Vasilek) mortar *214*, 215
45/5 modello 35 'Brixia' mortar *202–3*
50-PM mortar series 204
51-mm Mortar 212–13
82-PM mortar series *204*, 215
94 Shiki Kenju pistol 32
100 Shiki Kikanshoju (Type 100) *54*
107-PBHM 38 mortar 204, 217
120-HM 38 mortar *205*, 217
120-HM 43 mortar 205
160-HM 43 mortar 205
A5 shotgun *224*
AAT 52 machine-gun *167*
AAT F1 machine-gun 167
Abwehrflammenwerfer 42 193
AC556 assault rifle 125
AC556GF assault rifle *125*
Ack-Pack flamethrower 196
active-denial technology 235
AGS-17 Plamya grenade launcher *219*
Aisne, Battle of the *144*
AK-5 assault rifle 112
AK-47 assault rifle 81, *108*, 109, *120*
  and the Finnish Rk.60 *106–7*
AK-74 assault rifle 79, *121*
AK-101 assault rifle 79, 121
AK-102 assault rifle 79, 121
AK-103 assault rifle 79, 121
AK-104 assault rifle 79
AK-105 assault rifle 79, 121
AK-107 assault rifle 79
AK-108 assault rifle 79
AKM assault rifle 109, *120*
AKS-74 sub-machine gun 79
AKS-74U (AKSU) sub-machine gun *79*
Alvis OMC Casspir Mk III 236
Ameli machine-gun *173*
American self-loading pistols *44*
Ampulenyot 1941 System Kartukov *195*
AMT On Duty pistol *44*
AN-M2 machine-gun 155
anti-aircraft artillery (AAA) *179*
anti-tank weapons
  grenades *184*, 188, *189*
  improvised *188–9*
  PIAT *190*
  rifles *186–7*
  *see also* rocket launchers
AP/AV700 grenade launcher *219*
AR assault rifle, Galil 116
AR-10 assault rifle 81, *106*
AR-15/M16 assault rifle *122–3*
AR-18 paramilitary rifle *125*
AR70 assault rifle *117*
AR90 assault rifle 117
Arisaka type rifles *91*
Armalite
  AR-10 assault rifle 81, *106*
  AR-15/M16 assault rifle *122–3*
  AR-18 paramilitary rifle *125*
ARM assault rifle *116*, *117*
Armsel Striker shotgun *227*
Arwen riot-control weapon *240*
assault rifles *9*, *106–7*, *110–25*
  development *108–9*
AT 105 Saxon riot-control vehicles 236, *237*
Atchisson Assault Shotgun *231*
ATO-41 flamethrower 195
ATO-42 flamethrower 195
AUG, Steyr *110*
  AUG Para (Aug 9) *66*
Austro-Hungarian army *82*
Austro-Hungarian pistols, 8mm and 9mm *12*
Automaticky Pistole vz.38 (CZ 38) pistol *32*
AVS36 rifle 95
AVT40 rifle 95
Avtomaticheskaya Vintova Simonova (AVS36) rifle 95
Avtomaticheskii Minomet Vasilek *214*
Avtomat Kalasnikova *see* AK

'Baby Nambu' 15
Badger flamethrower 197
BAR light machine-gun *151*, *154*
Barrett
  M82 sniper rifle 138–9
  M95 sniper rifle 139
baton rounds *233*, *238*, *243*
bayonets
  revolver 21
  rifle *87*, 96
bazookas *178*, *191*
BDA-9C 36
BDA-9M 36
BDA-9S 36
bean bag rounds 234
Belholla-Selbsladepistole 18–19
Benét-Mercié machine-gun *143*
Beretta
  AR70 assault rifle *117*
  AR90 assault rifle 117
  Model 12 sub-machine gun *73*
  Model 81 pistol 40–1
  Model 92 series pistols 41–2
  Model 93R pistol *41*
  Model 98 pistol 41
  Model 99 pistol 41
  Model 1951 pistol *40*, 41
  modello 1915 pistol *14*
  modello 1934 pistol *33*
  Moschetto Automatico Modello 1 53
  Moschetto Automatico Modello 38/42 *53*
  Moschetto Automatico Modello 38A *53*
  RS200 shotgun *225*
  RS202P shotgun *225*
  SC70 assault rifle 117
  SC70 Short assault rifle 117
  Sniper *134–5*
  sub-machine guns *53*
Bergmann MP18 sub-machine gun 46
Berthier rifles
  mle 1907 84–5, 90
  mle 1907/15 84–5, 90
  mle 1907/15 M34 90
  mle 1916 85, 90
Blackhawk, Ruger 45
Bofors AK-5 assault rifle 112
Bond, James 38
Borchardt, Hugo 16, 26
Borchardt pistol 16
Boys anti-tank rifle 178–9, *188*
Brandt
  gun-mortars *218*
  mortars 214–15, *219*
Breda machine-guns *153*
Bren Gun 141, *157*, *174*
Brixia modello 1912 pistol 14
'Brixia' mortar *202–3*
Brizia 33
Browning
  Automatic Rifle (BAR) *151*, *154*
  Automatic shotguns *224*
  GP 35 automatic pistol *28*
  High Power (HP) pistol (modèle à Grande Puissance) *28*, *35*, *36*
  M2HB heavy machine-gun *176*
  M1917 machine-gun *150–1*
  M1919 machine-gun *155*
  machine-guns 140
  Modèle 1900 pistol *12*, 13
  Modèle 1903 pistol 12–13
  Modèle 1910 pistol *13*, *28*
  Pistol, Automatic L9A1 28
Buffel riot-control vehicles *236*, *237*
Bulldog riot-control vehicles 236

C/96 pistol, Mauser *18*
Cadet Traing Rifle L81A1 sniper rifle 137
Carabine FN-Mauser mle 1889 rifle 82
Carbine, Caliber .30, M1 *99*
Carbine, Caliber .30, M2 99
Carbine, Caliber .30, M3 99
Carbine Type 38 91
Carl Gustav (m/45) sub-machine gun *75*
Cassino, battles for *59*, *96*
CAWS (Close Assault Weapon System) 223, 231
CAW shotgun *231*
CETME
  Ameli machine-gun *173*
  Model L/LC assault rifle *118–19*
Chaimite vehicles 237
Chauchat light machine-gun *144–5*
Chemical Mortar, 4.2-in 211
Chinese machine guns *166*
Churchill, Winston *58*
CIS Ultimax 100 (3U-100) machine-gun *172*
clothing, protective *245*
Cobray M11 sub-machine gun 77
Colt
  Commando *122*
  Delta Elite *44*
  Lawman Mk III *45*
  M1892 *23*
  M1911A1 pistol *23*, *29*
  M1911 pistol *23*, *29*, *44*
  New Service M1917 *22*, 23, 31
  Python *45*
  revolvers *45*
  Trooper 45
Colt-Browning Model 1895 machine-gun *150*
Commando Mk III vehicles 237
Computer/Radio Subsystem (CRS) *245*
CS gas and grenades 238–9
CZ
  38 (vz.38) pistol *32*
  75 and family, of pistols *36–7*
  vz 61 Skorpion sub-machine gun/machine pistol *67*
  vz 63 sub-machine gun/machine pistol 67
  vz 68 sub-machine gun/machine pistol 67
Czech pistols *36–7*

'Deathshead' pioneers *14*
'Deer Gun' 29
Defender, Winchester *229*
Degtyarev
  DP light machine-gun *140*, *163*
  DPM light machine-gun 163
  DT light machine-gun 163
  DTM light machine-gun 163
Delta Elite, Colt *44*
Desert Eagle, IMI *40*
DP light machine-gun *140*, *163*
DPM light machine-gun 163
Dragunov combat sniping rifle *135*
DShK1938 heavy machine-gun *141*, *162*
DT light machine-gun 163

DTM light machine-gun 163

Eintoss Flammenwerfer tragbar 192
Enfield No. 2 Mk 1 pistol *24*
'Enfield' rifle (Rifle M1917) 87
Enforcer sniper rifle 136
Envoy sniper rifle 136
Euromissile HOT missile system *179*

F1 sub-machine gun *64*
Fabrique Nationale *see* FN
FAL, FN *81*, *111*, *112*
Fallschirmjägergewehr 42 (FG 42) rifle *94*
FA MAS assault rifle 81, *109*, *113*
FA MAS FELIN rifle *248–9*
FA MAS G2 assault rifle 248, 249
FAO machine-gun 152
Faustpatrone 180
Federal Riot Gun *243*
FELIN rifle *248–9*
FFV 890C assault rifle 116
FG 42 (Fallschirmjägergewehr 42) rifle *94*
fire and manoeuvre *8–9*
Flame-Thrower, Portable, No. 2 (Lifebuoy) *196*
flamethrowers *179*, *194–8*
  German *192–3*
  tanks as *193*, *194*, *199*
Flammenwerfer 35 flamethrower *192*, *193*
Flammenwerfer 41 flamethrower *192*
Flammenwerfer klein verbessert 40 192
Flammenwerfer mit Strahlrohrpatrone 41 192
Flammpanzer 38(t) 193
Flammpanzer I 193
Flammpanzer II *193*
Flammpanzer III *193*
Flare Pistol M1942 29
Flash-Ball launcher 235
FL-Selbstlader-Armee Modell Pistole 19
FMK-3 sub-machine gun *64–5*
FMK-5 sub-machine gun 65
FN 247
  303 'gun' *234*, 235
  2000 modular system *246*
  Carbine (FNC) assault rifle 112, *239*
  FAL assault rifle *81*, *111*, *112*, *247*
  FNC assault rifle 112, *239*, *247*
  MAG medium machine-gun *141*, *164*
  Minimi light machine-gun *141*, *165*
  Model 30 sniper rifle *130–1*
  Model 49 rifle *247*
  Riot Shotgun *224–5*
FN-Mauser mle 1889, Fusil *82–3*
foam, sticky 234, *235*
formations, army section *9*
French automatic pistols *37*
French Resistance, World War II *11*
Fucile anticarro 187
Fucile modello 91 rifle *85*
Fusil Berthier mle 90, 1907 rifle *84–5*
Fusil d'Infanterie mle 07/15 90
Fusil d'Infanterie mle 07/15 Mk34 90
Fusil d'Infanterie mle 1886 90
Fusil d'Infanterie mle 1886/93 90
Fusil d'Infanterie mle 1916 90
Fusil FN-Mauser mle 1889/93 rifle *82–3*
Fusil FN-Mauser mle 1889 rifle *82–3*
Fusil Gras mle 1874 90
Fusil Lebel mle 1886 (Lebel) *84*, 90
Fusil Lebel mle 1886/93 84, 90
Fusil Lebel mle 1886 rifle (Lebel) *84*
Fusil MAS36 rifle 90–*1*
Fusil-Mitrailleur Hotchkiss mle 1909 machine-gun *143*
Fusil-Mitrailleur mle 1915 (Chauchat; CSRG) *144–5*
Fusil-Mitrailleur mle 1924/29 152

G2 assault rifle 248, 249
G3 A3ZF sniper rifle 133
G3 assault rifle 81, *114*
G3 SG1 sniper rifle 133
G11 rifle 116
G36 assault rifle *116*
G41 rifle 116
Galil
  assault rifles *116–17*
  sniping rifle *134*
Gallipoli, aviators over *20*
Garand (Rifle, Caliber .30, M1) *98*
Gebirgsgranatwerfer 328(r) 204
Geweer tp 181110 anti-tank rifle 187
Gewehr 41 (W) rifle 94
Gewehr 43 rifle *94*
Gewehr 98 rifle 92
Gewehr 252(r) rifle 95
Gewehr 254(r) rifle 95
Gewehr 1898 rifle (Gew 98) *80*, *86*
GG-95 PDW 68
Glisenti modello 1910 (Glisenti) pistol 14–*15*, *33*
Glock pistols *34*
GME-FMK2-MO grenade 221
Goliath demolition vehicles *183*
Granatbüchse 39 *187*
Granatwerfer mortar
  42205
  176(i)203
  200(r)204
  205/1(r)204
  274/1(r)204
  274/2(r)204
  274/3(r)204
  378(r)205
Grande Chasse hunting rifle 131
'Grease Gun', M3 *60*
Grenade Discharger Type 10 *203*
grenade launchers *219–21*
grenades 220–1
  anti-tank *184*, 188, *189*
  phosphorus 188
  riot-control 234, *238–9*
Guardian vehicles 237

Haile Selassie *18*
Harvey flamethrower *197*
Hast and Glasser Revolver M.1898 12
Hawkins Grenades 189
Heckler & Koch
  CAW *231*
  G3 assault rifle *114*
  G3 A3ZF sniper rifle 133
  G3 SG1 sniper rifle 133
  G11 rifle 116
  G36 assault rifle *116*
  G41 rifle 116
  HK 4 pistol 38
  HK 11 machine-gun *168*
  HK 11A1 machine-gun 168
  HK 11E machine-gun 168
  HK 13 machine-gun *168*
  HK 13E machine-gun *168*
  HK 21 light machine-gun *114*, *168*
  HK 21A1 light machine-gun *168*
  HK 21E machine-gun 168
  HK 23E machine-gun 168
  HK 33 assault rifle *114*
  HK 53 assault rifle *115*
  HK 69A1 grenade launcher 221
  machine guns *168*
  MG 36 light machine-gun 168
  MP5 sub-machine gun 47, *70–1*
  MSG90 sniper rifle *133*
  pistols *38*
  PSG1 sniper rifle 133
  sniper rifles *133*
Heeres Pistole (HP) 27
helmets *245*
High Power, Browning *35*
Hilton multi-purpose gun *239*
Hinckley, John *72*
HK *see* Heckler & Koch
Hornet's Nest Sting Grenade 234
Hotchkiss
  medium machine-guns *144*
  mle 1897 machine-gun 144
  mle 1900 machine-gun 144
  mle 1909 (Hotchkiss Mk 1) machine-gun *143*
  mle 1914 machine-gun *144*
HP (Heeres Pistole) 27
Humber 'Pig' vehicles *237*
IKM machine-gun 170
IMI
  Desert Eagle pistol *40*
  Negev machine-gun *172*
  Uzi sub-machine gun *72*
Ingram
  Model 10 sub-machine gun *77*
  Model 11 sub-machine gun *77*
Israel Miltary Industries *see* IMI
Ithaca
  Model 37 shotguns 228
  Model DS shotgun 228
  Model LAPD shotgun 228
Iver Johnson Model 500 sniper rifle *138*

Jackhammer shotgun *230*
Japanese pistols *15*
Jati-Matic sub-machine gun *68*

Kalashnikov *see* AK
Karabiner rifles
  4394
  98b92
  98k*92* 108
  Karabiner-S rifle 107
  m59107
'knee mortars' *203*
Kord heavy machine-gun 171
KPV machine-gun 171
kurzer Granatwerfer 42 mortar 207
KV-8 flamethrower 195
KV-8S flamethrower 195

L1A1 grenade discharger 221
L1 assault rifle *81*
  L1A1 111, *112*
  L1A1-F1 112
L2A3 Sterling sub-machine gun *76*
L3 Lanciafiamme *194*
L4 Bren machine-gun 141, *174*
L9A1, Pistol, Automatic 28
L16 mortar *178*, *201*, *214*, *215*
L34A1 sub-machine gun 76
L39A1 sniper rifle 136
L42 sniper rifle *136*
L67A1 *239*
L81A1 sniper rifle 137
L85A1 (SA80) British Army rifle *109*, 124
L85A2 assault rifle 124
L86 Light Support Weapon *175*
  L86A1 124, *175*
L96 sniper rifle *126*, *136*–7
Lanchester sub-machine gun *55*
Lanciafiamme Modello 35 194
Lanciafiamme Modello 40 194
Land Warrior System *244–5*
Langenhan *19*
Lawman Mk III, Colt *45*
Lebel revolvers

Modèle 1873 13
Modèle 1874 13
Modèle 1892 (Lebel) *13*
Lebel rifles
Fusil Lebel mle 1886 (Lebel) *84*, 90
Fusil Lebel mle 1886/93 84, 90
leGRW 36 mortar *206*
Lehky Kulomet
vz 59 machine-gun *166–7*
ZB vz 24 light machine-gun 152
ZB vz 26 light machine-gun *152*
ZB vz 30 light machine-gun 152
leichte Gebirgs Infantreigeschütz 18 (leGebIG) 207
leichte Granatwerfer 36 (leGRW 36) mortar *206*
leichte Infantreigeschütz 18 (leIG) 207
Lewis machine gun 141, *148*
Liberator M1942 assassination gun *29*
Lifebuoy flamethrower *196*
Light Machine-Gun
Type 11 153
Type 96 *153*
Light Mortar 217
Light Support Weapon (LSW) *109*, 124, *175*
LMG 08 machine-gun 147
LMG 08/15 machine-gun 147
Luger (9-mm Pistole '08) *16–17*, *26*
Luger, Georg 16, 26
Lyran system *213*

M1, 60-mm mortar 210
M1, 81-mm mortar *211*
M1 (Carbine, Caliber .30) *81*, *99*
M1A1 99
M1 flamethrower *198*
M1A1 198
M1 (Rifle, Caliber .30, M1 (Garand)) *81*, *98*
M1 rocket launcher (bazooka) *191*
M1 Thompson sub-machine gun *58–9*
M2-2 flamethrower *198*
M2 (Carbine, Caliber .30) 99
M2 heavy machine-gun *156*, *176*
M2HB heavy machine-gun *156*, *176*
M2 mortar *210*–11
M3A1 sub-machine gun 60
M3 (Carbine, Caliber .30) rifle 99
M3 'Grease Gun' sub-machine gun *60*
M4/M4A1 assault rifle 122
M5-4 flamethrower tank 199
M6 mortar 212
M8 mortar 214
M9 (Beretta Model 92F) 41
M9 rocket launcher 191
M12 mortar 216
M14 sniper rifle *138*
M16 assault rifles *81*, *108*, 109, *122–3*
M16A1 *9*, 122, *220*
M16A2 122
M16A3 109
M18 rocket launcher 191
M19 mortar *210*
M21 sniper rifle *138*
M29 mortar 212
M30 mortar 216–17
M-38 mortar 215
M-40 mortar 217
M40 sniper rifle *139*
M/41C, 120-mm mortar 217
m/45 (Carl Gustav) sub-machine gun *75*
M-56 mortar 215
M-58 mortar 217
M60 (T44) machine-gun *141*, *177*
M-64 mortar 215
M65 pistol 25
M-65 Standard Mortar 217
M66 mortar (Soltam 160-mm) *216*, 217
M68 pistol 25
M79 grenade launcher 220, *221*
M82 sniper rifle 138–9
M95 sniper rifle 139
M-160 mortar 217
M203 grenade launcher *220*
M224 Lightweight Company Mortar *212*, 213
M-240 mortar 217
M252 mortar 214
M384 grenade 220–1
M406 grenade 220
M1892, Colt *23*
M1903 machine-gun 142, 143
M1903 (Springfield Model 1903 rifle) *89*, *97*
M1911 pistol, Colt *23*, *29*, *44*
M1911A1 pistol, Colt 23, *29*
M1917
machine-gun *150–1*
Revolver, Caliber .45 *22*–3, 31
Rifle (the Enfield) 87
M1919 machine-gun *155*
M1942 Liberator *29*
MAB PA15 pistol *37*
machine-gun groups, fire and manoeuvre 8, 9
machine-guns *140–77*
light, medium and heavy 141
Madsen
machine-guns 142–*3*
sub-machine gun *66*–7
Magazine Rifle, Calibre .30, Model of 1903 89, *97*
MAG medium machine-gun *141*, *164*
Makarov 9-mm pistol 25, 42
Mannlicher
M1903 pistol *12*
Modell 1895 rifle *82*
manoeuvre, fire and 8–9
'manstoppers' *21*
maquis *57*
Marine Corps, U.S. *126*
marksmanship, snipers and *128–9*
MAS
AAT 52 machine-gun *167*
AAT F1 machine-gun 167
FA MAS assault rifle 81, *109*, *113*
FELIN assault rifle *248–9*
FR-F1 and F2 sniper rifles *131*
G2 assault rifle 248, 249
Model 1950 pistol *37*
Modèle 1938 gun 49
Maschinengewehr
08 (sMG 08) machine-gun *146*
08/15 machine-gun 147
08/18 machine-gun *147*
MG 34 machine-gun *160*
MG 42 machine-gun *161*
Maschinenkarabiner 42(H) (MKb42(H)) *93*, 108
Maschinenpistole
43 (MP43) *93*
44 (MP44) 93, *108*
709(r) 63
716(r) 63
717(r) 62
722(f) 49
MAT 49 sub-machine gun *69*
Mauser
C/96 pistol *18*
Gewehr 1898 rifle (Gew 98) *80*, *86*
SP 66 sniper rifle 132
SP 86 sniper rifle *132*
Maxim machine-guns
Model 1905 147
Model 1908 *146*
Model 1910 *147*
Merlin Gun 150
MG 1 machine-gun 169
MG 2 machine-gun 169
MG 3 machine-gun *169*
MG 08/15 machine-gun 147
MG 08/18 machine-gun *147*
MG 26(t) light machine-gun 152
MG 30(t) light machine-gun 152
MG 34 machine-gun *140*, 141, *160*
MG 36 light machine-gun 168
MG 42 machine-gun 141, *161*, 168
Micro-Uzi sub-machine gun *72*
MILAN anti-tank guided weapon 178
Minenwerfer mortar 178
Mini-14 rifle *78*, *125*
Minimi light machine-gun *141*, *165*
Mini-Uzi sub-machine gun *72*
Mitrailleuse Hotchkiss mle 1897 machine gun 144
Mitrailleuse Hotchkiss mle 1914 machine-gun *144*
Mitrailleuse mle 1931 machine-gun 152
Mitrailleuse St Etienne mle 1907 machine-gun *145*
Mk 19 grenade launcher 220, *221*
MM1 mortar *211*
MM-1 multi-round projectile launcher *241*
Model 43 mortar 217
Model 48 pistol 25
Model 82 (Parker-Hale 1200TX) sniper rifle *137*
Model 83 sniper rifle 137
Model 85 sniper rifle 137
Model 1943 mortar *217*
Model L mortar, 105-mm 217
Model L mortar, 120-mm 217
Model L-L mortar 215
Model L-N mortar 215
Model LR gun-mortar *218*
Model SL mortar 217
modular systems, FN2000 *246–7*
Molotov cocktails *188*
Mortar L16 *178*, *201*, *214*, *215*
Mortar M1, 60-mm 210
Mortar M1, 81-mm *211*
Mortar M2 *210*–11
Mortar M19 *210*
Mortar M30 216–17
Mortar M252 214
Mortar MM1 *211*
mortars *178*, *200–1*
British *208–9*
French *202*
German *206–7*
gun-mortars *218*
heavy *216–17*
Italian *202*–3
Japanese *203*
light *212–13*
medium *214–15*
Soviet *204–5*
US *210–11*
Mortar T13 211
Mortar T25 211
Mortier Brandt de 81 mm moèle 27/31 *202*
Mortier MO 81-61 C 215
Mortier MO 81-61 L 215
Mortier MO-120-60 mortar 216
Mortier MO-120-AM 50 mortar 216
Mortier MO-120-LT mortar 216
Mortier MO-120-M65 mortar 216
Mortier MO-120-RT-61 mortar 216
Mosin-Nagant rifles *95*
Model 1891 *87*
Model 1891/30 rifle 87
Model 1910 87, 95
Mossberg shotguns
500 *228*
509 228

ATP-8SP 228
Mousqueton mle 1890 90
Mousqueton mle 1892 90
MOWAG Roland MR 8 vehicles 237
MP5, Heckler & Koch *70–1*
MP 18 sub-machine gun 46, 52
MP 28 sub-machine gun *52*
MP 34 sub-machine gun 52
MP 35 sub-machine gun 52
MP 38 sub-machine gun *50, 51*
MP 38/40 sub-machine gun 50
MP 40 sub-machine gun 50, *51*
MP43 (Maschinenpistole 43) rifle *93*
MP44 (Maschinenpistole 44) rifle 93, *108*
MP 738(i) sub-machine gun 53
MP 739(i) sub-machine gun 53
MP 749(e) sub-machine gun 56
MP 751(e) sub-machine gun 56
MPi 69 sub-machine gun *65*
MPi 81 sub-machine gun 65
MSG90 sniper rifle *133*
M SS 41 anti-tank rifle 187
Multi 163 vehicles 237

Nagant Model 1895 pistol *19*
Negev machine-gun *172*
Northover Projectors 188–*9*
NSV heavy machine-gun *171*
NSVT heavy machine-gun 171

Ofenrohr (RPzB) *182*
On Duty pistol, AMT *44*
Ordnance, ML 2-inch Mortar Mk II 208
Ordnance, ML 3-inch Mortar Mk II 208
Ordnance, ML 3-inch Mortar Mk IV 209
Ordnance, ML 3-inch Mortar Mk V 209
Ordnance, SB 4.2-inch Mortar 209
OSS Pistol 29
OT-34 flamethrower 195
Owen gun *48*

P5, Walther *39*
P7, Heckler & Koch 38
P8, Heckler & Koch 38
P 08 (Luger) pistol *16–17, 26*
P9, Heckler & Koch *38*
P10, Heckler & Koch 38
P.13 rifle 87
P.14 rifle *87*
P-64 pistol 42
P-85, Ruger 44
P88, Walther 39
P-89, Ruger 44
P-90, Ruger 44
P-91, Ruger 44
P-93, Ruger 44
P-94, Ruger 44
P-95, Ruger 44
P-97, Ruger 44
P99, Walther 39
P-944, Ruger 44
Pab 785(s) anti-tank rifle 187
Pancor Jackhammer shotgun *230*
Panzerabwehrbüchse
782(e) 188
783(r) 186
Panzerbüchse
38 186–7
39 *187*
Panzerfaust *180–1*
Panzerschreck (RPzB) *182*
Panzerwurfmine (L) anti-tank grenade *184*
PAPOP *248*, 249
Parachutist's Rifle Type 2 91
Parker-Hale sniper rifles *127*
Model 82 (Parker-Hale 1200TX) *137*
Model 83 137
Model 85 137
Patchett sub-machine gun 76
Pecheneg machine-gun 170
PepperBalls 234–5
PIAT anti-tank weapon *190*
Pindad SS1 assault rifle 112
Pistol, Automatic, Caliber .45, M1911 *29*
Pistol, Automatic L9A1 28
Pistol, Browning, FN, 9-mm HP No. 1 28, *36*
Pistol, Revolver 0.38/200, Smith & Wesson No. 2 30
Pistol, Revolver, No 2 Mk 1 24
Pistola Automatica Beretta modello 1934 *33*
Pistola Automatica Glisenti modello 1910 *33*
Pistol Automatic, Caliber .45, M1911 23
Pistole 08 (Luger) service pistol *16–17, 26*
Pistole 12(oe) 12
Pistole 75, 9-mm 43
Pistole 620(b) 12, 28
Pistole 621(b) 13, 28
Pistole 622(b) 13
Pistole 645(p) or 35(p) 31
Pistole Automatique Browning modèle 1910 *28*
Pistole Automatique Browning modèle à Grande Puissance (Browning HP) *28*
Pistole M 42
Pistole P 39(t) 32
Pistole P 671(i) 33
Pistolet-Pulyemet Degtyareva obrazets 1934g (PPD-1934) *63*
Pistolet-Pulyemet Shpagina obrazets 1941g (PPSh-41) *62*
Pistolet-Pulyemet Sudareva obrazets 1942g (PPS-42) 63
Pistolet Random wz.35 *31*
Pistolet ViS wz.35 31
Pistol M1942 29
Pistol Revolver Type 4 *15*
Pistol Revolver Type 26 15
Pistol Revolver Type 1914 Nambu 15
pistols 12–45
concealed carry *11*
self-loading *11*, 20, 34–5, *44*
types of service pistol *11*
use in combat *10–11*
Pistol Type 94 (94 Shiki Kenju) *32*
PK machine-gun *170*
PKB machine-gun 170
PKM light machine-gun *170*
PKMS machine-gun 170
PKS machine-gun 170
PKT machine-gun 170
PM, Makarov 25, 42
PM1910 (Maxim) machine-gun *147*
PMM, Makarov 42
POA-CWS 75 HI flamethrower tank 199
Portable Flamethrower
Type 93 *194–5*
Type 100 194–5
Port Said (m/45b sub-machine gun) 75
PP, Walther *27, 38–9*
PPD-1934 sub-machine gun *63*
PPD-1934/38 sub-machine gun 63
PPD-1940 sub-machine gun 63
PPK, Walther 27, *38–9*
PPS-42 sub-machine gun 63
PPS-43 sub-machine gun *63*
PPSh-41 sub-machine gun *62*
Pritchard-Greener revolver bayonet 21
PSG1 sniper rifle 133
PSM 5.45-mm pistol 42–*3*
PTRD 1941 anti-tank rifle *186*
PTRS 1941 anti-tank rifle *186*
Pulemet Maksima obrazets 1910 machine-gun *147*
Püppchen rocket launcher *184–5*
Python, Colt *45*

R4 assault rifle 116–17
Raketenpanzerbüchse (RPzB) rocket launcher *182, 185*
Raketenwerfer 43 rocket launcher *184–5*
Random wz.35 *31*
Redeye missile 179
Reichs-Commissions-Revolver
Modell 1879 18–19
Modell 1883 18
Reising
Model 50 *61*
Model 55 *61*
Remington
Model 11A shotgun 224
Model 12 shotgun 224
Model 870 Mk 1 shotgun 230–1
Model 870R shotgun 224, 230
Repetier Gewehr Modell 1895 (Mannlicher Modell 1895) *82*
Repetierpistole M.07, 8mm (Roth-Steyr) 12
Repetierpistole M.12, 9mm (Steyr-Hahn) *12*
Revolver 0.38/200 *30*
Revolver, Caliber .45, M1917 *22–3*, 31
revolvers *11*
RHINO programme 223
Rhino riot-control vehicles 236
Rifle, Anti-tank, 0.55-in, Boys, Mk 1 *188*
Rifle, Caliber .30, M1 (Garand) *98*
Rifle, Caliber .30, Model 1903 *97*
Rifle L39A1 sniper rifle 136
Rifle L42 sniper rifle *136*
Rifle L96 sniper rifle *136–7*
Rifle M14 sniper rifle *138*
Rifle M21 sniper rifle *138*
Rifle M40 sniper rifle *139*
Rifle M1917 (the Enfield) 87
riflemen, paired operations 9
Rifle No. 1 Mk III 87, *88*
Rifle No. 1 Mk III* *80, 88*
Rifle No. 3 Mk I *87*
Rifle No. 4 Mk I *96*
Rifle No. 4 Mk I* 96
Rifle No. 4 Mk I(T) 96
Rifle No. 5 Mk I *97*
rifles *80–1*
assault *106–25*
sniper *126–40*
Rifle Type 5 98
Rifle Type 38 91
Rifle Type 99 *91*
riot control *233–43*
Riot Gun Model 203A 243
Rk.60 assault rifle 106–7
Rk.62 assault rifle *106, 107*
Rk.76 assault rifle 107
Rk.95TP assault rifle 107
RM & M Dreyse *19*
Automatic, 7.65mm *19*
rocket launchers *182, 184–5*
bazooka *178, 191*
ROKS-2 flamethrower 195
ROKS-3 flamethrower *195*
Ronson flamethrower 197
Ross rifles *83*
Roth-Steyr pistol 12
RPG-7 anti-tank rocket 179
RPK machine-gun *170–1*
RPzB 43 rocket launcher 182, *185*
RPzB 54 rocket launcher *182, 185*
Ruger
AC-556 rifle 78
Blackhawk 45
K-Mini/14-20GB rifle 78
Mini-14 rifle *78, 125*
Model 77 rifle 78
P-85 44
P-89 44
P-90 44

P-91 44
P-93 44
P-94 44
P-95 44
P-97 44
P-944 44
revolvers 45
rifles *78*
Security-Six 45
Service-Six 45
Speed Six *45*
Russian heavy machine-guns *171*

S&W *see* Smith & Wesson
S1-100, Steyr-Solothurn *54–5*
s18-1100 anti-tank rifle 187
SA-7 missile 179
SA80 British Army rifle *109*, *124*
Sako Rk.75 107
Samozariadnyia Vintokva Tokareva (SVT38) rifle 95
Samozariadnyia Vintokva Tokareva (SVT40) rifle *95*
Samozaryadnyia Karabin Simonova (SKS) rifle *107*
Santa Barbara (CETME) Ameli machine-gun *173*
SAR21 assault rifle *118*
SAR80 assault rifle *118*
SAR88A assault rifle 118
SAR assault rifle 116
SARAC M1953 machine-gun 163
Satan flamethrower tank *199*
Savage
Model 1907 pistol 22
Model 1915 pistol 22
Saxon riot-control vehicles 236, *237*
SC70 assault rifle 117
SC70 Short assault rifle 117
scatter guns *223*
Schermuly gun *240–1*
Schwarzlose machine-gun *142*
schwere Granatwerfer 34 (sGrW 34) mortar *206–7*
SdKfz 251/16 mittlerer Flammpanzerwagen 193
SdKfz demolition vehicles *183*
sections, army (squads)
fire and manoeuvre tactics 8–9
formations 9
'gun' and 'rifle' groups 140
Security-Six, Ruger 45
Selbstladegewehr 251(a) 98
Selbstladegewehr 258(r) 95
Selbstladegewehr 259(r) 95
Service-Six, Ruger 45
SG43 machine-gun 162
SG550 assault rifle *119*
SG551 assault rifle 119
SG552 Commando assault rifle 119
sGrW 34 mortar *206–7*
Sherman Crocodile flamethrower tank *199*
Shorland vehicles 237
shotguns *222–31*
SIG
710-3 machine-gun *173*
SG550 assault rifle *119*
SG551 assault rifle 119
SG552 Commando assault rifle 119
SIG-Sauer P220 series pistols *43*
SK-1 and SK-2 vehicles 237
Skorpion
CZ vz 61 *67*
CZ vz 63 67
CZ vz 68 67
SKS rifle *107*
sMG 08 (Maschinengewehr 08) machine-gun *146*
Smith & Wesson
0.38/200 pistol *30*
Hand Ejector M1917 pistol *22–3*, *31*
Model 39 pistol 44
Model 59 pistol 44
No. 38 Bodyguard 45
No. 209 gas pistol 242
No. 210 shoulder gas gun *242*
revolvers *45*
S&W99 pistol 39
Sniper, Beretta *134–5*
sniper rifles *130–40*
snipers and *126–9*
Sniper's Rifle Type 2 91
Soltam
120-mm Standard Mortar *216*, 217
160-mm mortar *216*
Soviet Naval Infantry *42*
SP 66 sniper rifle 132
SP 86 sniper rifle *132*
SPAS-15 shotgun 226–7
SPAS Model 11 shotgun 226
SPAS Model 12 shotgun *226*
Spatengranatwerfer 181(r) mortar 204
Spectre sub-machine gun *74*
Springfield Model 1903 rifle *89*, *97*
squads *see* sections, army
SSG 69 sniper rifle *127*, *130*
SSG P11 sniper rifle 130
Stanchion Gun 188
Sten sub-machine gun 46, *56–7*
Sterling (L2A3) sub-machine gun *76*
Steyr
AUG assault rifle *110*
AUG Para (Aug 9) sub-machine gun *66*
M1912 pistol *12*
MPi machine pistol *47*
SSG 69 sniper rifle *127*, *130*
SSG P11 sniper rifle 130
Steyr-Hahn pistol *12*
Steyr-Solothurn S1-100 sub-machine gun *54–5*
Stinger missile 179
Sting-RAG 234
ST Kinetics assault rifles *118*
Striker shotgun *227*
StuG III assault gun *26*
Stummelwerfer mortar 207
Sturmgewehr 44 (StG44) rifle 81, 93, 108–9
Sturmgewehr 90 (StG90) assault rifle *119*
sub-machine guns *46–79*
Suomi m/1931 gun *49*
support weapons *178–85*
SVD Dragunov combat sniping rifle *135*
SVT38 rifle 95
SVT40 rifle *95*

T27 'Universal' mortar 211
T44 machine-gun 177
Tank Machine-Gun Type 91 153
tanks, flamethrower *193–4*, 195, *199*
tear gas *238*
Thompson sub-machine gun *58–9*
Tikagypt 25
Tir Sportif rifle 131
TM 125 vehicles 237
TM 170 vehicles 237
TO-34 flamethrower 195
Tokarev
rifles *95*
TT-30 pistol 25
TT-33 pistol *25*
'Tommy Guns' *58*
Transaif vehicles *237*
TRGG crowd-control 'weapon' *234*, 235
Trooper, Colt 45
TT-30, Tokarev 25
TT-33, Tokarev *25*
Type 11 light machine-gun 153
Type 53 mortar 215
Type 65 rifle 107
Type 74 machine-gun 171
Type 76 machine gun 166
Type 80 machine gun 166
Type 81 Squad Machine-Gun *166*
Type 95 Squad Machine-Gun *166*
Type 96 light machine-gun 153
Type 100 sub-machine gun *54*

UD M42 sub-machine gun *61*
Ultimax 100 (3U-100) machine-gun *172*
UR-416 vehicles 237
USP, Heckler & Koch 38
Uzi sub-machine gun *72*

Valkyr riot control vehicles *236*
Valmet m/60 (Rk.60) assault rifle 106–7
Valmet m/62 (Rk.62) assault rifle *106*, *107*
Valmet/Sako Rk.76 107
Vickers
machine guns *140*, *149*, *158*
Valkyr riot control vehicles *236*
Vickers-Berthier light machine-guns *159*
G.O. (Vickers K) machine gun *155*, *159*
Vintovka obrazets 1891(g) rifle 95
Voronezh front *26*
VP70, Heckler & Koch 38
VTP 2 vehicles 237
vz 9 gun 48
vz 61 Skorpion sub-machine gun/machine pistol *67*
vz 63 sub-machine gun/machine pistol 67
vz 68 sub-machine gun/machine pistol 67
VZ pistols (Czech) 36–7

WA2000 sniper rifle *132–3*
Walther
MKb42(W) assault rifle 108
P5 pistol *39*
P38 pistol *10*, *27*
P88 pistol 39
P99 pistol *39*
PPK pistol 27, *38–9*
PP pistol *27*, *38–9*
Walther WA2000 sniper rifle *132–3*
Wasp & Harvey flamethrowers *197*
Wasp flamethrower *197*
water cannons *235*
Webley
Mk 4 pistol 24
Self-Loading Pistol Mk I 20
Webley & Scott
revolvers *20–1*
self-loading pistols 20
Webley Fosbery revolver *21*
Winchester shotguns *229*

X3 sub-machine gun *64*
XL47E1 27

Yom Kippur War *120*

Z-84 sub-machine gun *75*
ZK 383 gun *48*
ZPU-4 heavy machine-gun *171*